Handbook of Solid Modeling

Handbook of Solid Modeling

Donald E. LaCourse, Editor in Chief

President
The Solid Modeling ExChange

McGraw-Hill, Inc.

New York San Francisco Washington, D.C. Auckland Bogotá
Caracas Lisbon London Madrid Mexico City Milan
Montreal New Delhi San Juan Singapore
Sydney Tokyo Toronto

Library of Congress Cataloging-in-Publication Data

Handbook of solid modeling / Donald E. LaCourse, editor-in-chief.
   p. cm.
  Includes index.
  ISBN 0-07-035788-9
  1. Engineering models. I. LaCourse, Donald E.
TA177.H36 1995
658.5′752—dc20   95-4022
                    CIP

1 2 3 4 5 6 7 8 9 0 DOW/DOW 9 0 0 9 8 7 6 5

ISBN 0-07-035788-9

The sponsoring editor for this book was Robert W. Hauserman and the production supervisor was Suzanne W. B. Rapcavage. It was set in Times Roman by North Market Street Graphics.

Printed and bound by R. R. Donnelley & Sons Company.

McGraw-Hill books are available at special quantity discounts to use as premiums and sales promotions, or for use in corporate training programs. For more information, please write to the Director of Special Sales, McGraw-Hill, Inc., 11 West 19 Street, New York, NY 10011. Or contact your local bookstore.

This book is printed on acid-free paper.

To my wife Sheila and my sons Steven and Derek for their valued encouragement and assistance.

Also to the memory of Robert Johnson, formerly president of Cimdata, Inc., who was unable to fulfill his desire of contributing to this work.

About the Author

Donald E. LaCourse has spent 17 years in product design in industrial, aerospace, and automotive applications. He writes and speaks on solid modeling technology and is president of The Solid Modeling ExChange, an Algood, Tennessee–based firm specializing in writing, editing, and distributing solid-modeling-related documentation for practical use and assistance to engineering professionals.

Note to Collectors

Copies of this handbook are available from the Editor in Chief's Collection and are personally stamped, signed, dated, and individually serialized by Mr. LaCourse at no additional charge beyond the publisher's list price.

For more information on the Editor in Chief's Collection write to:

The Solid Modeling ExChange
Handbook of Solid Modeling
Editor in Chief's Collection
P.O. Box 49336
Algood, TN 38506-0336

From zero to 3D in record time.

PE/SolidDesigner from Hewlett-Packard just made other CAD systems history.

Get ready to bring your products to market faster. The next generation 3D solid modeling system is here. And it's got everything you need to streamline and accelerate the product design cycle as never before.

SolidDesigner features "dynamic modeling" so changes can be made any time during the design cycle without knowing the design history and without having to start again

from scratch. This alone could trim months off many projects.

What's more, SolidDesigner is so intuitive and easy to use that even designers who are only familiar with 2D systems can be up and running in just a few days. Plus, existing 2D and 3D designs will translate directly and seamlessly into SolidDesigner using industry standard data exchange protocols.

It's all backed by HP's reputation for reliability and superbly engineered products and a global consulting network that's second to none.

In product design, it's not just who delivers but who delivers the fastest. With SolidDesigner from HP you'll scream to the finish line. And leave history based systems in your dust.

To discover how SolidDesigner can make your product design process easier, please call HP at **1-800-756-9597.**

 **HEWLETT®** **PACKARD**

Contents

Section 1   Overview

Chapter 1. Read This First   1.3

Chapter 2. Introducing Solid Modeling   2.1

Section 2   Techniques

Chapter 3. Solid Modeling Concepts   3.3

Contents

Chapter 4. Solid Modeling Database Structures   4.1

Chapter 5. Curves and Surfaces for Solid Modeling   5.1

Chapter 6. Modeling Strategies   6.1

Chapter 7. Editing Strategies   7.1

Chapter 8. Parametric/Relational Solid Modeling   8.1

Contents

Section 3   Applications

Chapter 11. Solid Modeling for Assemblies   11.3

Chapter 15. Solid Modeling for Numerical Control   **15.1**

Chapter 16. Customizing the Solid Modeling System   **16.1**

Chapter 17. Solid Modeling and Documentation   **17.1**

Section 4 Interfaces

Chapter 18. Graphical User Interfaces (GUIs)   18.3

Chapter 19. Solid Modeling and Rapid Prototyping   19.1

Chapter 20. Preparing for Data Exchange   20.1

Chapter 21. Solid Modeling and the Initial Graphics Exchange Specification (IGES)   21.1

Chapter 22. Solid Modeling and Product Data Exchange Using STEP (PDES/STEP)   22.1

Section 5   Implementation

Chapter 23. Solid Modeling Implementation Strategies   23.3

Chapter 24. Solid Modeling and Design   24.1

Chapter 25. Solid Modeling for Manufacturing   25.1

Chapter 26. Volumetric Solid Modeling

26.1

Chapter 27. The Role of Solid Modeling in Concurrent Engineering

27.1

Chapter 28. Managing Solid Modeling Data

28.1

Section 6   In the Field

Chapter 29. Solid Modeling at Sony Corporation

29.3

Chapter 30. Solid Modeling at Volkswagen Automotive Group   **30.1**

Chapter 31. Solid Modeling at Hewlett-Packard   **31.1**

Chapter 32. Solid Modeling at Eaton Corporation, Supercharger Division   **32.1**

Contents

Chapter 33. Roundtable Discussion   33.1

The Solid Modeling Adviser Master Table

These advisory entries are offered for their potential benefits and do not indicate strengths or weaknesses of any Solid Modeling systems.

Section	Topic	Group	Icon	SMA	Name	Orig	Pg
Overview	Introducing SM	B-Rep	FM	2.1	A B-Rep Misunderstanding	01	2.4
		Good to Know	⊕	2.2	It's a Good Idea	02	2.7
			⚠	2.3	Proceed with Caution	03	2.7
			✔	2.4	The Ten Commandments of an SM System	04	2.7
Techniques	Basic Concepts	Good Practices	⊕	3.1	Good Practices	06	3.12
				3.2	Knowledge and Capabilities	07	3.12
				3.3	What Skills Should Be Taught?	08	3.12
				3.4	Construction Plane Concepts	08	3.12
				3.5	Construction Plane Attributes	09	3.13
				3.6	Copying, Scaling, and Mirroring	09	3.13
				3.7	The Master Model Concept	09	3.13
				3.8	Think Like a Model Maker	09	3.13
				3.9	Coordinate Details	09	3.13
		Guidelines	✔	3.10	Orientation in 3D Space	10	3.13
				3.11	The Right-Hand Rule for Rotation	11	3.13
				3.12	The Right-Hand Rule for a Positive Axis	09	3.14
				3.13	Strive for Validity	09	3.14
				3.14	The Right Amount of Detail	12	3.14
		Point of View	◁	3.15	Do Not Be Discouraged	09	3.14
	Database Structures	Concepts	⚠	4.1	Platform Portability	13	4.9
		CSG	FM	4.2	Supported CSG Primitives	13	4.12
		B-Rep	FM	4.3	B-Rep vs. Traditional Surface Modeling	13	4.15
		Errors and Reliability	⚠	4.4	Sources of Database Errors	13	4.23
				4.5	Disabling Error Checking	13	4.23
				4.6	Reliability Precautions	13	4.23
			↖	4.7	Undetected Errors	13	4.23
				4.8	Correcting Database Errors	13	4.23
			⊘	4.9	Reliability & Geometry	13	4.23
			FM	4.10	Parametric Methods	13	4.23
		Point of View	◁	4.11	Newer vs. Older SM Systems	13	4.23
		Good Practices	⊕	4.12	Understanding and Evaluation	08	4.24
				4.13	Processing & Performance	13	4.24
				4.14	SM and Databases	13	4.24
				4.15	Failure Logs	13	4.24
				4.16	Vendor Bulletins	13	4.24
	Curves and Surfaces	Needed Improvement	✚	5.1	Surface Construction Methods	01	5.1
				5.2	Surface Types Abound	01	5.1
		Curves	⚠	5.3	Concatenating Curve Deviations	09	5.4
				5.4	Concatenating Composite Curves	05	5.4
			✔	5.5	Curve Techniques and Concerns	09	5.4
			⊕	5.6	Curve Modifications	09	5.4
				5.7	When Trimming Curves	09	5.4
				5.8	When Extending Curves	09	5.4
				5.9	When Modifying Curves Locally	09	5.4
		Surfaces	✔	5.10	Surface Techniques and Concerns	09	5.8
			⊕	5.11	When Trimming Surfaces	09	5.8
				5.12	When Extending Surfaces	09	5.8
				5.13	Surface Tangency	09	5.8
				5.14	Sculpted Surfaces	15	5.10
				5.15	When Modifying Curves Locally	14	5.10

Section	Topic	Group	Icon	SMA	Name	Orig	Pg
Techniques (*continued*)	Curves and Surfaces (*continued*)	Surfaces (*continued*)	✔	5.16	Variable Radii Blends	09	5.10
			FM	5.17	Surface Offsets	01	5.10
		Free-Form Associativity	⊕	5.18	Combining Associative and Nonassociative Elements	16	5.13
				5.19	Nonassociative Curves and Surface	16	5.13
				5.20	Variational Curves and Associative Surface	16	5.13
				5.21	Nonassociative Curves and Associative Surface	16	5.14
				5.22	Associative and Nonassociative Curves with Associative Surface	16	5.14
				5.23	Most Effective Modeling Approach	16	5.15
		Good to Know	⚠	5.24	System Tolerances	09	5.16
			⊕	5.25	Effective Color Usage	10	5.16
				5.26	Use Existing Edges	07	5.16
			FM	5.27	Approximation	01	5.16
	Modeling Strategies	Primitives	FM	6.1	Primitive Modeling	14	6.1
				6.2	A Primitive Eye	09	6.3
				6.3	Primitive Productivity	09	6.3
				6.4	Thinking in Shapes	08	6.3
		Geometric Operations	✔	6.5	Blending Concerns	14	6.5
				6.6	Sweep Concerns	14	6.5
			⚠	6.7	Extrusion Concerns	14	6.5
			✔	6.8	Profiles, Chamfers, and Fillets	21	6.5
			⊕	6.9	Plan Your Edge Sequence	21	6.5
				6.10	Copy Profiles First	06	6.5
			FM	6.11	Modifying Profiles	08	6.6
		Boolean Operations	⚠	6.12	Boolean Groups & Errors	14	6.7
			FM	6.13	Regularized Boolean Operations	13	6.7
			✔	6.14	Using Booleans on Coincident Faces	06	6.8
		Modeling Time	✔	6.15	To Reduce Modeling & Editing Time	14	6.10
			⊕	6.16	Subdivision Saves Time	14	6.11
				6.17	CPU Time vs. Constructions & Operations	14	6.11
			✔	6.18	The CPU Time Curve	14	6.11
				6.19	Simple Intersections First	14	6.12
				6.20	Obtain Basic Shape Early	14	6.12
				6.21	Make Intersections Final	14	6.12
		Clean Modeling	✔	6.22	For Clean Modeling	14	6.14
				6.23	Continuous Surfaces	14	6.14
				6.24	Revolution Seams	14	6.14
				6.25	Edge Precedence	14	6.14
				6.26	Rework Unclean Geometry	14	6.14
			⊕	6.27	Construct As Produced	14	6.15
				6.28	ADD Before SUBTRACT	14	6.15
				6.29	Discard Often	14	6.15
				6.30	Avoid Difficult Geometry	14	6.15
			FM	6.31	Cleaning the Model	14	6.15
				6.32	Exploding Solids	09	6.17
			✔	6.33	Select Actual Edges	06	6.17
		Modeling Errors	✔	6.34	To Reduce Modeling Errors	14	6.17
				6.35	Avoid Trimming Features	14	6.17
				6.36	Avoid Trimming Surfaces	14	6.18
			⚠	6.37	Avoid Latent Gratuitous Surfaces	14	6.18
			✔	6.38	Minimize Concurrent Intersections	14	6.18

Section	Topic	Group	Icon	SMA	Name	Orig	Pg
Techniques (*continued*)	Modeling Strategies (*continued*)	Modeling Errors (*continued*)	⚠	6.39	Large vs. Small Geometry	14	6.19
			✔	6.40	Minimize Size and Complexity of Intersections	14	6.19
			⚠	6.41	Accuracy Settings	14	6.19
		Intersection Errors	↖	6.42	Move Geometry	14	6.20
				6.43	Revolution Solution	14	6.21
				6.44	Surface–Surface Tangency	14	6.21
			⊘	6.45	Narrow Faces	14	6.21
			⚠	6.46	Twin Edges	14	6.21
			✔	6.47	Revolution Seams	14	6.21
				6.48	Vertex–Vertex Coincidence	14	6.21
			⊕	6.49	Intersection Error Debugging	14	6.21
			FM	6.50	Unreported Errors	14	6.21
			⚠	6.51	Multiple Shells Error	14	6.22
		Accuracy Errors	✔	6.52	Minimize Movement of Profiles	14	6.23
			FM	6.53	Accuracy versus Speed	14	6.23
		Modeling Work-Arounds	↖	6.54	Reordering Operations	14	6.23
			⊘	6.55	Avoid Offsets	14	6.23
		Checklist	✔	6.56	Keep Geometry Simple	14	6.24
				6.57	Procedural and Wireframe Rules	14	6.24
				6.58	Geometry Construction Tips	17	6.24
		Good Practices	⊕	6.59	Use Blocks	06	6.25
				6.60	Use a Plane to Split a Solid	06	6.25
				6.61	Use Local Operations	06	6.25
				6.62	Geometry Alignment	18	6.25
				6.63	Nonparametric Systems	08	6.26
				6.64	ID Checks	20	6.26
				6.65	Always Include Draft	17	6.26
				6.66	Testing Intersections	14	6.26
				6.67	Do Not Display Unused Geometry	14	6.26
			FM	6.68	SM Is a Science	14	6.26
				6.69	A System's Dynamic Range	15	6.26
				6.70	Adding Surface Regions	14	6.27
	Editing Strategies	Topology	FM	7.1	Adding and Removing Topology	14	7.2
				7.2	Topology vs. Mfg. Costs	14	7.3
			⚠	7.3	Surface Violations	14	7.3
		The CSG Tree	✔	7.4	To Reduce CPU Editing Time	14	7.5
			⚠	7.5	Associative Awareness	14	7.5
			✔	7.6	Eliminate Unused Operations	22	7.5
		Geometric Operations	⊕	7.7	Affecting Other Shapes	14	7.6
			⚠	7.8	NC Considerations	14	7.6
			FM	7.9	Blend Cross Sections	14	7.6
				7.10	Blend Segments	14	7.6
			⚠	7.11	The Blend Trajectory	09	7.7
			✔	7.12	Angle of Revolution	09	7.7
		Good Practices	⊕	7.13	Use Freeze and Unfreeze	06	7.7
			✔	7.14	Local Surface Deviations	14	7.7
				7.15	Editing Guidelines	14	7.7
				7.16	Surface Intersection Accuracy	14	7.7
			⚠	7.17	Surface Edges	14	7.7
			⊕	7.18	Indicating Changes	17	7.8

Section	Topic	Group	Icon	SMA	Name	Orig	Pg
Techniques (*continued*)	Parametric/ Relational Systems	Understanding History in Sequential Para-metric Systems	FYI	8.1	History Reflects Intent	06	8.3
				8.2	Order Is Important	06	8.3
			⊕	8.3	Analyze Design First	06	8.3
				8.4	Verify History Periodically	06	8.3
			↖	8.5	Modifying Events	06	8.4
		Constraints	FYI	8.6	Constraint Assumptions	04	8.10
			⚠	8.7	Constrained or Not Constrained	23	8.10
			FYI	8.8	Constraint Needs	23	8.10
		Features	FYI	8.9	Advantages of Feature-Based Modeling	09	8.12
				8.10	Relocating Features	09	8.12
				8.11	A Robust Feature-Based SM System	24	8.12
				8.12	With User-Defined Features	24	8.12
		Associativity	FYI	8.13	Clarifying Associative Dimensioning	23	8.16
			⊘	8.14	Tracking Associativity	23	8.16
		Using Parameters	⊘	8.15	Determine Range of Acceptable Values	06	8.16
				8.16	Use Parameters Wisely	06	8.17
		Equations	⊕	8.17	Relationship Editing	23	8.23
			FYI	8.18	Bidirectional Equation Solving	24	8.23
		Parametric Editing	⚠	8.19	Think Before You Delete	06	8.24
			FYI	8.20	Parametric/Relational Editing	09	8.24
			⚠	8.21	Precautions	09	8.24
		Good to Know	✔	8.22	When to Use What	24	8.24
			FYI	8.23	Parametric Characteristics	24	8.24
				8.24	Integration Issues	23	8.24
				8.25	Is There a Parametric Sketch Pad?	25	8.24
	Knowledge-Based Engineering	Geometry Failures	⚠	9.1	Approximations & Nonmanifold Conditions	26	9.10
				9.2	Rounding & Tolerance Errors	26	9.10
			↖	9.3	Preventive Strategies	26	9.10
			✔	9.4	Error Trapping	26	9.10
		Organizational Issues	✔	9.5	Data Management	26	9.11
				9.6	Implementation	26	9.11
			⊕	9.7	Pilot Projects	26	9.11
			FYI	9.8	Integration	26	9.11
	Viewing and Display	Shading	⊕	10.1	Always Plan Ahead	20	10.3
		Video/Film	FYI	10.2	Contacts	27	10.7
		Isometric Viewing	⊕	10.3	What's Wrong with Isometric Viewing?	12	10.9
				10.4	Explore Alternatives	20	10.10
			FYI	10.5	Getting It Right	20	10.10
		Hidden Lines	⚠	10.6	A Creative Balance	20	10.10
			⊕	10.7	Line Densities	20	10.10
				10.8	Think Hidden-Line Removal	20	10.10
				10.9	Wireframe Display	20	10.10
			✔	10.10	Interactive Hidden-Line Removal	29	10.10
			FYI	10.11	Not a Panacea	20	10.11
				10.12	Dual Models	20	10.11
		Light Source Shading	FYI	10.13	Time for Perfection	20	10.11
				10.14	Persistence Can Pay Off	20	10.11
		Translucency	⊕	10.15	Final View Angle	20	10.11
				10.16	Internal Components	20	10.11

Section	Topic	Group	Icon	SMA	Name	Orig	Pg
Techniques (*continued*)	Viewing and Display (*continued*)	Specular Lighting	⊕	10.17	Positioning Light Source	20	10.12
				10.18	Material Selection	20	10.12
			✔	10.19	For Good Results	20	10.12
			FYI	10.20	Controls, Controls	20	10.12
				10.21	Specular Reflection	20	10.12
				10.22	Curved vs. Flat Surfaces	20	10.12
		Static and Animated Views	FYI	10.23	Static vs. Animation	20	10.13
			⊕	10.24	A Static Selection	20	10.13
		Material Settings Nonmetallic	✔	10.25	Color	28	10.13
				10.26	Highlight	28	10.13
				10.27	Texture	28	10.13
				10.28	Reflection Map	28	10.13
		Material Settings Other	✔	10.29	Shiny Plastic	28	10.14
				10.30	Cloth or Dull Wood	28	10.14
				10.31	Glass	28	10.14
		Caution	⚠	10.32	Perspective Views	20	10.14
				10.33	Tiling	28	10.14
				10.34	Sharpness	28	10.15
		Recommended	⊕	10.35	Shadows and Ray-Tracing	28	10.15
				10.36	Texture Mapping	20	10.15
				10.37	For Video or TV Format	12	10.15
			FYI	10.38	SM and Video Training	29	10.15
				10.39	Using Special Effects	30	10.16
				10.40	User-Defined Views	20	10.16
			✔	10.41	Get What You Need	09	10.16
			✚	10.42	Automatic Silhouette Lines	29	10.16
Applications	Assembly Modeling	Assembly Modeling	⚠	11.1	Component Libraries	31/32	11.12
			✔	11.2	Assembly Model Objectives	31/32	11.13
				11.3	Hard-Disk-Space Requirements	31/32	11.13
				11.4	Assembly Model Management	31/32	11.13
			⊕	11.5	Visual Feedback	31/32	11.13
				11.6	Share Your Knowledge	31/32	11.13
				11.7	Model Representations	31/32	11.13
			FYI	11.8	Exploded Assembly Views	31/32	11.13
			⊕	11.9	Graphics Accelerators	09	11.13
			FYI	11.10	Purchasing Hard-Disk Space	09	11.14
		Interference Detection	⚠	11.11	Model Accuracy	09	11.14
			✔	11.12	Tolerance Considerations	09	11.14
			⚠	11.13	Sole Reliance	33	11.14
			✔	11.14	Dynamic Detection	31/32	11.14
				11.15	Reducing Calculation Time	31/32	11.14
			FYI	11.16	Usful Interference Checking Procedures	24	11.14
	Mass-Properties Analysis	Application	⊕	12.1	Details for Weight	07	12.6
			FYI	12.2	Modeling Containers	09	12.6
				12.3	Material Cost & Requirements	09	12.6
				12.4	Weight by Volume	09	12.6
				12.5	Surface Area	09	12.6
		Technical	⚠	12.6	Check Surface Normals	35	12.6
				12.7	Which Mathematical Definition?	22	12.6
				12.8	Maintain Closure	09	12.6

Section	Topic	Group	Icon	SMA	Name	Orig	Pg
Applications (*continued*)	Mass-Properties Analysis (*continued*)	Technical (*continued*)	⊕	12.9	Accuracy Checks	09	12.6
			⚠	12.10	Moments of Inertia Caution	34	12.7
				12.11	Volume Caution	34	12.8
			⊕	12.12	Is There Enough Detail?	36	12.8
	Kinematic and Dynamic Analysis	Guidelines	✔	13.1	Keys to Real SM Benefits	37	13.10
				13.2	Realistic but Simple	38/39	13.10
				13.3	Model Reference Frame	38/39	13.10
		Recommended	⊕	13.4	One Solid Per Rigid Body	38/39	13.10
				13.5	Part Instancing	38/39	13.10
				13.6	Joint & Force Identification	38/39	13.10
				13.7	Model Files	38/39	13.10
		Good to Know	⚠	13.8	Model Detail	38/39	13.10
			FM	13.9	Solid Modeling	38/39	13.11
				13.10	Animation Alternatives	38/39	13.11
				13.11	What Can SM Designers Do?	67	13.11
				13.12	Optionally Integrated SM Analysis	67	13.11
				13.13	Integrating Motion Simulation	67	13.11
	Finite Element Analysis	Controlling Mesh Density	⊕	14.1	Maximum Element Edge Length	14	14.13
				14.2	Maximum Face-Aspect Ratio	14	14.13
				14.3	Minimum Face-Edge Ratio	14	14.13
		Minimum Element Edge Length	FM	14.4	Subdivision	14	14.13
			✔	14.5	Typical Value	14	14.15
			⚠	14.6	If Set Too High	14	14.15
		Maximum Subtended Angle	✔	14.7	If Stress Is Important	14	14.15
				14.8	If Stress Is Not Important	14	14.15
			FM	14.9	More Elements on Curvature	14	14.15
				14.10	Prevailing Edge Length	14	14.15
		Minimum Element Face Corner Angle	✔	14.11	Recommended Value	14	14.15
				14.12	When to Use Higher Values	14	14.15
				14.13	Premature Termination	14	14.15
			FM	14.14	Dense and Coarse Regions	14	14.15
		Edge Mesh Density	✔	14.15	On a Curved Solid Edge	14	14.15
				14.16	Topology Issues	14	14.15
			FM	14.17	Additional Control	14	14.15
				14.18	Aligning Elements	14	14.15
		Surface Mesh Density	✔	14.19	Extending to Face Elements	14	14.15
				14.20	Number of Edge Nodes	14	14.15
		Volume Mesh Density	✔	14.21	Internal Volume Mesh	14	14.15
				14.22	Changes in Topology	14	14.15
				14.23	Initial Volume Elements	14	14.16
			⚠	14.24	Internal Element Edges	14	14.16
		Relative Mesh Density—Edges	✔	14.25	Edge Ratio Values	14	14.16
				14.26	Narrow Faces	14	14.16
				14.27	Meshing Order	14	14.16
		Relative Mesh Density—Faces	✔	14.28	For Difficult Faces	14	14.16
				14.29	Element Edge-Length Ratio for Faces	14	14.16
		Relative Mesh Density—Volumes	✔	14.30	Element Edge-Length Ratio for Volumes	14	14.16
				14.31	For a More Uniform Mesh	14	14.16

The Solid Modeling Adviser Master Table (*Continued*)

Section	Topic	Group	Icon	SMA	Name	Orig	Pg
Applications (*continued*)	Finite Element Analysis (*continued*)	Other Mesh Density Controls	✔	14.32	Dense Nodes	14	14.17
			⚠	14.33	Solid Model Problems	14	14.17
			ℱℳ	14.34	Local Control	14	14.17
				14.35	Global Control	14	14.17
				14.36	Available Parameters	14	14.17
				14.37	Default Parameters	14	14.17
				14.38	Mesh Density Conversion	14	14.17
				14.39	Naming Conventions	14	14.17
				14.40	When Parameter Values Are Not Obvious	14	14.17
			⊕	14.41	Parameter Sensitivity Study	14	14.17
		Elements	ℱℳ	14.42	Tetrahedron Elements	14	14.22
				14.43	Analysis Convergence	14	14.23
				14.44	Incompatible Mode Linear Hexahedron Elements	14	14.23
			✔	14.45	Quadratic Hexahedron & Tetrahedron Elements	14	14.23
				14.46	Number of Elements vs. Nodes	14	14.23
		Mesh Process	⊕	14.47	Automatic vs. Interactive	14	14.23
				14.48	Local Mesh Modifications	14	14.23
				14.49	The Mesh Algorithm	14	14.23
			✔	14.50	Uniform Element Edge Lengths	14	14.23
				14.51	Coarse Mesh	14	14.23
			ℱℳ	14.52	Mesh Sequence	14	14.24
				14.53	Mesh Order	14	14.24
		Geometry	✔	14.54	Curved or Varied Geometry	14	14.24
				14.55	Faces with Very Short Edges	14	14.24
				14.56	Small Features or Small Faces	14	14.24
				14.57	Complex Solid Models	14	14.24
				14.58	Fillets	14	14.24
			⚠	14.59	Large Faces	14	14.24
		Analysis	✔	14.60	Visual Inspection	14	14.25
				14.61	Preanalysis Test	14	14.25
		Good to Know	ℱℳ	14.62	FEA Results	10	14.25
			⊕	14.63	Program Overrides	14	14.25
			ℱℳ	14.64	System Capabilities	14	14.25
	Numerical Control	Managing Change	ℱℳ	15.1	Propagation Control	40	15.3
			✔	15.2	Release/Revision Management	40	15.3
			⚠	15.3	Constraining Modes of Operation	40	15.3
			⊕	15.4	Toolpaths and Process Plans	40	15.3
				15.5	Database Access	40	15.3
		Tolerances	✔	15.6	Tolerance Balancing	40	15.6
		Revealing Gaps	↖	15.7	Investigative Methods	40	15.7
			⚠	15.8	Gaps May Be Masked	40	15.7
			↖	15.9	Translate Out and Back	40	15.8
		Dimensioning	⊕	15.10	Datum Positions	40	15.8
		Surfacing	⊘	15.11	Difficult Areas	40	15.9
		Problem Detection & Troubleshooting	↖	15.12	Test for Hidden Problems	40	15.10
				15.13	Display Tolerance	40	15.10
				15.14	Display Curves (Isolines)	40	15.10
				15.15	Outside Offset	40	15.10
				15.16	Shading or Rendering	40	15.10
			⚠	15.17	Undetected Problems	40	15.11

Section	Topic	Group	Icon	SMA	Name	Orig	Pg
Applications (*continued*)	Numerical Control (*continued*)	Preferred Capabilities Recommended Practices	⊕	15.18	Solid Support	40	15.13
				15.19	Feature Support	40	15.13
				15.20	Gouge-Free Toolpaths	40	15.13
				15.21	Toolpath Verification	40	15.14
				15.22	SM Integration	40	15.14
				15.23	Associable Process Plans	40	15.14
				15.24	Parametric Constraints	40	15.14
				15.25	Primitive Preference	40	15.15
				15.26	Information Availability	40	15.15
			✔	15.27	Site Specific	40	15.15
				15.28	Determine & Identify	40	15.15
	Customizing	Customizing	↖	16.1	Debugging Macros	41	16.8
				16.2	Small Adjustments	41	16.9
			⊕	16.3	Start-Up Files	41	16.9
				16.4	Default Models	41	16.9
				16.5	Batch Mode Processing	29	16.10
		Writing Your Own SM Program	✔	16.6	Planning Checklist	41	16.10
				16.7	Planning Action	41	16.10
				16.8	SM Engines	41	16.10
				16.9	Graphics Libraries	41	16.10
				16.10	The Graphic User Interface (GUI)	41	16.10
				16.11	Start Small	41	16.11
			FM	16.12	Integration	41	16.11
		Good to Know	⊕	16.13	Productivity Aids	21	16.11
			FM	16.14	Tutorial Sources	41	16.11
				16.15	Off-the-Shelf Code	41	16.11
				16.16	Available Tool Kits	41	16.11
	Documentation	Associativity	⚠	17.1	Solid Errors and Cleanup	09	17.3
				17.2	Detailing Associativity	09	17.3
		Desktop Publishing	FM	17.3	Graphics Conversion	09	17.5
			⊕	17.4	Screen Images to Film	09	17.11
				17.5	The HPGL Format	41	17.11
				17.6	Image Processing	41	17.11
				17.7	SM, CE, and Desktop Publishing	20	17.11
		Detail Drawings	FM	17.8	What You Model Is What You Get	36	17.14
			✔	17.9	Control Drawings	17	17.15
			FM	17.10	Understanding Less Documentation	17	17.15
				17.11	SM Start to Finish for Die Castings	07	17.15
			↖	17.12	HPGL as a Translator	09	17.15
			FM	17.13	Cleaning Up	41	17.15
			✔	17.14	Zero Deviations	41	17.16
			⊕	17.15	Tesselation Lines	41	17.16
			FM	17.16	Overlapping Entities	41	17.16
		Hardcopy	↖	17.17	Long Plots	09	17.16
			FM	17.18	Patterns and Plots	41	17.16
			✔	17.19	Resolution	41	17.16
				17.20	Troubleshooting Checklist	41	17.16
Interfacing	Graphic User Interfaces (GUIs)	Design Principles	✚	18.1	Leverage Known Design Techniques	43	18.9
			✔	18.2	Design Characteristics	43	18.10
				18.3	Design Guidelines	43	18.10

Section	Topic	Group	Icon	SMA	Name	Orig	Pg
Interfacing (*continued*)	Graphic User Interfaces (GUIs) (*continued*)	Organization	✔	18.4	Order and Chaos	43	18.10
				18.5	Consistency	43	18.10
				18.6	GUI Screen Layout	43	18.11
				18.7	Relationships	43	18.11
				18.8	Navigability	43	18.11
		Economy	✔	18.9	Economic Guidelines	43	18.11
		Communication	✔	18.10	Achieve a Balance	43	18.12
				18.11	Layout	43	18.12
				18.12	Legibility	43	18.12
				18.13	Screen Backgrounds	43	18.13
				18.14	Readability	43	18.13
				18.15	Typography	43	18.13
				18.16	Symbolism	43	18.13
				18.17	Multiple Views	43	18.14
		Color and Texture	FM	18.18	What Is Color?	43	18.14
			✔	18.19	Accomplishments	43	18.14
				18.20	Similarity	43	18.14
				18.21	Consistency	43	18.15
		Color Economy	✔	18.22	Principles and Redundancy	43	18.15
				18.23	Enhancement	43	18.15
				18.24	Sequencing	43	18.15
		Color Emphasis	✔	18.25	Suggested Emphasis	43	18.15
				18.26	Hierarchy	43	18.15
				18.27	Viewer Differences	43	18.16
		Color Communication	✔	18.28	Central and Peripheral Colors	43	18.16
				18.29	Combinations	43	18.16
			FM	18.30	Area	43	18.16
			✔	18.31	High Chroma and Spectrally Extreme Colors	43	18.16
			⊘	18.32	Chroma and Value	43	18.16
				18.33	Combinations to Avoid	43	18.16
			✔	18.34	For Dark Viewing	43	18.16
				18.35	For Light Viewing	43	18.16
			FM	18.36	Interactions	43	18.17
		Color Symbolism	✔	18.37	Using Color Codes	43	18.17
			⚠	18.38	Connotations	43	18.17
		Good to Know	FM	18.39	Shortcutting the GUI	09	18.17
			✚	18.40	For the Occasional User	30	18.17
	Rapid Prototyping	STL Interface	FM	19.1	Surface Gaps	44	19.14
				19.2	Facet Adjustment	09	19.14
		SLA Part Modeling	⊕	19.3	Additional Modeling Effort	09	19.14
				19.4	Part Orientation	09	19.15
				19.5	Multiple Parts	09	19.15
			FM	19.6	Additional Features	09	19.15
			↖	19.7	Part Size	09	19.15
			✔	19.8	Model Closure	44	19.15
		SLA Supports	⚠	19.9	Internal Supports	09	19.15
			⊕	19.10	Self-Supporting Features	09	19.15
				19.11	Avoid Delays and Rework	09	19.16
				19.12	Review Support Structure Designs	09	19.16
				19.13	Support Generation	09	19.16
				19.14	Separate STL Files	09	19.16
			FM	19.15	Support Structure Software	44	19.16

Section	Topic	Group	Icon	SMA	Name	Orig	Pg
Interfacing (*continued*)	Rapid Prototyping (*continued*)	SLA Production	℻	19.16	Surface Finish	44	19.16
				19.17	Layer Thickness	44	19.17
				19.18	Resin Viscosity	44	19.17
				19.19	Photo Sensitivity	44	19.17
				19.20	The SLA Unit	44	19.17
				19.21	Production Time	09	19.17
			⊕	19.22	Unnecessary Geometric Features	09	19.17
		SLA Recommendations	⊕	19.23	Look for Stress	09	19.17
				19.24	Let the Polymer Drain	09	19.17
				19.25	Polymer Materials	44	19.18
		SLS	⊕	19.26	Thermal Stress	44	19.18
		LOM	⊕	19.27	Drafts and Radii	45	19.18
		Needed Improvements	✔	19.28	The Right Tool for the Job	44	19.18
			✚	19.29	A Push-Button System	44	19.18
				19.30	Build Directly	44	19.19
				19.31	Accept Smooth Surface Data	44	19.19
				19.32	Become Fiscally Sound	44	19.19
				19.33	Improve Price/Performance Ratio	44	19.19
				19.34	Education	44	19.19
			℻	19.35	Dispel the RP myths	44	19.19
			✚	19.36	Expand the Use of SM	44	19.19
	Data Exchange	Protection & Integrity	⚠	20.1	Security Plan	46	20.9
			⊕	20.2	Access Limitations	46	20.9
			✔	20.3	Security Measures	46	20.9
				20.4	Design for Data Integrity (DFDI)	46	20.9
		Legal Issues	℻	20.5	New Questions	46	20.9
				20.6	Anxieties and Perception	46	20.9
				20.7	The Uniform Commercial Code	46	20.9
			⊕	20.8	New Agreements	46	20.10
				20.9	Record Keeping	46	20.10
				20.10	Existing Agreements	46	20.10
			✔	20.11	Ten Commandments of Data Exchange	46	20.10
		Utilizing Existing Guidelines	⊕	20.12	Why Reinvent the Wheel?	46	20.12
			℻	20.13	AIAG Label Conventions	46	20.12
			⊕	20.14	Auto Company Guidelines	46	20.12
			℻	20.15	CALS Implementation	46	20.13
		Managing Expectations	℻	20.16	Time and Effort	46	20.13
			✔	20.17	Strive for Value, Not Perfection	46	20.13
		Evaluating Translator Capability	✔	20.18	Translator Flexibility	46	20.13
				20.19	Translator Accuracy or Granularity	46	20.13
				20.20	What to Look For	46	20.13
				20.21	What to Ask	46	20.13
		Delivery Mechanisms	✔	20.22	Check Compatibility	09	20.14
				20.23	Floppy Disks	09	20.15
				20.24	Tape-Drive Densities	46	20.15
			℻	20.25	UNIX Tape Archive (TAR) Utility	46	20.15
		Data Compression	℻	20.26	ASCII IGES Format	46	20.15
			⊕	20.27	UNIX Platforms	46	20.15
				20.28	Personal Computer (PC) Platforms	46	20.15

The Solid Modeling Adviser Master Table (*Continued*)

Section	Topic	Group	Icon	SMA	Name	Orig	Pg
Interfacing (*continued*)	Data Exchange (*continued*)	Checklists	✔	20.29	Rules for Data Integrity	46	20.15
				20.30	Data Integrity Checklist	46	20.16
				20.31	Contingency Plans	46	20.16
		Good to Know	FYI	20.32	2D Drawing File Sizes	36	20.16
				20.33	Organizational Preparation	46	20.17
				20.34	Macintosh Drives	46	20.17
			⊕	20.35	System ASCII Support	46	20.17
				20.36	Emerging Delivery Mechanisms	46	20.17
	IGES	Anatomy	✚	21.1	Custom Start Sections	46	21.7
				21.2	If Resulting Scale Is Too Large	46	21.7
		Entity Mapping	FYI	21.3	IGES Subsets	46	21.11
				21.4	Mathematical Approximations	46	21.11
			⚠	21.5	Entity Mismatch in Loop Testing	46	21.11
		Utilities	FYI	21.6	What IGES Utilities Can Do	46	21.13
				21.7	Pinpointing Pre- or Postprocessor Errors	46	21.13
				21.8	IGES Viewing Utilities	46	21.14
				21.9	Product Capability	46	21.14
				21.10	Product Reliability	46	21.14
			⚠	21.11	Human Understanding	46	21.14
		IGES Testing	⊕	21.12	Vendor Verification & Conformance Tests	46	21.14
			✔	21.13	Scope the Test	46	21.16
				21.14	Compare Entity Maps	46	21.16
			FYI	21.15	Visual Equivalence for Good Pictures	46	21.16
				21.16	Functional Equivalence for Good Data	46	21.16
			✔	21.17	Measuring Results	46	21.16
				21.18	Test Case Characteristics	46	21.17
				21.19	Test Case Sources	46	21.17
		Analysis and Debugging	FYI	21.20	Analysis & Verification	46	21.18
			✔	21.21	Debugging Hints	46	21.18
				21.22	IGES File Verification	46	21.18
			↖	21.23	If the IGES File Will Not Load	46	21.18
			✔	21.24	Plot-to-Plot Comparisons	46	21.19
		Judging and Documenting Test Results	FYI	21.25	The Final Judge	46	21.19
			⊕	21.26	Case Study Repositories	46	21.19
				21.27	Documentation	46	21.19
			✔	21.28	Record Keeping	46	21.20
		Overall Evaluation	FYI	21.29	An Iterative Approach	46	21.20
			⊕	21.30	Know the Model's History	46	21.20
		Contacts	FYI	21.31	CALS Test Network (CTN)	46	21.23
				21.32	The National IGES User Group and the IGES/PDES Organization (IPO)	46	21.23
				21.33	Translator and Utility Vendors	46	21.24
		Good to Know	⚠	21.34	Don't Jump to Conclusions	09	21.24
				21.35	Check Modeling Tolerances After Transfers	35	21.24
			⊕	21.36	Not Just SM Data	47	21.25
				21.37	View-Dependent IGES Transfers	08	21.25
			↖	21.38	Typical Record-Length Problem	46	21.25
			✚	21.39	Limited IGES File Size Acceptance	46	21.25
			FYI	21.40	Useful Facts About IGES Files	46	21.25

Section	Topic	Group	Icon	SMA	Name	Orig	Pg
Interfacing (*continued*)	IGES (*continued*)	Good to Know (*continued*)	⚠	21.41	Editing & Browsing	46	21.26
			◁	21.42	Standardization	48	21.26
				21.43	The Concept of an Object	48	21.26
	PDES/STEP	Contacts	FM	22.1	PDES, Inc.	48	22.8
				22.2	NIST and NIPDE	48	22.8
				22.3	The European Community	48	22.8
				22.4	The European Commission	48	22.9
				22.5	Other Contacts	48	22.9
		Good to Know	FM	22.6	Growth Path to STEP	47	22.9
				22.7	Application Protocols	24	22.9
			⊕	22.8	Know Your Process	48	22.10
			✔	22.9	Highly Integrated STEP (HISTEP™)	49/50	22.10
			FM	22.10	Important Technology Characteristics of STEP Tools	49/50	22.10
Implementation	Strategies	Change Management	✔	23.1	Implementation and Effectiveness	51/52	23.7
			⊕	23.2	Look Inward as Well	51/52	23.7
			✔	23.3	A Case in Point	51/52	23.7
			⊕	23.4	A Cultural Mind-Set	51/52	23.7
			✔	23.5	Easy for Change	51/52	23.7
			⊕	23.6	Marketing SM Internally	29	23.8
		Planning	⊕	23.7	Needs & Productivity Analyses	51/52	23.8
				23.8	Aiding Communication	51/52	23.11
				23.9	Internal Application Support	51/52	23.13
				23.10	Configuration & Performance	51/52	23.13
				23.11	Modeling Precision	51/52	23.13
			✔	23.12	Modeling Notes Improve Communications	51/52	23.13
			FM	23.13	Methods & Performance	51/52	23.13
				23.14	Lack of Commitment	51/52	23.13
				23.15	Executive Understanding	51/52	23.13
			⊕	23.16	Proficiency Tests	51/52	23.13
				23.17	Do Not Lose Sight of Goals	51/52	23.14
			✔	23.18	Backup & Archive Procedures	51/52	23.14
			⊕	23.19	Your Hardware Budget	51/52	23.16
		Good Practices	⊕	23.20	Documenting Project Costs	29	23.18
				23.21	Sharpen the Axe	29	23.18
				23.22	Cross-Fertilization	29	23.18
				23.23	For Designers and Engineers	29	23.18
			⊘	23.24	Avoid a Poisoned Attitude	29	23.18
				23.25	Hard Disk Space	09	23.18
				23.26	Monitoring Productivity	51/52	23.19
				23.27	Supported Functions	51/52	23.19
				23.28	Implementation Investments	51/52	23.19
			✔	23.29	Implementation Guidelines	36	23.19
			FM	23.30	A Never-Ending Story	29	23.19
			✔	23.31	Software Considerations	51/52	23.19
				23.32	Order of Accuracy	51/52	23.20
			⚠	23.33	Cost Per SM Workstation	51/52	23.20
				23.34	Benchmarking	51/52	23.20
			◁	23.35	The Right Tool for the Right Job	53	23.20
			✔	23.36	Factors to Consider	54	23.20

Section	Topic	Group	Icon	SMA	Name	Orig	Pg
Implementation (*continued*)	Manufacturing	Design	⊕	25.1	Principal Axes	40	25.5
		Features	⊕	25.2	Knowledge Utilization	40	25.8
		Process Planning	⊕	25.3	Exception Handling	40	25.11
			⚠	25.4	Operational Sequence	40	25.11
		Manufacturing	⊕	25.5	Standard Parts	40	25.13
			✔	25.6	Lowering NC Costs	40	25.13
			FM	25.7	Work in Progress	40	25.13
			⊕	25.8	Billet & Stock Management	40	25.13
		Robotics	FM	25.9	Part Handling	40	25.14
		Inspection	FM	25.10	Rigid Is Not Reality	40	25.15
		Patterns	FM	25.11	Casting Patterns	40	25.17
		Good Practices	✔	25.12	The Overall Design Process	40	25.19
				25.13	Modeling Advice	40	25.19
	Volumetrics	Display	FM	26.1	Display Interactivity	13	26.7
		Data Processing	FM	26.2	Critical Trade-Offs	13	26.7
				26.3	Acquisition Parameters	13	26.8
			⊕	26.4	Segmentation Procedures	13	26.8
				26.5	Database Access	13	26.8
		Data Representation	↖	26.6	Disadvantages of Volumetric Clouds	13	26.9
			✚	26.7	An Octree Disadvantage	13	26.9
			✔	26.8	Choosing a Representation Method	13	26.10
	Concurrent Engineering	Customer Focus	⊕	27.1	A Shared Vision	55	27.10
				27.2	Customer Contact	55	27.10
		People and Teamwork	⊕	27.3	Cross-Functional Teams	55	27.10
				27.4	A Supportive Culture	55	27.10
				27.5	Multiple Cycles	55	27.10
			FM	27.6	Take Ownership	20	27.10
			✔	27.7	Optimize the Design Process	20	27.10
				27.8	Organizational Barriers	20	27.11
		Systems	⊕	27.9	A Voice in the Process	55	27.11
				27.10	*Handbook of Solid Modeling*	55	27.11
				27.11	Support Human Communication	55	27.11
				27.12	Get Physical Fast	55	27.11
				27.13	Synchronization	55	27.11
				27.14	Product Data Management (PDM)	55	27.11
		Processes	⊕	27.15	All Things Considered	55	27.11
				27.16	A Value Chain	55	27.11
				27.17	Look Ahead & Behind	55	27.11
				27.18	Support Best Practices	55	27.12
				27.19	Capture Process Knowledge	55	27.12
				27.20	Seek & Use Appropriate Metrics	55	27.12
		Resources & Responsibilities	⊕	27.21	Administrative Functions	55	27.12
				27.22	The Total Product Life Cycle	55	27.12
		Manufacturing Infrastructure	⊕	27.23	External Resources	55	27.12
				27.24	Computer-Based Tools	55	27.12
				27.25	Integrate with Customers	55	27.12
				27.26	Invest in Special Relationships	55	27.12
				27.27	Old & New	55	27.12

Section	Topic	Group	Icon	SMA	Name	Orig	Pg
Implementation (*continued*)	Concurrent Engineering (*continued*)	Implementation	⊕	27.28	No Walls—One Team	25	27.12
			✔	27.29	CE Design Tips	17	27.13
			⊕	27.30	Hardware Capabilities	55	27.13
				27.31	SM Sells Ideas	55	27.13
				27.32	SM and X Terminals	55	27.13
				27.33	SM, Customers, and Suppliers	55	27.13
				27.34	Data Exchange	55	27.13
			FM	27.35	Not Just Geometry	55	27.13
		Common CE Pitfalls	⚠	27.36	Information Explosion	56	27.13
			🚫	27.37	Spurts Are Not Desirable	56	27.13
			⚠	27.38	Risk of Wasted Effort	56	27.14
				27.39	Possible Increase of Iterative Costs	56	27.14
				27.40	Errors May Build Up	56	27.14
	Data Management	Product Data Management (PDM)	⊕	28.1	PDM Is Imperative	01	28.4
			◁	28.2	Who Will Benefit Most?	36	28.4
			⊕	28.3	A PDM Assessment	57	28.5
			FM	28.4	Nine Things PDM Can Do	17	28.5
			✔	28.5	Knowledgeable Assets	36	28.5
			⊕	28.6	Attributes	36	28.5
				28.7	If PDM Is Not Used	36	28.5
				28.8	For Multiple Users	36	28.6
		Network Considerations	✔	28.9	Network Bandwidth	01	28.6
				28.10	Networking Voice and Video	01	28.6
		Needed	✚	28.11	Database Editing	08	28.6
				28.12	UNDO Applications	08	28.6
				28.13	Information Hooks	29	28.6
				28.14	Database Searches	29	28.7
		Good to Know	⊕	28.15	Smart Part Libraries	21	28.7
				28.16	SM Database Management Tips	17	28.7
				28.17	Using Alphanumeric Terminals	29	28.7
			✔	28.18	Data Access Management	29	28.7
			⊕	28.19	Data Links	09	28.8
In the Industry	At Sony Corporation	Applications	FM	29.1	Related Issues	58/59	29.11
			⊕	29.2	Where Used	58/59	29.11
		Optimum System Configuration	⊕	29.3	Exceed Minimum Requirements	58/59	29.13
			FM	29.4	Performance Resources	58/59	29.13
			⊕	29.5	RAM Disks	58/59	29.13
		File Management	⊕	29.6	File Directories	58/59	29.13
			⚠	29.7	Backup Files	58/59	29.13
		Data Management	⊕	29.8	Naming Files	58/59	29.13
				29.9	Managing Objects	58/59	29.13
		3D Orientation	FM	29.10	Local Coordinate Systems	58/59	29.13
			⊕	29.11	Orienting Objects	58/59	29.14
		Display	FM	29.12	Wireframe Displays	58/59	29.14
				29.13	Shaded Displays	58/59	29.14
			⊕	29.14	Color Management	58/59	29.14
				29.15	Display On/Off Functions	58/59	29.14
		Systems Information	FM	29.16	X-Windows System	58/59	29.14
			✔	29.17	Determining Machine Status	58/59	29.14

Section	Topic	Group	Icon	SMA	Name	Orig	Pg
In the Industry (*continued*)	At Sony Corporation (*continued*)	Good to Know	⊘	29.18	Fillets and Chamfers	58/59	29.15
			⊕	29.19	Less Is Good	58/59	29.15
				29.20	Feature Functions	58/59	29.15
			FM	29.21	Optimization of Facets	58/59	29.15
			⊕	29.22	Performance Evaluations	58/59	29.15
			✚	29.23	Management Reform	58/59	29.15
			↖	29.24	Interference by Offset	58/59	29.15
			FM	29.25	Hand Operations	58/59	29.15
	At Volkswagen Automotive Group	Good Practices	⊕	30.1	Flexibility & Acceptance	60/61	30.12
				30.2	Product Definition	60/61	30.12
				30.3	Integrate a Relational Data Management System	60/61	30.12
				30.4	A Distributed Object-Oriented Database	60/61	30.12
		Recommended Guidelines	✔	30.5	A Complete SM System	60/61	30.12
				30.6	Parameter Definition	60/61	30.12
				30.7	Standards	60/61	30.12
				30.8	CAE Tools	60/61	30.12
				30.9	Solutions for Plastic Parts	60/61	30.13
		Good to Know	FM	30.10	What to Expect	60/61	30.13
				30.11	Choosing Applications	60/61	30.13
	At Hewlett Packard Company	Hidden Limitations	⚠	31.1	Retraining	62	31.11
				31.2	Expectations	62	31.11
			FM	31.3	Information Overload	62	31.11
				31.4	Reengineering	62	31.11
				31.5	Company Culture	62	31.11
		Hidden Benefits	⊕	31.6	Creativity and Innovation	62	31.12
				31.7	Teamwork	62	31.12
				31.8	Morale	62	31.12
				31.9	Visionary Thinking	62	31.12
		Additional Limitations	✚	31.10	Expenses	62	31.12
				31.11	Integration	62	31.12
				31.12	Drawings vs. Models	62	31.12
				31.13	System Performance	62	31.12
			⊕	31.14	Networking and Communication	62	31.13
		General Advice	⊕	31.15	Think Long-Term	62	31.13
				31.16	Standardize	62	31.13
				31.17	Modularity	62	31.13
				31.18	Encourage Expertise	62	31.13
				31.19	Keep It Simple	62	31.13
				31.20	A Dual Strategy	62	31.14
				31.21	Visionary Goals	62	31.14
				31.22	Measure Progress	62	31.14
				31.23	Encourage Communication	62	31.14
			✔	31.24	Ease of Use	62	31.14
				31.25	Be Aware of the Learning Curve	62	31.14
				31.26	Continuing Education	62	31.14
			⚠	31.27	Culture and Social Issues	62	31.14
			FM	31.28	Expect Change	62	31.14

The Solid Modeling Adviser Master Table (*Continued*)

Section	Topic	Group	Icon	SMA	Name	Orig	Pg
In the Industry (*continued*)	At Eaton Corp., Supercharger Div.	SM Caution	⚠	32.1	Associated Detail Drawings	45	32.8
		Pitfalls	⚠	32.2	Organizational Culture	45	32.9
				32.3	Training in Techniques	45	32.10
				32.4	Lost or Corrupted Models	45	32.10
			⊕	32.5	Training Requirements	45	32.10
				32.6	Spot Training	45	32.10
			✚	32.7	Associativity, Good and Bad	45	32.10
		Needed Improvements	✚	32.8	Faster Affordable Hardware	45	32.11
				32.9	Increased Feature Modeling Capability	45	32.11
				32.10	Assembly Modeling	45	32.11
	Roundtable Discussion	Advice and Observations	◁	33.1	Meeting Your Needs	63	33.5
			⊕	33.2	Benchmarks and Reality	63	33.5
				33.3	A Plan for Change	64	33.5
			⊘	33.4	Make a Wholesale Commitment	64	33.6
			◁	33.5	Balance People, Processes, and Technology	65	33.6
			M	33.6	Cost Considerations	65	33.6
			◁	33.7	In Retrospect	36	33.6
				33.8	Drawings and Model Complexity	36	33.6
				33.9	Conventional Detail Requirements	36	33.6
			✚	33.10	SM Flaws	36	33.6
				33.11	SM of the Future	36	33.7
				33.12	More SM Flaws	17	33.7
			⊕	33.13	SM Hardware Selection	17	33.7
			✚	33.14	The Rest of the Story	29	33.7
			M	33.15	The Weakest Link	66	33.7
			◁	33.16	Design Dependence	66	33.8

The Solid Modeling Adviser Contributors List

01. Joel N. Orr, President, Orr Associates International, Chesapeake, Va.
02. Ted Craft, Support Specialist, Computervision Corp., Oakbrook Terrace, Ill.
03. Johannes Eisenkoelbl, Application Engineer, Computervision Corp., Vienna, Austria
04. Dr. Patrick J. Hanratty, President, MCS Inc., Scottsdale, Ariz.
05. Stephan Lewis, President, Think CAD Blue, Redondo Beach, Calif.
06. Nancy Anderson-Semple, Technical Editor, Computervision Corporation, Bedford, Mass.
07. Philip Johnson, Development Engineer, Emerson Electric Company, St. Louis, Mo.
08. George E. Mock, Member Technical Staff, AT&T Network Cable Systems, Norcross, Ga.
09. Don LaCourse, President, The Solid Modeling ExChange, Algood, Tenn.
10. Andrew Price, Manager Engineering Applications, Axis Technologies, Fairport, N.Y.
11. Forrest K. Blair, President, Microport Systems, Hyde Park, Utah
12. John R. Gowans, Applications Support Specialist, CRS Sirrine Engineers, Greenville, S.C.
13. Dr. Donald J. Meagher, President, Octree Corporation, Coopertino, Calif.
14. Dr. Richard D. Lowrey, Engineering Consultant, San Jose, Calif.
15. John Skibinski, Program Director, Eaton Corp., Milwaukee, Wis.
16. Mark Russell, Senior Systems Engineer, Intergraph Corp., Huntsville, Ala.
17. Howard W. Stolz, Product Designer, Sun Microsystems, Mountain View, Calif.
18. Scott McOlash, Engineer, Eaton Corporation, Milwaukee, Wis.
19. George R. Winton III, Mechanical Engineer, Micromeritics, Lawrenceville, Ga.
20. Keith Campbell, Engineer, V.P. Marketing, American Small Business Computers, Pryor, Okla.
21. Richard A. St.Arnauld, Sr. Tool Design Engineer, Pratt & Whitney Aircraft Div. of UTC, West Palm Beach, Fla.
22. Brian Moriarty, Senior Engineer, Hamilton Standard Space & Sea Systems, Windsor Locks, Conn.
23. R. Herschel Redd, Senior Marketing Support Representative, IBM Corporation, Dallas, Tex.
24. Mark J. Silvestri, Life Cycle Solutions, Inc., Avon, Mass.
25. Eldad Cohen, Engineering Consultant, Brookline, Mass.
26. Lawrence W. Rosenfeld, President, Concentra Corporation, Coventry, England
27. Jay Cole, Wavefront Technologies, Santa Barbara, Calif.
28. Mike Wilson, Product Marketing Manager, Wavefront Technologies, Santa Barbara, Calif.
29. Brian Ruuska, CAD/CAE Applications Engineer, 3M Company, St. Paul, Minn.
30. David E. Schaeg, Designer, Emerson Motor Company, St. Louis, Mo.
31. Graham A. Rae, Director, MSC/Aries Product Management, The MacNeal-Schwendler Corporation, Lowell, Mass.
32. Darrel J. Hamlet, Senior Sales Engineer, Rand Technologies, Natick, Mass.
33. Mason Deever, Consultant, Jamm Computer Services, Mesa, Ariz.
34. Victor E. Wright, Design & Eng. Consultant, Louisville, Ky.
35. Wally Frederick, Director Customer Support, Varimetrix Corp., Palm Bay, Fla.
36. Kevin P. Alexander, CAD/CAM/CAE System Administrator, Littleford Day, Inc., Florence, Ky.
37. James D. Price, Vice President, Marketing, Mechanical Dynamics, Inc., Ann Arbor, Mich.
38. Dr. Edward J. Haug, Director, Center for Computer Aided Design, The University of Iowa, Iowa City, Iowa
39. Rexford L. Smith, President, Computer Aided Design Software, Inc., Coralville, Iowa
40. Robert J. Byrnes, Vice President, Varimetrix Corp., Palm Bay, Fla.

41. Olaf Bellstedt, Senior Software Engineer, Varimetrix Corp., Palm Bay, Fla.

42. Bernd Engel, Product Marketing Engineer, Hewlett Packard Co., Mechanical Design Division, Boeblingen, Germany

43. Aaron Marcus, President, Aaron Marcus and Associates, Inc., Emeryville, Calif.

44. Terry T. Wohlers, President, Wohlers Associates, Fort Collins, Colo.

45. Donald N. Wentworth, Supervisor—Advanced Engineering, Eaton Corp., Supercharger Div., Marshall, Mich.

46. Harlan Stokes, V.P. Sales & Marketing, IGES Data Analysis, Inc., Minneapolis, Minn.

47. Hermann Ruess, Hewlett-Packard Co., Mechanical Design Div., Boeblingen, Germany

48. Michael A. Dincau, President, Graphic Systems Inc., Burbank, Calif.

49. Michael T. Wood, Principal Member Technical Staff, Industrial Technology Institute, Ann Arbor, Mich.

50. Mitchell Fleischer, Scientific Fellow, Industrial Technology Institute, Ann Arbor, Mich.

51. Victor Bradley, Mechanical Consulting Services Coordinator, Intergraph Corp., Huntsville, Ala.

52. Thomas Riddle, Independent Consultant, Atlanta, Ga.

53. Jack Marathe, President, Universal Technical Systems, Inc., Rockford, Ill.

54. George LaBlanc, Director Marketing, Matra Datavision, Tewksbury, Mass.

55. Peter Marks, Managing Director, Design Insight, Los Gatos, Calif.

56. Biren Prasad, Sr., Engineering Consultant, Electronic Data Systems (EDS), General Motors Corp., Warren, Mich.; also Managing Editor, *Concurrent Engineering: Research & Applications* (CERA), W. Bloomfield, Mich.

57. Michael Legros, PDM Marketing Manager, Digital Equipment Corp., Marlboro, Mass.

58. Seiji Ito, Manager, Planning and Control Dept., Management and Eng. Information Systems Div., Sony Corporation, Japan

59. Hajime Ikeda, Assistant Manager, Design Innovation Dept., Management and Eng. Information Systems Div., Sony Corporation, Japan

60. Dr.-Ing. Peter Kellner, Systems Analyst, Volkswagen Automotive Group, Wolfsburg, Germany

61. Dr.-Ing. Viet Vu-Han, Systems Analyst, Volkswagen Automotive Group, Wolfsburg, Germany

62. Peter Zivkov, MCAE Technologies Consultant, Corporate Eng., Hewlett Packard Co., Palo Alto, Calif.

63. Stephen Wolfe, Editor, Computer-Aided Report, San Diego, Calif.

64. Marc Halpern, Research Manager, D.H. Brown & Associates, Inc., Port Chester, N.Y.

65. Dave Burdick, Program Director CIM Service, The Gartner Group, Inc., Santa Clara, Calif.

66. Gisela Wilson, Program Manager, CAD/CAM International Data Corp. (IDC), Framingham, Mass., USA

67. Richard Kading, Manager of Engineering and Development, Computer Aided Design Software, Inc., Coralville, Iowa

Contributors

Dr. Lawrence L. Barinka President, Interactive Computer Modelling, Inc., Reston, Virginia *(Chapter 24: Solid Modeling and Design)*

Olaf Bellstedt Senior Software Eng., Varimetrix Corporation, Palm Bay, Florida *(Chapter 16: Customizing the Solid Modeling System; Chapter 17: Solid Modeling and Documentation)*

Victor Bradley Mechanical Consulting Services Coordinator, Intergraph Corporation, Huntsville, Alabama *(Chapter 23: Solid Modeling Implementation Strategies)*

Robert J. Byrnes Vice President, Varimetrix Corporation, Palm Bay, Florida *(Chapter 15: Solid Modeling for Numerical Control; Chapter 25: Solid Modeling for Manufacturing)*

Laura Carrabine Editorial Manager, Structural Dynamics Research Corporation, Milford, Ohio *(Chapter 33: Roundtable Discussion, Despite High-Tech SM Laurels, the Glory Remains in Making Parts)*

Michael A. Dincau President, Graphic Systems Inc., Burbank, California *(Chapter 22: Solid Modeling and Data Exchange Using STEP (PDES/STEP)*

Darrel J. Hamlet Sr. Sales Engineer, Rand Technologies, Natick, Massachusetts *(Chapter 11: Solid Modeling for Assemblies)*

Dr. Patrick J. Hanratty President, Manufacturing and Consulting Services, Inc., Scottsdale, Arizona *(Chapter 8: Parametric/Relational Solid Modeling)*

Dr. Edward J. Haug Director, Center for Computer Aided Design, The University of Iowa, Iowa City, Iowa *(Chapter 13: Solid Modeling for Kinematic and Dynamic Analysis)*

Hajime Ikeda Assistant Manager, Design Innovation Dept., Management and Engineering Information Systems Div., Sony Corporation, Yokohama, Japan *(Chapter 29: Solid Modeling at Sony Corporation)*

Seiji Ito Manager, Planning and Control Dept., Management and Engineering Information Systems Dept., Sony Corporation, Yokohama, Japan *(Chapter 29: Solid Modeling at Sony Corporation)*

Dr.-Ing. Peter Kellner Systems Analyst, Volkswagen Automotive Group, Wolfsburg, Germany *(Chapter 30: Solid Modeling at Volkswagen Automotive Group)*

Donald E. LaCourse President, The Solid Modeling Exchange, Algood, Tennessee *(Chapter 1: Read This First)*

Dr. Richard D. Lowrey Mechanical Engineering Consultant, San Jose, California *(Chapter 6: Modeling Strategies; Chapter 7: Editing Strategies; Chapter 14: Solid Modeling for Finite Element Analysis (FEA))*

Aaron Marcus President, Aaron Marcus and Associates, Inc., Emeryville, California *(Chapter 18: Graphic User Interfaces (GUIs))*

Peter Marks Managing Director, Design Insight, Los Gatos, California *(Chapter 27: The Role of Solid Modeling in Concurrent Engineering)*

Dr. Donald J. Meagher President, Octree Corporation, Coopertino, California *(Chapter 4: Solid Modeling Database Structures; Chapter 26: Volumetric Solid Modeling)*

Joel N. Orr President, Orr Associates International, Chesapeake, Virginia *(Chapter 2: Introducing Solid Modeling; Chapter 5: Curves and Surfaces for Solid Modeling; Chapter 10: Viewing and Displaying Solid Models; Chapter 28: Managing Solid Modeling Data)*

Graham A. Rae Director, MSC/Aries Product Management, The MacNeal-Schwendler Corporation, Lowell, Massachusetts *(Chapter 11: Solid Modeling for Assemblies)*

Thomas Riddle Independent Consultant, Atlanta, Georgia *(Chapter 23: Solid Modeling Implementation Strategies)*

Lawrence W. Rosenfeld President, Concentra Corporation, Coventry, England *(Chapter 9: Solid Modeling and Knowledge-Based Engineering)*

Rexford L. Smith President, Computer Aided Design Software, Inc., Coralville, Iowa *(Chapter 13: Solid Modeling for Kinematic and Dynamic Analysis)*

Harlan Stokes V.P. Sales & Marketing, IGES Data Analysis, Inc., Minneapolis, Minnesota *(Chapter 20: Preparing for Data Exchange; Chapter 21: Solid Modeling and the Initial Graphics Exchange Specification (IGES))*

Dr.-Ing. Viet Vu-Han Systems Analyst, Volkswagen Automotive Group, Wolfsburg, Germany *(Chapter 30: Solid Modeling at Volkswagen Automotive Group)*

Donald N. Wentworth Supervisor—Advanced Engineering, Eaton Corporation Supercharger Division, Marshall, Michigan *(Chapter 32: Solid Modeling at Eaton Corporation, Supercharger Division)*

Terry T. Wohlers President, Wohlers Associates, Fort Collins, Colorado *(Chapter 19: Solid Modeling and Rapid Prototyping)*

Victor E. Wright Design and Engineering Consultant, Louisville, Kentucky *(Chapter 3: Solid Modeling Concepts; Chapter 12: Solid Modeling and Mass-Properties Analysis)*

Peter Zivkov MCAE Technologies Consultant, Corporate Engineering, Hewlett-Packard Company, Palo Alto, California *(Chapter 31: Solid Modeling at Hewlett-Packard Company)*

Preface

Having spent to date 17 rewarding years in product design and engineering, what I regret most is never seeming to have enough time in the workday to fully explore all of the benefits and proper techniques of my Computer-Aided Engineering (CAE) tools. Unfortunately, the pressures of meeting the customer's needs, design specifications, reviews, and deadlines of multiple projects has time and again left me (like many in my field) seeking and accepting a path of least resistance. If the information most helpful to me was not right at my fingertips, I could not spare the time to find it.

In the case of Solid Modeling and related technologies this dilemma was compounded by the fact that I had made a disciplined effort to seek the information that I felt I needed—but then had difficulty finding it!

This handbook is the product of these frustrations. In its preparation I have been rewarded (and dismayed) by the fact that I was not alone in my search and encouraged by the willingness of so many professionals in the various consulting, development, and engineering communities to come forward and assist me in this task.

Although these pages are born of selfish need, I eagerly share them with you in the hopes of reducing your search for answers. I hope they provide even more assistance to you than they have already provided me and my colleagues during their preparation. I also encourage your feedback (good, bad, or otherwise) so that this handbook can continue to grow and provide the types of assistance we need. So let's be sure to keep this handbook at our fingertips. There's a good chance we're going to need it!

Acknowledgments

A very special thanks to A. Clinton Brooks and family and George M. Hunt III for their valued assistance in preparing the manuscript for this edition.

A deep appreciation to all the engineering professionals who have submitted tips and suggestions which did not make it onto the final pages of this edition. Your valued input is being reserved for future editions and publications.

An additional special thanks to the following individuals not credited elsewhere in this handbook who have provided valuable assistance, support, and advice.

Sue Arellano, Amy Hendrickson,
and Dr. Paul Jacobs
    3D Systems, Inc.

Peter May
    Algor, Inc.

Craig Hendrickson
    American Small Business Computers

Mary Abood
    Advanstar Communications

Ann Meister
    Ann E. Meister Company

Val Dyer
    Applicon, Inc.

Bill Barnes, Cindy Dooling, Marilyn Guerin,
Buzz Kross, Andrew Mackles, Beth McConahey,
UVL Narayana, Elizabeth Parkinson,
and Mike Tanner
    Autodesk, Inc.

Claudia Smith
    **Computer-Aided Design Software, Inc.
(CADSI)**

Bill Hasenjaeger
    CGTech

Lou Bodnar and Charley Ferrucci
    Cadkey, Inc.

John MacKrell
    Cimdata, Inc.

Ralph Ezard
    Cimplex Corporation

Steven Wolfe
    Computer-Aided Design Report

John Murphy and Laura Thompson
    Computervision Corporation

Christine Bingert
    Cubital America, Inc.

Linda Kesten
Cubital Ltd.

Kent Nutt
DTM Corporation

Charles Foundyller
Daratech, Inc.

Carol Cronan and Ann Guillow
Dassault Systemes

Tony Affuso, John Baker, Dan Dunbar,
Raj Khoshoo, and Dick Schenk
EDS Unigraphics

Jennifer Maher
Helisys, Inc.

Debbie Fuchs, Jim Gutowski, Ute Hillmer,
Debbie Madden, Matthew Nguyen,
and Marvel O'Connor
Hewlett Packard Company

Johny Bennett, Bob Clock, Ed Hamilton,
Todd McCall, Susan Mueller, John Sarsgard,
Sam Schrage, and Jim Staropoli
IBM Corporation

Tom Schaefer and John Wilson
**Concentra Corporation
(formerly ICAD, Inc.)**

Vicki Blaum, Chris Carroll, Kim Corbridge,
Bryan Floyd, Katharine Garstka, Neysa Holland,
Chris Nivens, Jeannie Robison, Brenda Stevens,
Shelly Tedin, Joe Tripiano, and Phil Williams
Intergraph Corporation

David Mattei
International TechneGroup, Inc.

Scott Hanratty and Maureen Nowland
**Manufacturing and Consulting Services,
Inc. (MCS)**

Drexel Ace, Julieann Martin, and Ken Morris
**The MacNeal-Schwendler Corporation
(MSC)**

Henry Fong
Mark Analysis, Inc.

Barbara Alvarado, Dave Howarth,
and Judy Wetzler
Matra Datavision, Inc.

Hayward Anderson, Jim Perkins, John Raeuber,
Steve Smith, and Tom Tyan
McCord Winn Sub. Textron, Inc.

Donna Westermann
McDonnell Douglas Corporation

Judith Jones
Multipoint Technology Group

Debbie Baione and Maureen Eddy
**National Computer Graphics Association
(NCGA) CAD Society**

Bill Anderson and Bob Kiggans
PDES, Inc.

Nancy Herzog, John Hudson, Amanda Radice,
and Liz Schelpt
Parametric Technology Corporation (PTC)

Beverly Beckert and John Krouse
Penton Publishing, CAE Magazine

Joy Folla and Pam Kerwin
Pixar, Inc.

Steve Stewart
Protogenic, Inc.

Bruce Haase
SBC Company

Andrea Hannahan, Jere King, Joe Kormos,
and Karen Kramer
SDRC

Stephen Schroff
Schroff Development Corporation

Jim Grim and David Merritt
Schaefer Visual Media Group (SVMG)

Nancy Mauter
Society of Manufacturing Engineers (SME)

Jane Patterson
Spaceball Technologies

Mary Stanley
Stratasys, Inc.

Suzanne Batt, Stan Kelley, Howard Wood,
and Mary Brahney
Ansys, Inc.

Raymond Kurland
TechniCom, Inc.

Mike Crown, Lennie Morrison,
and Mark Vorwaller
Varimetrix Corporation

Tom Reyburn
Wavefront Technologies

Donald E. LaCourse
Algood, Tennessee

Section 1
Overview

To Hell With a Fancy Headline.
Buy DesignCAD and Save Money!

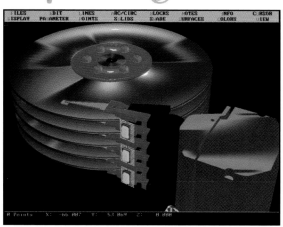

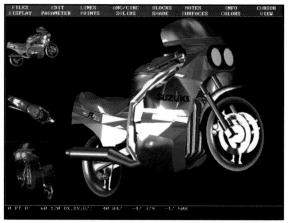

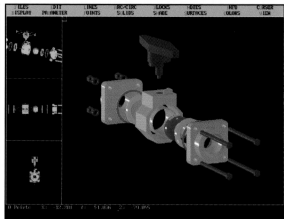

Designs submitted by actual users.

It *is possible* to get these results for under $500!

According to an independent study made by the California Department of Education. DesignCAD 3D beat all other PC Based, high-end, solid modeling programs in NINE MAJOR CATEGORIES! Plus, DesignCAD 3D did all of this for less than $500!

DESIGNCAD 3D COMES FULLY EQUIPPED WITH: Programming Language • Rendering With Textures • Boolean Operations • Solids Modeling • Volume and Surface Area Calculations • 3D Text and Dimensioning • Support of 10 File Formats • Macros

ONLY $499 (or less!)

Call Now for More Details and Ask About Your FREE Color Brochure and Demo Disk!

Phone (918)825-7555
Fax (918)825-6359

AMERICAN SMALL BUSINESS COMPUTERS
ONE AMERICAN WAY • PRYOR • OK • 74361

(CIRCLE READER SERVICE NO. 212)

Chapter 1
Read This First

Donald E. LaCourse
President
The Solid Modeling ExChange

On behalf of the entire *Handbook of Solid Modeling* (SM) team, I would like to welcome you to our first edition. This opening chapter is meant to offer an understanding of the *Handbook of SM*'s definition, purpose, structure, content, and usage. We hope that you will find this handbook entertaining, enlightening, and beneficial in your ongoing quest for knowledge.

1.1 What This Handbook Is

This handbook is the product of a coalition of active engineering professionals, consultants, and SM-related developers, all with a common goal—to keep industry informed and advised on SM technology and related issues. The *Handbook of Solid Modeling* is meant to be a practical and comprehensive guide for those who operate, manage, develop, and promote SM technology.

1.2 What This Handbook Is Not

This handbook is not meant to replace any SM system operations manuals but, rather, to complement and extend them. As such, all product (SM software)-specific information and much of the basic information found in operating manuals will not be found in this handbook.

There is no discussion on the vices or virtues of any one SM-related product or system over another. However, areas of concern and/or potential benefits discussed here may apply more or less to individual systems. We do not attempt here to make such distinctions.

Just as SM technology is not a panacea, this handbook is not a cure for all problem situations that may arise. Information and advice, however, is offered for many diverse topics. Always refer to your SM operations manual for software-specific issues.

1.3 The Solid Modeling Adviser

The Solid Modeling Adviser (SMA) is a separate but interrelated publication within this handbook. Advice and observations from active engineering professionals involved with SM on a daily basis, as well as software developers, industry consultants, and our own team of contributing authors, form recorded entries in The SM Adviser.

The SM Adviser is comprised of over 700 entries, all tabulated as a whole in the SMA Master Table at the front of this handbook. The majority of entries are located at the end of each chapter. Some entries, however, can be found at key locations within each chapter text. The SM Adviser entries appear in designated boxes separate from the general handbook text (see Fig. 1.1). Each box contains entries from a single source.

SMA.10.2   What's Wrong with Isometric Viewing

Many intricate solid models lose detail when viewed inproperly. If possible, avoid viewing from a true isometric view or where two sides are equal angles from the eye point. A slightly skewed angle will result in differing shades for each side, making the display of the model clearer. Where software allows, add more light sources to enhance background detail, but avoid overlighting the model.

John R. Gowans, Applications Support Specialist
CRS Sirrine Engineers, Greenville, S.C.

FIGURE 1.1   Sample entry box from The Solid Modeling Adviser. Note the categorical icon to the left of the entry (see Sec. 1.4.1).

The first line of each entry from left to right contains the entry number and entry name. The entry number begins with the letters "SMA" to distinguish it from regular chapter topics, continues with the number of the chapter in which the entry appears, and concludes with the consecutive number of the entry within that chapter. The example from Fig. 1.1 is the SMA entry from Chap. 10, number 2. In the lower right corner of each entry box appears a credit to the individual(s) who submitted all of the entries within that box. Entry boxes without credits are submitted by the chapter author(s). A complete list of the SMA contributors for this edition can be found following the SMA Master Table at the front of this handbook.

The SM Adviser is offered for your benefit. Each entry should be evaluated individually based on your needs. Some entries may not apply to your applications. Since SM technology is entirely system-dependent, those entries that suggest technology deficiencies or cautions may not apply to every system.

1.4   Handbook Structure

This handbook is structured for extended and repeated reference. Topics are grouped in logical sections and chapters, each designed to focus on SM-related issues. Categorical icons are used extensively throughout the handbook to allow the reader to focus in on categories of information regardless of content or origin. The categorical icons are discussed further in Sec. 1.4.1.

The handbook's page layout consists of two primary regions: the quick reference region and the primary data region (see Fig. 1.2). The quick reference region contains topic numbers, headings, SMA group headings, and categorical icons which correspond to text, graphics, and entries from the SM Adviser located in the primary data region. Some graphics and images are expanded and, as such, require the entire page area.

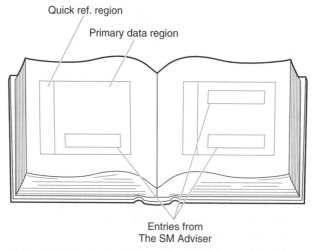

Quick ref. region

Primary data region

Entries from
The SM Adviser

FIGURE 1.2   The *Handbook of SM*'s page layout. There are two (2) primary regions and three (3) areas of information on a typical page.

1.4.1   Categorical Icons

To assist in locating categories of information regardless of section, chapter, or content, eight distinguishable categorical icons (see Table 1.1) appear throughout the handbook in the quick reference region of each page. These icons also appear in the SM Adviser entry table at the front of this handbook to assist in locating categories of entries. The icons mark the beginning and ending of that category of information.

TABLE 1.1   The Eight Categorical Icons Used in This Handbook

These icons appear in the Quick Reference region of each page as well as in The SM Adviser Master Table located at the front of this handbook.

Icon	Information Category	Icon	Information Category
	Caution Warns of possible danger and the reader is advised to be on the lookout.		**Work-Around** Indicates suggested ways to avoid potential problems.
	Avoid Indicates techniques or processes to avoid.		**Needed Improvements** Indicates areas where technology is lacking and improvement is suggested.
	Checklist Indicates rules, guidelines, and/or checklists of information to review.		**Point of View** Indicates a personal opinion or a particular point of view.
	Recommended Indicates recommended practices for optimum performance and productivity.		**For Your Information** Indicates information that is considered good to know.

1.4.2   Handbook Sections

Apart from the front and back matter and appendixes, the handbook is divided into six distinct sections, each focusing on a different aspect of SM technology. These sections are not necessarily arranged in the order in which one would encounter such information in the real world but, rather, in an order that will assist in understanding the technology as a whole.

Section 1: Overview

This section has only two chapters. Chapter 1, aptly named "Read This First" (and please do so), provides an orientation to the entire contents of the handbook. Chapter 2 provides an introduction to solid modeling.

Section 2: Techniques

This section has eight chapters and can be considered the heart of the entire handbook (from an operational standpoint). It begins with basic concepts and SM database structures. It continues with geometric-related chapters discussing the use of curves and surfaces with SM, as well as modeling and editing strategies. An entire chapter is dedicated to the parametric relational issues of SM from both a modeling and an editing standpoint. It should be noted that the bulk of the prior chapters on modeling and editing discuss strategies that are not parametric-related. The section continues with a discussion on SM and knowledge-based engineering, and concludes with viewing and displaying solid models.

Section 3: Applications

This section has seven chapters devoted to modular applications which can all be found completely integrated within the same SM system. The discussion begins with assembly modeling and continues with various forms of analysis, including mass properties, kinematics and dynamics, and finite elements. There is a discussion on SM for numerical control (CAM) and how to benefit from customization. The section concludes with a discussion on SM and various forms of documentation. These chapters focus on the SM-related issues of each of these applications.

Section 4: Interfacing

This section contains five chapters, all dedicated to methods of interfacing with SM technology from both a human and an electronic standpoint. The section begins with an overview of graphic user interfaces (GUIs) and provides extensive assistance on evaluating and developing a productive GUI. The discussion continues with extensive coverage of various rapid prototyping (RP) technologies. The remaining three chapters deal thoroughly with the exchange of CAD data. These chapters will be of great assistance to *all* professionals involved with CAD, not just SM professionals. They begin with preparing for data exchange and end with current exchange standards, including IGES and STEP.

Section 5: Implementation

This section has six chapters. The first chapter covers implementation strategies and recommended reading for all SM professionals—especially support personnel and managers. The next three chapters cover SM and its implementation in various disciplines such as design, manufacturing, and medicine (volumetrics). The section continues with an understanding of the role of SM in concurrent engineering methodologies and concludes with discussions on managing accumulating SM data.

Section 6: In the Field

This is the final section of the handbook and contains five chapters. The first four chapters present documented case studies of companies implementing SM technology around the world. The concluding chapter presents a roundtable discussion on SM technology today and in the future.

1.4.3   Reader Participation

Much of the knowledge that can most directly benefit SM-related professionals lies with you, our reader. There is no substitute for knowledge built from actual firsthand experiences. Many of the entries in the SM Adviser (see Sec. 1.3) have been submitted by active engineering professionals. If you have knowledge, information, advice, or observations concerning any SM- or 3D-related topic, or if you have any questions, comments, or criticisms concerning SM technology and/or this handbook, we would certainly like to hear from you. Your comments may be considered for inclusion in future supplements or editions of the *Handbook of Solid Modeling* and related publications.

To submit comments, simply make a copy of and fill out the Reader Comment and Submission Form shown in Fig. 1.3. If possible, try not to use the original form, so that others may copy it as well. Be sure to complete all portions of the form, including your telephone number, so that we may contact you if necessary. Sign your name where indicated and include a completed form with each submission you make. We also encourage you to duplicate and distribute this form to other professionals. If your submission includes previously copyrighted or published material in any form, from any source, the copyright holders must complete and sign the Material Release and Permissions Form shown in Fig. 1.4 and include it with each submission.

If possible, please follow these steps to complete each submission:

1. Include one (1) hard copy (printout) of all text.
2. Include three (3) original prints (preferably from a laser or higher-resolution printer) of any related graphics—one graphic per page.
3. Submit text for suggested headings and/or captions for each graphic separately (not as part of the graphic).

Reader Comment/Submission Form
Handbook of Solid Modeling

Use this form for general comments and submissions for <u>The SM Adviser.</u>
(Copying, distribution, and multiple submissions are encouraged.)

(Please type/print clearly, and attach business card.)

NAME

TITLE

COMPANY

ADDRESS

MAIL STOP

CITY/STATE/ZIP

TELEPHONE   FAX

Submission Category (Check all that apply.)

Handbook Categories
- ❏ 01 SM Concepts
- ❏ 02 SM Database Structures
- ❏ 03 Curves & Surfaces with SM
- ❏ 04 SM Building Strategies
- ❏ 05 SM Editing Strategies
- ❏ 06 Parametric/Relational SM
- ❏ 07 Knowledge Based Eng.
- ❏ 08 Viewing & Display SM
- ❏ 09 Solid Assembly Modeling
- ❏ 10 SM & Mass Properties
- ❏ 11 SM & Kinematics/Dynamics
- ❏ 12 SM & Numerical Control
- ❏ 13 Customizing SM
- ❏ 14 SM & Documentation
- ❏ 15 SM & GUIs
- ❏ 16 SM & Rapid Prototyping

- ❏ 17 Preparing for Data Exchange
- ❏ 18 SM & IGES
- ❏ 19 SM & PDES/STEP
- ❏ 20 SM Implementation Strategies
- ❏ 21 SM and Design
- ❏ 22 SM & Manufacturing
- ❏ 23 SM & Volumetrics
- ❏ 24 SM and Concurrent Engineering
- ❏ 25 Managing SM Data

Additional Categories
- ❏ 26 General Suggestion Box
- ❏ 27 What I Like About This Book
- ❏ 28 What I Don't Like About This Book
- ❏ 29 Question Box
- ❏ 30 Other: _____

Include Your Submitted Comments Here (Please type or print clearly. Attach additional material if desired.)

Category	Comment or Submission

Your comments cannot be used without your signature. (Please include an ASCII/DOS text file if available.)

Submission Agreement

I understand that the information that I have provided on or attached to this form will be considered for publication in **The Handbook of Solid Modeling** or related publications (Work) and is subject to these terms and conditions. I represent and warrant that this information is original to the best of my knowledge and that it does not violate or infringe any copyright, trademark, patent, statutory, common law, or proprietary rights of others, or contain anything libelous. I hereby grant and assign to the Editor in Chief all exclusive rights to this information under the United States copyright law and all international copyright conventions, including the right to copyright this information and any renewals thereof in the name of the Publisher, the Editor in Chief, or their assignees. I understand that I shall retain the right to use this information in professional journals and for internal use within my own firm without further permission from the Publisher or the Editor in Chief provided that the Work and the Publisher are given appropriate credit. I understand that if chosen for publication I will be given full credit where this information appears in every printed edition of the Work and that this credit shall constitute full payment to me. My signature below indicates that I have read and agree to these terms and conditions.

SIGN HERE   DATE   (EDITOR IN CHIEF)

PRINT YOUR NAME HERE

Return Submissions To:

**Handbook of Solid Modeling
Don LaCourse, Editor in Chief
c/o**

**The Solid Modeling ExChange
P.O. Box 49336
Algood, TN 38506-0336
Attn. Reader Submissions**

FIGURE 1.3 Reader comment and submission form. Complete, sign, and include a copy of this form with each submission. Please leave this form attached to this handbook so that other readers may copy it and make submissions as well. Copy and distribution of this form is encouraged.

Material Release & Permissions Form
Handbook of Solid Modeling
Use this form to release and grant permission to use copyrighted material.
(Copying and distribution of this form are encouraged.)

(Please type or print clearly)

NAME

TITLE

COMPANY

ADDRESS

MAIL STOP

CITY/STATE/ZIP

TELEPHONE   FAX

Material Released

❏ Text   ❏ Photographs
❏ Graphic Art   ❏ Other (attached)

Media Type Available

❏ ASCII Text Files   ❏ Text Printout
❏ Postscript Files   ❏ Color Photo/Slide
❏ TIFF Files   ❏ B/W Photo/Slide
❏ HPGL Files   ❏ DOS Diskette
❏ Camera Art   ❏ Photo Copy
❏ Laser Prints   ❏ None

Request and Material Description

To: Permissions Editor   **From: Don LaCourse, Editor in Chief**

Permission is requested to use the material specified below in a publication entitled
Handbook of Solid Modeling and in future supplements, editions, and/or
revisions thereof, published by McGraw-Hill, Inc.

Material Description

❏ **See Attached**

Credit Line

(1) As a footnote or credit line:
"From (name of author), (title of book or work), (publisher and place), (copyright date)," or "Courtesy of (Source)" or

(2) As a numbered reference keyed to the bibliography where the citation will be given in full.

It is understood, of course, that full credit will be given to your material. The acknowledgment of the source will be printed on the page where the material appears, as indicated above.
                                                                     Thank you.

Permissions Release

Your prompt consideration of this request will be greatly appreciated.
A release form is provided below for your convenience. Thank you
again.

SIGNED   DATE

PRINT NAME HERE

Return Permissions To:

**Handbook of Solid Modeling
Don LaCourse, Editor in Chief
c/o**

**The Solid Modeling ExChange
P.O. Box 49336
Algood, TN 38506-0336
Attn. Reader Submissions**

FIGURE 1.4   Material release and permissions form.

4. If you should share credit for any portion of your submitted material with any additional source, this source must submit a completed and signed form as well.

5. Include a 3½-inch DOS-compatible diskette which includes the following information files:

   a. Your submitted text in ASCII file format

   b. If possible, high-resolution color or black/white images of any figures in HPGL, Postscript®, or TIFF (preferred) file formats

   c. Any decompression utility files needed to expand your compressed files once they arrive, including a printout of the decompression command code.

6. Short, handwritten submissions (type or print clearly) are acceptable.

7. All submissions should be in English.

8. Mark all envelopes and packages "Reader Submissions" and mail to the address shown in Sec. 1.4.5. We encourage submissions from all interested parties regardless of affiliation or geographic location. Please respond.

9. Complete, sign, and include the Reader Comment and Submission Form shown in Fig. 1.3 with each submission.

10. Include signed copies of the Material Release and Permissions Form shown in Fig. 1.4, as required.

1.4.4 Reader Registration

One of the goals of this handbook is to create an interactive community representing a cross section of SM professionals among you, our readers, regardless of which SM system you may use or your degree of involvement with SM technology. We feel that there is a growing need for such global representation within the SM community.

We encourage your interaction. We would also like to keep you informed of future activities, supplements, and material related to this publication. Returning the Reader Registration and Service Reply Card located at the back of this book will assist us in doing so. You can also take this opportunity to request additional information on SM-related products and services advertised in this handbook. Circle the corresponding reader service numbers on the registration card to request information. Return the registration card as soon as possible so that we may process it and keep it on file.

If the registration cards at the back of this handbook are missing, make a copy of the one shown in Fig. 1.5. Please leave this figure intact so other readers may make copies. You may use Fig. 1.5 at any time to request product information after you have registered by mailing it to the address shown in Sec. 1.4.5. Thank you for participating.

1.4.5 Reader Correspondence

Please send all reader correspondence directly to the Editor in Chief at The Solid Modeling ExChange:

Editor in Chief
Handbook of Solid Modeling
c/o The Solid Modeling ExChange
P.O. Box 49336
Algood, TN 38506-0336

1.5 The Purpose of This Handbook

This handbook's purpose is manyfold, but focuses primarily on the need to inform and the desire to advise. Information that is easily available is the key to acceptance and usage of SM technology. Advice is often sought but seldom found in useful abundance. Information, collective advice, and you, our readers, are the three legs on which this handbook stands.

Handbook of Solid Modeling

First Edition

Reader Profile & Registration

Service Reply Card

(Please type or print clearly)

NAME

TITLE

COMPANY

ADDRESS

MAIL STOP

CITY/STATE/ZIP

TELEPHONE   FAX

A. Primary Business/Industry:
- ❏ 01 Computer: Service/Software
- ❏ 02 Manufacturing: Electronics/ Computer/Peripherals
- ❏ 03 Architecture/Architectural
- ❏ 04 Facilities Planning/Space Planning
- ❏ 05 Civil Engineering/Surveying/ Mapping/GIS
- ❏ 06 Chemical/Process Eng. or Mfg.
- ❏ 07 Federal/State/Local Government or Military
- ❏ 08 Manufacturing: Aerospace/

-     Automotive/Machinery/Industrial/ Process Equipment
- ❏ 09 Industrial/Process Engineering
- ❏ 10 Education/Training Institution
- ❏ 11 Scientific/Technical Research
- ❏ 12 Video-Film/Animation/ Publications/Printing/Graphics
- ❏ 13 Electrical Engineering
- ❏ 14 Other: _____

B. Primary Job Function:
- ❏ 01 Corporate/Senior Management

- ❏ 02 Project/Product Management
- ❏ 03 Designer/Engineer/Researcher
- ❏ 04 Data/CAD Management
- ❏ 05 Drafting Staff/CAD Operator
- ❏ 06 Sales/Marketing Staff
- ❏ 07 CAD Training
- ❏ 08 Consultant
- ❏ 09 Accounting Finance
- ❏ 10 Other (specify) _____

C. Use of Computer Graphics:
- ❏ 01 Large-Volume End User (ongoing or substantial purchases)
- ❏ 02 End User (occasional purchases)
- ❏ 03 Computer Hardware Manufacturer/ Software Developer
- ❏ 04 OEM/Systems Integrator/VAR
- ❏ 05 Dealer Distributor
- ❏ 06 Consultant
- ❏ 07 Other: _____

D. Do you specify, recommend, or buy computer-related design products or services?
- ❏ 01 Yes   ❏ 02 No

E. CAD functions used:
- ❏ 01 None   ❏ 04 3D Surfuce
- ❏ 02 2D   ❏ 05 3D Solids
- ❏ 03 3D Wire

F. Computer System:
- ❏ 01 PC/AT   ❏ 05 Apollo
- ❏ 02 PS/2   ❏ 06 DEC
- ❏ 03 Macintosh   ❏ 07 IBM
- ❏ 04 Sun   ❏ 08 Mframe/Mini
- ❏ 09 Other: _____

G. Current CAD software:
- ❏ 01 Primary: _____
- ❏ 02 Secondary: _____

H. Number of employees at this location:
- ❏ 01 0-10   ❏ 05 251-500
- ❏ 02 11-50   ❏ 06 501-1,000
- ❏ 03 51-100   ❏ 07 over 1,000
- ❏ 04 101-250

I. No. of individuals referring to this handbook copy:
- ❏ 01 0-1   ❏ 03 6-10
- ❏ 02 2-5   ❏ 04 over 10

J. No. of times per month you refer to this handbook:
- ❏ 01 0-1   ❏ 03 6-10
- ❏ 02 2-5   ❏ 04 over 10

K. To receive additional information on advertised products or services, circle the reader service numbers of your choice. Information will be sent directly to you.

201	202	203	204
205	206	207	208
209	210	211	212
213	214	215	216
217	218	219	220
221	222	223	224
225	226	227	228

FIGURE 1.5 Reader registration and service reply card. There are reply cards located at the back of this handbook. If they are no longer attached, copy, complete, and return this reply card to the address indicated in Sec. 1.4.5. Please leave this form attached to this handbook so that other readers may register as well.

1.5.1   In a Nutshell

Our purpose is perhaps best described by a true short story. During an on-site demonstration, the representative of a leading SM software developer related a recent experience with a customer interested in SM technology for the first time. This particular customer, being a leader in the field, was utilizing only 2D CAD.

The customer brought in many of the leading SM software developers. All were given an opportunity to present their products and services. Demonstrations, evaluations, and benchmarks were performed and compared. After much time and considerable effort, the customer called this particular representative back and asked if they could meet one last time. In the conference room, the customer looked across the table at the SM representative and asked, "I know that we have reviewed every aspect of what your company has to offer, but can you please explain to us one last time, why exactly do we need solid modeling?"

This story is typical of companies embracing SM technology for the first time. A clear understanding of the virtues and limitations of SM in relation to one's needs are necessary prior to any detailed evaluation of individual SM solutions. Our purpose is to offer a single source for this understanding—a source which can be referred to at leisure and in privacy.

1.5.2   Additional Roles

This handbook's purpose also includes the following:

1. *Ambassador-at-large*—To represent SM technology as a whole. All SM related professionals share a common technology regardless of product. This handbook can be a common source of reference.

2. *Bridging the gap*—To narrow any existing information gap prior to becoming actively involved and to bring the entry point of this involvement into sharper focus.

3. *To inform*—Being well informed can ease implementation and help avoid potential problems and overexpectations. We encourage all to be actively involved and to stay informed.

4. *To advise*—Individuals seek advice in times of uncertainty. This handbook seeks to offer advice in times of need. Advice can be found not only within The SM Adviser entries, but within each chapter text as well. We encourage everyone to take time to explore these pages for business and pleasure.

5. *To spark ideas*—With an emphasis on how to best exploit this technology, the *Handbook of Solid Modeling* focuses on techniques, strategies, and the sample applications of other companies.

1.5.3 Defining Limitations

Though the benefits of SM are many, this technology is not perfect or right for everyone or for all applications. Beneficial gains must always come at a price, either monetary or otherwise. Like any evolving technology, there are outer limits to its effectiveness. Defining and understanding both the physical and technical limitations of SM technology are the first steps toward extending and ultimately overcoming them. This is our ultimate purpose.

1.6 Using This Handbook

There are several suggested ways to use this handbook, based on your needs. These include:

1. Read entire chapters in any order or the entire handbook to gain knowledge of SM technology as a whole.

2. Use the Contents or the Index to locate topics in question.

3. To quickly obtain advice on a specified topic, use the SMA Master Table to locate entries relating to the topic in question.

4. To locate categories of information (such as cautions, things to avoid, checklists and guidelines, good practices, work-arounds, needed improvements, points of view, or things that are good to know), review the categorical icons in Table 1.1 and look for those icons in the quick reference area throughout the handbook.

This handbook is meant to assist a wide range of SM-related professionals as well as private individuals. Its use in varying fields of engineering can be readily understood. It is our hope that as the use of SM technology grows, new and innovative uses and benefits from this handbook will follow.

1.6.1 Who Can Benefit?

The groups of professionals that will benefit most from this handbook include, but are not limited to:

1. Designers and engineers
2. CAD/CAE and engineering managers
3. CAD/CAE applications engineers and analysts
4. Middle and upper managers
5. MIS managers
6. Students of engineering
7. CAD operators
8. Interested private individuals

These individuals will find interesting and informative reading and reference material, as well as advice from colleagues and other industry leaders.

1.6.2 A Deskside Reference

Perhaps the primary intended use of this handbook is as a deskside (or workstationside) reference. Professionals involved in the day-to-day operation and management of their SM applications will find reference material and advice when they need it most. This handbook is specifically structured for extended and repeated reference.

1.6.3 A Problem Solver

Despite the operational differences from one SM system to another, there are many issues of concern facing all SM professionals. Difficulties arise in the fundamental techniques of constructing and editing solid models as well as in data exchange, implementation, and management. This handbook is meant to provide inspiration, suggestions, and solutions for many of these issues.

1.6.4 For Implementation

There are few things more challenging than to be chosen to spearhead the implementation of new technology. Information can be scarce when available. There are many factors to consider and many paths to take. This handbook can be used to prepare an organization and individuals for implementing SM technology in the workplace by recommending strategies, highlighting concerns, and raising management issues.

1.7 Conclusions

We hope that you find this edition of the *Handbook of Solid Modeling* and The SM Adviser useful in your daily applications. Be sure to look for future editions and related publications. We encourage any feedback you may wish to make so that this work may improve in addressing your needs. After all, as SM professionals, this is our *Handbook of Solid Modeling.*

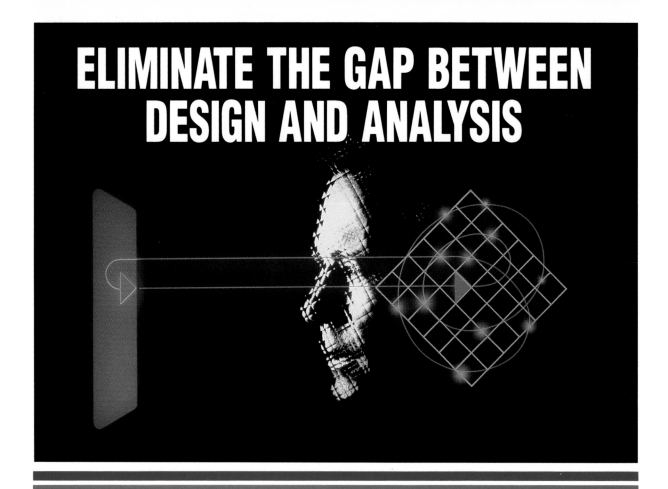

ELIMINATE THE GAP BETWEEN DESIGN AND ANALYSIS

Now all engineers can use advanced tools to make better designs because MSC has combined the two worlds of design and analysis into one world of Predictive Engineering.™ The power of MSC/ARIES solid modeling and automated meshing tools works hand-in-hand with the power and scope of the world's premier finite element analysis (FEA) solution, MSC/NASTRAN. For the first time, designers and analysts can work in the same solid-modeling-based environment, under one intuitive user interface, to rapidly create, analyze and optimize designs before expensive physical prototyping. Using Predictive Engineering for design optimization gives you higher quality, reduced development costs, and dramatically shortened time to market.

Solid benefits of the Geometry Bus™ and open systems philosophy.

The common tie among all mechanical engineers is geometry. MSC/ARIES has adopted ACIS, an industry-standard, non-proprietary modeling kernel. This standard geometry bus means you can easily exchange data with a variety of other CAD/CAM systems. You can choose best-in-class software solutions for drafting and manufacturing functions to complement the MSC/ARIES Predictive Engineering environment.

Two worlds become one.

Eliminate the gap between design and analysis with a Predictive Engineering solution that is scalable. From quick verification of straightforward designs on PCs and workstations to analysis of complex systems assemblies on supercomputers, we can meet your needs now and in the future. For more information on MSC's complete family of CAE technologies, call **800-642-7437, ext. 500.**

Chapter 2

Introducing Solid Modeling

Joel N. Orr
President
Orr Associates International

Integration of functions within the factory requires a product definition that is unique and consistent throughout the design and manufacturing process; it is computer graphics that makes possible a practical implementation of this dictum. At the heart of this definition is the geometry of the product—its shape. The world has three spatial dimensions, so computer models must be three-dimensional.

2.1   3D Geometric Forms

Three-dimensional CAD models can take three forms:

1. *Wireframe.*   Includes only points in space and the lines connecting them. Objects are represented by their edges.
2. *Surface.*   The edges of the wireframe are spanned by mathematically defined areas.
3. *Solid.*   The space enclosed by surfaces is defined and forms a closed volume.

Solid models are the least abstract and most realistic of the three forms; they necessitate far more computing power for their creation and management than the other two forms. Solid Modeling (SM) attracts designers because the construction of complex models, especially those that lack symmetry, is usually much faster than with surfaces. Wireframe representations of complex objects are very difficult to "understand" visually, because computer displays and paper plots seldom give an indication of depth. Seeing all the edges at once leads to perceptual confusion because of ambiguities.

A complex object can be decomposed into a much smaller number of solid components (called *primitives*) than surfaces, lines, or points; this is evident when one considers that a solid primitive can be decomposed into surfaces, which can be broken down into points and lines. With fewer parts to manipulate, a model is rapidly constructed. (See Chap. 6 for more on primitives.)

Solid and surface models also allow the generation of images with hidden lines and hidden surfaces removed, which are much more realistic than wireframe models.

Some shapes can be represented by surfaces but not by solids. Thus, even designers who believe in the essential superiority of solid representations are forced to resort to surfaces for certain complex objects. Many SM systems closely integrate surface and solid capability.

But by far the most important aspect of solids is that their integrity can be computationally determined. In other words, SM software with the aid of the computer can tell if a given object is a legitimate solid or not. Thus, objects designed in SM systems will be manufacturable, at least from the point of view of spatial integrity; the manufacturing engineer will not discover that the design engineer has handed over a spatial paradox to produce.

The reader is advised to keep in mind, however, that although a given solid may be valid or geometrically complete (forming a closed volume), this by no means guarantees it to be manufacturable by conventional methods (molding, cutting, stamping, etc.) in use today. This excludes the rapid prototyping techniques discussed in Chap. 19, whereby any valid solid can be produced.

Another important implication of the computational determinability of solid integrity is that SM systems can automatically test for and locate interferences among parts. Designers of large systems (aircraft, ships, offshore drilling platforms, chemical plants) find this to be of inestimable value. Chapter 11 discusses interference checking in greater detail.

What makes solids computationally verifiable is that they are described by topology in addition to geometry; that is, the properties of the shape that are unaltered by elastic deformations such as stretching or twisting (see Chap. 7). There are algorithms for determining if a given assemblage of geometry is a legitimate solid due to the topological peculiarities of 3D objects in 3D space (see Euler's formula in Chap. 4). One of the programming challenges in creating a user-friendly SM system is to permit designers a wide range of shape-changing operations while preventing them from unintentionally creating a nonsolid condition. Chapter 4 discusses topology in greater detail.

2.2 Why Is Solid Modeling Important?

Solid Modeling is important because it is the key to obtaining the productivity promises that computers offer designers. Let me explain.

Designing is a complex process. It is not simply a matter of filling in the blanks in a formula and obtaining an optimal answer; it is an iterative process that involves much trial and error, along with analysis. Analysis is heavily automated already; current work in this area focuses on making analysis tools accessible to designers who do not understand the mathematical details.

The next portion of the design process that is most susceptible to improvement through computers is design verification. In this phase, a prototype of a design is built and tested. Generally, the prototype is modified and tested many times before the design process moves to production.

Computers make it possible to build "software" prototypes. These are models that exist only within the memory of the computer. These models can be subjected to computer-based simulations of the prototype tests, and the results can be used to build a real prototype.

The major benefits of verifying the design within the computer are speed, cost, and flexibility. It is usually much faster to build a model within the computer than in a machine shop, and the costs are generally much lower. Moreover, computer-based simulations can often be better representations of real-world conditions than those to which physical prototypes are subjected.

For the software prototype to be practical, it must represent reality as faithfully as possible. Object geometry is commonly represented at three levels within CAD systems. As mentioned previously, the first and simplest level is called *wireframe;* in this representation, points, lines, curves, and text are modeled in two or three dimensions. Drawings can be created with wireframe geometry.

More realistic representations are required by some manufacturing tasks, such as metal cutting with numerically controlled (NC) machine tools. CAM systems for designing NC tool paths typically employ the second-level "surface" geometry in addition to wireframe, because the entire bounding area of a part must be represented in order to tell the cutting tool where to go.

But the highest form of realism requires that the interior of the part be represented as well. For that, we need level three: SM systems. Solid models can be used to faithfully represent the entire geometry of a part, not just that of its exterior. SM can therefore be used to determine if parts in an assembly will interfere with one another in operation—something that wireframe and surface representations cannot do.

The 130,000 manufacturers in the United States, and the comparable number in the rest of the world, all face similar problems. They need to become more productive in order to compete in the new world market, and they must all do so in the face of accelerating changes in labor, regulatory issues, and technology. The only hope for all is in automated computer integrated manufacturing, or CIM. CIM will be brought to pass by the progressive manufacturers, and will be supported by five important trends:

1. Solid Modeling
2. Integration
3. Computer networks
4. Database management systems (DBMS)
5. Humanization

Solid modeling is a prerequisite for CIM and is worthy, for that reason alone, of the close attention of engineering and manufacturing automation professionals.

Fulfillment of CAD/CAM's productivity promises rests on digital models. The automation of the drawing process is helpful, but its benefits are small when compared to what can be gained by automating all of design verification, and especially by unequivocally communicating those results to production.

And that is what SM is all about. Because solid models are less abstract (more real) than drawings or 3D wireframes, their behavior under a variety of simulated conditions can tell us enough about how the real thing will behave to make the modeling process worthwhile.

Solid models are easier to fix and easier to change than actual prototypes, and are sometimes less expensive as hardware comes down in cost. In fact, a digital model can be more faithful to the proposed product than can a prototype, because the limitations of prototype fabricating techniques often yield compromises that are very different from what will be made in the factory. A digital model does not suffer from the same constraints.

2.3 Types of Solid Modeling Systems

Several approaches to the representation of solid models have evolved; some have not been implemented commercially. The most popular of these are:

1. Constructive solid geometry (CSG)
2. Boundary representation (B-Rep)
3. Spatial enumeration by means of octrees (O-Rep)
4. Hybrids

Each approach is described briefly in the following sections, and in greater detail in Chap. 4.

2.3.1 Constructive Solid Geometry (CSG)

Geometric primitives are combined in this approach by means of boolean operations (see Chap. 6). CSG systems store a record of the primitives and the operations used with them; each time the part is to be displayed, it is computed from the "tree" of primitives and operations. Consequently, CSG databases are usually quite small relative to other representations, but display times are sometimes longer.

The trend toward making SM systems more accessible to factory professionals makes CSG systems attractive. Since this approach centers around solid objects, it facilitates a transition to feature-based modeling (see Chap. 8), which employs objects and operations corresponding to those in the normal mechanical design and manufacturing vocabulary. It is a small step from the mathematically oriented boolean operations to the factory operations familiar to the part designer and manufacturing engineer. By allowing the designer to work with features, rather than abstract geometries, the system preserves a record of the design intent. General design theory holds that this is important to the integrity of the ultimate design.

Since evaluation of the CSG model occurs at display time, systems can perform coarse evaluations for fast display, and fine evaluation for, say, the generation of NC toolpaths (see Chap. 15 for more on SM and NC).

2.3.2 Boundary Representation (B-Rep)

Traversing the dimensions of space sounds like a difficult concept, but that is just what is done implicitly in B-Rep systems (see Chap. 4). Making use of the fact that higher-dimension geometries are bounded by objects of lower dimensions, B-Rep systems maintain an explicit "tree" of boundaries: a solid is bounded by surfaces; a surface is bounded by lines; a line is bounded by points.

The coordinates of the points that bound the lines that bound the surfaces that bound the solids are explicitly stored in B-Rep systems; the geometric relationships are maintained by pointers. As a result, B-Rep files are much larger than CSG files of similar parts. But display performance is usually faster for B-Reps, because the model need not be "evaluated" at display time—that is, the boolean operations on primitives that are performed each time a CSG model is displayed do not have to be done.

B-Rep

SMA.2.1   A B-Rep Misunderstanding

B-Rep systems are sometimes thought to be inherently less precise than CSG systems, because storing geometry explicitly means that polyhedral approximations to surfaces must be made—and the degree of approximation is generally coarse, to minimize display times. This is a misunderstanding; B-Rep systems can be as precise as desired if the designer is willing to pay the corresponding price in performance.

2.3.3   Spatial Enumeration (Octrees)

While both CSG and B-Rep systems approach solid geometry from the point of view of the part, it is also possible to consider the part in the context of the space in which it resides. Space can be divided by a progressively refined grid of cubes, using cubes that stay completely within or completely outside the model, and smaller and smaller cubical partitions to approximate the boundaries of the model.

The name of the data structure most often employed for spatial enumeration is *octrees* (see Chaps. 4 and 26), which derives from the fact that in a regular division of space into boxes, each point can be a corner vertex of up to eight boxes. In an attempt to fit into a pleasing syntactic taxonomy, some researchers denote this approach as O-Rep, contrasting it with B-Rep and C-Rep for CSG.

O-Rep system performances degrade much more slowly with the complexity of the model than do B-Rep or CSG. Moreover, O-Rep is given to relatively simple parallelization. However, less development has been invested in the creation of SM systems employing this approach than in any of the others, for reasons that appear to be largely historical rather than technical.

2.3.4   Hybrids

Most of the SM systems on the market today are some form of hybrid of CSG and B-Rep. CSG is generally used for internal representation and B-Rep for the generation of views. Since CSG models are stored unevaluated, they are resolution-independent. B-Rep polygonization of models can be geared to the desired trade-off between resolution and display speed.

2.4   A Brief History

Most of the current SM systems on the market can be traced to a small number of seminal developments by research groups.

At an international conference held in Budapest in 1973, researchers from universities on opposite sides of the globe presented independent (but similar) proposals for the first SM systems. Braid and Lang, of the University of Cambridge, England, talked about their BUILD system; Okino and his colleagues, of Japan's Hokkaido University, described TIPS.

Both approaches built on the idea of creating complex shapes by combining geometric "primitives" in different ways. They differed in the ways in which data was represented within the computer; the Japanese system used what is now called *constructive solid geometry,* or CSG, while the English system employed the technique now known as *boundary representation,* or B-Rep.

A novel addition to the B-Rep approach was made in 1974 by Baumgart, of Stanford University, California. In his publication of that year, he described GEOMED, a system based on the "winged edge" representation (see Chap. 4). This technique affords substantial performance advantages over others.

The Technical University of Berlin's COMPAC system was described by Spur and his colleagues in 1975. It was used in a variety of ground-breaking projects in conjunction with German industrial concerns.

While most of the developments noted here occurred within the framework of mechanical design, Eastman and his colleagues at Carnegie-Mellon University of Pittsburgh, Pennsylvania, announced their architecturally oriented GLIDE system in 1977, funded by the U.S. Army Corps of Engineers.

In 1977, two other landmark publications appeared. Goldstein and his colleagues at MAGI, a software company in Elmsford, New York, described the generation of solids through a technique called *ray tracing* or *ray casting,* and Voelcker and Requicha of the University of Rochester, New York, published their work on PADL-1, a system that incorporated the advantages of CSG and B-Rep by maintaining a dual representation.

2.5   Applications

Mechanical design and manufacturing have been the areas in which SM has found greatest application to date. Architecture and construction can make productive use of solids, but have largely been prohibited from doing so until recently because of the cost of sufficiently large systems to handle architectural problems. In the heyday of the nuclear power generation industry, SM systems began to be used to design power plants. The cost of design errors showing up in construction was so great that expensive systems to avoid such problems were readily justified. But as the fortunes of that pursuit declined, so did the use of SM in architecture and construction.

Now that the cost of computer power is so low, plant design systems, in particular, are likely to turn more and more to SM.

2.5.1   Layout, Design, and Drafting

Since the computer system is able to algorithmically determine if a constructed object is a legitimate solid, it is a natural desire to create any needed drawings from the solid model (see Chap. 17). In this way, the design integrity is maintained and the drawings will be consistent among themselves. The value of reducing consistency errors in complex designs is very great.

Interference and clearance analysis make SM a desirable environment in which to generate layouts (see Chap. 11). There are many case studies of dynamic analyses performed on mechanisms with oddly shaped parts (see Chap. 13), such as the landing wheel compartment doors of aircraft, in which solids-based interference detection turned up interference conditions that would have been very expensive to remedy had they been found only after the construction of a working prototype.

2.5.2   Industrial Design

Industrial design is often considered to be almost a marketing function, rather than a part of engineering. By its nature, SM permits the relatively easy calculation of hidden-line and shaded images; the model "knows" whether a point is inside, outside, or on the surface of the object in question, which makes the generation of realistic images possible.

Aesthetics are important to the industrial designer, to be sure. But how much better for the manufacturer when the industrial designer is able to produce models that are not only aesthetically and ergonomically valid, but provide a usable geometric base on which the detailed design can be constructed.

2.5.3   Analysis

The interior of a solid model is implicitly defined, so mass properties (volume, weight, surface area, center of gravity, moments of inertia) are easy for the computer to calculate (see Chap. 12). And the fact that the SM software preserves the solid integrity of edited parts, or at least reports when that integrity is breached, means that the mass-property calculations can be reliably performed without fear of underlying geometric paradoxes invalidating them.

Models for finite element and other forms of structural analysis can be automatically generated from solids much more easily than from other geometric forms (see Chap. 14). The payoff for using solids is in complex designs, which are difficult to reconstruct into finite element models manually.

2.5.4 Manufacturing Engineering

One of the greatest beneficiaries of SM data in the manufacturing process is the numerical control programmer (see Chap. 15). A common problem of CAD-generated data for the part programmer are flaws such as missing geometry or unconnected surfaces. The computer-verifiable nature of solids obviates these problems. In particular, animated toolpath simulation is very helpful to the part programmer.

Animation of motion paths in an SM environment is also helpful to the programmer of robotic systems (see Chap. 25). Without solids, automation of process planning is almost impossible. With solids, it remains a challenge, but one that can be surmounted.

2.6 Current Limitations

Most apologists for the lack of SM use discuss the design tradition and the difficulty of use of contemporary packages. "Engineering professionals are simply accustomed to designing by drawing, and solids interfere with that process," said a professor from one of the leading engineering schools when I questioned him on the topic. "What's more, the SM packages are both hard to learn and hard to use."

That is certainly part of the story. But I now believe that there is a quantitative issue behind the slow propagation of this essential technology: large assemblies modeled in solids are simply too big (computationally intensive) for current computers, and will continue to be so for some time.

If SM is to be adopted by large manufacturers, something very different than what is currently available is required. A riddle will help to explain why: Which would you prefer, a million dollars, or a sum obtained by starting with one penny and doubling it every day for a month? If you do not remember the answer to this object lesson, do the multiplication. Even if the month is February, and it is not a leap year, you will wind up with 2^{27} pennies ($1,342,177.28). And if the month has 31 days, the amount is $10,737,418.24.

The same kind of impressive rapid growth occurs in the amount of time it takes to produce an image on a computer display from a solid model with each increment of growth in the model (see Chaps. 4 and 6). Make the model just a bit more complex by adding one more part to an assembly and you can easily double the amount of time it takes to display it.

Now you understand why large aerospace and automotive companies (even the ones that are committed to digital modeling and engineering—and not all of them are) do not produce solid models of entire airplanes or automobiles. Given existing SM software, they just do not have the hardware resources.

Everyone agrees that the key to improving design with computers is visualization. The ability to see all parts of a complex design and to interact with them is essential for the computer-aided engineer. But an airplane could have as many as 250,000 individual parts. Visualizing them individually is one thing, but looking at large subsets of them together is something else.

Moreover, the magnitude of the problem is such that even with three or four orders of magnitude increase in graphics processing power, you still will not be able to deal with an entire car or airplane. So, what is needed is a different modeling paradigm; a different way of representing geometry in the computer.

Also, another threshold is about to be crossed. Now that the light of the vision of solids as bearers of geometric truth is spreading, it is bringing the murky distinction between PCs and workstations into sharp relief. If one wants no more than to automate the drafting process, it is difficult to see why a computer more powerful than those based on the 80486 or 68040 chips is needed. But for the computation of solids, as well as for the shaded renderings thereof, the more power, the better!

But what is impeding the spread of solids? One bottleneck is in education. Although most educators recognize the value of SM, they do not have the equipment (or the experience) to incorporate it into design curricula.

Another bottleneck is the pressure of the market. The very forces which should lead manufacturers to seek new tools and incorporate them into their design processes to reduce time to market have the opposite effect. "We can't afford the time to experiment" is a common complaint. This applies to other MCAE tools, such as finite element analysis and simulation, as well.

The onus is on the providers of the products to reach out to the designers and understand their needs. Designers are, after all, looking for solutions to problems; they do not really care about tools or methods. The successful vendors understand this, and communicate in their language.

2.7 The Future of SM

Industry needs SM. Computer technology continues to evolve at a breakneck pace. It is a safe bet that convergence between the needs of industry and the ability of computers to provide the required performances will occur at some point. But when?

If we follow the accepted development curves for computer power, we see that it will be many years before current approaches will allow us to model an entire aircraft, or even an entire automobile, in solids, with subsecond response times. The problem lies in combinatorics: performance is proportional to the square of the number of elements in the model. Hardware is not improving fast enough. We must look to algorithmic improvements in SM systems to provide the needed performance.

One direction from which help may come is that of octrees (O-Rep). The one company presently offering a system based on this technology does not have the range of support tools required by CAD; the system is used for medical applications. But in CAD experiments, the vendor has demonstrated performances that are orders of magnitude faster than those of CSG and B-Rep systems.

Moreover, O-Rep systems are easy to implement in parallel computing environments. So, as computers become cheaper, it is possible to interconnect many of them in parallel and divide solution times by the number of processors. This approach shows great promise.

There is no doubt that all future modelers will be feature-based and have variational geometry capabilities (see Chap. 8). The concept underlying the power of solids is the interlinking of all aspects of the model, which results in the preservation of geometric integrity under a wide variety of conditions. Variational geometry carries the same concept a step further in the direction of generality by allowing the designer to link many different aspects of the model together for preservation of characteristics beyond the geometric and topological.

The other challenges facing SM are less likely to admit to easy solution. Allowing the creation of solids bounded by arbitrary surfaces is problematic, because the intersection of arbitrary surfaces is not a solved mathematical problem (see Chap. 4). There are endless special cases which are difficult to handle computationally.

Good to Know

SMA.2.2 It's a Good Idea[1]

It's a good idea to collect and present this advice. All too often companies let customers get frustrated by things they already know how to do better.

Ted Craft, Support Specialist
Computervision Corp., Oakbrook Terrace, Ill.

SMA.2.3 Proceed with Caution[1]

Switch on the brain first, then the computer.

Johannes Eisenkoelbl, Application Engineer
Computervision Corp., Vienna, Austria

SMA.2.4 The Ten Commandments of an SM System[2]

1. Thou shalt work with my existing data. A company's library of product files represents a huge investment in both time and money. SM systems should accept data from both existing and any external source (IGES, DXF, etc.).

2. Thou shalt make it easy to produce mechanical drawings. Drawings aren't dead yet. Ideally, a drawing should be part of the design database with two-way associativity between the model and the drawing, so that design changes are automatically reflected in the drawing.

3. Thou shalt have strong ties to manufacturing. Ideally, CAM should be as integral as mechanical drawing with two-way associativity between the design and tools paths.

(Continued)

Good to Know
(*Continued*)

4. Thou shalt let me make the changes I wish to make when I wish to make them. Design changes should not be limited by the order in which constraints were originally applied. Also, over- or underconstrained situations should be allowed.

5. Thou shalt not limit me to solids. Points, lines, arcs, splines, and basic and advanced surfaces should be supported as well as solids. If 2D is all you need for a particular job, you should be able to work in 2D.

6. Thou shalt allow me to share piece parts among designs. Model once, store, and reuse as required. Changes to the global piece parts should automatically be made to the individual instances within a design every time you open that part file.

7. Thou shalt let me specify absolute locations and distances as I develop my relational model. If a dimension absolutely, positively has to be 3.14159265 inches, let that dimension be locked into the design as it is created, without having to wait until the completed model is formally constrained.

8. Thou shalt not limit me to parametrics. When it is quicker, cheaper, and easier to do a proper and complete job using traditional modeling techniques, let it be so.

9. Thou shalt allow me to share my data easily. The ideal SM system provides binary data compatibility across platforms. Data exchange standards, such as IGES, STEP, and DXF should also be supported.

10. Thou shalt help me publish my work. Engineers look for the ability to output images from their SM system in a form that can be used by word processing, illustration, and desktop publishing systems.

Dr. Patrick J. Hanratty, President
MCS Inc., Scottsdale, Ariz.

References

1. Adapted from "Parametric Modeling Usage Tips," Revision 4.0.0, Nancy Anderson-Semple, Editor, Computervision Corporation, May, 1993.

2. Adapted from "The Ten Commandments," Patrick J. Hanratty, *Machine Design Magazine*, July 11, 1994, p. 122.

Section 2
Techniques

(CIRCLE READER SERVICE NO. 204)

Chapter 3

Solid Modeling Concepts

Victor E. Wright, P.E.
Design and Engineering Consultant

Solid Modeling (SM) requires the application of concepts that are academic in 2D drafting. The most obvious difference with SM, however, is that traditional engineering drawings are two-dimensional and solid models are inherently three-dimensional. While 2D drawings can be created manually or electronically, solid models must be created in an electronic "drawing universe." Solid models themselves are not physically accessible. CAD workstations are used to create, edit, and display 2D representations of the electronic solid model. The techniques used in building solid models compare to those of a conventional wood model shop without many of the physical limitations. This chapter will explore fundamental concepts that should be understood prior to embarking on any SM effort.

3.1 Basic Concepts

A solid model is an electronic description of a physical object or a group of physical objects. 2D and 3D CAD drawings are also electronic descriptions, but they do not contain information about the nature of space enclosed by the geometry used to describe the object. A 2D drawing presents the visual aspect of an object from a particular viewpoint in space.

A 3D drawing (wireframe or surface model) contains a description of the object's appearance, and is valid from any viewpoint. However, wireframe and surface models do not distinguish between the matter that makes up a solid and the surrounding empty space. A solid model contains information about the shape of an object as well as the matter that it is made of. This matter is known as the object's *mass properties*. Chapter 12 discusses SM and mass-properties analysis in more detail.

3.2 3D Coordinate Systems

Solid models are located in an electronic space that is defined in terms of 3D cartesian (rectangular) coordinates. This is known as the 3D *work space* or *model space*. This is the same application of 3D space employed by conventional wireframe and surface modeling systems. Some 3D systems provide an auxiliary 2D work space as well. This is sometimes referred to as *draw space* and is where 2D text and conventional details are located.

Three-dimensional coordinates are used to specify the location of points in space, the distances between pairs of points, and displacements between consecutive positions of a point. A coordinate system consists of an origin and a system of reference planes or axes. A coordinate system is sometimes referred to as a *coordinate frame*. The corner of the frame specifies the origin of the coordinate system, while the edges of the frame indicate the orientation of the system's *X, Y,* and *Z* axes. (Refer to Fig. 3.1.)

The location of a point is specified by giving its distance and direction from a given coordinate frame's origin. The location of an object is determined by assigning 3D coordinates to an origin point on the object. The orientation of the object is determined by assigning 3D coordinates to additional fea-

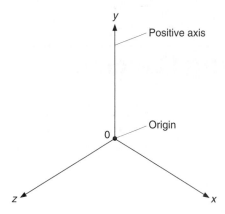

FIGURE 3.1 A cartesian coordinate frame consists of an origin (corner of the frame) and three vectors (edges of the frame) indicating the positive direction of the X, Y, and Z axes.

tures, or to a coordinate system local to the object's definition. Let's review a few different types of coordinate systems and how they affect 3D model space.

3.2.1 Global, World, and Local Coordinates

3D model space has at least one permanent coordinate system. This is called the *global*, or *world coordinate system*, and is typically the default coordinate system. For specific tasks, temporary or local coordinate systems can be defined relative to the global coordinate system, to points on an entity, or to an entity's coordinate system (see Fig. 3.2). Points or features of an object can be defined relative to that object's local coordinate system, just as the object and its local coordinate system can be defined relative to the global or world coordinate system.

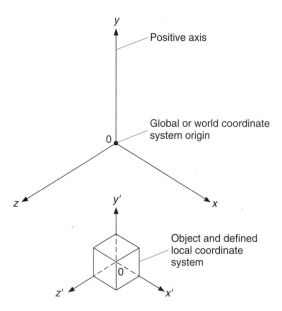

FIGURE 3.2 For specific tasks, auxiliary or local coordinate systems can be defined relative to an object or the global coordinate system.

3.2.2 Cartesian Coordinates

A cartesian coordinate system consists of three mutually perpendicular axes (the X axis, the Y axis, and the Z axis) which intersect at the origin. These axes extend away from the origin indefinitely in both a positive and negative direction. The location of a point is specified by listing three coordinates, one measured along each of the three axes, in the form x coordinate, y coordinate, z coordinate, the order is understood (see Fig. 3.3). The cartesian is the most common coordinate system used in SM systems today.

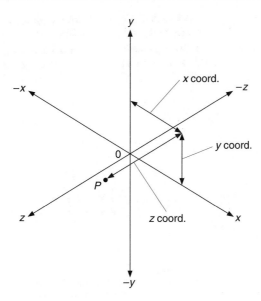

FIGURE 3.3 A cartesian coordinate system consists of three mutually perpendicular axes, crossing at the origin. A point P is specified in terms of three distances measured along the X, Y, and Z axes, respectively. When these distances are measured from the origin, they are coordinates.

3.2.3 Cylindrical and Spherical Coordinates

The location of an object can be specified in cartesian (rectangular) coordinates as described in Sec. 3.2.2, or in two alternative forms: cylindrical or spherical coordinates. Both forms can be used within the cartesian coordinate system. The choice of coordinate system format depends largely upon the nature of the task at hand.

Cylindrical Coordinates

The cylindrical coordinate of a given point P consists of the following information (see Fig. 3.4):

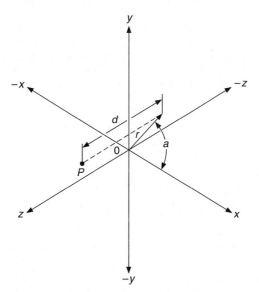

FIGURE 3.4 The cylindrical coordinate system. A point P is specified by the value of the radius vector r, angle a, and the distance d. This allows the location of a point to be specified in terms of two distances and one angle.

1. A radial distance r from a chosen reference frame's origin to the projection of the point of interest on that frame's X-Y plane
2. The angle a subtended by the X axis and the radial distance vector
3. The projected distance d of the point from the X-Y plane

Spherical Coordinates

The spherical coordinates of a given point P consist of the following information (see Fig. 3.5):

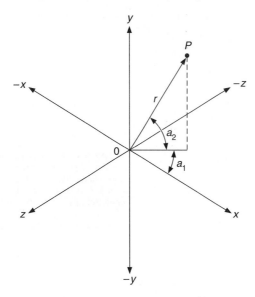

FIGURE 3.5 The spherical coordinate system. A point P is specified by the radius vector r, the angle a_1, and the angle a_2. This allows the location of a point to be specified in terms of one distance and two angles.

1. A vector r of radial distance from the origin to the point of interest
2. The angle a_1 between the X axis and the projection of the radial distance vector on the X-Z plane
3. The angle a_2 between the X-Z plane and the radial distance vector.

3.2.4 Reference Planes

Any two of the three axes in a cartesian coordinate system form a reference plane. There are three generic reference planes: the X-Y plane, the Y-Z plane, and the X-Z plane. A single coordinate value measures the distance from the reference plane formed by the other two axes. Thus, a z coordinate specifies the distance from the X-Y plane to a point, measured in a direction parallel to the Z axis.

A reference plane is divided by its two axes into four quadrants (see Fig. 3.6). In the first quadrant, both coordinate values are positive. In the second quadrant, the first coordinate value is negative and the second coordinate value is positive. In the third quadrant, both coordinate values are negative. In the fourth quadrant, the first coordinate value is positive, and the second coordinate value is negative.

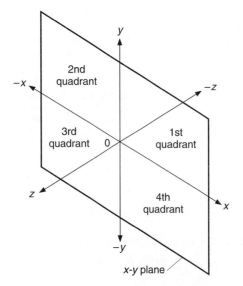

FIGURE 3.6 Two axes of a cartesian coordinate system form a reference plane and divide that plane into quadrants.

The three reference planes (*X-Y*, *Y-Z*, and *X-Z*) divide a cartesian coordinate system into eight octants. This division of 3D model space by reference planes occurs within the global, world, and all temporary or local coordinate systems (see Fig. 3.7).

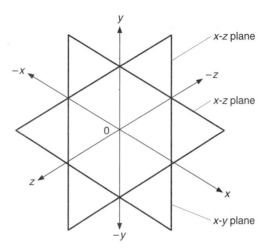

FIGURE 3.7 The three reference planes formed by the three different combinations of axes in a cartesian coordinate system divide the model space into eight octants.

3.3 Construction Concepts

Fundamental construction concepts are key to producing basic and complex solid models. Understanding these concepts and their applications will increase one's ability to grasp more advanced concepts, thus increasing the overall capabilities of an SM system.

3.3.1 Construction Planes

Although SM systems allow the construction of objects in 3D model space, the designer's interface consists of the monitor screen, pointing device, and keyboard, which are typically two-dimensional. Movement of the pointing device on a digitizer tablet or desktop is tracked by cross hairs, aperture boxes, or other screen cursors. These movements are two-dimensional.

During constructive operations the pointing device and screen cursor can be made to correspond to the default or active construction plane, a reference plane in 3D model space. When points and entities are entered with the pointing device and/or keyboard, they are typically assigned the elevation and orientation of the active construction plane.

If the global or world coordinate system is active, points and entities appear on the *X-Y* plane of that coordinate system. If a temporary or local coordinate system is active, its *X-Y* plane is typically the construction plane. In some systems, an elevation above or below the *X-Y* plane can be defined as a default value, so that the construction plane is parallel but not coplanar to the *X-Y* plane of the current coordinate system.

When a new construction plane is created, a complete local cartesian coordinate system is established with its *X-Y* plane typically defined as the new active construction plane. The graphic representation of construction planes may vary from system to system. Their display attributes can sometimes be modified to include a rectangular border, snap grids, to suppress the positive *z* axis, or to assign color to individual components. There may be many auxiliary construction planes defined in model space as needed while only one is current and active at any given time (see Fig. 3.8). The construction and modification of solid models is facilitated by creating and activating construction planes as needed. It is to be noted, however, that not all SM constructive operations require the use of a construction plane.

3.3.2 Building Blocks

A solid model of a complex object typically consists of several simpler objects, just as a 2D drawing consists of simpler geometric entities such as lines, circles, and arcs. Because lines, circles, and arcs are not

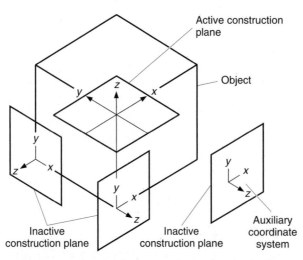

FIGURE 3.8 A construction plane is typically the *X-Y* plane of a temporary, auxiliary coordinate system. Construction planes are entities which can be translated or rotated about their own or the global coordinate system. There may be many construction planes defined in model space, while only one may be active at a given moment.

3D entities, they cannot enclose space and so cannot be assigned mass properties. Also, lines, circles, and arcs cannot be combined directly to yield a solid model, although they are used in the creation of a solid model's visual display.

Basic solid models are constructed from elementary solid objects or primitives (spheres, cylinders, prisms, slabs, etc.) (see Fig. 3.9). Each of these solid primitives is a shape that can be described simply. Solid primitives can be combined like building blocks to construct more complex objects. Thus, a model of a nail can be assembled from a cone and two cylinders. (Refer to Chap. 6 for more on SM primitives.)

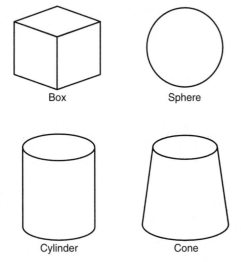

FIGURE 3.9 Solid models can be constructed from solid primitives which are simple regular shapes. Any resulting solid can also be used as a primitive. A few of the basic primitives are shown here. Refer to Chap. 6 for a complete discussion on primitives.

Advanced 3D surfacing techniques may be required to define very complex portions of a solid model. Many SM systems provide the integration necessary to apply the use of advanced surface and SM techniques. (Refer to Chap. 5 for more on curves and surfaces with SM.)

These building blocks are typically combined with the use of the three boolean operations (sometimes referred to as *set operations*): UNION, SUBTRACTION, and INTERSECTION (see Fig. 3.10). Boolean algebra is named after the English mathematician George Boole (1815–1864). (Refer to Chap. 6 for more on SM boolean operations.)

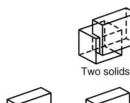

Two solids

Union   Subtraction   Intersection

FIGURE 3.10 Solid primitives are combined with the use of the three boolean operations UNION, SUBTRACTION, and INTERSECTION, to form a composite solid. Refer to Chap. 6 for a complete discussion on boolean operations. *(Courtesy of Hewlett-Packard Company.)*

3.3.3   Creating Solids from 2D Geometry

3D solids can be generated from 2D geometry by extruding, sweeping, or revolving a profile along an axis (see Fig. 3.11). Typically, the active reference plane is used to construct a 2D profile. When generating a 3D solid, the 2D profile must form a closed area. In conventional 3D wireframe and surface modeling, this closed condition is not required. The closed curve may consist of several linear entities connected end to end, depending upon the SM system used. (Refer to Chap. 6 for more on geometric operations.)

Extrusion   Sweep   Revolution

FIGURE 3.11 Solids can be created from geometric operations such as extrusions, sweeps, and revolutions. Refer to Chap. 6 for a complete discussion on geometric operations. *(Courtesy of Intergraph Corporation.)*

3.3.4   Groups and Assemblies

Physical products typically consist of parts and components organized into groups and/or assemblies. To reflect this hierarchical structure, solid models must also be organized into groups and assemblies.

The term *group* implies that the components of the group share a common level in the assembly process. The term *assembly* implies that the assembly is composed of components from a lower level in the assembly process. For example, a bolt, nut, and washer used to bolt two parts together may be treated as a group for ease of manipulation. Two parts, along with several bolt-nut-washer groups may form an assembly. As in real products, assemblies and individual components can be combined to form higher-level assemblies.

Groups and assemblies should not be confused with objects formed from solid construction techniques. Groups and assemblies are tools used to duplicate the organizational structure of the physical product. Solid construction techniques are used to facilitate the definition of complex solid objects. (Refer to Chap. 11 for more on assembly modeling with SM.)

3.4   Other Concepts

There are additional concepts fundamental to all 3D modeling environments. These include concepts for the manipulation and management of 3D objects.

3.4.1   Translations and Rotations

The location of an entity in a solid model can be modified by either translation or rotation. Translation shifts an object along one, two, or three axes without changing its angular orientation relative to any of the three axes (see Fig. 3.12).

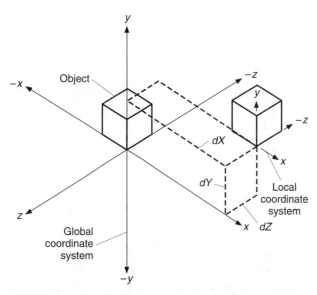

FIGURE 3.12   When an object is translated, every point is moved by the same displacement (distance and direction). The object's angular orientation does not change. In this example, the object is translated the distances *dX, dY,* and *dZ* from the global coordinate system. Notice that the orientation of the object's local coordinate system has not changed.

Rotation changes the angular orientation of an object relative to a local or global coordinate system. Rotation may occur about an arbitrary line (or axis) that is part of or separate from the object being rotated. Positive or negative rotation may occur based on the direction of the line or axis of rotation (see Fig. 3.13).

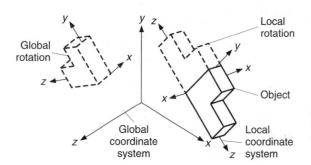

FIGURE 3.13   An object can be rotated about an axis. The axis may be a local or global axis or simply a linear edge separate from or part of the object itself. In this example, the object in question is rotated 180° about its local *Y* axis and 180° about the global *Y* axis. *(Courtesy of Varimetrix Corporation.)*

Translation and rotation often occurs simultaneously, as when an object is translated along a curved path but remains aligned with a line between the origin and a fixed point on the object.

Some workstations provide auxiliary controls to enable a designer to translate and/or rotate the solid model relative to the global coordinate system, active reference plane, or a reference line in the case of rotation, by turning knobs or repositioning other physical control devices. Such translations and rotation are hardware-controlled and are independent of the SM software.

3.4.2   Copying, Scaling, and Mirroring

Components of physical products are often duplicated. Bolts, nuts, and washers are examples. Some components occur in identical shapes, but varying sizes. If a specific component is used several times in a product, it need be modeled only once. Additional instances can be copied from the first.

Similarly, if a component is used in several different sizes, only one instance of the component need be modeled. Other instances of the component can be created by simultaneously copying and scaling the original component.

Many physical objects occur in different sizes, but only in similar form, such as valves. These objects cannot be scaled, because not all dimensions change by the same proportion between sizes. Thus, a 2-in valve is similar in appearance to a 1-in valve, but the dimensions of the 2-in valve are generally not twice those of the 1-in valve.

Physical objects often occur in left- and right-hand versions, or mirrored images. Automotive design, for example, utilizes this concept extensively. Once the right-hand version of a SM component is defined, the left-hand version can be created with a mirroring operation. In SM, the mirrored objects are symmetrical across a selected construction plane known as the *mirror plane.*

3.4.3 Layers

Layers, sometimes referred to as *levels,* are techniques used to organize and manage the solid model data for display. The term *layer* is derived from the overlay or pinbar methods used in graphic design. Sheets of punched Mylar are registered on a pinbar, so that a drawing can be separated into objects, colors, classes of objects, systems, etc. Each sheet of Mylar corresponds to a layer of the composite drawing (see Fig. 3.14). In SM, layers are expanded into the third dimension and are typically assigned portions of the entire composite model. Layers are convenient for storing reference geometry, design, and modeling notes, as well as system-dependent information.

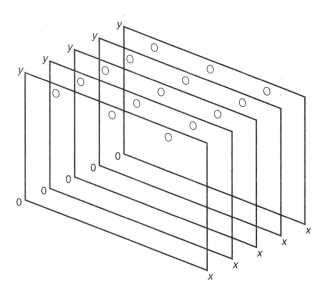

Layer name or no.	Color	Line type	Visibility	Entity type

FIGURE 3.14 Layers are model management aids and are similar in concept to pinbar registered overlays. An entity has a layer attribute as part of its definition. The layer attribute is used as an index into a table that can also specify color, linetype, visibility, etc., of the object.

In an SM system, layers are attributes or properties of objects. When an object is defined, a value is assigned to the layer attribute. The layer attribute can then be used to select objects for operations by specifying the layer name or value. Additional common uses for layers are to control the visibility, color, and linetype of a class of objects.

Good Practices

SMA.3.1   Good Practices[1]

1. *Read the prompts!*

2. Use a single displayed view when designing.

3. Discriminate layers.

4. Select entities by groups.

5. Use a separate layer for duplicate entities.

6. Use standard construction planes (*X-Y, X-Z,* and *Y-Z*) whenever possible.

7. Save multiple states of your design.

Nancy Anderson-Semple, Technical Editor
Computervision Corp., Bedford, Mass.

SMA.3.2   Knowledge and Capabilities

Some basic knowledge of CAD would be very helpful for learning SM. This would provide a familiarity with working in a menu- or icon-driven environment as well as being able to better anticipate which commands will do what. Once this is accomplished the transition to 3D or SM will be less painful. It would also help to know why you want to use SM. For manufacturing you will have to model parts to completion. For FEA you will not need to create parts in as great a detail. Select an SM package with the right capabilities to suite your needs.

Philip Johnson, Development Engineer
Emerson Electric Company, St. Louis, Mo.

SMA.3.3   What Skills Should Be Taught?

First and foremost, to effectively use SM, you need to understand 3D visualization and construction concepts. In order to fully adapt the 3D thought process, you should work primarily in one view, rotated as necessary. Other views should be used only occasionally to ensure against any ambiguities or to show a part or product in the traditional orthographic projections to others. Our experience has been that you either work completely in 3D or go back to 2D. This is especially true for those who have years of experience on the drafting board.

SMA.3.4   Construction Plane Concepts

Construction plane concepts vary with each SM system. To be effective, make every effort to thoroughly understand how to construct geometry in any plane using the techniques employed by the SM system of your choice. Once you are comfortable moving around within the part at any angle and on any plane, then you can quickly learn more sophisticated construction techniques and system features.

George E. Mock, Member Technical Staff
AT&T Network Cable Systems, Norcross, Ga.

Good Practices
(*Continued*)

SMA.3.5 Construction Plane Attributes

A simple or complex model can result in the creation of many construction planes. For organization and model clarity, the active construction plane should be given contrasting display attributes such as color and size. Form a habit of suppressing the display of or deleting construction planes that are not needed.

SMA.3.6 Copying, Scaling, and Mirroring

Always copy, scale, or mirror original geometry whenever possible. Not only does this save time, but in many SM systems, a more efficient model database will result. This can contribute to reduced file sizes and increased interactive performance. Note, however, that the exact coordinate location values of objects that are copied, scaled, or mirrored are subject to being rounded off by system tolerances.

SMA.3.7 The Master Model Concept

The most efficient SM environment is when the solid model is the single point of reference for all departments and subsequent operations—the master model. Try to avoid duplicating geometry or data in multiple locations. Strive to make the solid model file the single source of information concerning that part or product.

SMA.3.8 Think Like a Model Maker

It helps to think of yourself as a model maker when constructing solid models. In fact, the traditional model-making prototype process is often eliminated by your efforts in building an electronic model. Think in terms a model maker would use, such as cutting, turning, adding, and removing material. With SM, these processes are used for construction without the limitations of the physical model-making process.

SMA.3.9 Coordinate Details

Based on the master model concept mentioned in SMA.3.7, always coordinate the amount of detail needed in your solid model. There is no sense in wasting time modeling details into the solid if they are not needed (or wanted) by others who are to work with your solid model.

Don LaCourse, President
The Solid Modeling ExChange, Algood, Tenn.

Guidelines

SMA.3.10 Orientation in 3D Space

The most important thing to keep in mind when performing the operations of an SM system is your orientation in 3D space. Are you in absolute or relative coordinates? Which direction is the positive *Z* direction? How do you know which axis that profile will be turned about? These are some of the common questions asked by new SM users.

Andrew Price, Manager Engineering Applications
Axis Technologies, Fairport, N.Y.

SMA.3.11 The Right-Hand Rule for Rotation

The direction of rotation (positive or negative) about an axis or line can be determined by using the right-hand rule. Point the thumb of your right hand along the specified line or axis toward its positive direction. Curl your fingers toward your palm. Your fingers will wrap in the direction of a positive rotation (see Fig. 3.15).

Forrest K. Blair, President
Microport Systems, Hyde Park, Utah

FIGURE 3.15 The right-hand rule for rotation. (*Graphic courtesy of Hewlett-Packard Company.*)

Guidelines
(*Continued*)

SMA.3.12   The Right-Hand Rule for a Positive Axis

The direction of a positive axis in a cartesian coordinate system can be determined by placing your right hand, palm up, facing you, and your thumb pointing to the right. Your thumb will point in the positive direction of the X axis and your index finger will point in the positive direction of the Y axis. Now close the rest of your fingers but leave your middle finger pointing toward you. Your middle finger indicates the positive direction of the Z axis (see Fig. 3.16).

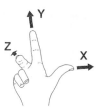

FIGURE 3.16   The right-hand rule for a positive axis. *(Graphic courtesy of Hewlett-Packard Company.)*

SMA.3.13   Strive for Validity

Remember that in SM your primary goal is to produce a clean and valid solid. Try to avoid operations that may cause unpredictable results. Do not depend on the SM system to alert you as soon as a problem occurs. It is always better to undo and redo operations than it is to fix the results of one. Always assume that a problem area that is fixed now (instead of being undone) will cause problems later.

Don LaCourse, President
The Solid Modeling ExChange, Algood, Tenn.

SMA.3.14   The Right Amount of Detail

It is important to remember not to overdetail a model. For example, if you are simulating a construction process, there is no need to model a perfect tractor or crane. Many simulation or animation programs are based on the number of polygons in a model, and the fewer the better.

John R. Gowans, Applications Support Specialist
CRS Sirrine Engineers, Greenville, S.C.

Point of View

SMA.3.15   Do Not Be Discouraged

Do not be discouraged when you encounter apparent limitations of SM technology. Remember that an obstacle is an opportunity. The limits of technology are extended by your efforts. Look for alternate methods of construction when necessary. For example, by merging advanced surfacing techniques into your solid, the geometric scope of your model can be unlimited.

Don LaCourse, President
The Solid Modeling ExChange, Algood, Tenn.

Reference

[1]Adapted from "Parametric Modeling Usage Tips," Revision 4.0.0, Nancy Anderson-Semple, Editor, Computervision Corporation, May 1993.

Chapter 4
Solid Modeling Database Structures

Donald J. Meagher, Ph.D.
President
Octree Corporation

By employing spatially "complete" models, Solid Modeling (SM) systems are able to apply computer power directly to the design of parts and assemblies rather than to lower-level details such as drawings. Much of the capability and operating characteristics of SM systems can be traced directly to the representation and modeling methods used in their databases. This chapter will introduce these methods and attempt to provide insight into how they influence system behavior at the design level.

4.1   Reviewing CAD Databases

One can imagine a variety of ways to mathematically represent solids. For example, an object constructed from toy blocks could be modeled by maintaining the location and orientation of cubes stacked on a plane. A successful SM system, however, must employ a representation scheme that provides general-purpose shape modeling for a variety of generation, manipulation, display, and analysis functions as well as support for external applications such as finite-element modeling (FEM) and numerical control (NC) machining. Such capabilities require a much more sophisticated database than those used to model lines and text in a 2D CAD system.

4.1.1   High versus Low-Level Design

To understand the function of various parts of a CAD database, it is useful to consider the information represented at different "levels" of an engineering effort. The global characteristics of a design are considered "high-level" information, while local details make up the "low level" of a design. Often a "top-down" design strategy is employed where the low-level design is derived from high-level design information, using various tools and methodologies. In computer programming, for example, a program is designed and written in a high-level language and then translated by a compiler into a low-level "machine language" for the actual control of the computer.

Early CAD systems were developed to model and manipulate the lower levels of a design, primarily drawings. Their databases performed mostly a bookkeeping function, keeping track of large numbers of points, lines, curves, and other items. With SM, however, CAD systems extend into the higher levels of design information, placing increased demands on the database.

4.1.2   CAD Generations

The primary function of any CAD database, solid or otherwise, is to symbolically represent certain characteristics of real or imagined 3D objects. The needs of the design community have encouraged the development of a progression of successively more powerful representation schemes to support increasingly higher levels of design, ultimately leading to the modeling of the "solidness" of objects. To classify this progression, CAD systems can be divided into four generations based on the characteristics modeled (see Fig. 4.1). These are as follows:

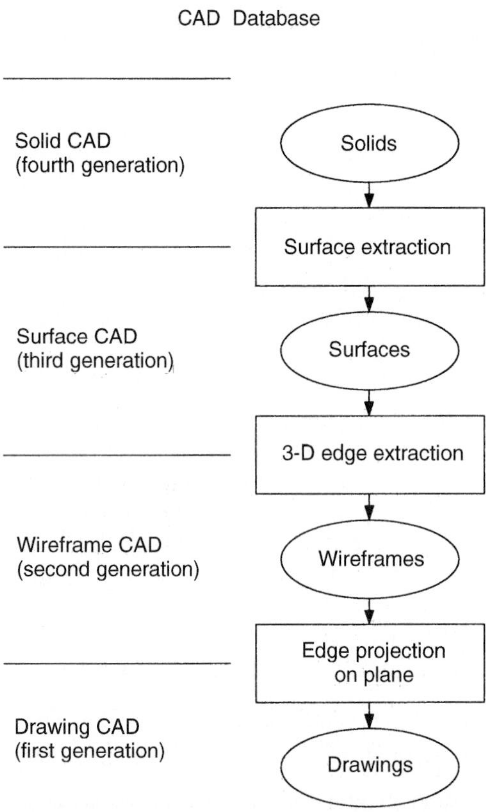

CAD Database

FIGURE 4.1 The four CAD database generations. Note that geometric information can be extracted from each database generation to provide the basis for the ones below it. *(Courtesy of Octree Corporation.)*

First Generation—Drawings. Objects are represented by the projections of selected edges on a 2D plane. Lines and text can be interactively entered and updated. Hardcopy can be generated automatically.

Second Generation—Wireframes. Selected edges are modeled in 3D. This supports 3D line display (wireframes) and the automatic generation of 2D views from any viewpoint.

Third Generation—Surfaces. Objects are represented by modeling selected surfaces. Realistic shaded images can be produced.

Fourth Generation—Solids. Objects are represented by the 3D space they occupy. Advanced features such as mass property calculations and interference detection can be performed automatically.

These CAD generations form a hierarchy that parallels the levels of a design. As noted in Fig. 4.1, top-down conversions can be used to convert solid models progressively to lower-level 3D surfaces, 3D wireframes, and 2D drawings (although the resulting 2D drawings usually need at least some "cleanup" by a draftsperson to improve readability).

A high-level design cannot normally be computed automatically from low-level information. For example, solids cannot be generated from drawings without additional information or manual intervention. This is because, in general, for any given drawing there are multiple solid models that could have generated it, most of which would be an erroneous interpretation of the designer's intent. For example, the drawing in Fig. 4.2*a* is ambiguous. It could represent any of the three solid objects in Fig. 4.2*b* (or a number of additional variations). With complex drawings, the number of possible solids quickly becomes astronomical. Of course, humans mentally perform these upward model translations with a high success rate (even in the presence of errors) because of intelligence, education, and experience. This partly explains the reason new designers are often amazed at what CAD can do, while experienced ones are amazed at what CAD can't do!

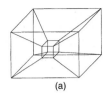

(a)

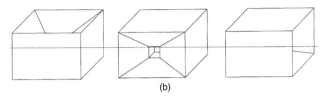

(b)

FIGURE 4.2 The spatially ambiguous nature of a drawing or wireframe representation: (*a*) 3D wireframe drawing; (*b*) multiple solid models that could have created the drawing. (*Courtesy of Octree Corporation.*)

4.2 Requirements

The only absolute requirement for an SM database is that its models be valid solids (spatially unambiguous). In other words, the system must know which regions of space are solid and which regions are empty. Mathematically, this can be reduced to the capability of determining if any given point is (1) solid (part of the object), (2) not solid (outside the object, including interior voids), or (3) on the surface. Given this raw capability, any mathematically well defined operation in the realm of a physical process can be performed on a modeled object (at least in theory!).

4.3 Basic Database Concepts

The following topics are intended to provide a well-rounded understanding of the basic concepts involved in an SM database. Depending on the types of SM systems encountered, some topics may apply more than others.

4.3.1 The SM Database

To a designer, the database is the part of a CAD system that holds what he or she sees on the screen and works with to create, modify, and analyze a design. The extent to which the system can help designers visualize and interact with such models is of critical importance. With a 2D drawing this is relatively simple because each element (point, line, item of text, etc.) can be viewed directly (although there may be subtle misunderstandings, such as lines that erroneously appear to meet).

With solid models, however, achieving a high level of understanding and interaction can be much more difficult than with a drawing. Here are a few reasons why.

1. Important details are often visually hidden or obscured in 3D views, hindering visualization and control.
2. With solids, the elements of a model are interrelated and must adhere to various rules needed to maintain model integrity. It is often difficult or impossible to comprehend the "health" of a model (to what extent it is actually in compliance with such rules).
3. SM operations are very powerful, but can have side effects that are not well understood (e.g., objects can become invalid).
4. Users do not view and interact with a single model in the database but with a collection of models that (more or less) represent various aspects of the object. Each such model has its own set of characteristics.

Because of these difficulties, an understanding of the SM database can help to reduce wasted effort, disappointment, and erroneous results when using SM systems.

It should be noted that modern CAD databases contain a wealth of information not directly related to the shape of a model. This includes text notes, unit and scale information, material properties, part numbers, modification history, and countless other pieces of information necessary to build facilities or design, manufacture, and ship products. While important, such information can usually be handled using standard database methods and will not be discussed here.

4.3.2   Representing Geometric Elements

Solid models are represented by sets of geometric elements that are somehow connected. While formulations vary, most all geometric elements of interest in CAD are ultimately defined by polynomials (equations where the exponents are positive integers and coefficients are constants such as $ax^2 + bx + c = 0$). While interesting shapes can be generated in other ways (e.g., equations with noninteger exponents), polynomials are favored because of the vast array of known and well-understood mathematical tools that can be applied to them (e.g., differentiation to compute surface normals).

Degree of Equations

The representational robustness of a geometric element is limited by the largest exponent used in its defining polynomial or set of polynomials. This is referred to as the *degree* of the equation.* With *linear* equations the largest exponent is 1 (e.g., $ax + by = c$). They can be used to represent straight lines and flat elements (e.g., planar polygons). While objects formed from linear elements are somewhat crude (no curved surfaces), the underlying mathematics is relatively simple and very reliable.

Quadratic equations have squared variables and can represent quadratic curves (arcs, parabolas, ellipses, etc.) and *quadric* surfaces (spheres, cylinders, cones, ellipsoids, paraboloids, and hyperboloids). For example, $x^2 + y^2 + z^2 = R^2$ defines the surface of a sphere where r is the radius. "Cubic" equations are of the third degree (e.g., $x^3 + ax + b = 0$). They provide for more robust shapes and are often used as the basis for advanced surface modeling. Higher-order equations such as "quartic" (fourth degree) polynomials are also sometimes used.

While modeling methods using equations of increasing degree are more powerful, they also become progressively more difficult to handle mathematically. This usually results in systems that have increased capabilities but that are more complex, require more powerful computers, and exhibit reduced reliability.

Sculptured Shapes

While many useful solid models can be constructed from geometric elements defined by quadric surfaces, there has been an increasing need for shapes with free-form or "sculptured" surfaces to fulfill aesthetic, functional, efficiency, or other requirements. Usually a sculptured shape (curve, surface, or solid) is defined by a formula and the location of a number of control points that may lie on, inside or outside the shape. Such schemes include NURBS (Non-Uniform Rational B-Splines) and Bezier shapes (see Chap. 5). In addition to providing increased representational freedom, geometric transformations (translation, rotation, and scaling) can be easily performed by transforming the control points, and local shape changes can often be made simply by moving nearby control points.

Common Representation

The geometric library of a fully functional SM system must have computer procedures that are able to mathematically handle the interaction of any combination of representable elements (e.g., determine the edge of intersection between a cylinder and a sphere, a cylinder and a cone, etc.). Traditional SM databases represent a wide variety of geometric elements and therefore require a large number of such procedures.

Since newer representation schemes such as NURBS are able to represent classical shapes (e.g., the quadrics) as well as sculptured shapes, their use may mean that only one or a small number of shape-representation formats are needed. This can simplify the database and greatly reduce the number of geometric procedures. However, the required procedures are often more complex, require more processing, and may be less reliable than many of those replaced.

---

*The term *order* is also used. Instead of the largest exponent, it is the number of coefficients (i.e., degree + 1). Thus, a cubic polynomial (degree = 3) is a fourth-order polynomial.

4.3.3   Classifying Geometric Elements

Geometric elements can be classified according to the following three characteristics (see Table 4.1):

1. ***Dimensionality of elements.***   Elements can be divided into points, lines (including curves), surfaces, and solids based on their dimensionality (defined as the number of dimensions they occupy):

Element	Dimensionality	Space occupied
point	0D	(none)
line	1D	distance
surface	2D	area
solid	3D	volume

2. ***Dimensionality of space.***   Geometric elements can exist in a universe of the same or higher dimensionality. For example, a point can exist in a 1D space (on a line) while a surface can exist only in 2D or 3D space.

3. ***Degree of defining equations.***   As noted in Sec. 4.3.2, equations of higher degree give an SM system the ability to represent more complex shapes.

TABLE 4.1   Dimensionality of Geometric Elements

This table categorizes the geometric elements commonly used in CAD according to the number of dimensions they occupy, the dimensionality of the space in which they exist, and degree of the equations that define them. (Courtesy of Octree Corporation.)

Points: Elements with dimensionality = 0 (do not occupy distance, area, or volume)		
Dimensionality of space	Degree of equations	Example
1D	0	Point on line
2D	0	Point on plane
3D	0	Point in space

Lines and curves: Elements with dimensionality = 1 (occupy distance, but not area or volume)		
Dimensionality of space	Degree of equations	Example
2D	1	Line on plane
2D	2	Quadric curve on plane
2D	3	Cubic curve on plane
2D	4	Quartic curve on plane
3D	1	Line in space
3D	2	Quadric curve in space
3D	3	Cubic curve in space
3D	4	Quartic curve in space

Surfaces: Elements with dimensionality = 2 (occupy area but not volume)		
Dimensionality of space	Degree of equations	Example
2D	1	Section of plane
3D	1	Plane or polygon in space
3D	2	Quadric surface in space
3D	3	Bicubic patch in space
3D	4	Biquartic surface in space

Solids: Elements with dimensionality = 3 (occupy volume)		
Dimensionality of space	Degree of equations	Example
3D	1	Polyhedron
3D	2	Triquadric solid
3D	3	Tricubic solid
3D	4	Triquartic solid

4.3.4   Bounded versus Unbounded Objects

Geometric elements can form a boundary for elements of the next-higher dimensionality. Thus, a point forms a boundary on a line (two points bound a segment of a line). Lines can form boundaries on surfaces and surfaces can bound 3D space (e.g., to enclose a volume).

In SM, an object is "bounded" if it has a complete set of enclosing surfaces that restrict it to a finite volume. An unbounded object can occupy an infinite volume. For example, a cylinder without end caps is an unbounded object and has infinite volume. Because of the mathematical problems this can cause, unbounded objects are often restricted or prohibited (or automatically clipped at the edges of a finite volume).

A half-space is a solid object consisting of all of the space on one side of a surface. A half plane, for example, is the space on one side of a plane. A half-space may be bounded (e.g., spheres) or unbounded (e.g., half planes and unbounded cylinders).

4.3.5   Geometry versus Topology

There is a fundamental distinction between the geometry and topology of a solid model stored in a database. Geometric information is the shape, size, and location of geometric elements. Topological information is the relationships between them (e.g., two faces share a common edge or two solid elements are unioned).

Consider the cube in Fig. 4.3, for example. It is composed of three types of geometric elements: points, lines and planes. Its geometric definition starts with 8 points. They define 12 lines which, in turn, define 6 planes. The topological definition specifies how the geometric elements are bounded (forming topological elements) and how they are connected. Thus, topologically, a cube is defined as a region of space bounded by six faces which are planes bounded by edges and connected to each other at edges. The edges are, in turn, lines bounded by vertices (points of intersection) and are connected to each other at the vertices. Note that the topological definition does not change if the geometric definition is modified (e.g., vertices moved to form a rectangular box or other shape; see Chap. 7). For a polyhedron, this association of the elements used in the topological definition and the related elements in the geometric definition is summarized as follows:

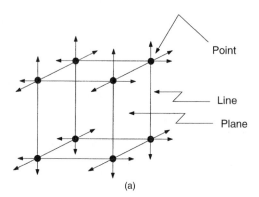

(a)

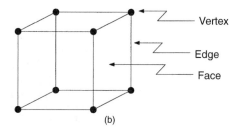

(b)

FIGURE 4.3 The geometric and topological elements that make up a cube: (*a*) geometric elements include points (defined by locations in space), lines (defined by two points), and planes (defined by two intersecting lines); (*b*) topological elements include vertices (a point defined by the intersection of three or more edges), edges (defined by the intersection of two faces), and faces (in this case, planer faces defined as segments of a plane bounded by an enclosing set of four edges). *(Courtesy of Octree Corporation.)*

Topological element	Geometric element
face	plane
edge	line
vertex	point

It should be noted that this distinction between geometry and topology exists in other areas of engineering. For example, in piping and electrical systems, geometric information is the "layout," while the topological connections are represented in the "schematic." (See Chap. 6 for more on topology.)

4.3.6 Evaluated Representations

Within an SM database, geometric elements can be represented explicitly (mathematically) or they may be defined implicitly by relationships between other geometric elements. A curve, for example, could be defined explicitly by an equation or defined implicitly as the intersection of two surfaces. An evaluated database is one in which the faces, edges, and vertices of solid objects are explicitly represented.

In practice, a database may be more or less evaluated. Often the actual mathematical definition of an element is computed from other elements in the database only when needed (saving overall processing and memory). For example, the equation of an edge may be computed from its two endpoints when needed for display and then discarded. If such computations are simple, fast, accurate, and reliable, the database is still considered to be evaluated.

4.3.7 Manifold versus Nonmanifold Objects

Mathematicians separate solids into *manifold* and *nonmanifold* objects. With a manifold object (also called an *object with manifold topology*), every surface point has a neighborhood (an infinitesimal sphere around it) that can be mathematically deformed into a locally planar surface. In other words, if the object was made of a perfectly elastic material, a small spherical region around any surface point could be flattened into a tiny flat disk without cutting or tearing the material. For example, one could imagine that a point on an edge of a rubber cube could find itself on a locally planar surface if it were pressed by a flat instrument.

While it may seem that all solid objects are manifold objects, this is not the case when modeling solids mathematically. Self-intersection is an example. Suppose edges A and B of the object in Fig. 4.4a were moved together so they became one edge as in Fig. 4.4b. The common edge would now bound four faces rather than the normal two. Given a point on this combined edge, its neighborhood could not be deformed into a planar surface on the solid because there are more than two faces attached to it. Self-interaction has caused it to become a nonmanifold object. Much more difficult nonmanifold situations can arise, especially when curved surfaces are allowed. Since some SM systems function properly only with manifold objects, such situations can cause problems. Often, checks are performed during or after operations in an attempt to detect illegal occurrences.

4.3.8 Primary versus Secondary Models

SM systems typically maintain several representations of objects. The solid model used by fundamental modeling algorithms is the *primary* or *working* model. Others are secondary models and may or may not be solid representations.

Often, secondary models are derived from the primary model to facilitate a specific function such as display, analysis (FEM, mass properties, kinematic analysis, etc.), manufacturing (rapid prototyping, machining, robot planning, etc.), documentation (drawings, etc.), or data exchange. Secondary files are sometimes stored along with the primary model to avoid time-consuming regeneration when they are needed.

The ability to establish a direct connection between models in a database is called *associativity*. For example, changes in a solid model might trigger an immediate update in related drawings. This would

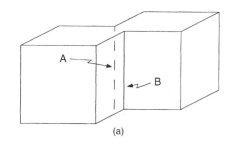

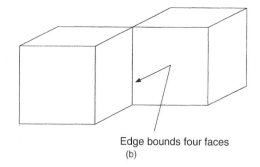

Edge bounds four faces
(b)

FIGURE 4.4 Example of a manifold object becoming non-manifold because of self-intersection: (*a*) a manifold object where edges A and B are distinct. The neighborhood of all surface points could be locally deformed to form a flat surface; (*b*) a nonmanifold object. Edges A and B are merged to become a single edge resulting in a self-intersection. The neighborhood of a point on the edge could not be deformed to form a flat surface because the point would be on four faces. (*Courtesy of Octree Corporation.*)

be an example of a top-down model translation. In some systems, parameters embedded in drawings or drawinglike databases are used to define solid models. A modification to a drawing can thus result in changes to the associated solid. (See Chap. 8 for more on parametric/relational modeling.)

Often the steps used in building and modifying an object are saved by an SM database in a journal or log file. This can be considered a secondary model (it represents the object by its construction steps). It can be used for documentation, to re-create a part at a later time (perhaps with modifications), and to support an "undo" capability to reverse SM operations (to correct errors and mistakes). Sometimes a "redo" command can also be used to repeat steps that had been erroneously undone.

4.3.9 Display Models

A secondary model that facilitates display is called a *display model*. This could, for example, be a list of lines and text used to regenerate a drawing or perhaps a set of polygons for rendering a shaded image. These models are important in an SM database because display requests are usually the most often requested operations.

Since the direct display of solids is slow, a two-stage approach is often used. This involves converting solid objects into a nonsolid display model, usually polygons or wireframe edges. This may take a considerable period of time, especially for complex models. When completed, however, the display model can be viewed rapidly.

While this compromise may be more desirable than the alternative (a display that is always slow), confusion can result from the fact that the primary model itself is not being viewed. The display model is the result of one or more translations that can introduce various subtle (and not-so-subtle) changes. For example, the display model is usually an approximation using linear elements (lines or polygons). When viewed close up, curves appear straight and curved surfaces appear flat. Small features may not be represented at all. And, of course, a regeneration of the display model is needed to view changes to the primary model.

4.3.10 Model Portability

It is often desirable to move solid models between different SM systems. Even with the availability of standard conversion formats this may be impossible if the solid representations have incompatible types of elements (although it may be possible with lower-level models such as surfaces, wireframes, and drawings). Sometimes only subsets of a model can be successfully translated, or subtle changes are introduced in certain geometric entities. (See Chaps. 20 and 21.)

Concepts

> ### SMA.4.1 Platform Portability
>
> It is possible to inadvertently change a model by simply moving it to a different type of computer (with the same SM system) because of differences in numeric representations. If such cross-platform transfers are contemplated, it would be advisable to obtain a written statement from the vendor specifying under what conditions this could occur, what steps should be taken to avoid it, how such changes could be detected and what problems could arise later.

4.4 Mathematical Methods

While much has been written about the intrinsic advantages of particular SM representations, perhaps the factor most critical to ultimate success is the development of robust and reliable mathematical methods to implement fundamental SM operations. Our goal in this section is to provide some insight into this often-neglected area.

4.4.1 Exact versus Inexact Mathematics

Computations of any kind can usually be classified as being exact or inexact depending on whether the result could differ from a mathematically perfect computation (having infinite precision). Integer addition and multiplication (e.g., $6 \times 20 + 30 = 150$), for example, are exact (assuming, of course, that the capabilities of the computer are not exceeded). With such operations the use of a computer with greater precision would not change the result. On the other hand, integer division (e.g., ⅓) and most floating-point operations (those involving real numbers such as 2.531) are inexact.

Because numbers are represented to a limited precision, the result of inexact operations can differ from the mathematically perfect result by a small amount due to round-off and other errors. For example, the computation of 1 divided by 3 is always inexact, because the exact value would require an infinite number of digits (0.3333 . . .). Note, however, that an inexact operation can generate an exact result (e.g., the floating-point division of 1.0 by 2.0 results in the exactly correct result 0.5). They just can't be guaranteed to generate an exact result in all cases.

4.4.2 Analytical versus Numerical Methods

An SM database relies on a comprehensive collection of subroutines to compute information about geometric elements. The mathematical methods employed by such routines can usually be divided into two classes: analytical and numerical.

In essence, analytical methods use mathematical formulas to directly compute a solution. For example, the edge of intersection between two planes (a straight line) is easily computed using analytical methods found in elementary geometry textbooks. Modern SM systems, however, use advanced modeling methods (e.g., NURBS) to represent sculptured surfaces. Unfortunately, there is often no known method (or no practical method) to analytically perform fundamental operations on such representations. For example, computing the curve of intersection of two bicubic patches is of great practical importance in SM. While it is possible, in theory, to use analytical methods, the resulting equation would be of degree 324! Since no formula is known for directly solving equations above degree 4, such methods are unusable.

In such cases, numerical methods must be used. This usually involves using repetitive mathematical procedures that attempt to converge on an approximate solution. In the case of intersecting bicubic patches, for example, numerical methods are employed to find approximations of points on the edge. This typically involves the execution of iterative procedures to generate points of increasing accuracy as the computations proceed. A series of such points can then be used to generate a spline curve representing the edge. This curve is an approximation and will not, in general, lie exactly on either patch. While this can cause errors, with sufficient processing the deviation can usually be made small enough to be essentially negligible for most purposes. It is, however, often difficult to determine how much processing should be devoted to increasing accuracy.

Unfortunately, numerical methods can fail to find a solution or fail to find all possible solutions. Also, they sometimes exhibit numerical instability. For example, instead of converging on a point of intersection, the procedure may try to iterate forever between two points on opposite sides of the edge. These problems are aggravated when geometric situations become complex.

4.4.3 Computational Complexity

In nonsolid databases, individual geometric elements are usually processed in isolation. An operation may be applied to many elements at once (e.g., moving a drawing), but can usually be accomplished by applying the operation to the elements individually (e.g., move a line). This is often not true with SM operations. While modeling functions such as boolean operations (see Chap. 6) are very powerful (e.g., determining the interference between two complex assemblies with a single intersection request), such power comes at a price. That price is global interaction. Each element can affect all others by the interpenetration of solid elements or by the intersection of surface elements (depending on how the model is represented).

This can result in operations where all pairs of elements must be processed. This is a problem because pairing is a quadratic growth operation in the number of elements. In other words, if each object has n elements, the number of pairs grows by n^2. To illustrate the problem, Table 4.2 tabulates the processing time for two hypothetical algorithms: one which exhibits pure linear growth and the other, quadratic growth as a function of the number of items processed. It assumes that 100,000 cases can be processed per second. The growth illustrated in the table shows why the dominant performance factor for an operation may not be dataset size but, rather, the computational complexity characteristics of the algorithms employed.

TABLE 4.2   Quadratic vs. Linear Growth of Algorithms

This table illustrates the growth of processing time with the size of the input data set for a pure linear growth algorithm and a pure quadratic growth algorithm, both processing 100,000 cases per second. (Courtesy of Octree Corporation.)

Processing Time at 100,000 Iterations Per Second		
Input items	**Linear growth**	**Quadratic growth**
1	0.01 ms	0.01 ms
10	0.1 ms	1 ms
100	1 ms	100 ms
1,000	10 ms	10 s
10,000	100 ms	17 min
100,000	1 s	1.2 days
1 million	10 s	3.9 months
10 million	1.7 min	31.7 years
100 million	17 min	31.7 centuries
1 billion	2.8 hours	317 millennia

Actual implementations of SM algorithms behave in complex ways and often take advantage of various speed-up mechanisms. Unfortunately, the underlying computational problems often remain, causing processing time to increase faster than model complexity. Chapter 6 provides some strategies for minimizing CPU time.

4.4.4 Graphs and Trees

Topological relationships are usually represented in a database with graphs. As shown in Fig. 4.5a, a graph is a set of *nodes* linked by *connections*.* Nodes represent items, while connections represent relationships. A path is a sequence of nonrepeated connections between two nodes.

---

*Connections are usually called *edges* by mathematicians. This terminology is not used here because of potential confusion with object edges.

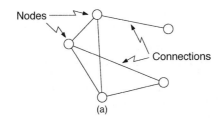

(a)

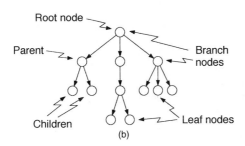

(b)

FIGURE 4.5 Sample graph and tree: (*a*) a graph is a collection of nodes which represent distinct items with any number of connections that represent relationships between items; (*b*) a tree is a restricted form of graph. One node is designated as a root node (traditionally drawn at the top). There are no loops in a tree (a path of connections which leave and return to the same node without crossing the same connection twice). Nodes that are connected to nodes at a lower level (farther distant from the root) are parent nodes; nodes directly below them are their children. A parent node with two or more children is a branch node. A node with no children is a leaf (or terminal) node. *(Courtesy of Octree Corporation.)*

A tree is a restricted form of graph in which all nodes spread out from a single "root" node and there are no paths that start and end in the same node (no "loops"). As shown in Fig. 4.5*b*, trees are traditionally drawn with the root node at the top. A node immediately below another node is a *child* (the upper node is its *parent*). Continuing this analogy, all the nodes above a node (back to and including the root) are its ancestors and all nodes below it are its descendants. A node and its descendants form a subtree (the node itself is the root of the subtree). Nodes with no children are *leaf* or *terminal* nodes while those with more than one child are *branch* nodes.

4.5 SM Database Considerations

The operating characteristics of an SM system are closely related to its representation scheme and the algorithms employed. What follows is a discussion on a few important database-related considerations.

4.5.1 Representational Capability

The domain of object shapes that can be modeled within an SM database ("geometric coverage") can be divided into four parts:

1. ***Allowable geometric elements.*** The types of elements allowed and the degree of their defining equations determine the representational capabilities of individual elements.
2. ***Object complexity.*** This refers to the number of geometric elements that can actually be used in a practical situation to construct an object. There is often a trade-off between using large numbers of simple elements (polygons, spheres, cones, etc.) versus a smaller number of more sophisticated elements (e.g., those with sculptured surfaces) which have greater storage and processing requirements.
3. ***Exact versus approximate.*** An SM system is called *exact* or *precise* if the precision of the original object definition is maintained in the primary model. Otherwise, it is an approximate modeler (e.g., polygons used to approximate curved surfaces).
4. ***Constraints.*** Some SM systems allow complete freedom in the construction and use of solid models, while others constrain designers to "reasonable" shapes in order to avoid geometric situations that are mathematically difficult to handle. While constraints may have the beneficial result of imposing a certain amount of discipline on a design, they also limit modeling freedom.

4.5.2 Performance

Performance is an important issue for SM systems because they have generally been found to be much less responsive to user requests than CAD systems that handle drawings. This can be a problem because a lack of interactivity can disrupt the activities of a designer, reducing productivity. As previously noted, the complexity of many fundamental SM algorithms grows faster than object or situation complexity. Such issues are often considered irrelevant because of the belief that ever-faster computers will solve performance problems. While this may be true for a fixed task, in applications where needs are growing (like most CAD uses), increased computational power will increase the advantage of efficient algorithms over inefficient ones. Larger data sets can be handled in either case but, as was illustrated in Table 4.2, the relative difference can increase dramatically.

4.5.3 Reliability

Reliability is one of the most critical considerations as design functions grow increasingly dependent on SM. While an ideal SM system would be as reliable as a hand-held calculator is with arithmetic, such is not the case. Refer to the SM Adviser at the end of this chapter for specific advice on SM-related database errors and reliability issues.

4.6 Constructive Solid Geometry (CSG)

CSG is one of two major schemes currently used for representing solids. An object is constructed using boolean operations (UNION, INTERSECTION, and SUBTRACTION) to combine simple solid shapes (spheres, blocks, cylinders, etc.). Such geometric elements are called *primitive solids* or simply *primitives* (see Chap. 6). As shown in Fig. 4.6a, CSG objects are usually stored using a tree database structure. Leaf nodes represent primitives, and branch nodes represent boolean operations. Note that each subtree also represents a legitimate solid.

This "classical" CSG tree can be extended by the use of transformation nodes. As illustrated in Fig. 4.6b, they can be used to change the location and orientation of an object or some part of an object represented by a subtree. This provides for the independent design of a part and its later incorporation into a larger object or assembly (as a subtree). Rather than using separate nodes, often geometric transformations are simply incorporated into each node. Auxiliary information such as material type or previously computed mass-properties data can also be attached to nodes.

CSG

SMA.4.2   Supported CSG Primitives

The types of solid geometric elements that can be used as primitives in a particular SM system is an important consideration. Sometimes they are restricted to planar and quadric shapes to simplify the underlying mathematics. More advanced SM systems allow the use of primitives with sculptured surfaces (usually requiring cubic or higher-degree equations).

4.6.1 Multiple Use of Subtrees

A powerful CSG feature is the use of multiple instances of a part. Figure 4.7 shows a subtree (node A and its two children) used to represent a countersunk hole. It is subtracted from a block in two places using transformation nodes (T_1 and T_2) to position the instances. Any change to the subtree definition is immediately reflected in both holes. Note that, technically, the overall CSG graph structure is no longer a tree because node A has two parent nodes.

4.6.2 Point Classification

Point classification is a mathematical operation used to determine if a specified point is outside, on the surface of, or inside a modeled solid. This is a fundamental operation used with great frequency within

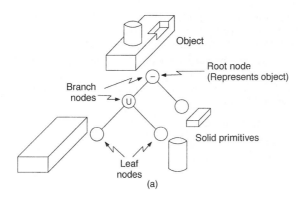

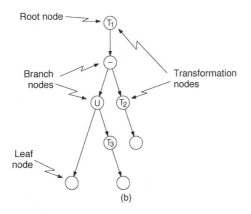

FIGURE 4.6 CSG data structure: (*a*) a tree structure is used to represent a three-primitive CSG object; (*b*) the CSG tree can be further extended with transformation nodes. Nodes T2 and T3 each transform a single primitive, while T1 transforms the entire object. (*Courtesy of Octree Corporation.*)

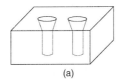

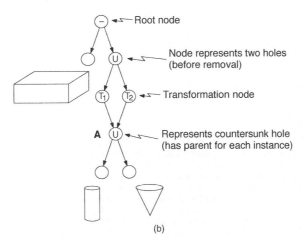

FIGURE 4.7 The use of transformation nodes to create multiple instances of an object: (*a*) a block with two countersunk holes; (*b*) node A represents the countersunk hole. Nodes T1 and T2 perform geometric transformations on A to create two instances of the hole. A change to node A is reflected in both hole locations. (*Courtesy of Octree Corporation.*)

SM systems when executing various modeling tasks. Examining how this is accomplished will provide a glimpse at the types of calculations that are performed behind the screen in SM systems and will illustrate the difficulty of making such systems compact, fast, and reliable.

For a CSG object, the process begins by classifying the point for each primitive—a simple computation for most shapes. A new classification is then computed at each branch node until the final classification is determined at the root. For example, a point classification for the result of a union between two parts (subtrees), A and B, would be:

Subtree A

		out	on	in
	out:	out	on	in
Subtree B	on:	on	?	in
	in:	in	in	in

Point classification for A ∪ B

The columns, left to right, indicate whether the point has been found to be outside, on, or inside object A. The rows, top to bottom, indicate the same for object B. The associated value indicates the classification for the combined object, A ∪ B. For example, if the point is outside both A and B, it is outside A ∪ B. If it is inside either object, it is inside A ∪ B. Figure 4.8 shows an illustration of this (2D rectangles are used for simplicity).

In Fig. 4.8*a*, point *P* is on the surface of one object (B) but outside the other (A). It is therefore on the surface of the resulting object. A problem called the "on-on ambiguity" arises when the point is on the surface of both objects (the "on-on" case). In Fig. 4.8*b*, the objects are on opposite sides of the common face (edge in this 2D example) and *P* finds itself inside the combined object. In Fig. 4.8*c*, the two

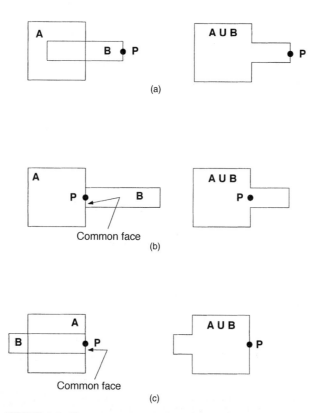

FIGURE 4.8 The "on-on ambiguity" problem while combining two objects. Similar cases occur for intersecting and subtracting objects: (*a*) *P* is on the surface of *B* and outside *A*. It is, therefore, on the surface of the union of *A* and *B*. There is no ambiguity; (*b*) when *P* is on the surface of both *A* and *B*, an ambiguity exists. Here *P* becomes an interior point; (*c*) *P* shares a common face and becomes surface point. The ambiguity cannot be resolved without knowledge of the neighborhood of *P* in each object. (*Courtesy of Octree Corporation.*)

objects are on the same side of the common face and *P* becomes a surface point. The new classification cannot be resolved with just subtree classifications (thus the "?" in the preceding table).

A solution is to have the computer analyze a spherical neighborhood of the point. The region of the sphere that is solid is computed for each primitive. This information is then combined at every CSG branch node to calculate the region or regions in the neighborhood that are solid. When combined at the root, if the entire neighborhood is solid, the point is classified as *interior*. If the neighborhood is completely empty, it is determined to be *exterior*. If it is partly solid, the point is determined to be *on the surface*. While conceptually simple, implementing this scheme is quite complex. One can appreciate the difficulty of maintaining and combining these "neighborhood balls" if, for example, the vertex points of many randomly oriented cones were to meet at the point being tested.

4.6.3   CSG Pros and Cons

CSG is a powerful, high-level representation scheme. CSG models can be created with a minimum of steps, are compact, and are always valid (since they're built from solid elements). Boolean operations are simple to implement and take little processing time (a new branch node for the resulting tree is simply generated and connected to the two CSG trees). Also, many designers find the addition and subtraction of solid primitives to be an intuitive design paradigm that parallels manufacturing operations (welding, drilling, etc.). This lends itself to top-down design approaches (see Chap. 11).

A pure CSG representation is severely limited in most SM situations, however, because it is unevaluated. An object's faces, edges, and vertices are not available in explicit form (mathematical equations). They are implicitly defined by the CSG structure itself. While such information can be computed explicitly for applications that need them, this is time-consuming. It also becomes mathematically difficult as the degree of the surfaces increases. Because of this, CSG primitives are sometimes limited to shapes with quadric surfaces or are first converted to polygonal approximations.

The unevaluated nature of CSG can also limit the design process. For example, since edges are defined implicitly, one cannot easily start with edges (perhaps from a drawing or wireframe representation) to define an object.

4.7   Boundary Representation (B-Rep)

B-Rep is the second of the two commonly used database methods of representing solids. Surface elements are assembled to form an "airtight" boundary that encloses the three-dimensional space occupied by the modeled object. Figure 4.9*a* illustrates a B-Rep half cylinder formed by four surface elements: three planar and one cylindrical. The topology can be represented using a graph where the nodes are faces and the connections represent shared edges.

B-Rep

SMA.4.3   B-Rep versus Traditional Surface Modeling

It is important to understand how B-Rep differs from a conventional surface modeling scheme. While a nonsolid CAD system may represent surfaces, a B-Rep system must also guarantee that the surfaces form a complete partition of space, even after being extensively modified. This is, in practice, a major challenge. If this separation of space fails for any reason, the model becomes invalid and the SM system has made a serious error.

4.7.1   Winged-Edge Data Structure

In practice, the B-Rep graph illustrated in Fig. 4.9*a* is usually expanded into what is known as the *winged-edge* data structure. As shown in Fig. 4.9*b*, edges are defined by vertices (their endpoints). Faces are defined by loops of edges and are connected at common edges to form a partition of space.

Figure 4.10 shows an expanded winged-edge representation of a simple triangular pyramid where the vertices, edges, faces, and the solid are explicitly represented. Topological elements are shown on different levels based on their dimensionality. Bottom-level nodes represent vertices. Above this are

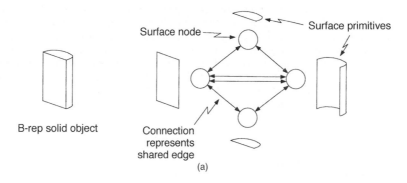

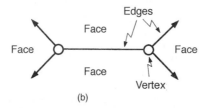

FIGURE 4.9 B-Rep database representation of a solid half cylinder: (*a*) graph where nodes represent faces (surface primitives), connections represent common edges; (*b*) winged-edge data structure where vertices are explicitly represented as nodes, connections as edges, and faces as loops (closed paths of connections). Bottom-level nodes determine geometric definition, while connections form topological definition. *(Courtesy of Octree Corporation.)*

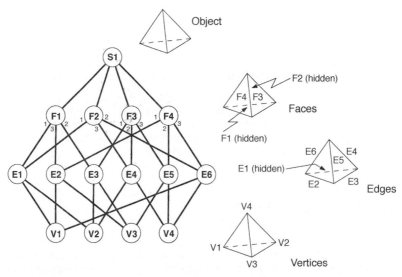

FIGURE 4.10 An expanded winged-edge representation of a simple triangular pyramid. *(Courtesy of Octree Corporation.)*

edges. Their downward connections point to two vertices (their endpoints). Nodes at the next-higher level represent faces. Each has connections to a loop of edges forming its boundary (three each in this case). Finally, at the top level, a single node represents the 3D solid. Its connections indicate the enclosing faces.

Faces used in B-Rep systems are orientable; that is, they have an inside surface and an outside surface. This information is typically encoded by numbering the edges in a sequence such that the right-hand rule (see Chap. 3) defines a vector that points outward from the object. Note that this is used to number the loop edges of each face of the pyramid. (See Chap. 12 for concerns related to the orientation of faces during mass-properties analysis.)

Note that the shape of the pyramid is completely determined by the location of its vertices. If one is moved, the attached edges and faces will move with it. This can be used to perform local shape changes on B-Rep objects (often called *tweaking*) without changing the topology. (See Chap. 7.)

4.7.2 Euler's Formula

A B-Rep object can be proven to be topologically correct if its elements are appropriately connected (e.g., all edges are connected to two vertices and bound two faces) and it adheres to an equation (derived by the 18th century Swiss mathematician Leonhard Euler) known as *Euler's formula:*

$$V - E + F = 2$$

where V = number of vertices
             E = number of edges
             F = number of faces

This can be easily verified for the pyramid of Fig. 4.10 ($V = 4$, $E = 6$, $F = 4$, and $4 - 6 + 4 = 2$) or for a cube ($V = 8$, $E = 12$, $F = 6$, and $8 - 12 + 6 = 2$). Topological correctness (all necessary geometric elements are present and connected properly) does not guarantee a valid solid, however. An example is shown in Fig. 4.11. If the geometry is changed such that a vertex inadvertently pierces a face (see Fig. 4.11c), the topological model no longer represents the actual shape of the object. The geometric and topological definitions of the model are contradictory, resulting in an invalid "nonsense" object.

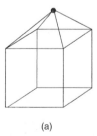 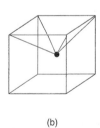 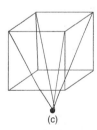

       (a)   (b)   (c)

FIGURE 4.11 Local surface modifications can create valid and invalid objects: (*a*) and (*b*) show surface modification that result in valid objects; (*c*) shows a surface modification that results in an invalid object. The four top faces now intersect the bottom face, resulting in new vertices, edges, and faces that are not represented in the original topological model. Should the new pyramid region below the original bottom be empty (forming a hole through the block) or solid? *(Courtesy of Octree Corporation.)*

While CSG methods lend themselves to top-down design, the classical method of generating B-Rep objects is a bottom-up construction from vertices, edges, and faces. Internal database operators are used to make incremental topological and geometric modifications. These topology operators are formulated to ensure that Euler's formula is not violated, and are commonly called *Euler operators.* Although powerful and effective, Euler operators are complex, operate at a low level, and are relatively difficult for a designer to use. In many B-Rep systems they are used internally to implement high-level operators (e.g., set operations) and are not directly available for general use.

4.7.3 Boolean Operations with B-Rep

Boolean operations are much more difficult to accomplish with B-Rep than with CSG because an evaluated model must be computed. This requires the merging of two interpenetrating structures of vertices, edges, and faces into a single structure. New edges and vertices must be created where faces intersect, existing faces split accordingly, and then all vertices, edges, and faces on the interior of the resulting object (for union) or exterior to the resulting object (for intersection and subtraction) must be dismantled and removed. An airtight surface structure with a flawless topological definition must result from this process.

Figure 4.12 illustrates the result when two B-Rep cubes are unioned. Of the original 16 vertices (8 on each cube), two lie within the combined object and must be eliminated. Three edges on each object penetrate faces of the other creating six new vertices for a total of 20 $(16 - 2 + 6)$. The original 24 edges all exist in the resulting object (although 6 are shortened). Six additional edges are generated where three faces on one cube intersect two faces each on the other, resulting in 30 edges $(24 + 6)$. Six of the original square faces become six-sided polygons, but the total number remains the same at 12. A quick calculation of Euler's formula $(20 - 30 + 12 = 2)$ confirms that the resulting object has the correct number of topological elements.

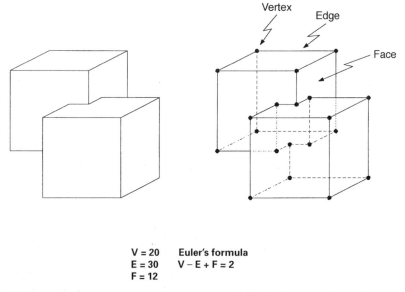

$$V = 20 \qquad \text{Euler's formula}$$
$$E = 30 \qquad V - E + F = 2$$
$$F = 12$$

FIGURE 4.12 The result when two B-Rep cubes are unioned. *(Courtesy of Octree Corporation.)*

Three fundamental problems can be seen to arise with B-Rep boolean operations. These are as follows:

1. The pairing of geometric elements to find intersections exhibits quadratic growth in the number of elements. As mentioned previously, this causes processing time to grow much faster than object complexity.
2. The new topological model is derived from geometric calculations. Errors in determining the topology can have unpredictable results.
3. If the two objects met at a common geometric element (e.g., an edge) a nonmanifold object can result (an illegal situation in some systems); see Sec. 4.3.7.

Although various techniques are used to reduce the occurrence or correct the results of these situations, they remain a continuing problem in B-Rep systems.

4.7.4 Polygonal Representations

A polygonal representation is an approximate B-Rep where all modeled surfaces are planar. Curved surfaces are represented by polygons to some specified tolerance. This has certain advantages because manipulating and intersecting planes is mathematically simple and very reliable. The results are not exact, however, and the number of polygons (and the associated processing time) can grow very large when the tolerance is lowered. Often, low-resolution polygonal models are used for conceptual design (for improved performance) and more accurate versions are used later for analysis, detailed design, and presentations.

4.7.5 B-Rep Pros and Cons

B-Rep database structures exhibit the benefits of being an evaluated representation. Edges and faces are readily available for display or other uses and can be specified directly or from drawings when constructing objects (rather than implied by intersections as with CSG). Also, higher-degree edges can be readily represented (they do not need to be computed from intersections). In some situations the ability to make local changes to topology and geometry (tweaking) is a major advantage. Also, B-Rep is well known for its effective modeling of swept objects.

The fundamental problem with the B-Rep database structure is the inability of the representation itself to guarantee object validity. Unlike CSG, B-Rep validity depends on the correctness of modeler algorithms, the quality of their implementation, and their sensitivity to the subtle computational errors that will inevitably occur. This has been found to be a major challenge with B-Reps. Applying internal constraints to prevent the occurrence of such problem situations (e.g., enforcing a fixed topology) can greatly increase reliability but reduces system utility (e.g., boolean operations may be restricted because they modify topology).

Also, maintaining an evaluated database can be a burden for B-Rep modelers in terms of system complexity, storage requirements, and performance. Construction of objects usually requires many more operations than with CSG (at least internally).

4.8 Other Database Representations

A large number of methods of mathematically representing solids have been proposed and developed over the years. While both CSG and B-Rep have emerged as useful methods, each has limitations that detract from its commercial viability. For this reason, strategies other than simply using CSG or B-Rep have emerged. This section will first present another representation scheme, the octree, which has a substantially different set of characteristics. This is followed by a discussion of hybrids where multiple representations are maintained to realize the advantages of each.

4.8.1 The Octree Database

An octree (also called an *O-Rep*) is an approximate solid representation in which nodes in an eight-way branching tree structure are used to represent the subdivisions of a cubical universe. As shown in Fig. 4.13, the root node of the tree represents the entire universe. There are eight children at the next-lower level representing the eight cubical octants of the universe. This subdivision process can continue to any needed level of resolution. Note that octrees are hierarchical in that the parent and its children represent the same region of space (the children being at a higher resolution).

Octree nodes are given one of three possible values: black, white, or gray. White (W) indicates that no part of the object exists within the represented space. Black (B) indicates that its space is completely occupied by the object. Otherwise, it is partly occupied (at least part of a surface is within the region) and the node is gray (G).

In the example of Fig. 4.13 a simple solid box is represented. Since it partly occupies the universe, the root is a G node. The universe is then subdivided. At this level two nodes, 4 and 5, are partly occupied and are given a G value. The rest are W nodes. The subdivision of the G nodes continues. One child of node 4 is completely occupied by the object and is made a B node. Two children of node 5 become B nodes. The rest are empty. Of significance is the fact that W and B nodes need not be subdivided because no additional information would be represented. Because of this it can be shown that the number of nodes in an octree is on the order of (limited by) the surface area of the object modeled.

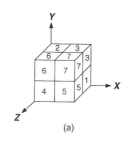

(a)

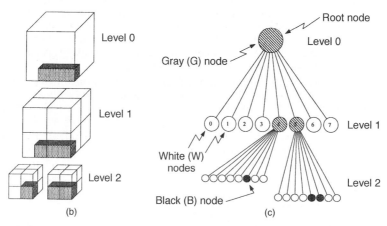

(b)   (c)

FIGURE 4.13   An octree representation of a simple solid box: (*a*) labeling of octree octants; (*b*) subdivision of octree universe; (*c*) octree data structure. (*Courtesy of Octree Corporation.*)

Perhaps the most important characteristic of the octree data structure is that it maintains a model in a spatially sorted format in which space can be searched efficiently. This can be used to eliminate or reduce many of the adverse computational complexity problems associated with SM operations.

Point classification is simple and fast (the octree is simply traversed to the appropriate leaf node). Set operations are also fast because there is no need to generate and examine all the possible pairs of elements between two objects. The two octrees are simply traversed simultaneously and compared node by node to generate a third octree. Display is fast because only the octree nodes on the outer visible surface of an object (from any particular viewpoint) need be accessed from an octree stored in memory (or generated from another solid representation) to produce an image.

Since they are hierarchical, octree algorithms can employ a "coarse-to-fine" processing strategy where low-resolution information is used to determine where the use of higher-resolution information is necessary. During interference detection, for example, progressively higher-resolution regions of the octrees are examined only in regions where there is a continuing intersection. This stops when an intersection is actually found (B nodes in both octrees for the same space) or it is determined that none exists (or a preset resolution limit is reached). Situations where objects are separated by wide gaps or where they intersect in large regions are resolved quickly, while more difficult situations require additional processing.

Octree Pros and Cons

The primary advantage of the octree database structure is the computational efficiency that results from its being hierarchical and spatially sorted. Also, its recursive nature often results in algorithms that are simple, compact, and fast. This, plus the almost exclusive use of integer arithmetic (rather than floating-point arithmetic) facilitates implementation in low-cost computers and hardware accelerators.

On the other hand, octrees are an approximate representation and are unevaluated. If stored, large amounts of system memory are required for octree models as the level of precision increases. For this reason they are often generated "on-the-fly" (computed as needed and discarded). Octree methods are currently used in CAD systems for computing mass properties, generating FEM meshes, and improving the efficiency of display. They are also used in "volumetric" SM (see Chap. 26).

4.8.2 The Hybrid Database

SM databases must support a wide variety of functions for both internal and external use. An ideal solid representation would exhibit all needed characteristics to effectively support them. Unfortunately, all existing database methods are deficient in certain critical areas. CSG supports high-level design, but the lower-level details (edges, vertices, etc.) are not readily available. B-Rep explicitly represents the details but lacks some of the design power and efficiency of working with solid elements and high-level tools. Plus, allowing a designer to directly manipulate low-level elements introduces reliability problems. Octrees can be seen as a "least common denominator" approximation that any solid can be converted into. While not suitable as a primary CAD representation, octrees can be effective in facilitating SM operations. They fulfill a role in SM similar to that of polygons in surface modeling.

This situation has led to the development of hybrid modeling schemes in which multiple database representations are employed in order to, hopefully, realize the strengths of each. The actual definition of a hybrid database is debatable because virtually all SM systems make use of secondary models for various purposes (e.g., polygon display lists). For this discussion, a modeler will be considered a hybrid if it employs two or more substantially different internal database representations that are valid solids and are actively maintained to support modeling functions.

The use of multiple representations has several undesirable aspects. The conversion between two formats may be difficult, impossible, inexact, or introduce subtle changes (potentially introducing serious inconsistencies). Because of this, conversion is often in one direction only (e.g., CSG to B-Rep). The use of multiple models also increases the size of programs and storage and increases processing requirements.

With most hybrid modelers the general strategy is to support a high-level CSG representation which can then be internally translated into a lower-level B-Rep model. Actual implementations range primarily from CSG systems that use B-Rep to facilitate display, to primarily B-Rep systems that maintain CSG or CSG-like object descriptions.

Boundary Evaluation

The translation of a CSG model to a B-Rep model is called *boundary evaluation*. This is generally reliable for linear and most quadric primitives. Objects with higher-degree primitives are more difficult to handle and usually are either converted to polygonal representations or processed using numerical methods. Because the general flow of models is from high-level to low-level models, a reverse conversion (B-Rep to CSG) is not normally required (and not easily accomplished).

Boundary evaluation generates an explicit (evaluated) representation from an implicit (unevaluated) one by locating and extracting surface intersections to form a B-Rep network of vertices, edges, and faces. It begins by generating the boundary of each CSG primitive. These boundaries are then paired to find intersections that generate candidate edges. These edges are then compared to the original CSG object to eliminate the ones which lie inside or outside the object. The remaining edges are boundary elements and are topologically connected to form a B-Rep object. This conversion is similar to B-Rep set operations and exhibits similar computational characteristics. The pairing of primitives is a quadratic growth operation and a large number of candidate edge segments may be generated as edges are subdivided (wherever they intersect a face).

Using Octrees

The need for greater interaction with solid models has sometimes led to the addition of an octree representation into the hybrid mix (see Sec. 4.8.1). With this scheme, an evaluated model is not needed for display (CSG models are displayed directly from octrees). To save computations, a solid model can be partly evaluated as needed by a particular operation (e.g., find the edge of intersection of two CSG primitives). Nonsolid entities such as surfaces, curves, and points can also be directly displayed, providing a powerful visualization capability.

4.9 The Parametric/Relational Database

In this discussion so far, solid models have been considered to be static shapes that were created by a series of operations requested by an operator. Major shape changes are difficult to accommodate in this environment, often requiring that an object be recreated from scratch. Parametric/relational design attempts to improve on this situation by making models flexible. Here we will discuss the impact such technologies have on database structures. Parametric/relational SM methods are presented in Chap. 8.

Basically, parametric models are defined by a set of parameters that can range from simple dimensional values (e.g., radius of a specific fillet) to global parameters that have an effect on an entire design (e.g., length of a crankshaft). The goal is to somehow capture the designer's "intent" in the model.

4.9.1   CSG

With CSG-based systems, this can be accomplished to a certain extent by providing a computer library of object construction and spatial-relationship subroutines. The designer essentially writes an object design program. Specific objects are generated by running the program using externally defined parameters. While effective, most designers prefer more traditional nonprogramming methods using interactive graphics.

4.9.2   B-Rep

With parametric/relational B-Rep, one strategy is to provide the designer with high-level tools that can be used to specify a topological definition while leaving the geometry defined by variables (e.g., length of base, radius of drill hole). This can often be done graphically using drawinglike methods. An internally generated procedure can then be run with a new set of parameters to change an object's shape. Spatial constraints can be automatically inserted into the procedure to help prevent incompatible parameters (i.e., those that would cause the generation of an object violating the topological model). This also helps to ensure that the object fulfills the original intent of the designer. The responsibility for keeping track of parametric information, relationships, and constraints is often placed in a separate "constraint manager" associated with the database.

4.9.3   Variational Design

A related technique is referred to as *variational design*. The parameters and constraints are encoded into a set of simultaneous equations. Instead of replaying a sequential design procedure, the equations are solved to determine a set of parameters to define the shape. This can be used for optimization and has been found to be especially helpful in refining 2D designs based on sketches. As the number of equations and their mathematical sophistication increases, however, finding solutions becomes more difficult and slow. Overconstrained situations can arise and designs can exhibit strange behavior.

4.9.4   Feature-Based Design

Feature-based design is another methodology that impacts the parametric/relational SM database. Essentially, this allows the designer to specify form features (e.g., fillets and flanges) using familiar engineering terms. If a through-hole was specified, for example, the bottom face of a subtracted cylinder would be automatically constrained to lie on the bottom of the object.

While popular with designers, form features are difficult to implement because it is not possible to simply define geometric elements in isolation and then add or subtract them in the database. Their shape depends on finding and analyzing a specific situation existing in the model. For example, a simple chamfer may require two planar faces meeting at a straight edge with sufficient space on each to locate the new plane (without hitting anything else).

As procedures that implement form features become more sophisticated and powerful, the programs that implement them must exhibit greater degrees of intelligence and the ability to perform spatial reasoning. It is often a major challenge for an SM database to support such capabilities. Because geometric elements such as vertices and edges play an important role, an evaluated representation (B-Rep or hybrid) is usually necessary.

**Database Errors
and Reliability**

SMA.4.4   Sources of Database Errors

Database-related failures usually occur when an SM system is unable to handle certain geometric situations that arise infrequently such as objects with self-intersections, faces that meet at very small angles, or objects with isolated parts. While such errors can result from programming bugs and over-sights, they can also be due to the inexact nature of geometric calculations.

SMA.4.5   Disabling Error Checking

Achieving a high level of reliability becomes increasingly difficult as (1) designs increase in complexity, (2) the operations demanded by the design community become more sophisticated, and (3) designers work at higher levels and become less intimately familiar with the details of their designs. Designers are sometimes allowed to disable certain levels of error checking to improve performance. This should be used with caution. Performance means nothing if the resulting design is invalid. It is good practice to perform a complete error analysis off-line after major design changes.

SMA.4.6   Reliability Precautions

No SM system should be considered 100 percent reliable. Steps should always be taken to facilitate recovery from errors (regular backups, etc.), especially after installing new program releases.

SMA.4.7   Undetected Errors

A new topological model (set of connections between new and existing faces, edges, and vertices) results from SM functions such as boolean operations. It is usually computed from the geometric models (how the elements of the objects being combined intersect). An error can introduce internal contradictions within an SM database. Serious problems can arise if such errors are undetected for some period while subsequent operations are performed (and perhaps design decisions made). If a database failure is encountered, try undoing several operations and modifying the modeling approach. This is one reason why a powerful undo feature is so important.

SMA.4.8   Correcting Database Errors

If detected, database errors can often be corrected. Sometimes the dataset can be modified automatically to remove the problem (e.g., slightly moving an edge or vertex). Or the system may attempt to undo the operation that caused the error and ask that you try something else. Clearly, systems that fail or require manual intervention will become less usable as designs become more complex and the design process becomes more automated.

SMA.4.9   Reliability and Geometry

Reliability is enhanced when you are intimately familiar with the design. Operations that cause difficult geometric situations should be avoided when possible.

SMA.4.10   Parametric Methods

SM systems often use extensive procedures to detect internal errors. Such procedures are, however, difficult to implement, lower performance, and usually cannot guarantee that all possible errors will be detected. SM systems may force limits on a design by imposing various constraints. When using parametric methods, for example, the designer may be called upon to first specify an object's topology, often by drawing it. Any parameter changes that would violate this fixed topology are rejected. This approach greatly reduces failures, but can also reduce system flexibility and capability.

Point of View

SMA.4.11   Newer versus Older SM Systems

Newer, more sophisticated SM systems usually incorporate advanced capabilities (e.g., sculptured surfaces), but they also tend to be less reliable and more difficult to use than more mature systems. If your situation does not require all the latest capabilities, it may be desirable to consider a more mature SM system.

Good Practices

SMA.4.12   Understanding and Evaluation

When evaluating SM systems, first determine your needs. Certain database structures are better suited for specific applications. For example, polygonal (faceted) modelers are not well suited for output to machining or NC operations because they do not precisely define surfaces. However, a polygonal modeler can be faster at times and allow you to work dynamically with the model shaded. (*Editor's Note:* This is true for certain situations, but not all.)

So, determine if you need accurate surface representation for CAM output or perhaps good visual representation for product aesthetics. Once you determine your needs, then you can more effectively evaluate different SM systems.

George E. Mock, Member Technical Staff
AT&T Network Cable Systems, Norcross, Ga.

SMA.4.13   Processing and Performance

When dealing with operations where processing time grows faster than object complexity, a strategy to enhance performance is to minimize the size and interaction of objects. It is usually desirable to break a design into as many separate pieces as is practical and to operate on them in isolation for as long as possible (see also Chap. 6).

SMA.4.14   SM and Databases

Designers are sometimes surprised when they cannot directly access their models in the database. If CAD models are needed for uses not supported by the CAD vendor, clearly understand your ability to read from and write to a database using an external program before making a purchase commitment.

SMA.4.15   Failure Logs

Always monitor reliability in your environment. A log should be kept, including details of the operations being undertaken at the time of a failure. Be sure to record all error messages. Isolate failures that can be traced to system problems (lack of swap space, disk full error, etc.). Look for failure patterns (i.e., unusual geometric situations being attempted). Report unresolved problems to your SM vendor; ask if such errors have occurred elsewhere (usually they have) and what steps are being taken to correct them.

SMA.4.16   Vendor Bulletins

Designate someone in your organization to maintain and review all vendor bulletins, especially those related to reliability. Often fixes or work-arounds have been developed.

Suggestions for Further Reading

Chiyokura, Hiroaki, *Solid Modelling with DESIGNBASE,* Addison-Wesley, 1988.

Samet, Hanan, *The Design and Analysis of Spatial Data Structures,* Addison-Wesley, 1989.

Hoffmann, Christoph, *Geometric and Solid Modeling: An Introduction,* Morgan Kaufmann, 1989.

Mantyla, Martti, *An Introduction to Solid Modeling,* Computer Science Press, 1988.

Mortenson, Michael, *Geometric Modeling,* John Wiley & Sons, 1985.

Chapter 5

Curves and Surfaces for Solid Modeling

Joel N. Orr
President
Orr Associates International

The history of graphical communication is biased by the availability of media upon which such communications could be recorded. Stones, cave walls, clay tablets, skins, parchments, paper, and more recent synthetic materials have all borne the marks of artisans and artists who wanted to convey meaning in the form of a picture to someone in another place or time. In most cases, pictorial communications were chosen over verbal ones because they were able to impart information difficult to put into words or numbers; the earliest drawings may have predated written language.

All of these media shared an important attribute: they were two-dimensional. In order to represent three-dimensional, real-world objects on them, drawers had to invent ways to abstract information from the object so that it could be recorded on a 2D surface. Over time, these methods became standardized; today, engineering professionals have little difficulty deciphering drawings from many sources, even if their text is not in the professional's native tongue.

But, to this day, the representation of curved 3D objects in drawings still presents difficulties. No simple way to express their graphical complexities has emerged. Happily, the difficulties are disappearing for other reasons, chief among them being computer-based geometric modeling.

Within the computer, it is possible to create models of 3D objects without consideration for the constraints of flat paper. The mapping between the real world and the 3D world inside the computer is direct and easily comprehended.

A different set of difficulties now comes to the fore: how to represent arbitrarily curved shapes—things like fuselage-wing intersections, automobile fenders, and consumer products—within the mathematical necessities of the computer. Each surface seems to require a different mathematical model to describe it. The advent of Solid Modeling (SM) has exacerbated the problem, because solids demand that the surfaces bounding them meet perfectly within system tolerances at edges and corners—and it is difficult to ensure that surfaces constructed on different models will in fact meet. If they do not, the topology of the resultant model will reflect its lack of connectedness.

Needed Improvements

SMA.5.1 Surface Construction Methods

Practical SM systems that incorporate curved surfaces accommodate a wide variety of shapes, and create them piecewise through the use of patches. There have been many ingenious developments, but no "field theory" which could accommodate any shape by varying a universal template. Construction methods for the incorporation of complex surfaces in solid models are not well developed. Many are simply interactive representations of underlying mathematical forms which ignore the customs of manual surface creation that are characteristic of the prospective users of such systems.

SMA.5.2 Surface Types Abound

An SM system should allow designers to create models with surfaces of any desired shape. Ideally, one should not have to know the differences among the various types of surfaces used, but we are far from that ideal. The wise buyer of SM systems must still know what kinds of surfaces can and cannot be used to produce the shapes needed by their applications, and determine if the SM system under consideration supports them.

This chapter discusses these developments and those aspects of the present state of the art that would be of interest and benefit to someone acquiring or operating an SM system.

5.1 Curves, Surfaces, and Computers

The problem of representing curves in computers derives from their nature. Curves are by definition continuous; digital computers comprehend a discontinuous framework for the representation of numbers. You cannot directly store a curve in a computer; you must reduce it either to a series of points whose coordinates are stored or to a mathematical equation—an algebraic expression. Storing curves as points is, in general, impractical; too many are needed to enable the computer to reproduce the curve smoothly.

Also, the correspondence between the geometry of curves and the algebra of their representations is tricky. Curves that appeal aesthetically to designers are often difficult to represent mathematically. And the intersection of curve-based surfaces with each other can yield curves that are even more difficult to represent.

Moreover, the manipulation of curved surfaces within the computer is normally accomplished through the manipulation of control points, whose locations define the curves that prescribe the surface. However, many of the most popular surface-defining curves have their control points located off the surface, which tends to invite confusion.

This problem first appeared when aircraft designers attempted to produce mathematical definitions of surfaces that intersected a given set of points or a given set of curves. Powerful techniques falling under the general heading of parametric surfaces were developed to deal with these issues. But no single technique is applicable to every circumstance.

5.2 Curve and Surface Usage

More than any other aspect, the construction of curves and surfaces in SM systems reflects the history of manual approaches to the design of shapes. Ideally, a designer should be able to specify curves and surfaces in whatever way is convenient, and not be forced to understand their mathematical underpinnings. Motivation for the current approaches derives from two principal sources: automotive and aerospace design.

Automotive designers were—and still are—primarily concerned with aesthetics. In recent years, aerodynamics and their effects on fuel economy and speed have begun to be taken into account as well. But the look of the automobile, and especially the character of the reflective qualities of its surfaces, dominate automotive design parameters. Consumer products, such as kitchen appliances and home-use electric hand tools, follow a similar pattern.

Airplane designers are interested in putting an aerodynamically shaped skin around a tightly constrained physical design in which structural strength, function, weight, size, cost, and other factors are traded off against one another to produce a design solution. Like ship designers of old, the airplane designer is given a set of sections that must be smoothly interconnected by surfaces, or a set of edges for which a "patch" must be designed so that the resultant shape is smooth. This process is termed *lofting*.

Automotive designers start with artistic sketches. The design progresses through many iterations of review before any attempt is made to convert the artistic conception to 3D geometry. Airplane designs, on the other hand, move rapidly to a phase in which the precise mathematical nature of the surfaces becomes a concern.

When a design is initiated analytically, the result is usually a mesh of precisely defined points which must be interpolated into a surface. There is no general surface that can be made to fit an arbitrary collection of points smoothly; that is the main reason for the existence of a variety of mathematical surface types.

Another reason for the confusing proliferation of mathematical surface types is the search for a variety whose construction is "natural" for a particular category of designers. Bezier curves and surfaces, for example, are considered "natural" by designers whose primary initial consideration is the matching of a curve or surface to a predetermined set of points. However, since the control points for these forms lie off the curve or surface, many other designers find them unnatural.

5.3 Curves and Splines

A sample of the types of curves that SM systems ought to produce include[1]:

1. Straight lines
2. Conic sections: circles, parabolas, hyperbolas, ellipses
3. Superconics: generalization of conics in which the degree of the terms in the defining polynomial differs from 2
4. Free-form parametric curves: B-splines, NURBS, etc.
5. Intersection curves: curves resulting from the intersection of two surfaces.

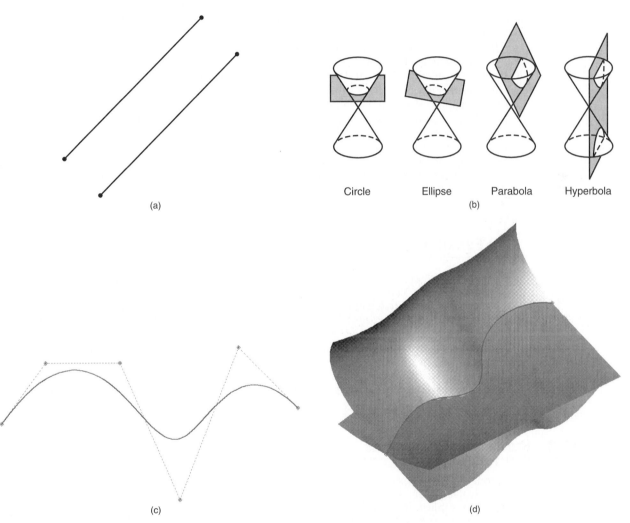

FIGURE 5.1 Curve types: (*a*) straight lines, (*b*) conics, (*c*) free-form parametric (NURBS), (*d*) intersection. (*Courtesy of Electronic Data Systems, Inc., EDS/Unigraphics, and Varimetrix Corporation.*)

Splines are by definition flexible pieces of wood or metal used by ship and aircraft designers to draw smooth curves. Spline curves have a loose kinship with such devices; they are curves that run smoothly through an empirically selected set of points. The mathematical derivation of these shapes has a long and somewhat tortuous history; various methods have been employed at different times by researchers in aerospace and shipbuilding organizations, as well as by academicians.

As each mathematical approach was developed, further work was required to put it into a form digestible by loftsmen and other design workers. Much of this foundational work took place in the sixties and early seventies, when interactive graphic systems were not yet widely accessible. Designers had to be given rules to follow in terms of their drafting orientation, rather than the math of the solution. Few such professionals view curves in terms of matrices or partial differential equations.

The methods that ultimately found most favor in industry were those that worked from measurable factors in the design—the datums and sections to which drafters and loftsmen were accustomed.

5.3.1   Bezier, B-Splines, and NURBS

At Renault in the 1960s, Pierre Bezier developed a definition of a system of curves that combines features of interpolating and approximating polynomials. (Interpolating polynomials pass through a given set of control points; approximating polynomials pass near the control points.) In a Bezier curve, the first and last control point precisely define the endpoints of the curve; intermediate control points influence the path of the curve; and the first two and last two control points define lines which are tangent to the beginning and end of the curve. Bezier curves can therefore blend nicely together, as can Bezier surfaces. The point at which two curves (not only Beziers) are joined is called a *knot*.

Blended Beziers give good local control; if a control point is moved, the curve changes only in the immediate vicinity of the control point. But construction constraints can sometimes be restrictive for the designer; under such circumstances, B-spline curves may be useful.

B-spline curves, unlike Beziers, can employ an arbitrary number of control points. They are generated by multiplying an approximating function in terms of the parameter u, where $0 \le u \le 1$, by a matrix containing a subset of the control points in the vicinity of the B-spline curve.

Since conic sections are common in manufactured forms, using rational B-splines often makes sense in this context; they run precisely through the defining points of the conic sections. Symmetrical forms yield a uniform distribution of knots. But when combining B-spline curves and surfaces, knots may appear in nonuniform distribution. The family of curves used for creating such shapes has come to be known as NURBS, or nonuniform rational B-splines.

5.3.2   Curve Functions

Curves must be represented by algebraic functions. Such functions generally fall into two categories—rational and polynomial. Rational curve functions can represent any point precisely, but lead to excessive computational requirements. Polynomial curve functions limit the computational requirements, but forego smoothness of shapes. Most modern systems use a combination of rational and polynomial functions, although some attempt to use polynomials almost exclusively.

Polynomial functions result in facets in surfaces, which are far easier to compute than smooth rational surfaces. Hence, it is common to retain dual representations—one for display and one for computation (see Chap. 3). In older systems, this computational burden was often insuperable, and sometimes led to a lack of robustness—such systems were easy to "break" by attempting to construct odd shapes.

5.3.3   Curve Representations

Various representations of curves have been applied in CAD systems over the years. A *representation* is the syntax of the mathematical arrangement used to describe the curve. Representations can be implicit or explicit. In an implicit representation, one of the variables is defined as a function of the other. Explicit representations are simpler, but can change wildly under mathematical operations.

Parametric representations of curves became popular because they allowed the accommodation of a wide variety of curve types, although they are not universal. They are also, however, more difficult to comprehend in geometric terms than simpler nonparametric forms.[2]

Curves

> **SMA.5.3   Concatenating Curve Deviations**
>
> Always remember that the result of two or more concatenated curves can deviate from the original curve paths. Be on the lookout for any deviations that can leave gaps between mating curves. Your SM system should alert you if a deviation has occurred.
>
> *Don LaCourse, President*
> *The Solid Modeling ExChange, Algood, Tenn.*

Curves
(Continued)

SMA.5.4   Concatenating Composite Curves

If the option is available, use the composite curve selection to maintain original curve definitions. This is due to the fact that concatenating lines and curves may redefine their mathematical definition when exploded. For example, lines and arcs may be redefined as splines.

Stephan Lewis, President
Think CAD Blue, Redondo Beach, Calif.

SMA.5.5   Curve Techniques and Concerns

Table 5.1 lists some of the more common methods of constructing curve geometry in SM as well as traditional CAD systems. Our emphasis here is to outline concerns during curve construction that can ultimately affect their usage in solid models. The following list of SM concerns are keyed to their applicable curve techniques listed in Table 5.1.

SM Concerns

1. Curve endpoints that are required to connect should always remain coincident.

2. Concatenated (joined) curves should not deviate from their disjointed curve paths. Look for deviations close to their joined endpoints.

3. Local curve modifications should not unknowingly affect associated curves and surfaces.

4. Be aware that some curves are approximations (such as those generated from the intersection of two surfaces or the result of a curve projected onto a surface).

5. It is preferred that curves be generated from existing curves and surface boundaries whenever possible.

6. Reference curves not used in SM construction should be kept on a separate layer.

7. Techniques that maintain curvature and tangency with other curves are recommended.

8. Large offset distances of fluctuating curvatures can produce unexpected results.

9. Only curve deviations within specified system tolerances are acceptable.

SMA.5.6   Curve Modifications

During curve construction for their subsequent use in solid models, always be aware of impacts of creating and modifying geometry. Curves as they are discussed here are a means of constructing complex surface geometry that cannot be developed directly by available SM functions.

SMA.5.7   When Trimming Curves

Curves may be trimmed to other curves or boundary of curves. In the case of lines and arcs, the results of trimming are well understood. In the case of spline curves, however, the resulting trimmed portion of the spline may differ slightly from its previous state. Only those deviations within the specified system tolerance are acceptable. Make a habit of checking for gaps and spline endpoints, particularly if they should form closed connections with other curves.

SMA.5.8   When Extending Curves

Curves may be extended to boundaries or by specified distances. The results of extending lines and arcs are predictable. Extending splines can be unpredictable. Planar 2D spline curves can be expected to remain planar after extension. Extending nonplanar 3D spline curves are the least predictable. If you extend spline curves be aware of local deviations and make sure the resulting endpoints are where you anticipate them to be.

SMA.5.9   When Modifying Curves Locally

Spline curves can be modified locally by adding, deleting, or moving middle or ending control points. Always be aware of the results of such modifications, especially if other geometry is dependent of the affected curve. For SM, local curve modifications can be used to ensure that curve endpoints are coincident when they should be.

Don LaCourse, President
The Solid Modeling ExChange, Algood, Tenn.

TABLE 5.1 Curve Techniques and SM Concerns

There are concerns specific to the construction and modification of curves for use with solid models. Refer to SMA.5.5 for a description of each concern indicated here. (Courtesy of the Solid Modeling Exchange. Graphics courtesy of Varimetrix Corp.)

Curve techniques		Description	SM-related concerns
Through points		A curve that passes through multiple points	(1) (3) (9)
Control points		A curve weighted by control points	(1) (3) (9)
Concatenate		Two or more curves joined end to end	(1) (2) (3) (9)
Project		Curve projected onto a plane or surface	(3) (4) (9)
Edge		Curve generated from existing surface boundary	(1) (5) (9)
Surface intersect		Curve of intersection between two planes or surfaces	(3) (4) (5) (9)
Silhouette		Curve generated from the silhouette of existing surface	(6) (9)
Through tangent		Curve whose endpoints are tangent to given vectors	(1) (3) (7) (9)
Offset		Curve offset from existing curve	(1) (7) (8) (9)
Blend		Curve blend from two existing curves	(2) (3) (7) (9)
Isoline		Curve generated from isoline of existing surface	(3) (4) (5) (9)
Segment		Curve generated from existing curve segment	(1) (3) (9)

5.4 Surfaces

SM systems with surfacing capability generally offer the ability to create the following surfaces types:

1. Planes.
2. Quadric surfaces: conic sections including cylinders, cones, spheres, and ellipsoids.
3. Superquadrics: shapes resulting from raising the sines or cosines to some power other than 1 in a standard parametrization of a quadric. This classification applies to superconics, cyclides, and torus.
4. Free-form parametric surfaces.
5. Blended surfaces.

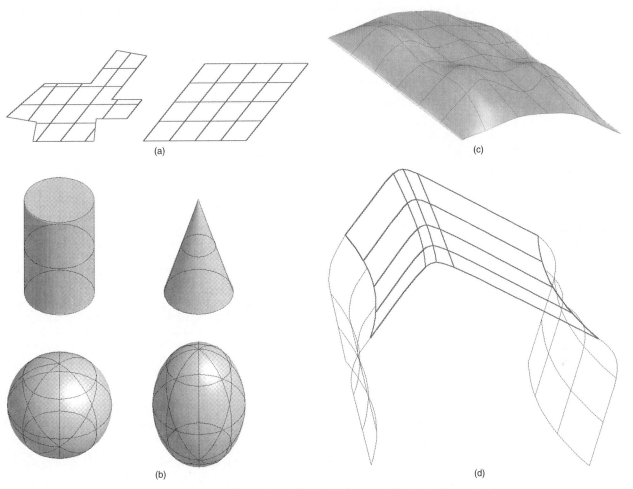

(a)

(c)

(b)

(d)

FIGURE 5.2 Surface types: (*a*) planar, (*b*) quadrics, (*c*) free-form, (*d*) blends. *(Courtesy of Varimetrix Corporation.)*

To this list we may also add procedurally defined surfaces, whose descriptions are algorithmic rather than mathematical.

Each surface type has qualities that make it useful under a given set of circumstances. In general, designers should seek to employ the simplest surface type that meets the requirements of the situation, because simple surfaces require fewer computational resources than complex ones. But, since each surface type has qualities not shared by others, most real-world designs require an aggregation of different surface types. Commercial systems vary greatly in the ease with which disparate surface types can be combined.

5.4.1 Surface Representations

There is often confusion between surface types and surface representations. The preceding list of surface types names varieties of geometric shapes. All can be represented by different mathematical means.

Surfaces

SMA.5.10 Surface Techniques and Concerns

Table 5.2 lists some of the more common techniques for constructing surface geometry in SM as well as traditional CAD systems. Please note that this listing is by no means complete. There are many additional advanced surface techniques in use which are beyond the space available in this edition. Again, our emphasis here is to outline concerns during surface construction that ultimately affect their usage in solid models.

SM Concerns

1. Watch for surfaces that have the potential to self-intersect. These include sweeps due to trajectory, revolves due to rotation angle, rules due to curve relationships, and offsets due to curvature.

2. All surface areas have seams (as in a revolve) or boundary curves. When positioned in a resulting solid topology, these seams and boundaries should be located away from other edges or vertices. Vertices or edges should never coexist within system tolerances unless they in fact share common boundaries.

3. Surfaces generated directly from boundary curves such as rules and patches are preferred over surfaces that are excessively trimmed.

4. When possible, always share existing vertices and edges between surfaces.

5. Techniques such as lofting, meshing, and patching approximate surface curvature between defining boundaries.

6. If possible, when techniques generate new boundaries on surfaces (such as with fillets), reconstruct mating surfaces from the new boundaries rather than trimming existing surfaces.

7. Techniques that maintain surface tangency are recommended.

SMA.5.11 When Trimming Surfaces

Surfaces may be trimmed or divided by curve and/or other surface boundaries. This is a very convenient and powerful technique to seemingly discard unwanted surface areas. However, trimmed surfaces pose concerns for the development of solid models and for data exchange through neutral formats (see Chap. 21, "Solid Modeling and IGES").

Many trimmed surfaces in a single model will increase database size and complexity since more information is required for storage (original surface, trim boundaries, and resulting trimmed surface). Also, the resulting surface edge is dependent on the accuracy and dependability of the system's surface-trimming functions. Airtight surface enclosures are required for solids, so always check trim boundaries that should mate with other surfaces.

SMA.5.12 When Extending Surfaces

Surfaces may be extended in either or both the *U* and *V* directions. Extending surfaces is very helpful during the development of surface geometry (for example, to establish an additional section curve further away from a surface's current boundary or to allow the continued tangency of subsequent surface functions). As a rule, surface extensions are used as a means to an end rather as an end in themselves. The development of new surface boundaries is generally the result of surface extensions.

SMA.5.13 Surface Tangency

Some surface operations (such as fillets and corners) maintain surface tangency during their construction. Such surface areas should not be reconstructed from their boundaries in lieu of trimming as recommended here for other surface areas unless subsequent tangency constraints can be applied. Even though their boundaries would be the same, the surface patch operation may not automatically take tangency into account, and the resulting surface may differ from the one it is intended to replace.

Don LaCourse, President
The Solid Modeling ExChange, Algood, Tenn.

TABLE 5.2 Surface Techniques and SM Concerns

There are concerns specific to the construction and modification of surfaces for use with solid models. Refer to SMA.5.10 for a description of each concern indicated here. (Courtesy of the Solid Modeling Exchange. Graphics courtesy of Varimetrix Corp.)

Surface techniques		Description	SM-related concerns
Sweep		Sweep a curve along a specified trajectory	(1) (2) (3) (4)
Revolve		Rotate a curve about a specified axis	(1) (2)
Rule		Rule a surface between two curves	(1) (2) (3) (4)
Offset		Offset a surface by a specified distance	(1) (2) (4)
Grid		Surface through a regular grid	(2) (4) (5)
Extrude		Extrude a curve along a linear trajectory	(2) (3) (4)
Loft		Loft a surface between dissimilar curves	(2) (5)
Mesh		Mesh a surface through control curves	(2) (4) (5)
Patch		Patch a surface between boundaries	(2) (3) (4) (5)
Control points		Surface through regular or irregular control points	(2) (4) (5)
Rolling ball		A constant or variable fillet between two dissimilar surfaces	(2) (4) (6)
Corner		A tangent corner patch between three surfaces	(2) (4) (7)

Surfaces
(*Continued*)

SMA.5.14   Sculpted Surfaces

Sculpted surfaces are at best painful to construct when subsequent features are to be attached or added. It is best to create any nonsculpted surfaces or features first, and then use the existing edges to create the final sculpted surfaces in place.

John Skibinski, Program Director
Eaton Corp., Milwaukee, Wis.

SMA.5.15   When Modifying Curves Locally

Surfaces may be modified locally. Any deviation that maintains a surface's current boundaries and thus the solid's current topology is acceptable unless the surface deviation internally or externally pierces another solid face. Local surface deviations take several forms. Here are a few:

1. *Radius dome.*   A smooth radiused surface deviation computed to fit a selected surface.

2. *Section dome.*   Replaces an entire planar surface with a blended, extruded, or swept sculptured surface.

3. *Local push.*   Smoothly deforms a circular or rectangular surface region.

Dr. Richard D. Lowrey, Lowrey Consulting
San Jose, Calif.

SMA.5.16   Variable Radii Blends

Sometimes a blend of four or more surfaces may be required, each with different converging fillet radii along their edges. In many cases this blend must be performed manually and would require a complex surface patch. At first, the solution (the resulting patch) may seem overwhelming to achieve. The steps provided here can be applied to both simple and complex surface blends (see Fig. 5.3). The surfacing capability of some systems may eliminate the need for this procedure.

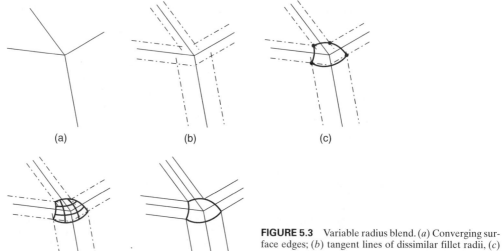

(a)   (b)   (c)

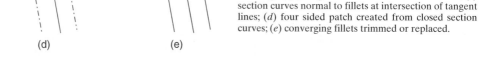

(d)   (e)

FIGURE 5.3   Variable radius blend. (*a*) Converging surface edges; (*b*) tangent lines of dissimilar fillet radii, (*c*) section curves normal to fillets at intersection of tangent lines; (*d*) four sided patch created from closed section curves; (*e*) converging fillets trimmed or replaced.

1. Start by defining the tangent lines of the converging radii. Where two intersect, a corner will be defined. Use this method to define each corner of the required patch.

(Continued)

Surfaces
(*Continued*)

2. Generate a section curve between corner points normal to and through each converging fillet surface. These curves will produce a closed boundary.

3. Use the closed boundary curves to generate the surface patch. If your SM system can apply surface tangency constraints, use them now.

4. Trim the converging fillets to the boundaries of the new surface patch. It is recommended that the fillets be replaced by ruled surfaces instead of trimming.

5. If there are more than four boundary curves, the resulting patch may be stretched or twisted. Even though this surface may not be desired, cut a section curve through it to approximate the definition of a new curve boundary and thus divide your required patch in two or more patches of three or four sides each. Use this approximated curve as a reference to generate a new curve that is tangent at its endpoints.

6. Validate the resulting surface patch to ensure that it blends smoothly along its entire surface as well as at the fillet boundaries. Here are some ways to perform this validation.

   a. Change the display settings to show a large number of isolines on the surface patch and then rotate the model to see if the patch looks smooth.

   b. If the preceding visual test appears to indicate a problem, generate section curves through the surface patch where it intersects the mating fillets. These curves should indicate a smooth transition.

Don LaCourse, President
The Solid Modeling ExChange, Algood, Tenn.

SMA.5.17   Surface Offsets

Some desirable operations introduce mathematical complexities that have no general solution—the offset operation, so useful in the design of numerical control toolpaths, is one such operation. While most SM systems support offset surfaces in one way or another, they all impose restrictions to keep the resultant surfaces within the realm of expectation while maintaining mathematical integrity.

5.5   Solid Modeling Considerations

Constructing curves and surfaces for use in solid models carries an additional set of considerations above and beyond normal recommended practices for these techniques. These concerns parallel those of the NC programmer whose job depends on all surfaces being present, that they meet, and that there are no hidden cracks or gaps. A little extra care and consideration is all that is required when constructing curves and surfaces for SM.

5.5.1   Geometric Progression

The inherent integrity of SM functions when used properly will result in valid closed 3D volumes. When the geometry of a design becomes too complex for existing SM functions to model properly, designers are forced to utilize curve and surface techniques to supplement the model-building process. This deviation from the SM environment carries a price. A governing rule for model validity (surface closure) must be addressed manually during construction (see Fig. 5.4).

There is a logical progression of geometric elements that, when constructed properly, will help ensure model closure. This process is referred to here as *modeling for closure*. Modeling for closure begins with points, and progresses to a closed solid volume. This progression includes:

1. Points on curves
2. Curves on surfaces
3. Surfaces on solids

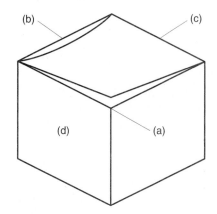

FIGURE 5.4 Modeling for closure. (*a*) Mating points should be coincident; (*b*) mating edges should share existing boundaries; (*c*) mating edges should have equal segments; (*d*) surface to boundaries instead of trimming when possible. These rules apply to all simplified (as shown) or complex surface models.

Points on Curves

Points are the most basic geometric elements. They form the basis of all geometric curves. Ensuring model closure begins with the proper creation and manipulation of points and curves. Control points for planar curves should always remain coplanar. Endpoints of connecting curves should always remain coincident. Remember that during wireframe and surface operations, internal controls for model integrity and closure found in SM are not automatically applied. Develop good point and curve strategies.

Curves on Surfaces

Just as points are the defining elements for curves, curves are the defining elements for surfaces. Whenever possible, always generate curves from existing surfaces. Be aware of how local curve modifications can affect associated surface geometry. Always use simple curves (lines and arcs) instead of splines whenever possible.

Surfaces on Solids

Surfaces must form a closed volume to define a solid and should always share curve boundaries when they meet. If possible, mating curve boundaries should always share equal segments. Difficult surface areas should always be redone rather than piecing small surface segments together. The endpoints of connecting boundary curves for mating surfaces should always remain coincident.

5.5.2   Levels of Integration

There are many levels of integration among wireframe, surfaces, and solids. SM systems that closely integrate these three representation schemes in a common database are more flexible than those that do not. Usually, such systems allow the creation, joining, and exploding of surfaces into and out of solids as needed without any loss of data or integrity. Until SM functions can accurately represent and model complex surface areas, the need to closely integrate wireframe and surface functions into the SM database will remain great.

5.5.3   Preferred Geometry

In surfacing, just as with any craft, there are preferred methods. Again, always try to construct surfaces to defined boundaries rather than performing extensive trimming. This is especially true if models are to be exported to dissimilar systems via neutral formats. Try to use ruled surfaces instead of surface patches whenever possible. Ruled surfaces require only two boundary curves, whereas a surface patch requires three or more defining boundaries. Any technique that simplifies construction and requires fewer database resources is recommended. SM databases can and will become quite large. Early simplification saves time and worries later. The techniques can't be overstressed.

5.6 Conclusions

The only measure of quality for curves and surfaces in an SM system is the extent to which the facilities meet the designer's needs. Systems and approaches to these issues are far too diverse at this time to admit to a linear ranking. All present products are somewhat deficient in robustness; that is, the user can create shapes that will "break" any system. Designers should know the limitations of the systems they are considering, and expect them to degrade "gracefully" when they "break," without loss of data.

Free-Form Associativity

SMA.5.18 Combining Associative and Nonassociative Elements[3]

In general, the greater the extent of associativity in a model, the less you can modify the model through direct curve or surface manipulation commands. In many cases, a fully associative model can be modified only by changing the parent elements or the dimensions driving the associative elements. However, by carefully combining associative and nonassociative elements in a single model, you can create a model that is modifiable both through dimension edits and through direct manipulation commands. Four common examples follow.

SMA.5.19 Nonassociative Curves and Surface[3]

Figure 5.5 illustrates a simple example of a nonassociative surface placed through nonassociative curves. Note that Fig. 5.5a shows the original curves and surface. Figure 5.5b shows the result after one of the curves is modified. Note that the surface does not follow the modified curve. You would then have to delete the original surface and create a new one. Figure 5.5c shows the result of moving poles on the surface. Note that, although the surface has been modified in the middle, the edges were not modified. However, if the surface had been modified such that the edge row of poles moved, the surface would deviate from the curves.

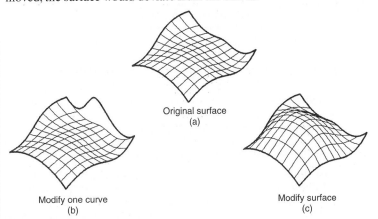

Original surface
(a)

Modify one curve
(b)

Modify surface
(c)

FIGURE 5.5 Nonassociative curves and surface: (*a*) original surface; (*b*) after modifying curve; (*c*) after modifying surface. *(Courtesy of Intergraph Corporation.)*

Advisory Notes. Since both the curves and the surface are nonassociative, either the curves or the surface may be modified. However, the drawback is that there is no intelligence between the surface and the curves, and if one of the endpoints of a curve is moved, the adjacent curve will not be connected to the modified curve.

SMA.5.20 Variational Curves and Associative Surface[3]

This example shows how you can construct an associative free-form surface from fully constrained variational profiles. Although the concept of a fully constrained free-form surface may sound like a contradiction in terms, this surface is fully dimensionally constrained. Once the four profiles mak-

(Continued)

ing up the boundaries of the surface are fully constrained, you can then modify any of the dimensions to modify the surface.

In Fig. 5.6 the dimensional constraints for both cross sections are all proportional to the overall width and height of the first cross section. By setting proportional expressions, you can then modify the surface predictably by simply changing the height and/or width. As shown in Fig. 5.6, the height is changed from 2.5 to 1.25 and the width is changed from 3.5 to 5.0. This causes the surface to update to match the new cross-sectional shapes.

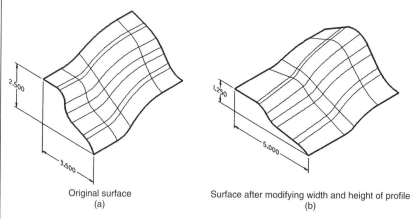

Original surface
(a)

Surface after modifying width and height of profile
(b)

FIGURE 5.6 Variational curves and associative surface. (*a*) Original surface; (*b*) surface after modifying width and height. (*Courtesy of Intergraph Corporation.*)

Advisory Notes. There are three important items to note about the example in Fig. 5.6:

1. Since both the cross-section curves and the trace curves are variational profiles with coincidence defined between the endpoints of the curves, the curves will always remain connected at their endpoints. When the cross sections are modified, the trace curves update to remain connected. This is important since the skinning surface would have problems if the endpoints were not connected.

2. Since the surface is associative to the curves, when the curves are modified, the surface updates accordingly.

3. Depending on the SM system used, you may not be able to modify either the curves or the surface with direct manipulation commands since they are both associative. Standard constraint modification techniques may be the only way to make changes.

SMA.5.21 Nonassociative Curves and Associative Surface[3]

This example shows one of the most useful combinations for pure free-form modeling. In this case we created nonassociative curves and then passed an associative skinning surface through the curves. The big advantage here is that you can use any of the available wireframe modification techniques to directly manipulate the curves. The associative surface will update to reflect any changes made to the curves. As shown in Fig. 5.7, the original surface is shown, then the resulting surface after directly modifying the poles on the curves.

Advisory Notes. The important point about the example in Fig. 5.7 is that you do not have to re-create the surface to see the result of free-form modifications to the curves. This lets you do "what-if" studies on a free-form, or aesthetic, shape without re-creating surfaces. The drawback is that, depending on the SM system used, you may not be able to directly modify the surface, and you must be careful not to modify the curves so that the endpoints lose their connections.

SMA.5.22 Associative and Nonassociative Curves with Associative Surface[3]

In this example, both associative and nonassociative curves are used to construct an associative surface. This method lets you modify some aspects of a surface through direct curve manipulation commands, and other aspects through dimension edits.

In Fig. 5.8, two variational profiles are used for the cross sections. The single trace curve is a nonassociative B-spline. The reference planes, on which the two cross-section profiles are constructed, are created through the endpoints of the B-spline. Therefore, the B-spline can be modified in any way and the cross-section profiles will still remain at the ends of the B-spline trace curve. Figure 5.8*a* shows the orig-

(Continued)

**Free-Form
Associativity**
(*Continued*)

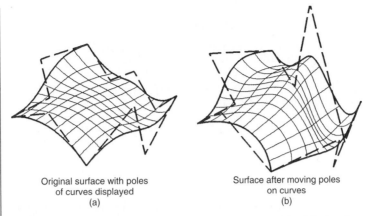

Original surface with poles
of curves displayed
(a)

Surface after moving poles
on curves
(b)

FIGURE 5.7 Nonassociative curves and associative surface: (*a*) original surface with poles of curves displayed; (*b*) surface after moving poles on curves. (*Courtesy of Intergraph Corporation.*)

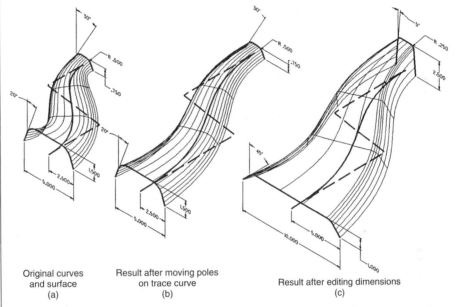

Original curves
and surface
(a)

Result after moving poles
on trace curve
(b)

Result after editing dimensions
(c)

FIGURE 5.8 Associative and nonassociative curves with associative surface. (*a*) Original curves and surface; (*b*) result after moving poles on trace curve; (*c*) result after editing dimensions. (*Courtesy of Intergraph Corporation.*)

inal curves and surface, a skinning surface created with the B-spline trace curve and two open profiles for cross sections. Figure 5.8*b* shows the result of modifying the B-spline trace curve. Figure 5.8*c* shows the subsequent result of modifying the dimensional values on the two profiles as shown.

Advisory Notes. In both cases in Fig. 5.8*b* and 5.8*c*, the surface updates according to the changes made, since the surface is associative to the cross sections and trace curve. The important thing to note here is that you have some flexibility in modifying the surface. You can either manipulate the trace curve or modify the profiles.

SMA.5.23 Most Effective Modeling Approach[3]

The examples above present a few ways in which you can combine nonassociative elements, associative elements, and variational profiles into a single model, particularly as they relate to free-form surfaces. The examples given are only a few of the possible combinations. The important thing to remember is that a model does not have to be fully associative to be useful. Oftentimes the most effective modeling approach will include a combination of variational profiles and other associative and nonassociative elements.

*Mark Russell, Senior Systems Engineer
Intergraph Corp., Huntsville, Ala.*

Good to Know

SMA.5.24   System Tolerances

Be aware of your system's tolerance. Any deviations from your system tolerance limits may result in unacceptable gaps and cracks. Modifying your system tolerance to obtain closure is not recommended. The proper solution is to employ techniques that will allow the generation of curves and surfaces within specified tolerance limits.

Don LaCourse, President
The Solid Modeling ExChange, Algood, Tenn.

SMA.5.25   Effective Color Usage

Use differences in color and layers effectively. When duplicating or projecting curves, arrange it so that the resulting new curve will be a different color or layer than the original. A newly constructed curve may differ only very slightly from an existing one. Color coding causes less confusion when a selection is required. This use of color and layering will also make it easier to identify each entity as well as to manipulate entities as a group. Blanking and deleting can be done by color and layer on most SM systems.

Andrew Price, Manager Engineering Applications
Axis Technologies, Fairport, N.Y.

SMA.5.26   Use Existing Edges

When adding a feature to a solid model using surfaces or when sewing surfaces together, try to use existing and common edges for curve boundaries. This will make the model easier to change later in the design cycle and will keep gaps from appearing between surfaces. Gaps cause problems when converting to a solid and in downstream operations such as NC.

Philip Johnson, Development Engineer
Emerson Electric Company, St. Louis, Mo.

SMA.5.27   Approximation

Many SM systems employ a CSG representation. The developers of CSG systems introduced the concept of applying boolean operations to solid shapes. These work fine when all surfaces are planar. But with surfaces of any greater complexity, intersections can result in complex curves. Such curves may not be precisely defined in the context of a particular SM system. Rather than applying an analytic solution, the program must employ numerical approximation techniques to express these intersections.

References

1. The taxonomy of curves and surfaces is based on "Geometric Methods for CAD," by Michael J. Pratt, in *Fundamental Developments of Computer-aided Geometric Modeling,* Academic Press, 1993.

2. A full treatment of curve representation can be found in *Computer Graphics for Engineers,* by Bruce R. Dewey, Harper & Row, 1988.

3. Adapted from "Freeform Modeling and Associativity," by Mark Russell in *The Intergraph Mechanical Quarterly,* first quarter 1993, no. 6, Intergraph Corporation.

Don't Limit Your Choices.

UNIGRAPHICS...WORK WITH A FULL SET OF TOOLS

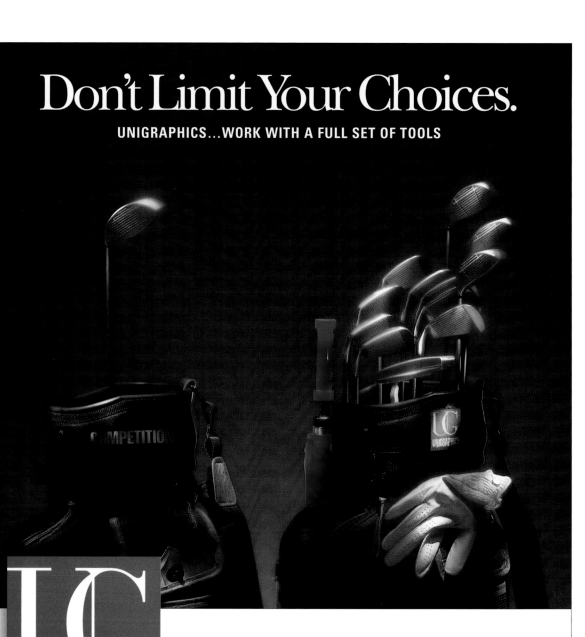

In golf—and business—the winner is best equipped to play the game from start to finish. • Pure parametrics handicap you by constraining your designs, causing constant rework. And unexpected system traps make it difficult to cut metal. Traditional parametric/variational systems face integration hazards, also adding strokes to your cycle time. • But with the new Unigraphics, you work with a complete set of advanced, integrated tools. A breakthrough hybrid modeler, offering a variety of modeling capabilities, allows you to quickly create winning designs. Advanced drafting and CAE tools speed production and analysis. And unmatched power and range in CAM provide confidence in cutting the most difficult of parts.

Rendered with UG/Photo

Work with a full set of tools— Unigraphics. Call 314-344-2687.

EDS Unigraphics

(CIRCLE READER SERVICE NO. 205)

Chapter 6
Modeling Strategies

Richard D. Lowrey, Ph.D.
Mechanical Engineering Consultant

Solid models are built using the capabilities provided by a given Solid Modeling (SM) system. Such capabilities often include solid primitives, operator-defined profiles swept along a path, features (see Chap. 8), and surfaces (see Chap. 5). SM system operators may combine these shapes in many and various ways to meet the requirements of a given design.

Every SM system must provide a base set of geometric construction capabilities apart from related functions such as drafting, analysis, parametric/relational definition, or data exchange. This chapter discusses these capabilities as well as construction strategies, guidelines, system errors, and ways of working around difficulties.

6.1 Attributes

Solid Modeling attributes include surface finish, threads, location tolerance, position tolerance, annotation, display color, etc. The solid model definition is incomplete without these. Please note that not all SM systems include this type of data in export files. Tolerances are so important that most SM systems treat them as a separate entity group.

6.2 Solid Primitives

A primitive is a volume defined by simple, standard geometrical shapes, such as a box, cone, and cylinder. Primitives are used by the CSG modeling method (see Chap. 4). There is a limited set of ready-made primitive shapes, each requiring very little input. Primitives can be defined using simple menus and can be combined to form complex geometry. Input can be relative to local or global coordinate systems or other existing geometry. Table 6.1 illustrates a typical set of solid primitives along with their input requirements.

Primitives

SMA.6.1 Primitive Modeling

Very complex shapes can be created by combining primitives through the use of boolean operations discussed in Sec. 6.4. The resulting complex solid can then be saved and treated as an operator-defined primitive.

TABLE 6.1 Sample Group of Primitives

Many primitives other than those shown here are available, each with varying input parameters. (Icons courtesy of Varimetrix Corporation.)

Primitive	Description	Typical input required
BoxPln	**Box** A box is a right rectangular hexahedron. That is, it has six rectangular faces.	**Box** Length, width, height, and location. The center point and orthogonal edge vectors as well as two diagonally opposite corners are specified with some systems.
ConePln	**Cone** A cone has a base circle, a curved exterior surface tapering to a point, and an axis of revolution normal to the base circle. All lines on the curved exterior surface between the base circumference and the apex are linear.	**Cone** Base radius, height or length, and the base center point as a location.
FrusDir	**Frustrum** A frustum is typically defined as the portion of a cone that lies between two parallel intersecting planes.	**Frustrum** Bottom center point for location, an axial direction, bottom radius, top radius, and length.
CylDir	**Cylinder** Cylinders are defined by a constant diameter bounded on each end by right-angular, parallel circles of equal radius. The axis is normal to the ends.	**Cylinder** Direction, base point or location, radius, length.
PrsmIns	**Prism** A prism is similar to a right rectangular box, except that it has more faces.	**Prism** Base point or location, directional vector, the radius of the defining circle, and length. Prisms may be inscribed or circumscribed about the defining circle. Some systems also allow the number of equilateral edges or facets on its base to be specified.
TetCir	**Tetrahedron** A tetrahedron has an equilateral triangular base and three triangular sides.	**Tetrahedron** Base point or location, directional vector, the radius of a defining circle, and length or height. The base may be inscribed or circumscribed about the defining circle. A variation is known as *pyramid,* defined by four sides and a rectangular base.
SphCtr	**Sphere** A sphere is the volume generated by a semicircle revolved about an axis passing through its end points.	**Sphere** Spherical radius and the center or polar point.
TorDir	**Torus** A torus is generated by revolving a circle about an axis in the plane of the circle. The axis must not pass through the center of the circle, and must lie outside the circle in most SM systems.	**Torus** Radius of the circle, the radius from the center of the circle to the axis of revolution, and the direction of the axis must be defined. A hollow tube is created when two concentric circles of differing radii are revolved.

Primitives
(Continued)

SMA.6.2   A Primitive Eye

A primitive eye for modeling is a skill to be nurtured and developed over time. Given the same geometric part, a process engineer and a traditional CAD designer would each see the part in terms of the manufacturing processes required for production and the parts geometric entities such as edges and surfaces. An SM designer, however, would also see and recognize the basic shapes or primitives required for the part's construction.

SMA.6.3   Primitive Productivity

There will be many ways of constructing the same part. Maximum productivity is gained by determining the least number of primitives required and their combining sequence for overall construction.

Don LaCourse, President
The Solid Modeling ExChange, Algood, Tenn.

SMA.6.4   Thinking in Shapes

A benefit of thinking in shapes (primitives) is that you begin to think more in terms of "how I would make this part." Your manufacturing people will love you for this. When you think about it, most machining operations deal in basic shapes, especially milling and drilling. Think of using primitives to build tools to be used in shaping your base solid.

George E. Mock, Member Technical Staff
AT&T Network Cable Systems, Norcross, Ga.

6.3   Geometric Operations

Geometric operations in SM are volumes created using cross-sectional planar profiles and dragging functions, such as blends, extrudes, sweeps, revolves, fillets, corner rounds, and local surface deviations. It should be noted here that in an SM system these geometric operations result in a single closed solid entity. Similar operations are available in surface modeling that result in one or more individual surface entities.

These SM volumes may have constant or variable cross sections and linear, multilinear, curvilinear, or axisymmetric paths. The common naming conventions used for such entities are: *extrude, sweep, blend* or *transition,* and *revolve.* Figure 6.1 illustrates common geometric operations.

6.3.1   Blends or Transitions

A blend or transition has a variable cross section swept along an arbitrary path as illustrated in Fig. 6.1*a.* Its definition consists of two or more closed planar profiles of equal number of segments and a trajectory curve. The blending operation causes the cross section between defining profiles to be approximate.

The trajectory may be a spline curve passing through the ordered sequence of profiles. The cross section blends from segment to segment from one profile to the next. The profiles are generally normal to the trajectory, but may be allowed to be normal to another surface as the profile moves along the trajectory. Two profiles and a linear trajectory can be used to create a linear blend.

Blending Example

An engine intake manifold which is of a circular profile at the intake valve quickly blends along a tight three-dimensional curve into a rectangular profile with large fillets (due to space limitations), and then more gradually blends along an increasing radius into an elliptical profile before again becoming circular. The cross-sectional area must remain unchanged along the length, requiring accurate approximations of intermediate cross sections to be made.

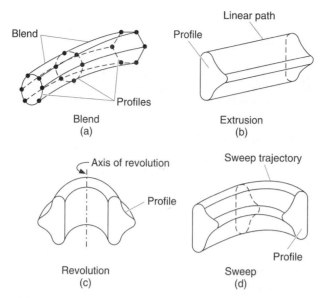

FIGURE 6.1 Common geometric operations. Typical examples are shown, system-dependent variations are available. (*a*) Blend or transition consists of two or more closed planar profiles swept along an arbitrary trajectory curve; (*b*) extrusions consist of a closed planar cross-section profile dragged along a single linear path; (*c*) revolutions are created by revolving an arbitrary planar cross-section profile about an axis; (*d*) sweeps are created by sweeping a planar cross-section profile along an arbitrary curve. (*Courtesy of Lowrey Consulting.*)

6.3.2 Extrusions

Solid extrusions have a constant cross section dragged along a single linear path. The profile does not rotate about the extrude line. Consequently, lines on the cross-section profile generate prismatic surfaces.

The extrude operation generally uses a closed planar profile that is extruded along a line normal to the profile. In SM, planar profiles have a front and a back side. *Normal to the profile* means that the front of the profile is facing the direction of extrusion. The *extrude line* may be defined as a distance offset from the planar profile, parallel to a straight edge of the solid, or may extend between two parallel planar faces.

An outside planar profile and a nonintersecting inside planar profile on the same plane can be used to create a hollow tubelike extrusion. A single SM volume results.

6.3.3 Revolutions

A solid revolution is a volume created by revolving an arbitrary planar cross-section profile about an axis. The profile should be closed and not cross the axis. If the profile is open, the axis must pass through its endpoints.

6.3.4 Sweeps

A solid sweep is a volume created by sweeping a planar cross-section profile along an arbitrary curve. A sweep operation uses a closed planar profile that is generally normal to and swept along a multiple segmented curvilinear sweep trajectory. The adjacent segments of the sweep trajectory are usually required to be tangent.

Sweeping a Helix

Multiple sweep trajectories are sometimes allowed. One sweep trajectory is used to define the sweep path, and another controls the profile's local axis orientation (i.e., the rotation of the profile along the trajectory). For example, the sweep trajectory may be a helix, and the local axis trajectory for a noncircular cross section may lie along the long axis of the helix. The local axis of the profile will always point toward the long axis of the helix. A helix of circular profile requires only one trajectory.

Geometric Operations

SMA.6.5 Blending Concerns

1. Additional profiles to control cross sections may be difficult to position accurately if the trajectory curve varies rapidly.

2. Due to their approximate nature, blends can be created, sectioned where refinement is desired, new improved profiles constructed at the cross sections, and a new blend created.

3. As additional cross sections are added, check for surface continuity between profiles, as waviness can be introduced.

4. The number of segments per profile is required to be equal, as each segment is blended in consecutive profiles. Arcs and lines of profiles may need to be subdivided.

5. Blends are sometimes restricted to profiles on parallel planes.

SMA.6.6 Sweep Concerns

The sweep volume must not self-intersect along the sweep trajectory as it would if a figure-eight trajectory were used. Arc or spline segments of the trajectory that are small compared to the profile can cause self-intersection.

SMA.6.7 Extrusion Concerns

Two or more nonintersecting outside planar profiles on the same plane can be extruded simultaneously to create multiple unconnected parallel solid primitives. Unconnected objects can define a valid solid, but applications such as automatic finite element meshing and automatic NC toolpath generation cannot use a solid of multiple volumes.

SMA.6.8 Profiles, Chamfers, and Fillets

When sweeping cross-section geometry into a solid, keep that geometry as simple as possible. Do not include fillets, radii, and chamfers (unless you have an incomplete or nontangent one). Adding these features to the resultant solid keeps them as intended (a fillet/blend is a fillet/blend—not a rounded solid face) and in some systems you are limited to the number of entities that you are allowed to sweep. Also, make sure that your geometry is planar before it is swept. Some nonplanar geometry can be swept, but may result in an invalid or unstable solid.

SMA.6.9 Plan Your Edge Sequence

Before attempting to apply fillets or radii to a solid, spend some time studying the model and plan the sequences of edges to which you want to apply them. Think about the way the model would be manufactured. Use the "undo" command (if your system has this feature) when the result is not as expected.

Richard A. St. Arnauld, Sr. Tool Design Engineer
Pratt & Whitney Aircraft Div. of UTC, West Palm Beach, Fla.

SMA.6.10 Copy Profiles First[1]

Before you use a profile in a sweep operation, copy the profile in place to another layer, and use the copied profile for the sweep. Some SM systems do this automatically.

(Continued)

Geometric Operations
(Continued)

Benefits

1. Makes it easier to see which parameters control each part of the model since, if desired, you can display only the layer on which the 2D profile and its parameters resides

2. Helps later on in the modeling process, such as when you remove corners or sides of the solid in future operations

3. Avoids any problems you may have if you do not copy the 2D profile, such as not being able to tell how parameters control the model if they hang in space after implementing future boolean operations

Nancy Anderson-Semple, Technical Editor
Computervision Corp., Bedford, Mass.

SMA.6.11   Modifying Profiles

One thing to look for when evaluating SM systems is which techniques are available for modifying profiles. Some systems allow you to change profiles by changing dimensions. Some require that you extract the defining curve, modify it, then replace the original curve. Or, you can just replace the curve with a new one. Other systems won't let you modify the profile. You must delete the part and start over, or modify it with boolean operations.

George E. Mock, Member Technical Staff
AT&T Network Cable Systems, Norcross, Ga.

6.3.5   Formula-Defined Shapes

Formula-defined shape operators define the entire shape using one or more equations. The geometry is implicit. This method can model complex parts such as bottles with aesthetic shapes required to improve product marketability. Simpler shapes, such as hyperbolic paraboloids, oblate spheroids, prolate spheroids, and ellipsoids, can also be formula-defined. The intersection curves generated from two formula-defined shapes can be of relatively high degree. (See Chap. 3 for more on implicit geometry and the degree of defining equations.)

6.4   Boolean Operations

A solid boolean operation is the mathematical joining by UNION, SUBTRACTION, or INTERSECTION of two or more solids into a single new solid object (see Fig. 6.2). Any valid solid can be used in boolean operations, including primitives, geometric operations, or the results of previous boolean operations.

The resulting solid will be either (1) the combined volumes of the prior solids, (2) the net volume of subtracting one solid from another, or (3) the volume common to both prior solids. Boolean operations give SM highly productive capability by modifying large amounts of geometry (each solid) in a single command operation. (Boolean algebra is named after the English mathematician George Boole, 1815–1864.)

6.4.1   Combining Solids

The boolean combine operation is typically named ADD, COMBINE, JOIN, MERGE, or UNION. The new solid is equal to the combined volumes of each selected solid. Typically, two or more solids can be selected for a single join command. However, the SM system will join each solid separately and display the final result.

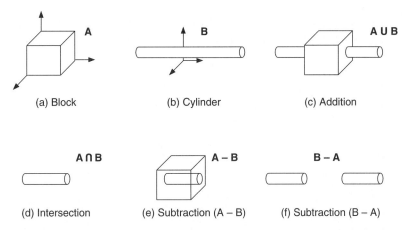

FIGURE 6.2   Boolean operations. With the use of boolean operations, two or more solids can be combined in one of three ways: (*a*) solid block A; (*b*) solid cylinder B; (*c*) results of UNION operation of A plus B; (*d*) results of INTERSECTION operation of A and B; (*e*) results of SUBTRACTION operation of A minus B; (*f*) results of SUBTRACTION operation of B minus A. (*Courtesy of Octree Corporation.*)

6.4.2   Subtracting Solids

The boolean subtract operation is typically named CUT, DIFFERENCE, REMOVE, or SUBTRACT. Only two solids are typically selected for a subtract operation. The base solid is usually selected first, followed by the subtracted solid. The resulting solid is defined as the volume of the first less the volume of the second.

6.4.3   Intersecting Solids

The boolean intersect operation is typically named COMMON, CONJOIN, or INTERSECT. Two or more solids can be selected for the intersect operation, and the order of selection is allowed to vary. If more than two solids are selected, the underlying database will perform each intersect sequentially and display on the end result. The resulting solid is defined as the volume common to the original solids.

Boolean Operations

SMA.6.12   Boolean Groups and Errors

Some SM systems allow the selection of a group of solids that require the same boolean operation. Remember that each operation is performed sequentially and only the accumulative result is displayed. If any of the operations should fail, the erroneous operation should be undone and the model saved in this uncorrupted state. One additional boolean may require being undone to remove the corrupted operation because, frequently, the error is not known to the SM system or the designer until one boolean operation after the actual error has occurred.

SMA.6.13   Regularized Boolean Operations

As illustrated in Fig. 6.3, certain difficulties can arise when using boolean operations. An intersection operation between objects A and B is used to remove the part of object A to the left. The desired result is shown in Fig. 6.3*b*. But since objects A and B share a face, the intersection leaves it "dangling in space" as shown in Fig. 6.3*c*. This part of the object occupies no volume—an illegal condition in many SM systems. To prevent the occurrence of this and related conditions, specially

(*Continued*)

Boolean Operations
(*Continued*)

formulated versions called "regularized" boolean operations are often used. They are sometimes indicated with an asterisk superscript (*).

Donald J. Meagher, President
Octree Corp., Coopertino, Calif.

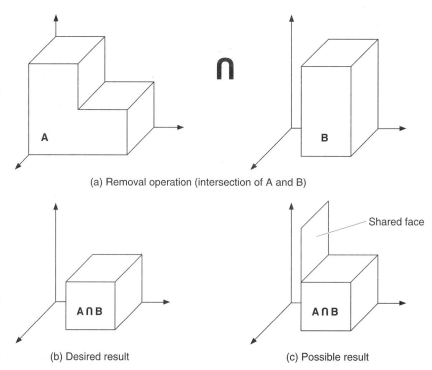

(a) Removal operation (intersection of A and B)

(b) Desired result   (c) Possible result

FIGURE 6.3 Regularized boolean operations. (*a*) Removal operation by the intersection of A and B; (*b*) desired result; (*c*) possible result. (*Courtesy of Octree Corporation.*)

SMA.6.14 Using Booleans on Coincident Faces[1]

A boolean operation on objects having coincident faces may fail in some cases, such as when faces adjacent to the coincident faces are tangent. **Solution:** Use any of the following alternate construction techniques instead of a boolean operation.

1. Always creates a single profile to be swept along the same drive curve (trajectory).

2. Rather than sweeping a profile, then sweeping a face of the result, and then joining the two objects, sweep the profile once. Use local operations to move faces when possible.

3. **Guidelines:** You should also keep the following guidelines in mind to avoid coincident faces, which may cause a boolean to fail:

   a. Fillet a resulting solid after a boolean, so a large number of coincident or tangent faces do not result. **Exception:** In a few cases (such as a vertex with four edges), if attempts to fillet the resulting solid fail, try filleting the objects first.

   b. When splitting or trimming solids, extend the trimming surfaces beyond the faces of the solid being modified so that the "knife" protrudes outside the solid.

   c. Position boolean operands that make through-holes so that they extend beyond the faces being punched, rather than making them flush.

Nancy Anderson-Semple, Technical Editor
Computervision Corp., Bedford, Mass.

6.5   Modeling Guidelines

The modeling guidelines discussed here are generally applicable to all CSG and B-Rep SM systems and most surface modelers, even though implementations vary. These guidelines are organized into three groups addressing:

1. Minimum modeling time
2. Model size and complexity classifications
3. Clean modeling

The terminology UNION, SUBTRACT, and COMMON used here reflect CSG boolean terminology. However, the information is also applicable to B-Rep modeling. Merely substitute ADD, CUT, and TRIM as required.

6.5.1   Minimum Modeling Time

The ideal CSG tree will have several levels of constructions as shown by the model classes in Fig. 6.4. The class 1 CSG tree should never be used for complex models. The ideal B-Rep model is also built using constructions. CSG and B-Rep modeling and editing time will both be greatly reduced with the use of multilevel constructions. Because the model is built in levels, deleting the boolean associations of constructions to the model, or of individual shapes to each construction, will delete only a few specific boolean or surface intersection associations.

Fig. 6.5 illustrates the amount of modeling time required versus the number of operations in a class 1 model. Figure 6.6 shows the same model subdivided into six constructions of a class 2 model. Note the amount of CPU time saved during construction.

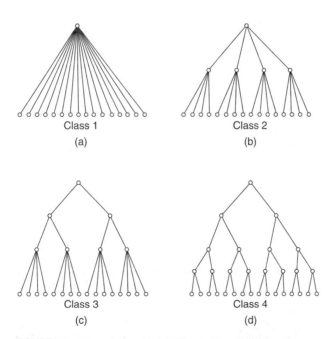

FIGURE 6.4   Classes 1 through 4 CSG trees. The subdivision of operations into discrete constructions within a solid model creates four distinct classes of representing CSG trees. (*a*) Class 1 models have a single level of constructions; (*b*) class 2 models have two levels of constructions; (*c*) class 3 models have three levels of constructions; (*d*) class 4 models have four or more levels of constructions.

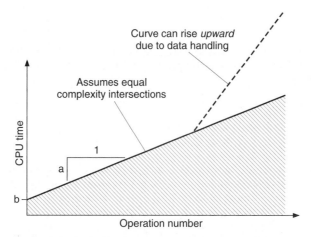

FIGURE 6.5 CPU time vs. number of operations, class 1. In a class 1 model, the time necessary to perform a boolean or surface intersection operation has a small overhead time "b." If the operation fails immediately, the CPU time "b" is still expended. Each subsequent operation of the same complexity takes a little longer ("a") because more model surfaces must be checked for possible intersection with the current shape. If all SM operations are to a single root object, then the total CPU time is equal to the area under the curve shown. Note that the curve can rise dramatically in later operations due to data handling.

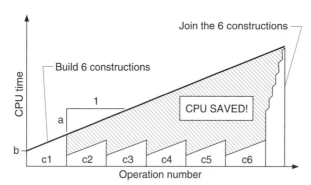

FIGURE 6.6 CPU time vs. number of operations, class 2. In a class 2 model like the one represented in Fig. 6.5, six equal subdivided constructions can be made and then joined at the end. The subdivision process causes each construction to require relatively equal CPU time. Since the accumulative CPU time "a" is not encountered, a large portion of the CPU time required in the class 1 model is saved.

Modeling Time

SMA.6.15   To Reduce Modeling and Editing Time

1. Perform simple intersections first.

2. Perform basic shape operations first.

3. Avoid trimming features.

4. Construct detail and features last.

5. Add features to subdivision constructions.

6. Minimize the extent of intersections.

(*Continued*)

Modeling Time
(*Continued*)

SMA.6.16 Subdivision Saves Time

As illustrated in Figs. 6.5 and 6.6, a complex solid model can often be subdivided into logical regions called *constructions*. Each construction can be individually modeled and then combined to achieve the final solid. Dividing the model into logical regions can save 50 percent of modeling time and 80 percent of editing time. Please note, however, that smooth, continuous surfaces should not be broken in the subdivision process.

SMA.6.17 CPU Time versus Constructions and Operations

A solid consisting of 100 primitives and geometric operations can be built in many ways. For example, the model could have 100 constructions of one primitive each, 50 constructions of two primitives each, etc. The relative CPU time to build such a model is compared in Fig. 6.7. Ideal modeling is achieved when the total number of constructions equals the total number of operations per construction.

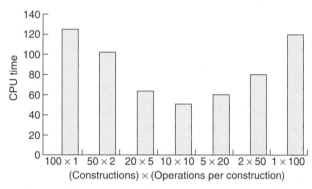

FIGURE 6.7 CPU Time for a 100-operation solid. For a solid having 100 operations, using 10 constructions of 10 operations each yields the minimum required CPU time; 20 constructions of 5 operations each or 5 constructions of 20 operations each requires only slightly more time. At the extremes, model creation requires over twice the minimum time. A poorly constructed larger model can consume over three times the minimum modeling time.

SMA.6.18 The CPU Time Curve

As shown in Fig. 6.8, the boolean (CSG) or intersection (B-Rep) CPU time curve is greater for a series of complex surface intersections than for a series of simple surface intersections. The number of intersections grows rapidly with each succeeding operation, causing all succeeding operations to perform even more intersection checks. Keep it simple whenever possible.

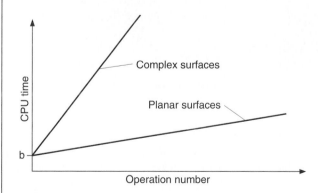

FIGURE 6.8 CPU time vs. operations and surface complexity. The CPU time curve is greater for a series of complex surface intersections than for a series of simpler surface intersections.

(*Continued*)

Modeling Time
(Continued)

SMA.6.19   Simple Intersections First

Perform simple intersections first when possible (see Fig. 6.9). As much as 80 percent of the total CPU time can be saved by following this rule, although 30 to 50 percent savings is probably more typical. Modeling speed and efficiency considerations become very important when a real-world part with actual manufacturing surfaces must be created. Most moderately complex parts require at least 50 shapes or surface intersection operations. A transmission housing or engine block, for example, can easily require 300 to 500 operations. The sheer magnitude of the data quickly fills the database when finite element meshes, drawings, NC toolpaths, etc., are included.

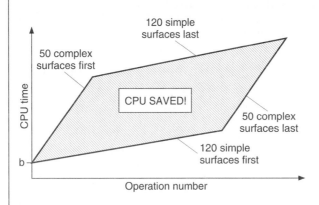

FIGURE 6.9   Perform simple surface operations first. By doing so, dramatic savings in CPU time can be realized.

SMA.6.20   Obtain Basic Shape Early

Perform basic shape operations early so that the net shape is attained while the number of surfaces is limited. Extra material only means that subsequent operations may look for more unnecessary intersections. This is depicted in Fig. 6.10. As a result, the total CPU time will be reduced. Boolean operations of an ADDITION nature especially reduce geometry.

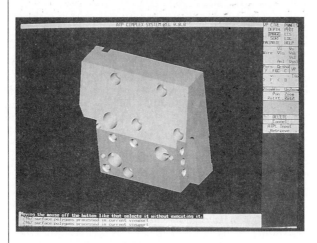

FIGURE 6.10   Perform basic-shape operations before details. Always finalize the basic shape first so that subsequent detailing will minimize the number of intersection checks required. *(Courtesy of Ingersall Milling and Machine Company.)*

SMA.6.21   Make Intersections Final

Perform operations in such an order that intersections created are final, and are never trimmed or otherwise modified again. Intermediate operations that cannot be avoided in the modeling process should be made to simpler surface intersections when possible.

6.5.2   Model Size and Complexity

Model size must be well understood in order to properly determine the ideal modeling strategy. The model classifications shown in Fig. 6.4 can be further identified by the number and complexity of required surface intersections. The larger and more complex the final model, the more difficult and time-consuming each subsequent boolean or surface intersection will be.

The CPU time required to perform a boolean or surface intersection is a function of the following:

1. The number of intersecting segments of all surfaces that must be checked during the operation
2. The number of new intersection segments produced in the current intersection
3. The order in which the intersection operations are performed
4. The accuracy of the intersections computed
5. Other factors such as the data transfer rate with the database, how I/O is performed, etc.

A complete intersection check requires more time to perform than a local intersection check. Some SM systems limit the number of surfaces checked for possible intersection with the current object by checking only at surfaces selected. An intersection may be missed during a local operation if complex surfaces are nearby. In some cases, the option of performing the complete intersection check when desired or required is available.

Model size can be approximated by measuring the number of boolean operations for primitive and geometric shapes plus features (CSG), or the number of surface intersection operations (B-Rep). In Table 6.2, model classifications are further identified by the total operations involved.

TABLE 6.2   Model Classifications by Number of Operations

Model class	Number of operations	Descriptive examples
1	15	Simple models; bearing cap, bracket
2	10–75	Complex surfaces; piston, crankshaft
3	50–200	Complex surfaces; manifolds, windage tray
4	>150	Complex surfaces and constructions; engine block, cylinder head

The number of operations and complexity of class 3 models are near the capability limits of some SM systems. When class 3 or class 4 models are created using high precision, later boolean or surface intersections can take several minutes to perform. Consequently, simplified models are sometimes created which may not be useful for all applications. An understanding of SM fundamentals can partially alleviate this problem.

As surface complexity increases, the time required to perform intersections can increase dramatically; hence the intense need to control the model structure well. Without proper direction, modeling time for a 300 operation solid can easily grow exponentially.

6.5.3   Clean Modeling

Clean modeling techniques allow designers to avoid creating excess geometry and always take precedence over all other guidelines. If a model is not clean of excess geometry, the following conditions may occur:

1. Automatic finite element meshing will generate more nodes and elements, and the mesh will become more difficult to control.
2. NC toolpath generation will require stepping over extraneous edges and surfaces.
3. Graphic displays may be inconsistent.
4. Drawings are incorrect, ambiguous, and undimensionable.
5. Tolerances and surface finishes cannot be specified properly.

Clean Modeling

SMA.6.22   For Clean Modeling

A clean solid model is more useful than an unclean one to all downstream applications. Remember the following:

1. Always create continuous surfaces (see SMA.6.23).

2. Always remove unwanted material.

3. Construct as produced.

4. Avoid offsetting surfaces.

5. Minimize narrow faces.

6. Avoid small corner angles.

SMA.6.23   Continuous Surfaces

Clean models have continuous surfaces wherever possible (see Fig. 6.11). This requires that the total number of surfaces are kept to a minimum: surfaces have the fewest vertices, edges, and no gaps. Do not break a continuous surface unless absolutely necessary.

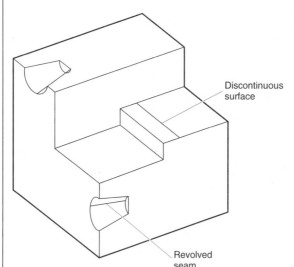

Discontinuous surface

Revolved seam

FIGURE 6.11   Clean models have continuous surfaces and seams whose vertices are not within system tolerance proximity or each other.

SMA.6.24   Revolution Seams

Revolved (axisymmetric or turned) shapes sometimes have a seam present that will remain on the solid and near another edge. The revolve can be rotated before performing the SUBTRACT operation to move the seam away from other edges or to eliminate it entirely (see Fig. 6.11).

SMA.6.25   Edge Precedence

Perform intersections in an order to produce the fewest number of vertices, edges, and surfaces. The edges of shapes added usually take precedence over existing solid model edges. Depending on the SM system, existing edges may take precedence over the added edges, both sets of edges may remain, or all edges on continuous surfaces are automatically removed (this is the cleanest model).

Unnecessary edges will cause an automatic finite element mesh to possess many more nodes and elements, and NC toolpaths will encounter more surfaces, etc.

SMA.6.26   Rework Unclean Geometry

Always rework unclean geometry rather than covering it up or simply trimming it off. The solid will retain more operations due to creating unclean geometry and covering it up than it will if the geometry is remodeled properly. The additional operations can contribute to future errors and cause later operations to consume more time than is necessary.

(Continued)

Clean Modeling
(Continued)

SMA.6.27 Construct As Produced

Solids should be constructed similar to the way they will be machined, as illustrated by Fig. 6.12. Build a SUBTRACTion construction in the shape of pockets to produce cleaner pockets, rather than subtracting a series of solids. Build a UNION construction to produce a cleaner appendage, rather than UNIONing a series of solids. Fillets should be created last as fillet features.

SMA.6.28 ADD Before SUBTRACT

Perform boolean ADDs before SUBTRACTs when possible so that cavities and pockets are not erroneously filled in. Another identical SUBTRACT can be built to clean up such an error, but coincident surface intersection errors might then result.

SMA.6.29 Discard Often

A cleaner model will result if you eliminate primitives, geometric operations, and features as soon as they are no longer needed.

SMA.6.30 Avoid Difficult Geometry

Unclean geometry such as short edges, narrow faces, and small angles between edges can lead to application difficulties. As previously mentioned, any revolved construction can be rotated about its axis so that the seam does not intersect near another vertex or edge. Fillet radii can sometimes be increased within the normal design tolerance to eliminate an unnecessary adjacent surface. The design might be adjusted to eliminate small surfaces by relocating a surface.

SMA.6.31 Cleaning the Model

When too many extra vertices, edges, and surfaces are created, the model can usually be cleaned by creating and subtracting from the model another construction which is outside the solid and coincident with its surfaces.

In some cases, the extra edges and surfaces may be removed from the model, but the vertices may remain. Removal of a finite amount of material may be required to remove the vertices. Alternatively, a construction can sometimes be built internal to the model and coincident to its surface, and a UNION performed.

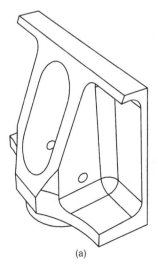

FIGURE 6.12 Construct as produced. An approach to modeling prismatic parts is to simulate the actual manufacturing methods used. The method of removing material as in a machining process helps keep a model clean for downstream processes. (*a*) Sample bracket part. *(Continued)*

(a)

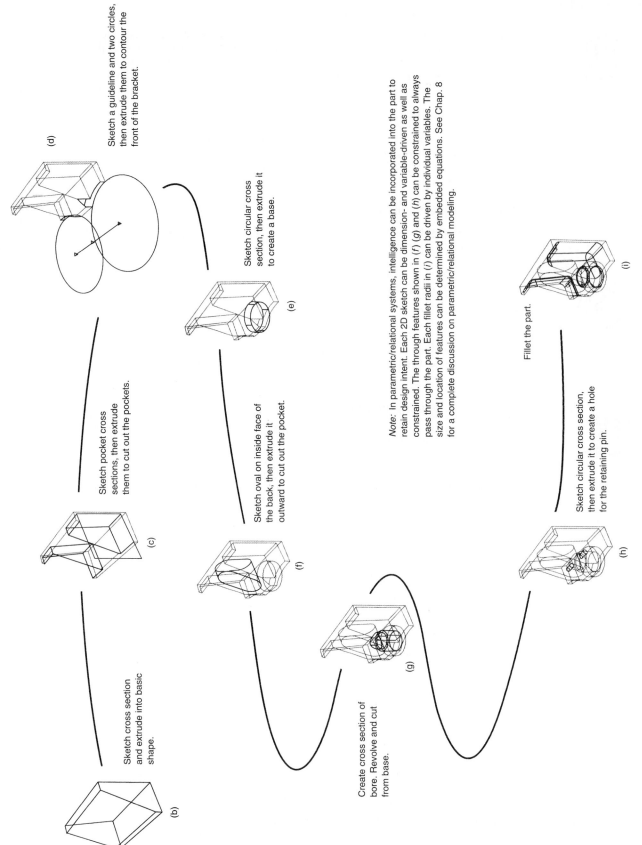

FIGURE 6.12 (*b*) sketch cross section and extrude into basic shape; (*c*) sketch pocket cross sections, then extrude them to cut out the pockets; (*d*) sketch a guideline and two circles, then extrude them to contour the front of the bracket; (*e*) sketch circular cross section, then extrude it to create a base; (*f*) sketch oval on inside face of the back, then extrude it outward to cut out the pocket; (*g*) create cross section of bore, then revolve and cut from base; (*h*) sketch circular cross section, then extrude it to create a hole for the retaining pin; (*i*) fillet the part. (*Courtesy of Structural Dynamics Research Corporation, SDRC.*)

The following text labels appear within the figure:

(b) Sketch cross section and extrude into basic shape.

(c) Sketch pocket cross sections, then extrude them to cut out the pockets.

(d) Sketch a guideline and two circles, then extrude them to contour the front of the bracket.

(e) Sketch circular cross section, then extrude it to create a base.

(f) Sketch oval on inside face of the back, then extrude it outward to cut out the pocket.

(g) Create cross section of bore. Revolve and cut from base.

(h) Sketch circular cross section, then extrude it to create a hole for the retaining pin.

(i) Fillet the part.

Note: In parametric/relational systems, intelligence can be incorporated into the part to retain design intent. Each 2D sketch can be dimension- and variable-driven as well as constrained. The through features shown in (*f*) (*g*) and (*h*) can be constrained to always pass through the part. Each fillet radii in (*i*) can be driven by individual variables. The size and location of features can be determined by embedded equations. See Chap. 8 for a complete discussion on parametric/relational modeling.

6.16

Clean Modeling
(Continued)

SMA.6.32 Exploding Solids

Some SM systems allow the solid to be exploded into individual surfaces without loss of definition. Surface areas can then be cleaned up, rejoined, and made into a solid once again. Geometry required for function must not be eliminated, of course.

Don LaCourse, President
The Solid Modeling ExChange, Algood, Tenn.

SMA.6.33 Select Actual Edges[1]

When selecting a solid edge for an operation, make the selection on an actual edge, not a meshed line. ***Rationale:*** Future operations may change a mesh pattern. If so, selecting a meshed line will cause regeneration to fail. ***Usage tip:*** You can distinguish if something is an actual edge by using selection filters.

Nancy Anderson-Semple, Technical Editor
Computervision Corp., Bedford, Mass.

6.6 Navigating Errors

SM systems, as well as those professionals who develop and operate them, are by no means perfect. Productivity with any advanced technology is achieved only relative to one's ability to navigate through errors and inconsistencies. This section is devoted exclusively to this effort.

6.6.1 Modeling Errors

Modeling errors are almost always due to one of the following:

1. Exceeding array sizes in the computer code. A particularly complex operation may require storing more entities such as edges than the software was coded to handle.

2. Exceeding the memory size of the computer's CPU. A complex operation may require more memory than is available.

3. Imprecise geometry.

Modeling Errors

SMA.6.34 To Reduce Modeling Errors

1. Avoid trimming features.

2. Avoid trimming surfaces.

3. Avoid latent gratuitous surfaces.

4. Minimize concurrent intersections.

5. Create final intersections directly.

6. Perform boolean ADDs before SUBTRACTs.

7. Minimize concurrent operations to avoid software array limits.

8. Eliminate extra operations.

9. Newer edges have precedence over coincident older edges.

SMA.6.35 Avoid Trimming Features

If at all possible, avoid trimming features (such as through-holes) by basic-shape boolean or surface intersections. All intersections at exterior faces will have been needlessly performed twice. If a

(Continued)

Modeling Errors
(*Continued*)

single intersection fails to be determined, the entire boolean or surface intersection will fail. Always perform basic shape operations first.

SMA.6.36 Avoid Trimming Surfaces

Trimming surfaces can lead to more boolean and surface intersection errors later in the modeling process due to the extra geometry and the extra operations not required with an untrimmed surface. It is always best to build a surface to its trimmed location. However, the definition of a complex surface at the desired boundaries are not always known; hence, the trimmed surface is used. Trimmed surfaces can also be a cause of lost geometry when translating to neutral formats. (See Chap. 21, "Solid Modeling and IGES.")

SMA.6.37 Avoid Latent Gratuitous Surfaces

Latent or gratuitous surfaces are those that are no longer visible after the boolean or intersection operation because they lie inside or outside the solid. As shown in Fig. 6.13, after a SUBTRACTION has been performed, the box ADDITION operation may fail due to its coincidence with the now-latent surfaces of the box SUBTRACT, especially if complex surfaces are present. This error can often be corrected with a shorter box SUBTRACT or a longer box COMMON where the coincidence does not occur.

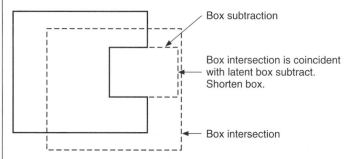

FIGURE 6.13 Avoid latent gratuitous surfaces. Surfaces that are no longer visible after a boolean or surface intersection operation can cause problems for subsequent operations. As shown here, the box INTERSECTion operation may fail because it is completely coincident with the latent surfaces of the previous box SUBTRACTion operation. Try to avoid complete coincidence with latent surfaces.

SMA.6.38 Minimize Concurrent Intersections

The hub in Fig. 6.14 should be intersected with just one spoke, and the resulting solid intersected to the rim. The remaining spokes should then be intersected to the model, one at a time. Alternatively, but to be avoided, all of the spokes can be intersected to the hub first. However, intersecting the rim will then entail numerous simultaneous intersections of the rim to all the spokes. The intersections look as though they are all identical; but due to orientation, positioning, and accuracy errors, they differ. If just one intersection segment of a spoke to the rim fails, the entire intersection operation fails.

FIGURE 6.14 Minimize concurrent intersections. In this example, a single spoke should first be UNIONed to the hub and then to the rim. The remaining spokes can then be UNIONed separately. The possibility of intersection errors is reduced. (*Courtesy of Cimplex Corporation.*)

(*Continued*)

Modeling Errors
(*Continued*)

SMA.6.39   Large versus Small Geometry

Accuracy-related errors can occur when very large and very small geometries exist within close proximity. In Fig. 6.15 the existence of the small radius is clouded by the precision lost with the occurrence of the very large radius. The precise locations of the intersections at the radii clearly require that the geometry possess more than eight digits of accuracy. Consequently, the intersection may fail.

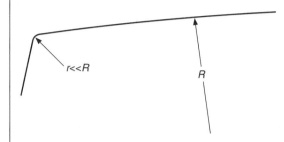

FIGURE 6.15   Large vs. small geometry. The coexistence of very large and very small geometry can produce accuracy errors. The accuracy required by the small radius r is clouded by the imprecision generated from the large radius R when the two are required to be tangent. Perhaps radius r can be left sharp or increased without undue impact to the design.

SMA.6.40   Minimize Size and Complexity of Intersections

To reduce memory and CPU requirements, always minimize the size and complexity of intersections. Software array limits can overflow. As illustrated in Fig. 6.16, the order in which boolean operations are performed can help minimize the size and complexity of intersections.

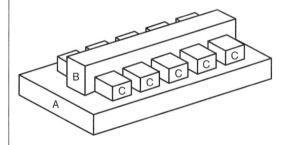

FIGURE 6.16   Minimize the size and complexity of intersections. In this simplified example, part B should be intersected with part A prior to the intersection of parts C to reduce the risk of possible intersection errors. Also see SMA.6.38.

SMA.6.41   Accuracy Settings

In Fig. 6.17, the search for the intersection of the large and small geometries will not be successful if the search path is too coarse. Coarseness greatly speeds up the search process, but at the cost of accuracy. If the SM system allows the temporary tightening of intersection tolerances, extreme caution should be exercised in doing so.

Tighten search accuracy.
Reset accuracy after intersecting.

Coarse polygonalized
intersection search line

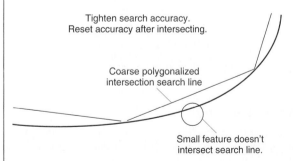

FIGURE 6.17   Accuracy settings. The coarseness of the system's accuracy settings can cause small features to appear not to intersect when they actually do. In this example, the coarse polygonalized intersection search line along the curve misses an intersecting feature. Do not modify the system's accuracy settings unless absolutely necessary.

Small feature doesn't
intersect search line.

Caution: Reset the accuracy to the default value for later intersections. Also, changing accuracy from one intersection to another may cause errors in later intersections.

6.6.2 Intersection Errors

Intersection errors generally result from reduced accuracy, which causes geometry to be very slightly noncoincident or nontangent when it should be. The geometry types for coincidence and tangency errors are vertex–vertex, vertex–edge, vertex–surface, edge–edge, edge–surface, and surface–surface. An example of each is given in Fig. 6.18.

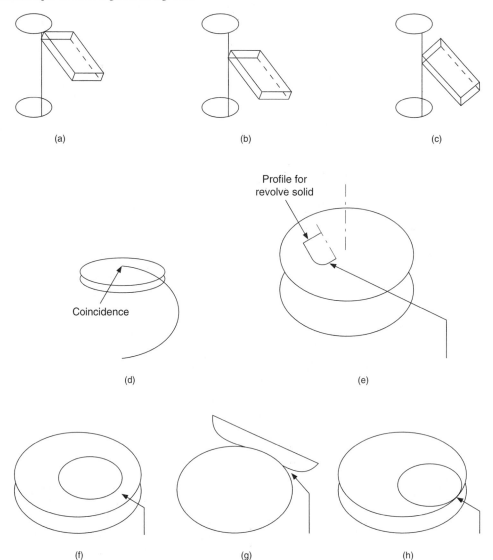

FIGURE 6.18 Intersection errors. Coincidence and tangency relationships of vertices, edges, and surfaces can be altered due to system accuracy. Generally these relationships should be avoided: (*a*) vertex–vertex, (*b*) vertex–edge, (*c*) edge–edge, (*d*) vertex–surface, (*e*) vertex/edge–surface, (*f*) surface–surface (coplanar), (*g*) surface–surface (tangent and coincident), (*h*) surface–surface (cylindrically tangent).

Intersection Errors

SMA.6.42 Move Geometry

When situations such as those illustrated in Fig. 6.18 are encountered, and if precise repositioning of geometry can be performed, then do so. However, during an intersection error it is often hard to identify which is the offending geometry. Also, the imprecision which caused the mislocation may also prevent accurate relocation. Zooming the display larger might show a near-coincidence condition, but the graphics display accuracy is typically much less than the geometry accuracy. Query the actual locations of each vertex or curve, and reposition as appropriate.

(Continued)

SMA.6.43   Revolution Solution

Intersection errors can sometimes be worked around easily if at least one of the shapes is a revolution. For example, right-circular forms of a cylinder, tube, cone, sphere, torus, or a general revolved profile can be rotated about its axis of revolution without altering the subsequent solid, other than changing where the seam line(s) will be. Always rotate by small angles, such as 1°. The intersection search curve of the revolved shape may now find an intersection with the solid. A rotation of 90° would likely have the same phasing as the original intersection search curve; the intersection may still fail.

SMA.6.44   Surface–Surface Tangency

Errors can often be overcome by extending and embedding one surface inside another solid or surface. Transition and torus surface tangency errors are the most prevalent, due to the variable radius and double curvature conditions present in these geometries. Be perceptive. In some cases a different solid will be the result and the design may change, making this an unacceptable alternative.

SMA.6.45   Narrow Faces

If narrow or small faces should exist, a subsequent finite element mesh will probably be uncontrollably dense at this location. The narrow surfaces may create more difficulty for the NC programmer, and/or the NC software. For example, the width of a narrow face may be much smaller than the end of the tool bit, causing the NC software to interpret this condition as an error.

SMA.6.46   Twin Edges

The topology of a polyhedron (solid body) can be defined as: (1) both ends of every edge is a vertex, (2) edges bound an infinite surface into a face, and (3) exactly two faces (polygons) meeting along each edge of the solid (see Chap. 3).

The two edges of adjacent faces are known as *twin edges* because they are coincident and identical. If a gap or overlap in the faces of the solid occurs here, the solid is invalid. The twin of each edge at the gap or overlap cannot be identified mathematically at this location.

Automated applications, such as finite element mesh generation or NC tool path generation, cannot use such geometry. Note that some gaps and overlaps may be within system tolerance levels. Also check to see that downstream operations are not operating at a tighter tolerance level.

SMA.6.47   Revolution Seams

Care should be taken so that the seam lines of a revolution do not occur very near anticipated intersection edges. The revolve should be rotated so that the intersected revolved surface is either not divided at all, or the surface created is divided by the seam line(s) into nearly equal size faces. If a 90° rotation is desired, and a prior intersection attempt failed, the actual rotation should be 91° for proper phasing of the intersection search curve. Also see SMA.6.43.

SMA.6.48   Vertex–Vertex Coincidence

Two vertices must coincide precisely (to about 12 significant figures) or must be at clearly different locations (differing by at least one digit in the fifth significant figure) or a boolean or surface intersection error becomes more probable.

SMA.6.49   Intersection Error Debugging

If it is noted which and when error messages occur, and what the source of the error is, then debugging becomes possible. A flowchart can then be constructed similar to Fig. 6.19, where the message suggests the possible causes, and each path suggests possible situations that will cause this message and solutions to overcome the error. This practice applies to all system and operational error messages as well.

SMA.6.50   Unreported Errors

Unreported errors can occur but not be immediately obvious if no error message is reported. For example A UNION B should result in A and B being trimmed. If the intersection curve is not found, A and B will be displayed with no trimming of their surfaces. Similarly, A SUBTRACT B can result in only A being visible if no intersection is found. The next boolean or surface intersection opera-

(Continued)

Intersection Errors
(*Continued*)

tion usually reports that an error has occurred, but it is really the previous boolean or surface intersection that has failed.

SMA.6.51   Multiple Shells Error

A valid solid can be created in most SM systems with two or more totally disconnected surfaces or shells. For example, a solid can be cut into two distinct portions. Similarly, a shape can be subtracted from the interior of a solid, leaving a void with a surface that is not connected to the exterior surface.

A valid solid in an SM system or by design is not necessarily a valid solid in other applications. For example, automatic solid finite element mesh generators in commercial systems do not currently mesh multiple shells of either type. Also, a solid with an internal void cannot be machined.

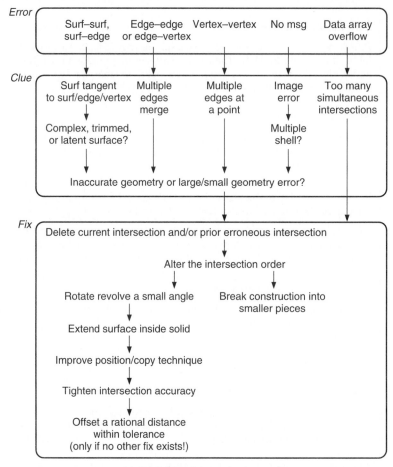

FIGURE 6.19   Intersection error debugging. Always note the contents, source, and occurrence of error messages. Such information makes error debugging possible. Over time, gather this information into a flowchart similar to the one shown here. Such information will be invaluable in saving time and avoiding errors in the future.

6.6.3   Accuracy Errors

General accuracy errors can occur such that profiles are not flat to the required precision, or geometry is not positioned properly, causing minute geometry errors. Extra edges are often created resulting in large/small geometry accuracy errors. Calculations performed at twice precision are almost always necessary to overcome these problems. Very systematic modeling procedures can overcome accuracy problems in some cases.

Accuracy Errors

SMA.6.52   Minimize Movement of Profiles

Try to minimize the movement of profiles, particularly relating to rotations. The round-off errors in PI and every arithmetic operation lead to cumulative errors that can cause incorrect solids to be built with these constructions.

SMA.6.53   Accuracy versus Speed

The speed of computations is a function of computational word size, accuracy of the intersection search algorithm, and the accuracy to which the intersection is computed.

If the SM system performs all computations to double precision, then the computations will take up to 10 times longer than if done using only single precision. NC toolpaths and other operations performed using single-precision results may not be of sufficient quality.

If the intersection search algorithm is coarse, intersections can be found faster, but some may be missed as shown previously in Fig. 6.17.

6.6.4   Modeling Work-Arounds

Any change in modeling technique that creates the correct model, but in a different way, is acceptable. Work-arounds are very important because software problems encountered can take a long time to document, report, correct, build into new software modules, deliver, and install! Guidelines exist for many cases, though not all are well documented.

A work-around is quite acceptable if:

1. The same solid model can be created in another way.
2. The resulting changes are within acceptable design tolerances.
3. The function and quality of the design have not been violated.
4. All applications can still utilize the solid model without additional difficulty.

Modeling Work-Arounds

SMA.6.54   Reordering Operations

Alter the order of booleans or intersections if the initial sequence fails. The model created will be the same solid, although the edges produced may vary due to the precedence of the later shape's edges over the former's edges.

SMA.6.55   Avoid Offsets

Try to avoid offsetting geometry in an attempt to eliminate an intersection error. The model design is clearly changed. Subsequent operations can create very short edges or very small angles, degrading the effectiveness of all applications using the model.

If offsetting is used as a last resort, the value might be less than the design tolerance, but larger than the large/small accuracy value. For example, an offset of a half percent of the radius or a tenth percent of the object length will be much less damaging than some infinitesimal value which will often lead to large/small type accuracy error.

6.7   Cautions and Needed Improvements

Solid modeling systems are by no means without need of improvement. Here is a short list of recommended cautions and improvements.

1. Feature definitions in CSG and B-Rep modelers are generally incomplete. For example, a hole feature is not complete unless the input allows inclusion of countersink angle and depth, counterbore diameter and depth, fillet radii, tool radii, threads, surface finishes, dimensional tolerances, etc.
2. The feature types provided for are generally incomplete. By adding feature types, the need to overlay modeling operations to produce other features not provided for is reduced.

3. Attribute definitions are often incomplete. For example, threads are not just defined as pitch diameter and threads per length, but must also be identified by the thread standard (UNF, UNC, UNS, etc.), depth of good threads, class of fit, thread orientation (male, female), and thread type (standard, tapered, pipe, machined).

4. The overlapping interface between SM for mechanical and electrical design needs to be improved. Product development teams will be more efficient when this process is robust. Interfaces to other fields should also be evolved.

6.8 Conclusions

As seen from these discussions, the road to productive construction of solid models can be a minefield of considerations. After all, one cannot expect to simply reap the benefits of technology without addressing the basic issues of good planning, operational practices, and management along the way.

For those who are designing simple to moderately complex parts, many of the considerations discussed here may not apply. However, if an SM design consists of complex surfaces or large amounts of geometry, proper strategies can save vast amounts of time and money, and reduce data management burdens.

Checklist

SMA.6.56 Keep Geometry Simple

For example, whenever possible:

1. Use arcs and lines rather than splines.

2. Use extrudes rather than sweeps.

3. Use sweeps rather than blends or transitions.

4. Use single rather than double curvature.

SMA.6.57 Procedural and Wireframe Rules

These rules are primarily for efficiency when working with the wireframe data for large, high-precision solid models. Briefly, they are:

1. Create wireframe geometry first. Often, certain geometry can be copied, offset, etc., to produce adjacent geometry. Great caution and forethought should be used, as the accuracy of all geometry is already set at this stage.

2. Perform all operations for a single construction (model subdivision). Preview the construction by solid-shading the shape surfaces.

3. Boolean or intersect shapes to create the first construction.

4. Make the display of previous constructions invisible so that graphics redisplay time is not increased.

5. Proceed to the next construction.

6. Reset all viewing controls while the object is not shaded. Shading of complex solids is time-consuming. Unnecessary reshading should be avoided.

SMA.6.58 Geometry Construction Tips

1. Don't use boolean operations unless absolutely necessary.

2. Keep part files small. Keep temporary or construction geometry in a separate file.

3. Model all drafted surfaces.

4. Use modeling construction techniques that avoid rounding errors. For instance, an array of features may end up on uneven distance locations.

(Continued)

Checklist
(*Continued*)

5. It is not necessary to model every instance of a feature in a series of features (such as vents or holes). Model a few copies of the feature on either end of the pattern; then indicate on a drawing how many times the feature is to be repeated. This will reduce the size of the database.

6. Don't fillet edges unless required for design reasons (i.e., leave off "typical" fillets). Perform filleting operation as late as possible in the design process. Once a corner is filleted, the corner is no longer available for reference.

7. *Save frequently!* Save after each major operation. Archive layouts daily.

8. Develop a company "CAD Geometry Construction Methodology." In order to allow all designers to work on the same database, they must know what to expect. A similar approach to constructing typical geometry features will allow designers and drafters to understand and modify each other's work intuitively.

Howard W. Stolz, Product Designer
Sun Microsystems, Mountain View, Calif.

Good Practices

SMA.6.59 Use Blocks

Save portions of your design as blocks and use instances of these blocks when the same geometry appears in several places in a drawing or when creating components and assembling them in an assembly drawing.

Rationale: A block is treated as a single element during recalculation. You can manipulate block instances much more quickly than with the equivalent number of individual elements. They also require much less time when resolving constraints because the system does not have to recalculate the constraints within each block every time you make a change to a drawing.

SMA.6.60 Use a Plane to Split a Solid

When splitting a solid, use a plane rather than a line or a surface. ***Purpose:*** To ensure that you have an infinite cutting surface. When you use a plane, model alterations won't fail as they might if the model changes and the line or surface no longer cuts through the solid.

Exception: If you must use a line or a surface, make sure that it cuts across the solid as needed by relating the extremities of the cutting entity to the solid being split.

SMA.6.61 Use Local Operations[1]

Wherever possible, use local operations rather than boolean operations. ***Purpose:*** To avoid long regeneration. ***Rationale:*** With boolean operations, the system considers all faces of a solid or surface before execution. With local operations, the system considers only the face you select and its adjacent faces.

Exception: If the case is relatively complex, and you are unsure of how many faces will be involved, a boolean operation may be more appropriate.

Nancy Anderson-Semple, Technical Editor
Computervision Corp., Bedford, Mass.

SMA.6.62 Geometry Alignment

Use aligned construction geometry (that which is prealigned, touching, and sharing common vertices, edges, etc.) to create features on a solid model for a more robust mathematical representation.

Scott McOlash, Engineer
Eaton Corporation, Milwaukee, Wis.

Good Practices
(Continued)

SMA.6.63 Nonparametric Systems

When developing mating parts in nonparametric SM systems, it is often the case, for example, that the holes in a plate will be moved (revised) before the 2D drawing is generated. When it is suspected that this might be the case, you can save time by not subtracting the holes; just leave cylinders. This will allow the holes to be quickly moved. When it is time to document the part, the holes can be quickly subtracted from the plate.

George R. Winton III, Mechanical Engineer
Micromeritics, Lawrenceville, Ga.

SMA.6.64 ID Checks

Watch out for the integrity of your entities (objects) after you perform a boolean operation. A worthwhile CAD program will have some sort of ID (identification) command allowing you to grab an object to find out information about it. It doesn't hurt to ID your objects after boolean operations so you don't build more complex things on top of a faulty foundation.

Keith Campbell, Engineer, VP Marketing
American Small Business Computers, Pryor, Okla.

SMA.6.65 Always Include Draft

Designers tend not to draft features with "typical" or minimum draft in order to save time. Although the draft angle is usually obvious, the toolmaker must guess which end of a feature to draft. Modeling all drafted surfaces eliminates the guesswork, phone calls, and delays. Draft surfaces as late in the design process as possible. Undrafted geometry is easier to modify, copy, offset, etc.

Howard W. Stolz, Product Designer
Sun Microsystems, Mountain View, Calif.

SMA.6.66 Testing Intersections

Surface intersections can be trial-viewed by shading the nonintersected geometry. Faceted displays may need to use finer polygons and/or smooth shading for this technique to be most useful. If positioning is incorrect, the intersection and subsequent editing time is avoided.

SMA.6.67 Do Not Display Unused Geometry

To speed redisplay, make all unnecessary geometry and constructions invisible. Finding the ideal orientation for current operations can be less time-consuming.

SMA.6.68 SM Is a Science

The rules of productive SM are primarily based on underlying mathematics. Fortunately, being a mathematician is not a prerequisite to being productive. When well understood, it becomes clear that SM is a science, and not a mysterious and obscure art.

SMA.6.69 A System's Dynamic Range

SM systems have dynamic ranges and may not be able to have many small- and large-feature entities in the model simultaneously. The same is true for some parametric systems that have limited solver capabilities to handle many multiple-referenced datums or parametric features. When the dynamic range in either case is exceeded, not one additional feature can be created without a problem.

John Skibinski, Program Director
Eaton Corp., Milwaukee, Wis.

Good Practices
(Continued)

SMA.6.70   Adding Surface Regions

Solid modeling systems may not allow for creating surface regions on continuous surfaces. Designers may need to create a surface region to ease the use of the solid model in other applications.

For example, a pressure may reside on a portion of a surface. Or a concentrated force may be applied to a small region of a surface. For analysis accuracy, the finite elements generated should not cross the boundary of the region, and the finite element analysis software may not allow for applying the pressure to a region of the complete surface. Hence, the finite element analyst may desire the surface to be broken into regions via edges, while the NC programmer needs the surfaces continuous.

Regions can be created on a surface in some SM systems using surface intersections or booleans. A surface-coincident shape can be placed inside the solid and a UNION performed or the shape may be surface-coincident and external to the solid and a SUBTRACT performed. Which technique is appropriate will depend on the edge precedence algorithm of the SM system.

Some SM systems leave no edges when surfaces are fully coincident. If no surface is visible after such an operation, the next boolean is usually required before the designer learns if the lack of edges was by design, or if the solid is actually corrupt at this time, and no longer usable.

Reference

1. Adapted from "Parametric Modeling Usage Tips," Revision 4.0.0, Nancy Anderson-Semple, Editor, Computervision Corporation, May, 1993.

Chapter 7
Editing Strategies

Richard D. Lowrey, Ph.D.
Mechanical Design Consultant

Editing solids is very important because it frequently occurs late in the product development cycle when changes can drastically impact product cost, quality, schedule, and profitability. Editing which alters only geometry may have limited impact, while that which alters topology (the total number of vertices, edges, and faces) usually results in an impact of much greater consequence. (Refer to Chap. 8 for a discussion on parametric/relational editing.)

7.1 Occurring Types of Change

During the course of product development, three types of changes will usually occur before the solid model is released for manufacturing. These include the areas of (1) geometry, (2) topology, and (3) cosmetics.

7.1.1 Geometry Changes

If editing alters only geometry, then associativity is valid, and associated applications of the solid will not be measurably impacted. Notifications sent to the affected applications about the geometry changes permit the applications to generate new or additional views, update notes, etc.

Editing that typically affects geometry includes only changes in the surface intersection accuracy value, units, and minor changes in dimensions, angles, dimensioning scheme, and tolerances which alter the number of decimal places of dimensions and angles. The topology is unchanged, as noted by no changes in the number of vertices or edges of each face, and no change in the number of faces (see Fig. 7.1).

 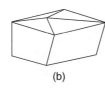

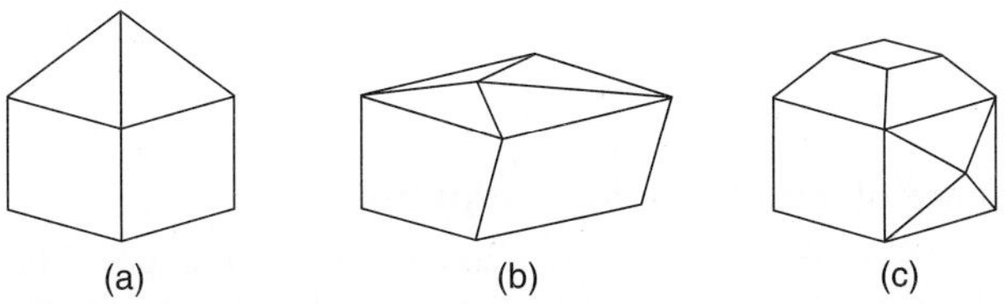

(a)   (b)   (c)

FIGURE 7.1 Editing geometry and topology. (*a*) Original solid; (*b*) editing geometry allows vertices to move and both edges and faces to be stretched and or truncated; (*c*) editing topology adds or deletes vertices, modifies, adds, or deletes faces, and modifies the total number and relationship of vertices, edges, and faces.

7.1.2   Topology Changes

Topology changes can invalidate associativity by modifying the total number of vertices, edges, and faces of a solid, often forcing complete rework and delays in associated applications (see Fig. 7.1). Labor costs in the associated applications occur with each change. Later in the product development cycle, costs may also include product retesting, new or modified manufacturing processes and fixtures, packaging changes, etc.

7.1.3   Cosmetic Changes

Some design information is only cosmetic to the solid model and is not evaluated into the SM geometry or topology. This information usually conveys design intent to other applications.

Cosmetic information never changes geometry or topology and includes changes in dimension locations, material specifications, notes, and attributes. SM attributes are entities such as tolerance, surface finish, surface plating and coating, nonevaluated threads, flatness, perpendicularity, angularity, concentricity, parallelism, straightness, runout, and circularity.

7.2   Editing Solids

Solids can be edited directly for all operations that modify only geometry as well as those operations that modify topology without adversely violating surfaces. There is an exception, however, in SM systems that prevent modification of an evaluated root solid. Direct editing of solids can include:

1. Geometry
2. Topology
3. Dimensions
4. Surface intersection accuracy

7.2.1   Editing Geometry

Dimensional and angular changes frequently alter the size and location of surfaces without altering topology. This editing can be performed directly on the individual shapes without editing the CSG tree, as discussed later in this chapter. The primary solid or local details can be stretched in one or more directions, details repositioned, and parameters changed (see Fig. 7.1b). Editing functions are typically accessed via a MODIFY menu. Editing choices under MODIFY may be for each primitive or geometric operation type or for each editing operation type such as STRETCH, BEND, MOVE, ROTATE, ENLARGE, WARP, TWEAK, or CHANGE.

7.2.2   Editing Topology

Topology editing changes the number of vertices or edges of some faces, or the number of faces (see Fig. 7.1c). Editing that adds, removes, or modifies topology without causing unwanted surface violations can be performed directly on a solid.

Topology

SMA.7.1   Adding and Removing Topology

Topology edits that remove material are generally of minor impact. These edits can include adding holes, chamfers, and minor details such as pockets and slots. Manufacturing can sometimes add a tool and toolpath to machine these changes, and additional analysis might not be required. However, removing holes, chamfers, etc., may cause parts already manufactured to become scrap. Topology edits which add material are generally a greater problem. For example, bosses, fillets, and draft usually require major rework in applications.

(Continued)

Topology
(Continued)

SMA.7.2   Topology versus Manufacturing Costs

Topology edits that substantially increase the number of surfaces will almost always increase product development costs and production costs. Manufacturing may require more tool changes, setups, and toolpaths. These changes may be justified if they increase product quality. Conversely, topology changes that substantially reduce the number of surfaces and simplify the product can decrease product development and production costs.

SMA.7.3   Surface Violations

Unwanted surface violations can result when the geometry of a primitive or geometric operation is changed such that it protrudes through a surface not intended. The offending shape must be removed from the solid, its geometry changed, the offending region of this shape removed, and the modified shape again joined with the solid.

7.2.3   Editing Dimensions

Dimensions are typically edited by changing the dimension values, relations, scheme, or changing tolerances. The product development team will have used varying techniques to determine the ideal parameters for optimal product quality, manufacturing time, and cost characteristics. By this process, critical dimensions are identified, critical tolerances are tightened, and noncritical tolerances are loosened. These techniques require time to perform and, consequently, may require editing the solid model.

The dimensioning scheme and related tolerances will cause a particular tolerance stack-up. They convey to manufacturing which dimensions and tolerances are most important for achieving product quality, and which are not as important. In some SM systems changing a tolerance will change the number of decimal places in the dimension to which the tolerance is applied.

7.2.4   Editing Surface Intersection Accuracy

Changing the surface intersection accuracy will affect all subsequent intersections. A full model regeneration will of course recompute all intersections at the new accuracy. The accuracy is sometimes tightened to refine geometric and topological data for manufacturing.

7.3   Editing the CSG Tree

The CSG tree (see Chap. 4) must be edited when:

1. Unwanted surface violations occur during direct SM editing.
2. Editing will be faster when performed on CSG constructions.
3. The modeling scheme must be changed due to major redesign.
4. The logical shape of constructions has changed or a different number of constructions must be used.
5. Editing is required on an unevaluated shape such as the root primitive, or an extrude, sweep, blend, or revolve geometric operation.
6. A shape type must be changed. For example, a revolve geometric operation must be replaced by a cone primitive, a blend geometric operation, or a construction.

If your SM system is associative, the CSG tree is edited by breaking the associations of the shapes to be edited from the tree, editing the necessary shapes, and then reconstructing the CSG tree associations (see Fig. 7.2). The associations broken may be of the root shape to individual primitives, solid geometric operations, or constructions composed of primitives and geometric operations. Only remove as many associations as necessary to limit the amount of rework. Surface intersections that were performed to create the B-Rep boundary object are also broken and again performed upon reconstruction.

Breaking the CSG tree associations is usually performed using a function called MODIFY SOLID, DELETE SOLID, REMOVE SOLID, SMASH SOLID, etc.

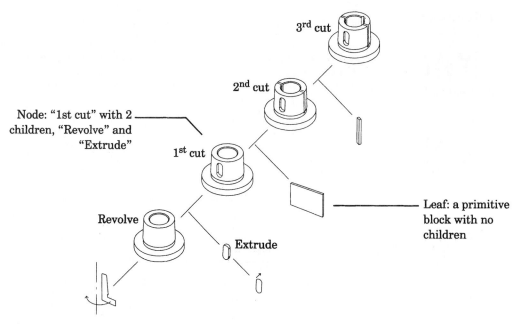

FIGURE 7.2 Graphic CSG tree example of a single solid. Associations between leafs and nodes can be broken, modifications made, and associations reestablished to achieve a desired result. (*Courtesy of Structural Dynamics Research Corporation, SDRC.*)

Edited shapes may be individual primitives and geometric operations. Hence, a construction removed from the solid for editing must in turn have the associations and intersections of the shapes to be edited removed from its CSG tree.

7.3.1 Editing Order of Shapes

It may be necessary to edit the order of constructions in a solid model, or shapes in a construction because:

1. A shape fills or removes a portion of another shape.
2. Computational and labor time can be saved during subsequent reevaluations by shifting simpler shapes to earlier positions.
3. The design is better understood, allowing intuitive ordering.
4. Modeling operations can be grouped better.

7.3.2 Adding or Removing Shapes

Shapes can be added or removed from the solid model as required for design changes. Shapes added will be placed at the highest level in the CSG tree. For example, a shape added to the root solid will be placed at the highest level of the entire CSG tree; a shape added to a construction (node) will be placed at the highest level of the CSG tree of that construction; and a shape added to a leaf node (basic shape) may be added at a lower level.

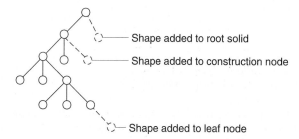

FIGURE 7.3 Shapes (leaf nodes) may be added or removed from the CSG tree to achieve a desired change. Shapes may be added to leafs, intermediate nodes, or the root solid.

The CSG Tree

SMA.7.4 To Reduce CPU Editing Time

A solid model that was built using class 2, 3, or 4 CSG constructions (see Chap. 6) can be edited in an order-of-magnitude less time than if a class 1 CSG construction was used. Refer to Fig. 6.4 for examples of each CSG tree class. The number of associations and boundary intersections that must be recomputed during this process is substantially reduced by using the proper class of CSG tree.

For example, if a solid is built using six equally sized constructions in a class 2 CSG tree, and two constructions must be modified, then over 90 percent of the CPU time required for editing will have been saved versus a class 1 CSG tree (see Fig. 7.4).

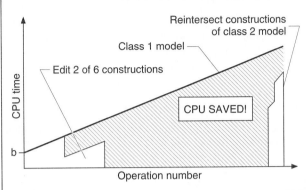

FIGURE 7.4 Editing the solid model of a class 2 vs. a class 1 CSG Tree. Note that over 90 percent of the CPU time required for editing is saved. This is illustrated by the shaded area.

SMA.7.5 Associative Awareness

Shapes that are positioned and/or dimensioned relative to a shape being deleted or moved must be redimensioned prior to removal to avoid corruption. A warning message is usually issued if position associativity exists. If your SM system is associative, a general awareness during all editing procedures is highly recommended.

SMA.7.6 Eliminate Unused Operations

Solids created with boolean operations should be edited or modified to eliminate unused operations and "scabbing-on" other operations. For example, don't increase a hole diameter by subtracting a larger cylinder from a solid without deleting the original subtraction operation.

Brian Moriarty, Senior Engineer
Hamilton Standard Space & Sea Systems,
Windsor Locks, Conn.

7.4 Editing Solid Primitives

Solid primitives are edited by changing their parameter values. (Refer to Chap. 6, Table 6.1, for the parameters of a sample set of primitives.) For example, a cone may be edited by changing its base radius, height, base point, axis, and coordinate system of definition.

Each primitive usually has its own set of parameters accessed via a function called EDIT PRIMITIVE or MODIFY PRIMITIVE.

7.5 Editing Solid Geometric Operations

Solid geometric operations such as Extrude, Sweep, Blend or Transition, and Revolve can be edited by replacing, adding, or removing a cross-section profile curve. Substantial changes in surface definition can occur. (See Chap. 6, Fig. 6.1, for an example of each of these geometric operations.)

7.5.1 Editing Blends

A blend can be edited by reorienting a cross section, changing a cross-section shape, replacing one cross section with another, adding or removing a cross section to the set of cross sections, or by modifying the trajectory curve(s).

7.5.2 Editing Extrusions

A solid extrusion can be edited by reorienting the cross section, changing the cross-section shape, replacing the cross section with another, or changing the linear path length and/or direction.

7.5.3 Editing Revolutions

A solid revolution can be edited by reorienting the cross section, changing the cross-section shape, replacing the cross section with another, or changing the revolution angle and direction of revolution.

7.5.4 Editing Sweeps

A solid sweep can be edited by reorienting the cross section, changing the cross-section shape, replacing the cross section with another, or by replacing or modifying the trajectory curve.

Geometric Operations

SMA.7.7 Affecting Other Shapes

To edit an Extrude, Sweep, Blend, or Revolve, redisplay the original cross-section profile curves. Determine if the cross section or any segment(s) of it are used to define any other shapes. For example, a cross section may be used to extrude in one direction and sweep in the opposite direction. If so, determine if editing or deleting the cross section will affect the other shape as well. The other shape may have its own copy of the cross section, which is not associated to the cross section being edited. Determine if others are to be modified also.

SMA.7.8 NC Considerations

Replacing an arc with a spline in a cross-section profile of an Extrude, Sweep, Blend, or Revolve will alter the surface definition produced. Toolpaths become more difficult to produce. Conversely, replacing a spline with an arc can have a desirable affect.

SMA.7.9 Blend Cross Sections

It is often necessary to change a particular cross section of the blend to attain a new cross-section shape, area, perimeter, etc. The number of segments in the cross section must not change unless all cross sections are modified to use the new value. Some SM systems allow a new cross section to be built and the current cross section then replaced with the new one.

SMA.7.10 Blend Segments

Cross sections are generally added or removed from the original set, or a cross section is reoriented in order to alter the surface between blend segments. The original surface may be too wavy between cross sections, or have inadequate clearance with surrounding components. Remember that blends are approximate and are controlled only at their defining cross sections.

Geometric Operations
(*Continued*)

SMA.7.11 The Blend Trajectory

If the blend trajectory is curvilinear, use arcs instead of splines when possible. It is easier to parametrically control a single radius value than multiple control points of a spline. Also, be careful not to allow the resulting blend to intersect itself while modifying its trajectory.

SMA.7.12 Angle of Revolution

The cross-section profile for a solid revolution should be rotated not more than 360° during its generation. Make sure that any subsequent modifications do not result in an angle that exceeds 360°, which would result in a self-intersecting solid. SM systems may allow this to occur, although the resulting solid is invalid and should be avoided.

Don LaCourse, President
The Solid Modeling ExChange, Algood, Tenn.

Good Practices

SMA.7.13 Use Freeze and Unfreeze[1]

Use the Freeze and Unfreeze options to freeze portions of your drawing. ***Purpose:*** To make sure the selected portions of your drawing are not affected by any changes to the rest of it.

Rationale: SM systems may recalculate only the elements that remain unfrozen. By working with fewer variables, you can reduce the time needed for recalculation. You can also control which portions of a design change without adding constraints (which impact regeneration time).

Rule: You may not be able to move frozen elements, either by dragging with the mouse or as a result of a constraint solving, but you may still be able to delete them.

Nancy Anderson-Semple, Technical Editor
Computervision Corp., Bedford, Mass.

SMA.7.14 Local Surface Deviations

Local modification operators facilitate minor or local modifications of standard geometry. If an operator to produce local deviations in the solid causes imprecise geometry, minimize its usage. The surface may be difficult to dimension and NC. These operators are used to bend, blend, stretch, tweak, warp, push, and offset.

SMA.7.15 Editing Guidelines

Always:

1. Model to accommodate editing.

2. Edit early.

3. Simplify the design.

4. Avoid topology changes late in the product development cycle.

SMA.7.16 Surface Intersection Accuracy

If tightening the surface intersection accuracy value changes the number of vertices or edges of any face or the number of faces, then the original value was inadequate. Determine if additional tightening is required before proceeding.

SMA.7.17 Surface Edges

If one edge of a surface is moved entirely past an opposing edge, an invalid surface will be produced. Software logic may prevent the operation and issue a warning, or the solid may become corrupt upon operation execution.

Good Practices
(Continued)

SMA.7.18   Indicating Changes

When parts are made from an SM database instead of from fabrication drawings, indicating changes can be difficult. Work with the vendors to establish a standardized process for communicating changes. When sending changes to vendors send the following:

1. Complete part file

2. New geometry only

3. Old geometry that went away

4. A control drawing (see Chap. 17)

Howard W. Stolz, Product Designer
Sun Microsystems, Mountain View, Calif.

Reference

1. Adapted from "Parametric Modeling Usage Tips," Revision 4.0.0, Nancy Anderson-Semple, Editor, Computer-vision Corporation, May, 1993.

The perfect tool.

For companies large and small, CATIA helps make designing and building products a snap.

For several years, Snap-on® Tools used a unique, patented handle for its famous line of screwdrivers.

When the patent expired, "look-alikes" seemed to come out of the woodwork to threaten Snap-on's valuable market share.

So they turned to IBM and CATIA.®

Before long, an all-new handle design was created that surpassed even their original in aesthetics, comfort and torque capability.

The beauty of the new ergonomic handle is obvious. The beauty of the handle story is that Snap-on used CATIA to shave *months* off its normal development cycle.

The same way hundreds of small, medium and large companies are doing today for a wide range of products—from cars to washer/dryers to toasters.

Bottom line:

No longer exclusive to only huge manufacturers of the world, thanks to IBM, CATIA can help any size company get a better handle on higher quality and cost efficiency.

For more details on how to reduce cycle time and enjoy CATIA's other long-term benefits, including the advantages of full-scale concurrent engineering, call us:
1 800 395-3339.

IBM

Chapter 8

Parametric/Relational Solid Modeling

Patrick J. Hanratty, Ph.D.
President
Manufacturing and Consulting Services, Inc.

No technical area has been more affected by new concepts in recent years than Solid Modeling (SM). From its introduction by Ian Braid in the late 1970s until 1988, the underlying structure of all SM systems was basically the same. Whether they were true mathematical or faceted representations, the procedures which were applied to build and create complex geometric entities used the same mathematical approach. In 1988, the first general *dimension-driven* SM system made its appearance. While we use the term *dimension-driven* today, these were originally identified as *parametric solids*.

The purpose of this chapter is to illustrate the advantages that can accrue to a designer using an SM system which has a parametric structure superimposed over it. *Parametric structure* is a generic phrase which implies that the SM system does not only make use of variables and constraints in its generation and modification, but that it is also governed by both mathematical and topological relationships.

While the term *relational structure* is a more accurate description of what will be described, convention and usage have dictated the use of the phrase *parametric structure*. Our compromise will be the use of *parametric/relational* (P/R) to cover the categories of dimension-driven, parametric, relational, feature-based, and variational SM, albeit we must recognize that a strict definition of each term would show that they are not synonyms.

It is suggested that the definition of the following terms be reviewed in the Glossary at the back of this handbook before continuing. For those new to the concepts of parametric/relational modeling, doing so will provide a foundation of knowledge on which to continue.

Algebraic function

Assembly

Boolean operations

Boundary representation (B-Rep)

Constructive solid geometry (CSG)

Dimension-driven

Dimensionally constrained

Entity

Features

Feature-based modeling

Mathematical rectification

Parameter

Part

Rectification

Relational rectification

Sculptured solid

Select

Subassembly

Topological rectification

Transcendental function

Variational engine

8.1 The History of Parametrics in Solid Modeling

The use of constraints to define geometry first appeared in 1963 in early work by Sutherland.[1] Sutherland made use of constraints as a design aid in the creation of parts, but did not use geometric constraints for definition and modification of part geometry. Geometric constraints for definition and modification of part geometry first appeared in 1977 when Requicha[2] used directive graphs to represent the relationship between dimensions and geometry. The first use of directed graphs to define and modify geometry in an interactive CAD system occurred in 1978 by Gopin.[3] This CAD system restricted the part geometries to rectilinear (i.e., straight line) segments and dimensions.

Almost concurrent with Gopin, Hillyard and Braid[4,5] showed that small variations in geometry could be related to variations in dimensions by a rigidity matrix. In 1980, Light and Gossard[6,7] showed that generalized dimensional constraints could be used to modify geometry through large shape variations and that geometric properties could be used to constrain geometry. Most of the aforementioned work was done at the Massachusetts Institute of Technology (MIT), University of Rochester, and the University of Cambridge in England. Credit should be given to Computervision Corporation (Bedford, Massachusetts)[8] for supporting a significant amount of the work at MIT in the early 1980s in variational systems.

In the late 1980s, the term *parametric solid modeling* was applied to a product from Parametric Technology Corporation (PTC) (Lowell, Massachusetts),[9] which produced the first commercial example of what we call today *parametric/relational* (or dimension-driven) SM. By January 1994, there were at least seven significant dimension-driven and/or variational SM systems in the marketplace, with more appearing every few months. This is a direct result of the impact that the PTC products had on the CAD/CAM marketplace. It is doubtful that any robust CAD or CAM system will be produced from this time forward which does not contain robust parametric/relational capabilities.

8.2 Parametric/Relational versus Variational Solid Modeling

In comparing P/R SM with variational SM we must be careful to recognize two sets of definitions for P/R SM, one for systems which existed prior to 1992 and those which were developed subsequent to this date.

Pre-1992 P/R SM systems were described by sets of decoupled equations which were solved sequentially. This meant that the P/R functionality depended entirely upon the order in which dimensions and constraints were created. Post-1992 P/R SM systems incorporate the variational capability of processing nonsequential dimensions and constraints. This allows dimensions and constraints to be applied in any order and to be modified and analyzed in any order. It also allows for the analysis and updating of a small segment of a model when changes have been made in that segment only. The result of this isolated analysis provides a speed-up in regeneration which can, in extreme instances, be over 100 times faster than that available from pre-1992 P/R SM systems.

These post-1992 modelers incorporate not only the ability to determine the positions of geometric elements specified by predefined combinations of geometric constraints, but also have equation solvers which allow a set of engineering equations to be used to set the value of dimensions, based on either engineering parameters or values of other dimensions. In addition, these solvers take into consideration conditions of parallelism, perpendicularity, colinearity, concentricity, etc. Since this capability corresponds to the definition of a variational SM system, the post-1992 P/R SM systems should be considered a subset of a full variational modeler.

The major difference between P/R and variational SM systems is that a robust variational SM system provides an essentially unlimited number of engineering relationships to be associated with the solution of the positioning and relational equations. These engineering relationships and constraints, such as area, volume, analysis of degrees of freedom, etc., are what gives a variational modeler its power and richness.

The comparison would not be complete without recognizing that the number of designers who could effectively use a variational SM system is a small percent of those who use P/R (dimension-driven) SM systems. This is because more emphasis is placed on form than on function in consumer products. For example, a vacuum cleaner must be able to move a certain amount of air in order to be effective. Once the motor for controlling air volume has been designed (the *function*) the major design process (how it is held, moved, stored, etc., that is, the *form*) commences.

8.3 Anatomy of a Parametric/Relational Solid Modeling System

Classical P/R SM systems are composed of five major components. These are:

1. The sketcher
2. The SM system
3. The dimensional constraint engine (DCE) (also called *variational engine* and *parametric engine*)
4. The feature manager
5. The assembly manager

Editor's Note: Many of these concerns are eliminated in newer systems.

Understanding History in Sequential Parametric Systems[10]

SMA.8.1 History Reflects Intent

Parametric modeling captures the operations you use to build a product. The captured operations, called *parametric history,* reflect your design intent (any geometric relationships you establish) and strictly adhere to that intent as sizes of the design change.

Importance: During the life cycle of a design, the product matures and design intent can change. As a result, you may have to redesign portions of the product. You can use many techniques to incorporate flexibility into the parametric history of a model, such as with equational constraints, so that it is easy to handle certain design-intent changes.

SMA.8.2 Order Is Important

History is time-dependent. *Importance:* Parametric modelers record operations in a chronological order and maintain any relationships you define with displayed parameters. Because operations are order-dependent, they are aware of a model's state only at the time you insert them. Operations do not know about any future operations you may enter. When regenerating a model, the system may not conduct an operation if either of the following occur:

1. A previous operation negates it. (*Example:* If you change the parameter of a solid so that it no longer intersects with any other entities, any boolean operations in which the solid is an operand will fail.)

2. It requires another operation before it, but you placed the needed operation after it.

SMA.8.3 Analyze Design First

Parameters drive a model, so it is important to plan ahead. Analyze the design and then determine the structure of a part. *Importance:* Before you begin to create a model, take the time to think about how your design is likely to change. The system uses the command options and construction constraints you enter to regenerate the model. The parameters generated by each command drive the model. You need to make sure parameters exist or that you can write equations that will enable you to make anticipated changes.

SMA.8.4 Verify History Periodically

As you build a model and relationships get more complex, take the time to periodically review dependencies. *Purpose:* Using these options can show which entities are dependent on a selected command or operation so that you can verify history independence.

Example: If you create an entity that contains more than one operation of the same name, you may be able to display the history number of each operation. You can then be sure you are selecting the desired operation for something, such as the removal of a hole.

(Continued)

Understanding History in Sequential Parametric Systems[10]
(Continued)

SMA.8.5 Modifying Events

You can typically make two kinds of parametric changes:

1. You can remove an operation from the parametric history of a model.

2. You can change the value of a parameter to alter such things as the size, shape, and location of an entity.

Depending on the SM system, you may not, however, be able to modify a parametric event. ***Example:*** You may not be able to create a general radius fillet having four radius values and later add two more radius values.

Possible work-around: If you know you may need to add radius values, create that fillet with extra but equal values. Later in the design process, you can change parameters as required or use constraints to build relationships between the values.

Nancy Anderson-Semple, Technical Editor
Computervision Corp., Bedford, Mass.

8.3.1 The Sketcher

The sketcher is one of three common ways in which geometry (profiles and features) are supplied to a P/R SM system. The other two ways are geometry which is created using standard CAD and SM construction techniques and geometry which is imported from external design systems.

The original intent of a sketcher was to allow a designer or engineer to have the same freedom for conceptualizing as when sketching on a coffee shop napkin. The sketchers that exist in all major P/R SM systems today are as far from that original concept as an automobile is from a skateboard.

Sketchers today are another form of entering planar (or, in some of the more sophisticated systems, 3D) preliminary designs. Since most P/R SM systems allow sketching with a grid, it is possible for a "sketch" to have the same dimensional accuracy that a figure constructed in any other part of the SM system would have.

Sketching typically provides for the entry of line, arc, and (in some cases) spline data. Most P/R SM systems allow for lines to be constrained under a designer's control. Thus, it is possible to constrain all lines to the closest 45.0° angle, or the closest 10.0°, or 1.0° angle, etc.

Also, most sketchers today incorporate implication engines which examine the geometry as it is sketched, and if it meets certain implications, assigns attributes to the geometry. For example, if two lines are approximately parallel, then as a first guess, the sketcher will supply the constraint "parallel" to these lines. If two arcs have approximately the same radius, then most sketchers will imply that the radii are meant to be equal.

A sketch is typically used to generate the profile for either an axial or a rotational sweep, for user-defined features which can be generated from an axial or rotational sweep, or for *hard-coded* features. *Hard-coded* or *canned* refers to features which are selected from a menu (choice list), icon, or other mechanism for identifying a predetermined geometric configuration, the methods for controlling its placement, and the types of variables it can contain. Sketches are ordinarily controlled by modals. These allow the designer to influence the implication engine.

Sketch types include, but are not limited to:

1. Chain (i.e., "heel and toe")
2. Centerline
3. Axis-symmetric

Examples of sketch modals are:

1. Snap angle
2. Sketch mode
   a. Linear
   b. Nonlinear
3. Fillet mode
   a. Automatic between linear sketch curves
   b. No fillets between linear sketch curves

4. Dynamic notch

5. Dynamic round

    a. Semicircular

    b. Free angle

6. Sketch closure

    a. Direct to start point

    b. Horizontal, then vertical to start point

    c. Vertical, then horizontal to start point

    d. Direct to start point with fillet between first and last curves

Figure 8.1 illustrates some of the more common chain sketch modes and the results of varying control modals during the sketching process.

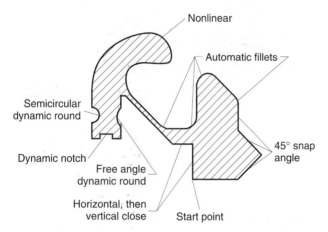

FIGURE 8.1 Common chain sketch modes. Sketching was originally designed to represent free-hand drawing. By using a computer's ability to turn on and off various control modals, it is possible to generate sketches that are still aesthetic and represent, very closely, the object which is being designed. Control modals are represented here by snap angle, automatic fillets, linear and nonlinear sketching, dynamic notches, and the types of closure to get back to the start point. *(Courtesy of Manufacturing and Consulting Services, Inc.)*

8.3.2 The Solid Modeling System

The solid modeler is the area in which planar profiles and 3D curves are turned into solid objects by axial or rotational sweeps, general surface enclosures, or creation of analytic solids (cubes, spheroids, cones, toroids, right-circular cylinders, etc.). While the objective of all P/R SM systems is to generate solid models, that fact is often obscured by the sketcher, relational edit, feature generation, and assembly capabilities. All of these components would be useless without a mechanism for creating the actual solid.

The most common ways of generating a solid are by either an axial or rotational sweep. However, robust P/R SM systems include a significant number of additional ways to produce solids (see Chap. 6). These include:

1. Curve-driven solids (see Fig. 8.2)

2. General surface enclosure (GSE) (see color insert, Fig. 8.3)

3. Analytic solids or *primitives* (see Fig. 8.4)

4. Blended solids, in which profiles are blended together either as straight blends (see Fig. 8.5*a*), as smooth blends (see Fig. 8.5*b*) or as rotated blends (see Fig. 8.5*c*).

5. Surface-to-surface blends (see Fig. 8.6)

6. Shell produced from existing solids (see Fig. 8.7)

Each P/R SM system has special cases for producing a solid model. However, the axial and rotational sweep as well as boolean operations which are applied to the results of these sweeps produce a large percentage of the solids in any given system. (Refer to Chap. 6 for specific modeling strategies.)

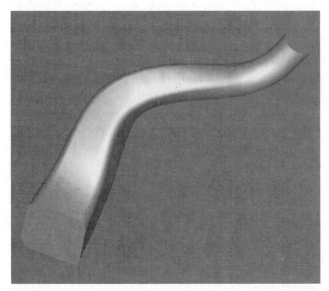

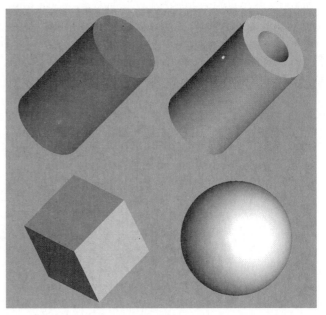

FIGURE 8.2 Example of a curve-driven solid. This curve-driven solid was generated by driving the rectangular closed profile with filleted corners along a spline which exists from the center of the profile to the center of the circle at the opposite end. The transition was made from rectangular to circular shape in the blending process. The reason it is called "curve-driven" is because the sweep that takes place follows a curve (in this case a 3D spline) through space while transitioning from one shape to another. *(Courtesy of Manufacturing and Consulting Services, Inc.)*

FIGURE 8.4 Example of analytic solids or primitives. This illustrates the more common analytic solids. They are a right-circular cylinder, a right-circular pipe, cube, and spheroid. *(Courtesy of Manufacturing and Consulting Services, Inc.)*

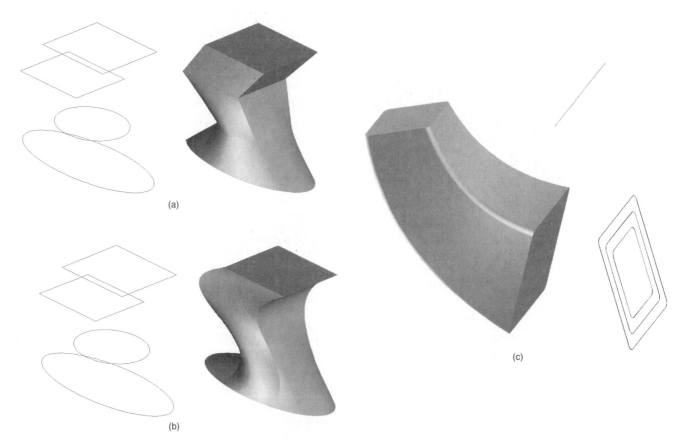

(a)

(b)

(c)

FIGURE 8.5 Three categories of blended solids. (*a*) Curves which are connected by ruled surfaces and can be discontinuous from one solid segment to the next, known as *straight blends;* (*b*) smooth blends which are continuous across each of the solid segments defined by each set of curves; (*c*) rotational blends in which each set of curves of a family of curve sets is rotated about an axis a different number of degrees and the transitions between these rotated curve sets are blended so as to be continuous from one curve set to the next. *(Courtesy of Manufacturing and Consulting Services, Inc.)*

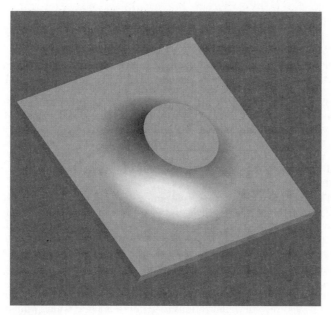

FIGURE 8.6 Example of surface-to-surface blend. The surface-to-surface blend effectively results in a fillet blend from two coplanar surfaces separated by a distance. *(Courtesy of Manufacturing and Consulting Services, Inc.)*

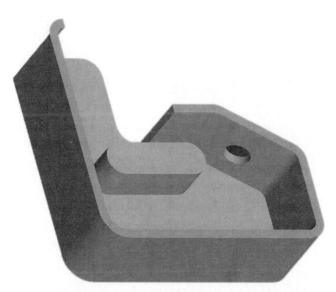

FIGURE 8.7 Example of solid shell. This is an example of a solid which has been shelled by having its top and four selected faces removed, giving a constant shell thickness to the remaining material. Most P/R SM systems allow for the shell thickness to vary as well as being constant. *(Courtesy of Manufacturing and Consulting Services, Inc.)*

8.3.3 The Dimensional Constraint Engine (DCE)

The DCE (also called *variational engine* and *parametric engine*) provides for the modification of dimensions (variables) associated with the model and the regeneration of the model after variables have been changed. The DCE is the P/R segment which provides for the following:

1. The establishment and modification of dimensions
2. The establishment and modification of topological relationships between geometric entities (a topological relationship is used here to mean the way geometry is arranged relative to other geometry)
3. The creation and modification of mathematical relationships in which one entity is constrained by arithmetic values associated with parameters of one or more other entities

The DCE is the heart of a P/R SM system and often contains most of the functionality of a "variational" engine. (See Sec. 8.2 for a discussion on the distinction between a DCE and variational engine.) The DCE is a software component which manipulates geometric designs to satisfy given dimensions and topological constraints. When geometry is changed, either directly or by changing an associated dimension, it is the function of the DCE to analyze the impact of that change on other geometry in the design and to modify the geometry corresponding to the constraints and relations which have been established for that design.

The DCE also determines whether a particular design is (1) underdimensioned, (2) dimensioned correctly, or (3) overdimensioned. In the event that a design is underdimensioned, a typical DCE flags the geometry which is not dimensioned adequately so that the designer can add the dimensions necessary to make a "correctly" dimensioned part. Regardless of the dimensional state of a design, a proper DCE should operate for each of these situations.

DCEs are typically concerned with evaluating geometry in a 2D subspace of 3D. They typically allow points, lines, circles, conics, and splines as the representative geometry, along with geometric constraints such as concentric, parallel, perpendicular, tangent, and coincident. A significant amount of work is currently under way in several organizations to generate a DCE which will handle full three-dimensional geometry. The discussions of this chapter assume that the DCE is evaluating a two-dimensional subspace of a 3D world.

Five factors determine the usefulness of a DCE (a discussion of each follows):

1. Dimension types recognized
2. Degree of geometric constraints
3. Freedom to postpone dimensioning
4. External compatability
5. Configuration of variables

Dimension Types Recognized

This refers to the number and type of dimensions supported by the DCE. Every major design and/or manufacturing organization adheres to a drafting standard. While specific standards vary throughout the world, there is usually one significant standard within a particular country. It is important that geographically dependent dimensioning standards be acceptable to the DCE. If the DCE forces a particular mode or type of dimensioning which is inconsistent with the standard used by the industry in which it is operational, that particular DCE is of academic and not industrial value.

If varying types of dimensions are accepted by the DCE, they should include, but not be limited to:

1. Angle
2. Baseline
3. Diameter
4. Horizontal
5. Ordinate
6. Parallel
7. Parallel with reference line
8. Radius
9. Thickness
10. Vertical
11. Coupled with true position tolerancing

Degree of Geometric Constraints

This refers to the number and type of geometric constraints supported by the DCE. A robust DCE should provide support for, but not be limited to:

1. Coincident arcs
2. Concentric arcs
3. Colinear endpoints
4. Colinear lines
5. Fixed (datum)
6. Horizontal
7. Vertical
8. Normal
9. Parallel
10. Points on a curve
11. Tangent

Freedom to Postpone Dimensioning

This refers to the freedom available to postpone actual dimensioning until late in the design process. Early DCE implementations forced designs to be completely dimensioned before any variations could be attempted. This is contrary to the way in which designers/engineers ordinarily work and puts unreasonable constraints and limitations on the design process. Newer DCE implementations allow for any level of dimensioning to be evaluated and changes made which are consistent with the scope of the actual dimensions provided.

External Compatibility

This refers to the ability of the DCE to make use of external files from other systems. This includes IGES files, files from the standard geometry and dimensioning modules of the system in use, or sketched files. The source of geometry and dimensions should be unimportant to the other segments of the P/R system; that is, the solids module should not care where or how the curves used in solid generation were created, the relational engine should not care how or where the dimensions were created, etc.

Some DCEs provide software "scanning" of existing dimensions so that "old" designs and designs from other systems can be utilized.

Configuration of Variables

This refers to the symbolic name associated with the value for each dimension. Obviously a variable defined as a number such as

```
LEN123=2.5
```

allows for simultaneous changes of all instances of LEN123, but otherwise provides limited design choices in that it has no relationship to other dimensions.

Allowing for the use of parameters associated with otherwise unrelated geometry provides for a richer design environment. In the following example LEN123 equals one-half the sum of curve lengths LEN18 and LEN23 minus the radius RAD291.

```
LEN123=0.5*(LEN18+LEN23)-RAD291
```

A complete set of transcendental functions (any function which is not algebraic, such as $y = \sin x$) coupled with all parameters associated with each piece of geometry, and the operations available in most programming languages, provides maximum design capability.

In the following example, the start angle of ARC29 is equal to the square root of the start slope of curve321 times the end slope of curve42, plus the tangent of the radius of ARC28 divided by the radius of ARC819, plus twice the start angle of ARC21. Thus the start angle of ARC29 is a function of five other geometric entities.

```
GOANG29=SQRT(GOSL321*ENDSL42)+TAN(RAD28/RAD819)+2.0*GOANG21
```

Constraints

SMA.8.6   Constraint Assumptions

Assumed constraints are fine as long as the system allows the designer to override all implications in a simple manner. For example, if a sketch is to be constrained to within 10.0° increments, and a line sketched at 4.5° is made horizontal, this is acceptable. However, if that line is forced horizontal throughout the design process, without an easy mechanism of eventually defining the line to be canted 5.0°, then capability is lacking in the sketcher.

SMA.8.7   Constrained or Not Constrained

Be aware that simple parts can be misleading. If a part is sufficiently complex, it is not always obvious what is and is not constrained. If the system will not allow over- or underconstrained situations, it can become very frustrating to try to determine what has to be changed. This situation is highly system-dependent.

SMA.8.8   Constraint Needs

Look for these constraint capabilities in a P/R SM system:

1. Incorrect constraints are automatically flagged in a fully constrained approach.

2. The ability to undo or abort constraint operations is allowed.

3. Over- or underconstrained situations are temporarily allowed.

4. If autoconstrained, the system allows the designer to choose whether the autoconstraints apply to all or part of the model.

R. Herschel Redd, Senior Marketing Support Representative
IBM Corp., Dallas, Tex.

8.3.4   The Feature Manager

The feature manager provides for the addition of pockets, slots, holes, bosses, ribs, etc., and user-defined features to any face or faces of a model. The functionality which contributes to the dramatic increase in performance of a feature-based P/R SM system over a traditional CSG/B-Rep hybrid SM system is the intelligence which is imparted by features. A necessity in any feature-based P/R SM system is a user-defined feature. This allows the geometric and topological characteristics of the feature to be totally defined by the designer and then applied to existing solids.

Many P/R SM systems also provide a full selection of default (hard-coded) features including, but not limited to:

1. Constant offset pockets

2. Circular and rectangular arrays of holes

3. Free slots

    a. Straight or two-point slots

    b. Three-point T and L slots

    c. Four-point U slots

    d. Circular slots

    e. Slots parallel to a boundary

4. Necks or protrusions

5. Flanges

Figure 8.8 illustrates many common features in the view in which they are sketched (i.e., the "top" of the feature). Obviously, anything which can take away material (e.g., a slot, a pocket, a hole) can also be considered a boss if material is added rather than removed; thus, circular slots become circular ribs, pockets become bosses, holes become bosses, etc.

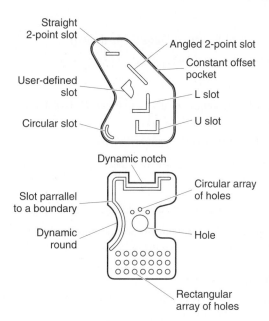

Straight 2-point slot

Angled 2-point slot

Constant offset pocket

User-defined slot

L slot

Circular slot

U slot

Dynamic notch

Slot parrallel to a boundary

Circular array of holes

Dynamic round

Hole

Rectangular array of holes

FIGURE 8.8 Example of common "hardcoded" features. In many cases, the top view of features are sketched. Features which remove material (slots, pockets, holes, etc.), can also be considered bosses if material is added rather than removed. *(Courtesy of Manufacturing and Consulting Services, Inc.)*

Traditional SM systems that are not feature-based or P/R force designers to use CSG boolean operators (see Fig. 8.9 and Chap. 6) in order to create complex objects from simple components. P/R SM systems use not only CSG boolean operators, but all of the geometry associated with embedded features as well. Thus a hole, a slot, a groove, and a pocket are recognized for what they are and do not require the creation of additional geometry which is subtracted (using boolean operations) from the base geometry. While some of the earlier P/R systems have the boolean operations embedded in the feature codes, most modern (post-1991) P/R systems use entirely different mathematics, leveraging off of the knowledge inherent in features, to generate the required geometry. This "feature-driven" philosophy both speeds the design process and simplifies the underlying database.

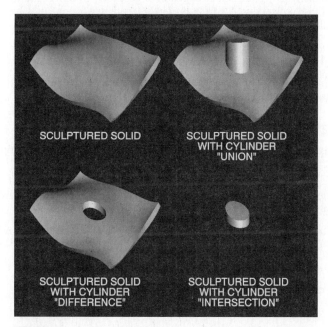

SCULPTURED SOLID

SCULPTURED SOLID WITH CYLINDER "UNION"

SCULPTURED SOLID WITH CYLINDER "DIFFERENCE"

SCULPTURED SOLID WITH CYLINDER "INTERSECTION"

FIGURE 8.9 Traditional CSG boolean operators. Traditional SM systems require CSG boolean operations to produce features such as holes, slots, grooves, and pockets. P/R SM systems embed feature-based modeling techniques. *(Courtesy of Manufacturing and Consulting Services, Inc.)*

Features

SMA.8.9 Advantages of Feature-Based Modeling

Designing with features provides a number of advantages.

You can:

1. Insert intelligent parametric geometry into a model without having to create intermediate construction geometry.

2. Associate a variety of information to portions of a model.

3. Create features with attributes unique to your specific design requirements.

Additional advantages:

4. Conventional CSG boolean operations which are time-consuming are not required.

5. Embedded feature characteristics are conveyed more intelligently to manufacturing applications such as NC. Holes are holes, pockets are pockets, etc., instead of simply raw surface geometry.

SMA.8.10 Relocating Features

Although highly productive, the P/R intelligence of feature definitions and their subsequent geometric locations places additional burden on the designer in the form of forethought and planning. Options for relocating features are limited to those that would result in equal topology.

Example: Relocating a boss feature on a flat surface close to an edge may not be possible. If the boss has a base radius which intersects the edge radius, the existing topology is violated.

Don LaCourse, President
The Solid Modeling ExChange, Algood, Tenn.

SMA.8.11 A Robust Feature-Based SM System

1. Supports many viewpoints on a collection of geometry as well as multiple geometric representations of those collections. Also, the preferred geometry for one may be free-form surfaces while for another it may be B-Rep solids.

2. Detects when a feature's intent has been violated. For example, when a blind hole is changed to a through-hole by a transaction subsequent to its insertion, the designer is notified of the change in design intent.

3. Supports feature suppression.

SMA.8.12 With User-Defined Features

User-defined features are of utmost importance. With a user-defined feature, designers can:

1. Name a feature.

2. Associate geometric representations and specify ranges of values, deriving functions, and geometric, algebraic, and positional constraints for those representations.

3. Associate nongeometric attributes and specify ranges of values, deriving functions, and constraints for those attributes.

4. Modify old features to form new ones.

5. Make a feature as a composition of other features.

6. Make a feature which inherits attributes from more than one feature.

Those familiar with the object-oriented paradigm and conceptual clustering techniques will see many similarities to this modeling approach.

Mark J. Silvestri
Life Cycle Solutions, Inc., Avon, Mass.

8.3.5   The Assembly Manager

The assembly manager provides for the creation of subassemblies from piece-parts and the creation of assemblies from piece-parts and/or subassemblies. The assembly manager also controls the regeneration of assemblies and subassemblies when changes have been made to individual piece-parts. In addition, it controls the modification of the way in which assemblies are put together. Last, assembly management provides for the explosion of assemblies into their component piece-parts and subassemblies.

During the design phase, adequate planning often identifies those components which can or should be used as subassemblies based on design function or the manufacturing processes required.

There are two distinct ways of placing parts when creating a subassembly or assembly: (1) relative placement and (2) boolean placement. Each is discussed here, along with gathering operations for placing and relating parts in an assembly or subassembly. (See Chap. 11 for more on solid modeling for assembly.)

Relative Placement

In this method parts are placed relative to each another. This placement can be thought of as "loosely gluing" the parts to form a unit. The idea is that at some point in the future it would be desirable to explode or unrelate the assembly back into individual parts. Figure 8.10 illustrates this method.

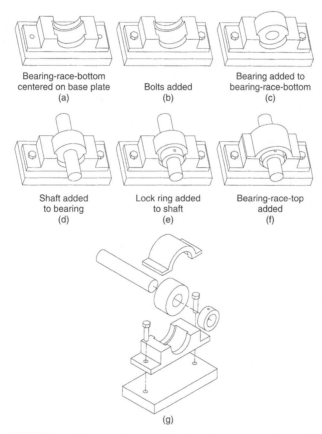

FIGURE 8.10   Example of bearing assembly model built up from individual piece-parts. (*a*) Bearing-race-bottom centered on the base plate; (*b*) bolts added; (*c*) bearing added to the bearing-race-bottom; (*d*) shaft added to the bearing; (*e*) lock ring added to the shaft; (*f*) bearing-race-top added to the bearing-race-bottom; (*g*) assembly exploded to original parts. (*Courtesy of Manufacturing and Consulting Services, Inc.*)

Boolean Placement

This method utilizes boolean operations. The result is the formation of a new single part, typically referred to as a *constructive solid geometry* (CSG, see Chap. 4) solid combined from two or more parts. The CSG solid usually cannot be exploded or unrelated easily. The best way to see the differences between boolean placement and relative placement is to compare Fig. 8.11 to Fig. 8.10. Notice how the shaft, bearing, and lock ring are handled in each method.

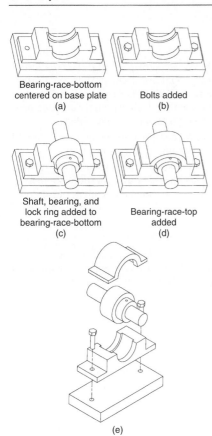

Bearing-race-bottom
centered on base plate
(a)

Bolts added
(b)

Shaft, bearing, and
lock ring added to
bearing-race-bottom
(c)

Bearing-race-top
added
(d)

(e)

FIGURE 8.11 Example of bearing assembly model using both individual piece-parts and CSG solids. (*a*) Bearing-race-bottom centered on the base plate; (*b*) bolts added; (*c*) bearing, shaft, and lock ring added to the bearing-race-bottom. These three parts were previously combined with Boolean placement techniques. (*d*) Bearing-race-top added to the bearing-race-bottom; (*e*) assembly exploded to original parts. Note that bearing, shaft, and lock ring remain combined. (*Courtesy of Manufacturing and Consulting Services, Inc.*)

Gathering Operations

Subassemblies and assemblies are created by the use of "gathering" operations. These operations define and retain relationships among parts. Gathering operations include, but are not limited to:

1. Align axes
   a. Match centers
   b. End to end
   c. Offset from end
   d. Normal to face-centered on face
   e. Normal to face-centered on normal point
   f. Normal to face-centered on face-offset
   g. Normal to face-centered on normal point-offset
2. Align corners
   a. Both flush
   b. Offset first
   c. Offset second
   d. Offset both
3. Align definition coordinate system (DCS)
4. Align edges
   a. Flush
   b. Offset
5. Align faces
   a. Align faces
   b. Center aligned faces
   c. Offset face from a face

6. Align features
   a. Centered
   b. Align an edge
7. Logical union (addition, A + B)
8. Logical difference (subtraction, A − B)
9. Logical intersection (both A and B)

8.4 Dimension-Driven Editing

In a P/R SM system, dimensions are typically assigned a symbolic variable name at one of three times: (1) when they are created, (2) when they are automatically scanned by the system, or (3) when they are chosen for use with a profile. In most systems the variable name can be generated by the system or supplied by the designer, and it is usually displayed below or near the dimension value.

There are three classes of edits that can be performed on dimensions or variables. These are (1) value, (2) reference, and (3) appearance editing. Each is discussed in the following sections.

8.4.1 Value Editing

The first and most obvious way to change the value of a dimension is to select it and enter a new value. A second method is to select the name of a part or feature, or to select one of its profile curves. When this is done, many systems display a list of the pertinent variables and dimensions for that item, allowing the designer to enter one or more new values (see Fig. 8.20).

A third method for editing a dimension value is to key in the symbolic variable name followed by an expression that establishes the relationship between this dimension and other dimensions or variables. If a dimension is assigned an expression, the expression is usually displayed in place of the dimension name.

8.4.2 Reference Editing

Reference editing refers to the ability to toggle the reference status of a dimension. This gives the designer an option of displaying a dimension on-screen without having it affect the operation of the dimensional constraint engine (DCE).

Normally, a dimension is active and considered in all relevant relational operations. But if the dimension status is switched to reference, it is displayed but otherwise ignored. This can be useful, for example, if a design is overdimensioned. Changing one or more dimensions from active to reference allows the designer to eliminate the overdimensioning while still being able to view the information in those dimensions.

8.4.3 Appearance Editing

The first and most obvious method of appearance editing is changing a dimension's location. This is sometimes necessary after a dimensional change to a model. P/R SM systems do position dimensions automatically, but the ability to adjust the position manually allows the designer to improve both the legibility and the aesthetics of the annotated design. There are other methods of appearance editing which include:

Shared Dimensions

This method allows a dimension to be shared by more than one location in the design. This reduces clutter on the display while constraining the geometry just as if the extra dimensions were there.

Selective Viewing

Controls over the centering of dimension text and the selective display of portions of the dimension are also available. At times, a designer needs to see only the value of a dimension, but not its symbolic name, or vice versa. The ability to selectively blank the unwanted part of the dimension makes a P/R SM system friendly and easy to work with.

Similarly, the ability to blank and unblank complete dimensions is essential. A designer should be allowed to do this for both individual and groups of dimensions. These groups can be based on such criteria as their association with a solid, or with a profile, or their presence on a given logical level (layer) or range of logical levels within the model file.

8.5 Bidirectional Associativity

Associative dimensioning implies that a dimension is automatically updated when the geometry it is dimensioning changes. Dimension-driven implies the ability to change a dimension and have all affected geometry change. Bidirectional associativity implies that both update methods are available.

Associativity

SMA.8.13   Clarifying Associative Dimensioning

With associative dimensioning, a dimension is associated with geometry such that if the geometry is changed, the dimension is updated automatically. An example would be a dimension that changed to reflect that a line had been stretched. This capability does not change the length of the line if the dimension is changed. A P/R SM system adds this last step, where changes to dimensions or parameters drive geometry changes.

SMA.8.14   Tracking Associativity

While associativity can be a very powerful tool when used properly, it could be disastrous if not implemented properly. A master model that is used in multiple assemblies cannot be changed without consideration of each instance of its use. Each change to a model should be tracked. One cannot have an effective engineering system if changes can be propagated without each person who uses the data being aware that changes have been made. An integrated tracking system should allow those affected by a change to approve or deny it.

R. Herschel Redd, Senior Marketing Support Representative
IBM Corp., Dallas, Tex.

8.6 Example Parametric/Relational Design Process

Perhaps the best way to conclude our chapter is to review step by step an example P/R design process. Our example has 12 steps, beginning with a sketch and ending with a final part which captures design intent during the process. Each step is illustrated for clarity. This example was chosen to illustrate the process and capability of a P/R SM system. Actual design applications will, of course, vary in complexity.

Using Parameters[10]

SMA.8.15   Determine Range of Acceptable Values

At critical stages in the modeling of a design, you should stop and determine what the range of values will be for a given parameter or combination of parameters in order for the model to regenerate successfully. If needed, you should build constraint equations to ensure that the model will keep regenerating in the future.

Purpose: To avoid any regeneration failures.

(Continued)

Using Parameters[10]
(Continued)

Rationale: You must be aware of any limitations that could be imposed on your model in the future. For example, height, width, and radius values may change. By determining if a range of parameter values is unacceptable, you can choose an alternate modeling technique that will produce an acceptable value so that the model will regenerate.

SMA.8.16 Use Parameters Wisely

Parameters drive your model. Like layers, the management of parameters is very important early on in the design process to minimize the complexity of your design. When creating them, keep the following in mind:

1. Choose parameter values according to the extents of your part, which are impossible to change.

2. Take the time to structure your parameters. Use layers, make those parameters not being used invisible, and place all parameters in a reasonable position.

3. Minimize the number of parameters by referencing existing geometry or using constraints, making sure that you do not hinder any future flexibility to make modifications.

4. Think about how you want your model to work rather than how you want a production drawing to look. The parameters needed may coincide, but they may not. For example, you may want to create a line in parametrics using parameters for angle and length because they are subject to change when modeling. Although these parameters may not be needed in a production drawing, they are what you need to control the entity parametrically.

Nancy Anderson-Semple, Technical Editor
Computervision Corp., Bedford, Mass.

Step 1: Sketching and Dimensioning

This step illustrates a part profile after it has been relationally dimensioned but prior to being relationally rectified (see Fig. 8.12). Note that the right vertical dimension, VD4, is a function of the length of the horizontal entity, HD2. HD10 is equal to HD6; thus, HD6 is equal to HD10, meaning that either variable can change and the other one will have the corresponding change. Likewise, VD11 is equal to VD8, and the converse is also true. All of the fillet radii are a function of RD3 and thus change whenever RD3 changes. Note there is no dimension on the canted line. This has been intentionally left free to pivot, or rotate, so that changes can be made to either side of the line which change the shape of the design significantly. The actual value of the dimensions shown are odd-looking because the original profile was sketched as opposed to having been constructed.

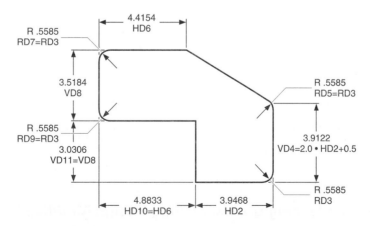

ACTIVE PIECE–PART: PIECE • PART • 1

FIGURE 8.12 Example parametric/relational design process, step 1—sketching and dimensioning. *(Courtesy of Manufacturing and Consulting Services, Inc.)*

Step 2: The Dimensional Constraint Engine

This step (see Fig. 8.13) shows the same profile after it has been processed by a dimensional constraint engine (DCE). The constraints which force all radii to be equal and which force certain lines to be equal in length to others have been satisfied.

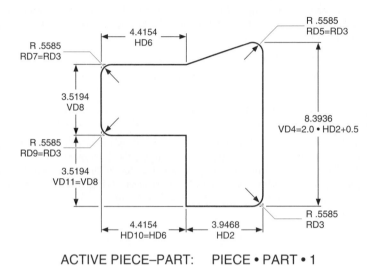

ACTIVE PIECE–PART: PIECE • PART • 1

FIGURE 8.13   Example parametric/relational design process, step 2—the dimensional constraint engine. *(Courtesy of Manufacturing and Consulting Services, Inc.)*

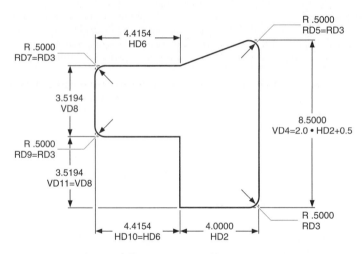

ACTIVE PIECE–PART: PIECE • PART • 1

FIGURE 8.14   Example parametric/relational design process, step 3—cleaning up and making design modifications. *(Courtesy of Manufacturing and Consulting Services, Inc.)*

Step 3: Cleaning Up and Making Design Modifications

This step (see Fig. 8.14) shows the same profile after HD2 has been "cleaned up" (i.e., a true design value has been placed on it) and the corresponding change has taken place in VD4. Also, RD3 has been modified and all corresponding radii updated.

Step 4: Making Design Modifications

We now see what dramatic results can be obtained by making simple changes (see Fig. 8.15). RD3 was first changed to 0.5 and is reflected by the modified radii throughout, and VD8 was changed from a 3.5194 to 5.0. Note that since VD8 was changed, VD11 also had to change and became a 5.0, which means the total dimension on the left side of the figure is now 10.0. Also note that the canted line has gone from a positive slope to a negative slope.

The power of a P/R SM system is that very small changes can be made to achieve very large modifications in the model.

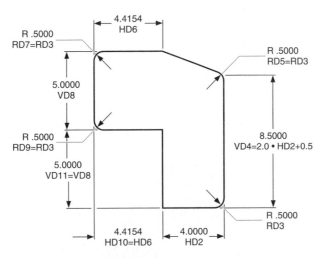

ACTIVE PIECE–PART: PIECE • PART • 1

FIGURE 8.15   Example parametric/relational design process, step 4—making design modifications. *(Courtesy of Manufacturing and Consulting Services, Inc.)*

Step 5: More Design Modifications and Preparations

This step (see Fig. 8.16) shows one additional modification wherein HD6, the top horizontal dimension, is changed to 4.5. This is in preparation for the next phase of the design.

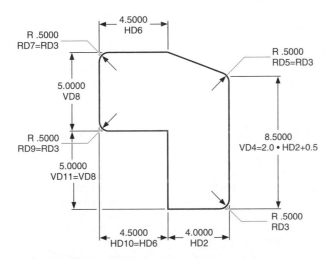

ACTIVE PIECE–PART: PIECE • PART • 1

FIGURE 8.16   Example parametric/relational design process, step 5—more design modifications and preparations. *(Courtesy of Manufacturing and Consulting Services, Inc.)*

Step 6: Creating the Base Solid

This step (see Fig. 8.17) shows the result of an axial sweep (also referred to as an *extrusion*) in which the depth of the profile was sketched in a 3D sketch mode. We now have a solid to which we can add features. Each of the features will be sketched and will have actual engineering values placed on them at a later time.

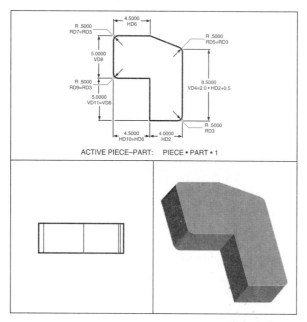

FIGURE 8.17 Example parametric/relational design process, step 6—creating the base solid. *(Courtesy of Manufacturing and Consulting Services, Inc.)*

Step 7: Sketching the First Feature

This step (see Fig. 8.18) shows the first feature, a constant offset pocket at a depth of approximately one-half the thickness of the axial sweep. Upon completion of the pocket feature, the designer is requested to indicate where the name of this feature will be placed (i.e., which curve it will be placed on) and where the thickness dimension for the constant offset should be placed. POK12, located above the bottom curve, is the name which has been supplied. Most P/R SM systems allow the designer to either enter a name or to have the system supply one. In this case, the system has supplied all of the names for the horizontal, vertical, radial, and thickness dimension, as well as the name of the feature.

Step 8: Sketching Three Additional Features

This step (see Fig. 3.19) illustrates the addition of three more sketched features identified as SLOT13, RIB14, and HOLE15. SLOT13 is a slot with rounded ends. RIB14 is a rib rather than a slot because we are adding material to the part, whereas a slot removes material. SLOT13 is a through-slot (i.e., it will go through the bottom of the part regardless of how the dimensions of the part are changed in subsequent operations). Again, the system automatically named these features as they were sketched, while the designer indicated the curves which would be associated with the feature name, and also the position of the thickness dimensions.

The designer is forced into a relational edit mode as soon as the feature creation is completed. In this example, SLOT13 has been defined as being centered on and parallel to HD6, and centered on and perpendicular to VD8; RIB14 is centered on HD2 and is a distance from the end of the rib to HD2 of 2.0. HOLE15 is centered on the canted line of the profile and is a distance of 1.50 from the hole center to the line. The top thickness dimension, 1.0 (T) over TH15 indicates that the value of TH15 is 1.0. The (T) indicates that this is a thickness dimension.

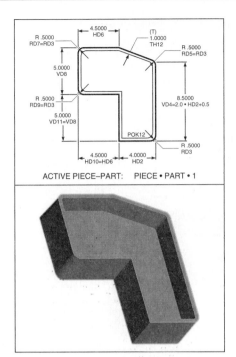

FIGURE 8.18 Example parametric/relational design process, step 7—sketching the first feature. *(Courtesy of Manufacturing and Consulting Services, Inc.)*

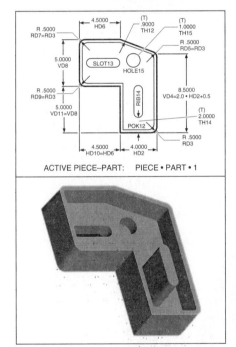

FIGURE 8.19 Example parametric/relational design process, step 8—sketching three additional features. *(Courtesy of Manufacturing and Consulting Services, Inc.)*

Step 9: Adding Draft

Having generated the features, we now see how easy it is to finish our part by applying, first, a blend to the outer profile coupled with a draft to 15°. The outer profile is identified as Piece_Part_1. The top Z value (TOP1) is 0.0000, the depth 2.7250, the draft 15.0°, and the blend has a value of 0.2000 (see Figs. 8.20 and 8.21).

Step 10: Adding Feature Blends

All of the feature blends (see Fig. 8.22) were applied at one time by entering a single value to be applied to the tops of all features. In addition, POK12 has a bottom blend on it of 0.1000.

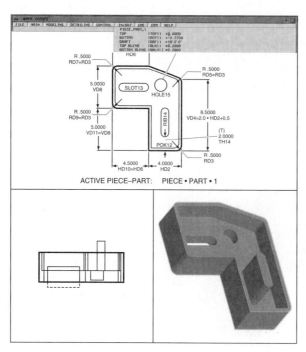

FIGURE 8.20   Example parametric/relational design process, step 9. *(Courtesy of Manufacturing and Consulting Services, Inc.)*

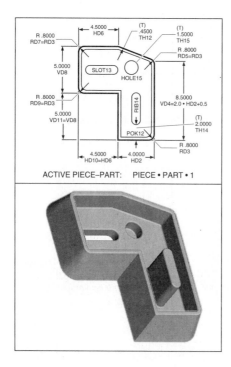

FIGURE 8.21   Example parametric/relational design process, step 10—adding draft. *(Courtesy of Manufacturing and Consulting Services, Inc.)*

Step 11: Final Design Modifications and Reviewing Constraints

This step (see Fig. 8.22) illustrates the true power of a P/R SM system. After changing the hole distance from the canted line, the widths of SLOT13 and RIB14, and the length of RIB14, we had a figure almost identical to Fig. 8.21. However, here we changed VD8 from a value of 5.0 to a value of 2.75. Since VD11 is equal to VD8, it also changed to 2.75, changing the height of the left side of the solid from 10.0 to 5.5, and generating the changes which you see. Note that all constraints that govern the positioning of the

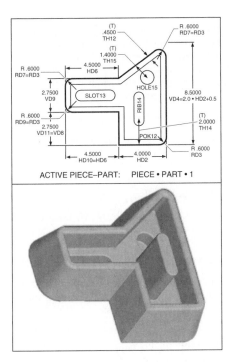

ACTIVE PIECE–PART: PIECE • PART • 1

FIGURE 8.22 Example parametric/relational design process, step 11—adding blends and final design modifications. *(Courtesy of Manufacturing and Consulting Services, Inc.)*

features still hold. SLOT13 is still centered on and parallel to HD6, and centered on and perpendicular to VD8. HOLE15 is centered on and a distance from the canted line, and RIB14 is centered on and a distance of 2.0 from HD2.

Step 12: The Final Part

The final part is shown incorporating the designers current intent. (See color insert, Fig. 8.23.)

Equations

SMA.8.17   Relationship Editing

The ability to edit parameter relationships of a design is extremely important. Parameter identities (name tags) can become quite confusing and the process of editing a complex design can be tedious, particularly if the person making the change is not the original designer. It is advisable to keep design relationship notes within the model file, perhaps on a separate text layer set aside for this purpose.

R. Herschel Redd, Senior Marketing Support Representative
IBM Corp., Dallas, Tex.

SMA.8.18   Bidirectional Equation Solving

One characteristic to be most acutely aware of is whether an SM product provides bidirectional equation solving. This commonly occurs as an issue when:

1. A discrete part has many relationships.

2. Many intercomponent constraints are established between assembly components.

3. More than one perspective needs to be applied to a product solution domain.

For example, if the algebraic equation $a = b + c$ is established, then $c = a - b$ can also be solved. More specifically, consider a vise where the width of the slot for a sliding bar may be equal to the width of

(Continued)

Equations
(*Continued*)

the sliding bar plus a 0.03 space for lubricants. A design engineer may want to define the bar width for stress reasons, and propagate the change to the slot width dimension. A manufacturing engineer may want to define the slot width dimension based on ease of manufacturing, and propagate the change to the bar width dimension. As more perspectives and relationships are added, the problem is obviously compounded. Without bidirectional equation solving, the relationship propagation direction has to be redefined for each perspective.

Mark J. Silvestri
Life Cycle Solutions, Inc., Avon, Mass.

Parametric Editing

SMA.8.19 Think Before You Delete[10]

Think before you delete any entities. It is often better to use the Undo Operation and Remove Operation options to undo the last one or two commands or place parametric entities you want to delete on a *garbage* layer.

Rationale: If you delete entities:

1. You may leave behind parametric dimensions that do not appear to reference anything. SM systems may remove parameters that are not being used. If a parameter remains, it is usually because it is being referenced by another operation.

2. The system may remove the entity, but if it is still referenced, it may not remove its history. This slows the regeneration of the model.

3. You may not be able to undo the deletion if it does not appear in the command history.

Exception: In some cases, such as when you want to reference a construction entity and use only its parameters, you may want to delete the entity. An option is to make the entity invisible or change its layer.

Nancy Anderson-Semple, Technical Editor
Computervision Corp., Bedford, Mass.

Editor's Note: This concern may be reduced or eliminated in newer systems.

SMA.8.20 Parametric/Relational Editing

Editing a parametrically constrained solid is easiest when the model's topology is not altered. Much variation in a part or family of parts can be achieved without altering topology. As mentioned previously, the topology of a solid refers to its total number and relationship of vertices, edges, and faces. It should be noted here that a face can be either flat or with curvature. Editing that modifies the arrangement but not the total number of these elements is most easily allowed.

SMA.8.21 Precautions

Save your model prior to parametric editing and undo any operations that are not well understood or have unexpected results. Also, if the system's undo utility will not override its auto-backup utility, turn autobackup off prior to extensive parametric editing. Utilizing autobackup when available should be standard procedure except for temporary situations.

Don LaCourse, President
The Solid Modeling ExChange, Algood, Tenn.

Good to Know

SMA.8.22 When to Use What

Use feature-based modeling when you can envision reusing the results more than once. Use variational modeling when the problem domain is well known such that it can be defined by equations. Use parametric modeling when reexecution of a all or a portion of the work will yield a foundation to add differences to the original.

(*Continued*)

Good to Know
(Continued)

SMA.8.23   Parametric Characteristics

One key characteristic of parametric SM is that it allows designers to undo operations and readily reexecute; it is essentially an infinite undo-redo capability. A parametric edit causes reexecution of the affected nodes in the history tree guided by embedded design intent like *middle-of* and *coplanar-to,* as well as previously recorded geometric transactions and interactions.

The history tree can be order-dependent, with preceding steps dictating intermediate results and relationships for succeeding steps, or, in more sophisticated implementations, bidirectional equations can break the order dependency. In the latter case, loops may occur in the reexecution, and designers may be required to set some variables constant in order to direct the solution.

Mark J. Silvestri
Life Cycle Solutions, Inc., Avon, Mass.

SMA.8.24   Integration Issues

Here are some issues to be considered before integrating a new P/R SM system:

1. Can existing models be migrated to the new system and parameterized if appropriate?

2. Can the exchange of models with customers and suppliers continue at the current state of productivity?

   a. What if each has the same software but different version levels?

   b. Database compatibility is critical when the master model is used to drive a downstream process such as NC.

   c. If communicating via tape or disk, there may not be associative links between machines that were not networked.

R. Herschel Redd, Senior Marketing Support Representative
IBM Corp., Dallas, Tex.

SMA.8.25   Is There a Parametric Sketch Pad?

I would like to see capability now or in the future of a front-end sketch-pad approach. When an engineer sketches his or her model on the pad, geometry for SM is created, adding AI to the process.

Eldad Cohen, Engineering Consultant
Brookline, Mass.

References

1. Sutherland, I. E., *Sketchpad: A Man–Machine Graphical Communication System,* MIT Lincoln, Lexington, Mass., January 1963.

2. Requicha, A. A. G., *Part and Assembly Description Languages: Dimensioning and Tolerancing,* Production Automation Project, University of Rochester, Rochester, N.Y., May 1977.

3. Gopin, A. M., "Development of a Dimension Based Data Structure for Two-Dimensional Computer Graphics," unpublished Master's thesis, MIT, Cambridge, Mass., 1978.

4. Hillyard, R. C., and Braid, I. C., "Analysis of Dimensions and Tolerances in Computer-Aided Mechanical Design," *Computer-Aided Design,* vol. 10, no. 3, June 1978, pp. 161–166.

5. Hillyard, R. C., "Dimensions and Tolerances in Shape Design," Technical Report No. 8, University of Cambridge Computer Laboratory, Cambridge, U.K., 1978.

6. Light, R. A. "Symbolic Dimensioning in Computer-Aided Design," unpublished Master's thesis, MIT, Cambridge, Mass., 1980.

7. Lin, V. C., Gossard, D. C., and Light, R. A., "Variational Geometry in Computer-Aided Design," *Proceedings of SIGGRAPH,* 1981.

8. Computervision Corporation is a solid modeling software developer headquartered in Bedford, Mass.

9. Parametric Technology Corporation (PTC) is a solid modeling software developer headquartered in Lowell, Mass.

10. Adapted from "Parametric Modeling Usage Tips," Revision 4.0.0, Nancy Anderson-Semple, Editor, Computervision Corporation, May 1993.

more than just geometry...

Engineering is a lot more than geometry - it's materials, costing, analysis, simulation, manufacturability, and a lot more besides. If that sounds like your kind of engineering then check out ICAD.

ICAD software products are used by major companies worldwide to help automate their engineering, yielding order-of-magnitude improvements in lead-time, full CADCAM integration, reduced engineering costs and maximum product quality.

The bike? The LotusSport Pursuit Bike used by Chris Boardman for Olympic Gold. Not just a pretty shape - engineered for optimum weight, strength, ergonomics, stability, and airflow by Lotus Engineering. Using ICAD.

Learn more about ICAD's technology in Chapter 9.

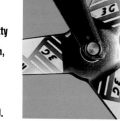

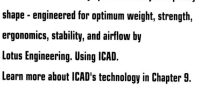

ICAD
the power to automate engineering

ICAD Inc.,

USA, Asia (617) 868 2800

Europe (UK) 0203 692323

Chapter 9

Solid Modeling and Knowledge-Based Engineering

Lawrence W. Rosenfeld
President
Concentra Corporation

Knowledge-based engineering (KBE) is a recent arrival to the engineering software market. KBE software provides a tool by which an engineering company can achieve wide-scale integration and automation of the engineering process. This integration may involve activities from the engineering of a single, highly complex component such as a jet engine turbine blade to the schematic packaging of a complex assembly such as a satellite.

A theme common to all KBE applications is the creation and manipulation of geometric data. This data may range from simple wireframe schemes to detailed solid models of complete assemblies. Engineers and managers involved in the selection and procurement of Solid Modeling (SM) systems should be aware of the possible roles that a KBE system may have when integrated with their chosen SM system. This chapter will explore the issues that should be considered.

9.1 Knowledge-Based Engineering (KBE)

Knowledge-based engineering is a technology founded by Concentra Corporation (Cambridge, Massachusetts) in 1984. To apply this technology, a KBE system is needed which provides a language for defining an engineering design process and a user interface that allows the activation of the design process definition and the subsequent creation of a design.

The design process definition is called a *product model,* which can store all the information that relates to a product. This includes information such as geometry, material type, and performance, as well as process information—the processes by which the product is analyzed, optimized, manufactured, assembled and tested.

The design process information stored in the product model can be considered an entity in itself—a "knowledge base." In many respects the KBE knowledge base—the "product model"—can be considered analogous to a design procedure's manual with the ability to:

1. Improve through feedback from actual manufacture, test, and field experience.
2. Capture knowledge which can be applied long after the human experts are gone.

However, unlike a design manual, which is a passive object, a KBE product model is active; it can create new designs automatically. Furthermore, because a product model is able to produce a design, it is possible to identify and correct inconsistencies that might not be noticed in a design manual. In fact, the product model can be so complete that it can create a design better and faster than a "best-practice" design that could be produced by an entire engineering team.

Once engineering knowledge has been collected and stored in a product model, the real advantages become apparent. Design engineers can generate and evaluate new designs by changing input specifications for the product model. Or they can modify existing designs by extending or changing the model.

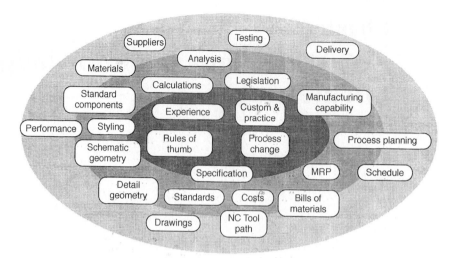

FIGURE 9.1 A KBE product model can encompass all aspects of a design, not just geometry. KBE technology is a powerful integration tool and can be used to link SM with analysis, manufacturing, and costing programs. *(Courtesy of Concentra Corporation.)*

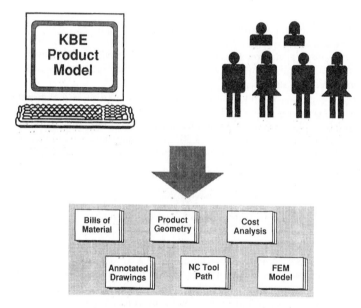

FIGURE 9.2 A KBE product model can produce a better design than an entire engineering team. This is because it never forgets, and can compute hundreds of design possibilities in the time that the engineering team might take to produce just one design. *(Courtesy of Concentra Corporation.)*

A KBE product model can cut down repetitive, time-consuming engineering tasks dramatically. As a result, there is much more time for creative design work—and much less likelihood of expensive errors.

9.1.1 A Typical Application

Engineering organizations have always looked for a complete, nonambiguous means of specifying systems and components. For the most part, this role has been fulfilled by detailed engineering drawings which are archived to form a master definition of the design artifact. Recently, the advent of sophisticated computer-based mechanisms for Solid Modeling (SM) have begun to form the basis for a new type of master model. Unfortunately, a single solid model which satisfies all groups involved in the design is often impossible to define. As a result, a more comprehensive master model is required. The following example illustrates this situation.

Modern commercial aircraft are highly complex. They contain hundreds of thousands of components, many of them similar, but each part is ever-so-slightly different. Beneath the skin of an aircraft are spars, ribs, stringers, and clips. Generally, the smaller the components, the more similar they become. Yet each of these items may differ from its neighbor. It has to, because weight is critical for an aircraft. It may be a small change in radius or thickness, but it will save weight. So, how do you ensure that the SM geometry will match the geometry that was calculated and defined by the stress department for those thousands of similar parts?

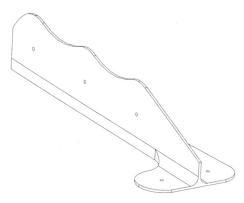

FIGURE 9.3 Solid model of an aircraft stringer clip. Aircraft have hundreds of these in their wings. Each one is individually engineered. Using a KBE system they can all be automatically produced from a single product model. *(Courtesy of Concentra Corporation.)*

Some of the parts will have a completely different topological form from other parts which are designed to perform the same function. This may be due to any one of many engineering design factors which, at a critical value, dictate a different shape requirement. How do you ensure that the solid model always represents a valid engineering solution and that its form follows its function?

Now consider how designs evolve. For instance, a new material becomes available. The critical stress calculations indicate that weight can be saved from some clips by reducing the thickness of particular features in those clips. How do you ensure that the modification is made correctly, consistently, and accurately to every clip?

This is a classic example of an application best handled by a KBE solution. A KBE product model can contain a full representation of the engineering process, and can generate a complete topological range of designs. A KBE product model can be integrated with a CAD system and any analysis systems such that it will automatically extract the necessary geometry inputs from the aircraft, compute the correct design, and automatically transfer the final solid model designs back into the CAD system. The ability to represent multiple geometric views of the design means that the CAD output may include not just the component geometry but the geometry of any associated special tools, fixtures, and processes. Because the product model represents the complete design specification, there is a considerable reduction in design time and effort.

Finally, because the KBE product model is a functional model, engineers have the freedom to optimize the component design based on functional criteria such as material, weight, and manufacturing time, as well as the geometric inputs.

9.1.2 Process or Geometry?

A KBE product model can be viewed as a model of a design process. A sharp distinction can be drawn between this concept of modeling an engineering process and modeling a geometric design, as with a parametric SM system or a CAD system.

With geometric modeling systems, an engineer creates a geometry model that conforms to the design requirements, using individual or collective experience. However, important elements of the design rules, such as calculations, manufacturing feasibility, analysis, and costing, cannot always be embedded in the model. A geometric system captures part of the process and the end result, but cannot easily capture the entire design process. If a change is required, or if the process is iterative, designers will have to repeat any engineering steps affected by the change (such as those just mentioned), record the outcome again on their geometric modeler, and then re-create any dependent data. This is very time-consuming, but, because it is the way engineering is traditionally done, the impact of this process has been accepted as a "natural" part of engineering rather than a major inefficiency.

The advent of parametric/relational SM systems has gone some way toward easing this problem, but until such systems can embed all design knowledge in a model, the requirement for "off-line" engineering alongside the geometric modeler will continue. Many companies use engineers to perform such off-line engineering. Some are now integrating KBE systems with their geometric modeler to assist in performing this function.

9.1.3   Object-Oriented

The underlying basis of a KBE system is an object-oriented structure. Conventional computing environments require two things:

1. The collection of information that describes how a set of input data can be transformed into a result

2. The correct order of information for solution—the flowchart

The information that describes the job is usually available, but getting it into some kind of order is less easy. This is done with flowcharts, which are normally the biggest headache for a computer programmer working on complex applications.

An object-oriented system doesn't need information to be ordered "correctly." It can work the order out for itself. The nature of the computing environment is such that it is necessary to describe the engineering information only when defining the application. Flowcharts are not required. Instead, the information about a product is grouped logically. All the information related to the design of a seat, for example, would be found in one place called (logically enough) "seat." And, technically speaking, "seat" is a kind of "object."

Objects are not passive; they have a capacity to actively interact with other objects. An object is something that can create and store information and act in response to external stimuli, either by demanding information from another object or sending information to another object. In the case of a product model of an aircraft, "aircraft" would be an object. It would compute its total mass by asking each subsystem (wings, tail plane, fuselage) for information about its total mass. And, as each subsystem is an object, it knows its total mass by asking its associated subsystems for their mass, etc.

The definition of an object is wholly self-contained and can be developed and tested in isolation from its final environment. That makes the process of building a KBE product model much easier. It is more analogous to writing a design manual procedure than to "computer programming." So product KBE models are normally developed by engineers rather than by computer programmers.

The same object definition can be used and reused in many different contexts or engineering situations. That makes the development of later KBE product models much faster, because parts of them will already have been written.

In practice, therefore, a KBE product model developer is concerned with the creation of relatively small objects, such as features and components, and other small objects which are assemblies of the feature/component objects. The object description of even the most complex product is still small because it simply describes an assembly of other smaller objects. This modularity cascades down to the lowest level of detail, which might be a geometric feature, an equation, a database selection algorithm, or perhaps a process definition.

9.1.4   Two Types of KBE Engineer

There are two types of KBE engineer; the product model developer and the run-time user. In some companies, they may be separate people, while in others they are the same person.

Product model developers usually work in small teams to create KBE applications for the run-time users. The KBE development team requires a number of roles to be filled. Team members must be trained in the programming of the KBE system; they should preferably be engineers; and they must have access to the experts who understand the task being automated.

KBE product models are never completely automatic. Indeed, many product models have a high degree of interactivity. This allows the run-time user to create a valid design without infringing on the creative scope of the task. Because of this need for creative input, the run-time user is normally a designer or engineer.

Run-time users are effectively customers of the developers. They are the ones who derive benefit from the KBE application. They will not usually require training in KBE techniques, since the application will be designed by the product model developers to have a natural easy-to-use interface.

9.1.5   Jargon

One of the most bewildering aspects of evaluating any new technology is the jargon. Engineering automation is no exception. Parametrics, constraints, expert systems, and artificial intelligence are terms that are used without discrimination when people talk about new engineering technology, and they mean different things to different people. It is worth comparing KBE with the more frequently misused jargon in terms of functionality.

Is KBE Parametric?

Yes, by any definition—change an input and you get a different output. Note, however, that the current market custom and practice is to define a parametric system as one that can create a geometric representation in which making changes to a particular dimension can change the size of other dimensions but not change the design topology (the number and relationship of faces, edges, and vertices)—dimensional parametrics. This is useful for improving the task of geometry creation and modification but inappropriate for modeling the actual engineering process where many engineering functions are involved, where iteration to an optimum is useful, and where much of the engineering actually relates to nongeometric factors such as material and component choice, analysis, manufacturing process, and cost. KBE vendors refer to this as "functional parametrics."

Is KBE a Type of Expert System?

Not from a computer science perspective, but there are similarities. Like an expert system, KBE works with instructions, definitions, and rules. The way in which rules are solved is completely different, however, and this gives each type of system its own strengths.

Expert systems are strongly suited to advisory, diagnostic, and real-time applications in which the expertise or data is incompletely defined or where a *fuzzy* (an algorithmic approach to problem solving) result is sufficient. Expert systems do not have a built-in data structure allowing geometry to be manipulated; some expert systems do have the capability to link to geometry modelers, but typically require additional computer programming.

Furthermore, because of their architecture, expert systems are subject to performance limitations when applied to large problems involving thousands of rules. Engineering is really a task of synthesis, not diagnosis; engineers create a good design by combining many principles into a single design. KBE systems are designed to work best with engineering definitions based on synthesis and are able to efficiently handle engineering tasks with thousands of rules.

Is KBE Artificial Intelligence (AI)?

No. The AI approach to engineering would be to model the engineer! This has proven to be a daunting task and one that is still unrealized. The functionality of KBE shares some of the software concepts developed in support of AI, but it is focused on modeling an engineering process which is known and to faithfully repeat that process.

A KBE product model does not replace the engineer's role of thinking, improving, and innovating. Instead it rigorously combines and applies a large number of tried and tested engineering rules to create a new design that conforms to them all. In a fraction of the time it would normally take to create a new design. And it encourages engineering innovation by providing a unique means of fully testing the implications of a new idea. One may introduce a new factor and see how it affects everything that is already known about the product in one computer iteration.

9.1.6   Who Can Benefit from KBE?

KBE is language-based. This means that to create geometry you must define it in terms of the KBE system language rather than interactively, as with a CAD system. An example is shown in Fig. 9.4.

Language-based definitions are, by their nature, slower to build than interactive definitions. User experience has shown that the time taken to build a product model can be two to three times longer than the time taken to produce a single design "conventionally." For this reason, KBE is best suited to applications in which the geometry definition forms a minor part in the engineering design of the prod-

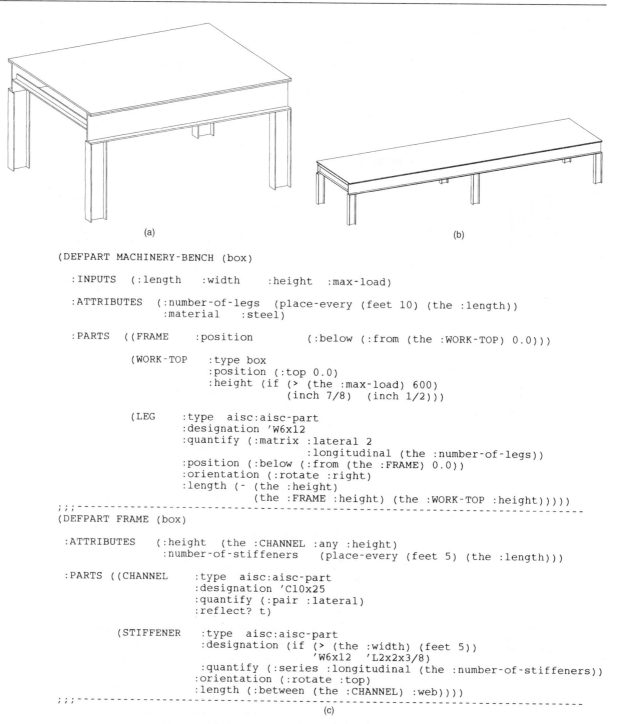

(a)

(b)

```
(DEFPART MACHINERY-BENCH (box)

   :INPUTS  (:length   :width     :height   :max-load)

   :ATTRIBUTES  (:number-of-legs  (place-every (feet 10) (the :length))
                :material   :steel)

   :PARTS  ((FRAME     :position            (:below (:from (the :WORK-TOP) 0.0)))

            (WORK-TOP    :type box
                         :position (:top 0.0)
                         :height (if (> (the :max-load) 600)
                                    (inch 7/8)  (inch 1/2)))

            (LEG    :type  aisc:aisc-part
                    :designation 'W6x12
                    :quantify (:matrix :lateral 2
                                       :longitudinal (the :number-of-legs))
                    :position (:below (:from (the :FRAME) 0.0))
                    :orientation (:rotate :right)
                    :length (- (the :height)
                               (the :FRAME :height) (the :WORK-TOP :height)))))
;;;-------------------------------------------------------------------------
(DEFPART FRAME (box)

   :ATTRIBUTES  (:height  (the :CHANNEL :any :height)
                :number-of-stiffeners   (place-every (feet 5) (the :length)))

   :PARTS ((CHANNEL     :type  aisc:aisc-part
                        :designation 'C10x25
                        :quantify (:pair :lateral)
                        :reflect? t)

           (STIFFENER   :type aisc:aisc-part
                        :designation (if (> (the :width) (feet 5))
                                       'W6x12 'L2x2x3/8)
                        :quantify (:series :longitudinal (the :number-of-stiffeners))
                        :orientation (:rotate :top)
                        :length (:between (the :CHANNEL) :web))))
;;;-------------------------------------------------------------------------
```

(c)

FIGURE 9.4 Design graphics and language rules for a simple KBE product model. (*a*) 6 × 4 × 3 ft machinery bench having four legs and an L-section cross-members; (*b*) 21 × 5 × 3 ft machinery bench produced by the same product model (note the I-section cross-member and extra legs); (*c*) complete design language description for the machinery bench product model. (*Courtesy of Concentra Corporation.*)

uct and in which the benefits of design automation—instant, optimal, error-free design—outweigh the costs of defining the product model.

For example, an industrial design consultancy servicing the consumer products industry (toasters, kettles, refrigerators, hair dryers) is likely to work on a number of projects at any one time. The design of these products is strongly influenced by appearance (i.e., geometry) rather than engineering perfor-

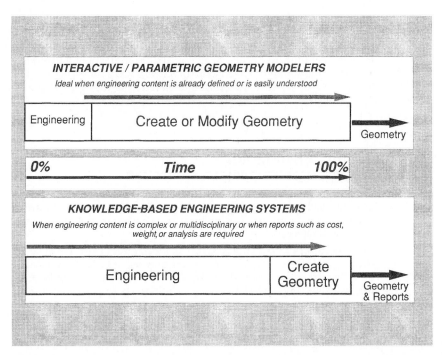

FIGURE 9.5 KBE is best used for applications with large engineering content. Applications in which the geometric design forms a large part of the design time are often better done with interactive/parametric geometry modelers. *(Courtesy of Concentra Corporation.)*

mance. Unless the consultancy has a steady stream of, say, toaster projects, it would not gain much benefit from investing time in the creation of a KBE product model for toasters. The transient nature of this business environment, together with the small size of individual projects, would not justify the use of KBE. Interactive or parametric/relational SM would be the more likely choices in this instance.

In contrast, a manufacturer which specialized in a particular consumer product, with, say, a whole range of toasters to suit all sectors of the market probably would use a KBE solution in conjunction with a CAD or SM system. This is because a toaster is much more than a geometric object. There is a large amount of engineering required to create a suitable design—from electrical regulations and standards to the size of the packaging on the store shelf. The engineering behind each toaster is very similar, even if the appearances are not. The time spent in defining the KBE model would be justified because the same model could be used time and again across the complete product range.

9.2 CAD and KBE

The principal descriptor of any design is its geometry. Both CAD and KBE work with geometry, and this can lead to confusion: "If I have KBE do I need CAD?," "Aren't CAD and KBE the same?," and so on. In fact, CAD and KBE are complementary technologies—wherever you find a KBE system you will usually find it working alongside a CAD system.

Each system has its own strengths and weaknesses; together they can form a powerful tool. The principal strength of a KBE system is its role as an integrator—combining such things as costs, layouts, geometry, manufacturing, and so on. Designers using KBE can create geometry which meets the design requirements perfectly, but in most cases they do not follow that geometry through to the production of detailed drawings, because it is quicker to complete it using the CAD system.

Depending on the CAD system, the KBE system may work directly within the CAD system geometry environment, or, where this is not possible, it will generate geometry by creating either a command or a geometry file.

KBE applications can be built and grown organically: top down, bottom up, or middle out. Unlike conventional programming environments, there is no need to specify a flowchart before starting. Because of this, KBE designers normally start on one small part of the overall engineering process—where it is most cost-effective—and then extend the application outwards.

The organic approach is particularly effective for design scheming—the creation of bid proposals in the industrial sector and of concept packaging and layout in the automotive and aerospace sectors. A notable benefit of this approach when used in conjunction with CAD is that the KBE system can be used to manage the overall design and subsystem interactions and output schematic geometry in a fully engineered form to the CAD system. Later, as more detailed KBE applications are built, they can be plugged into the schematic product model, reducing the effort required by the CAD users to create detail geometry.

9.2.1 Geometry Construction

KBE systems provide libraries of geometric "primitives" (objects). These include 2D and 3D wireframe objects as well as surface and solid objects. Geometry can be constructed using any combination of these geometric primitives. This means that solid geometry can be constructed using constructive methods, or by stitching surfaces, or both.

KBE designers will often use KBE solid techniques even when the required output from the KBE system is just 2D wireframe geometry for drawings. Or even if no geometry output is required at all! This is because SM can provide useful shortcuts in the creation of a KBE product model. KBE developers will generally use SM for any applications whose output must include the following attributes:

1. ***Drawings.***   Building a 3D solid model of a product and then using hidden-line removal can be the simplest way of creating 2D views of complex machines.
2. ***Sectioning.***   2D section views are also simple if you build a 3D solid first.
3. ***Mass properties.***
4. ***Clash detection.***

Solid Modeling techniques also lend themselves to geometries which are best described by the result of a physical process. Figure 9.6 shows an example of a car steering component. The engineering requirement is for a barrel that supports two bearings. The body is a pin-jointed cantilever that flares around the barrel. The internal geometry of the barrel is determined by the location requirements of the bearings, the need for a shaft through which to pass, and the need for a machining process in which all surfaces can be machined by simple boring.

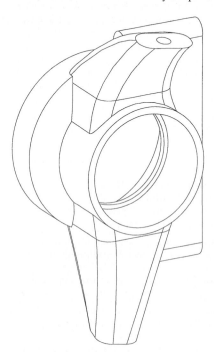

FIGURE 9.6   A KBE solid model of a car suspension upright consisting of a bearing support structure and a flared vertical cantilever which forms the steering axis. A large proportion of the design work for this type of component is nongeometric. The best design is found by multiple iterations. This is an ideal KBE application. *(Courtesy of Concentra Corporation.)*

The KBE product model that produced this geometry created a lofted surface to describe the cantilever solid, and then used constructive techniques to combine cantilever with barrel, cut the bearing seats, and cut the shaft. Because the KBE model construction process is emulating the physical machining process, the result is guaranteed to be manufacturable.

A similar application is the use of KBE for process planning. In this case, KBE is used to integrate physical geometry with manufacturing resources such as tools, fixtures, and machining centers. The process plan documentation from the KBE application contains factory/machine routing, NC programs, and drawings of the component at the end of each machining stage. The drawings are produced using a solid model which is successively machined using "virtual" tools defined by each manufacturing node in the KBE model.

9.2.2 Topology

The object-oriented nature of KBE provides designers and engineers with a much more powerful ability to describe a design than do parametric/relational modelers alone. A KBE product model can be easily programmed to produce a completely different topology, depending on the design inputs. A simple example is illustrated in Fig. 9.7 in which a block may be required to position itself anywhere between two "towers"; three different topologies can result. A real-world example is shown in Fig. 9.8 (see color insert), in which two very different machines are automatically designed by the same KBE model.

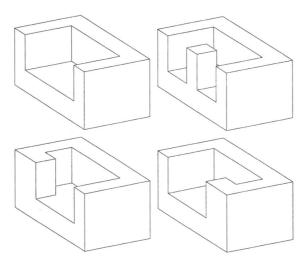

FIGURE 9.7 Multiple topologies from a simple KBE product model. The design requirement of a simple column that may need to be located at any lateral position results in four topologies. KBE does not require the user to produce a separate model for each topology—one is sufficient. *(Courtesy of Concentra Corporation.)*

9.2.3 Solid Modeling Kernels

KBE vendors do not create proprietary SM geometry engines (kernels); they license them or use the kernel of a host CAD system. The interface between the KBE system and the kernel is unseen by the engineer or designer. From their point of view, a set of geometric operations is defined by the KBE language; the methodology in which the operations occur is the responsibility of the KBE vendor.

The separation of requirement (language) from computation (geometry kernel) creates an interesting characteristic of some KBE systems: the ability of a single product model to be defined with the superset of all possible SM operations. These include constructive operations such as boolean addition defined by CSG modelers and synthetic operations, such as surface stitching, defined by B-Rep modelers. The KBE system transforms the operations requested by the product model definition into those that are suitable for the chosen kernel, whether CSG or B-Rep. This means that a product model defined at a time when the CAD system currently used is based on a B-Rep kernel would work at a later date with a new CAD system based on a CSG kernel.

9.3 Future Developments

KBE systems can work as stand-alone or in tandem with an SM system. The KBE and SM integration can be in client-server or server/client mode; that is, a KBE application can be driven from either the SM user interface or from the KBE user interface. Currently, the choice of KBE and SM systems which offer these capabilities is limited. It is reasonable to assume that such choices will increase in the future.

As more industries move toward the goal of improving the design process, a more complete representation of the master model will be required. This master model will not be centered on the geometry of the system but, rather, on the process-level specification of the design. KBE technology is ideally suited to facilitate this movement, thereby providing companies who adopt it with a significant competitive edge.

Geometry Failures

SMA.9.1 Approximations and Nonmanifold Conditions

SM operations can fail. This is because the underlying process is based on approximation and iterative solution of mathematical relationships that can fail to converge. When geometry is created by rules or parametric constraints, there is also the possibility of a failure when the inputs to the model attempt to produce a nonmanifold topological model in a situation that was not recognized by the engineer. For example, attempting to fillet between parallel surfaces or holes located outside a component which they should pierce are really instances of an underdeveloped model. It is the former, mathematical, type of failure which can be most bothersome to the KBE developer.

SMA.9.2 Rounding and Tolerance Errors

A type of failure in KBE systems can occur when creating a large-scale application which integrates data from multiple sources—for example, an application that imports surface geometry from a CAD system and a proprietary analysis program, reads data from a database, computes a design, and builds the solid model for another CAD system. The problem is rounding and tolerance errors. Each of the systems may work to different levels of "accuracy." Or, more simply, how small does a number have to be before the computer decides it is zero? This can manifest as surfaces which won't stitch together and parts that won't unionize correctly because they are infinitesimally misplaced.

There are strategies to avoid these problems. The most fundamental is to ensure that the tolerances are set uniformly throughout, rather than to use the default tolerance of the various subsystem program applications. Sometimes the input data from another system is simply bad, and there is nothing you can do to persuade the upstream supplier of data to change. In those circumstances it is necessary to create further rules to "parse" the input data into a more accurately defined form.

SMA.9.3 Preventive Strategies

A failure with an interactive modeler can be annoying, but the reason is usually obvious to the designer, who will then attempt the operation by other means until a successful result is achieved. With KBE and parametric/relational modelers, a higher level of expertise is required from the software developer, who must be sensitive to the possibilities of failure and who must adopt strategies which avoid their possibility. With KBE systems these strategies may range from taking care to correctly order a series of SM operations to changing the size of a particular component which might otherwise create an invalid operation downstream.

SMA.9.4 Error Trapping

KBE systems incorporate error flags in operations that may fail mathematically. It is the responsibility of the engineer who develops the product model to ensure that when such errors arise they are handled properly by using these flags correctly. The error flags can be rather clever in that they test for a failure without letting the model itself fail. This allows the product model to "test" a potentially fatal operation before it actually commits itself. Depending on the preferences of those who develop the product model, it is then defined to either (1) inform the user of a failure, its likely cause, and suggested work-arounds or (2) perform automatic fix-ups until a solution is found.

In both cases, the behavior is defined by the product model developer based on an understanding of the possible problems and a determination of the best strategies to resolve such problems.

Organizational Issues

SMA.9.5 Data Management

Data management is best accomplished using existing in-house electronic data management systems. KBE systems differ from most computer systems in that the requirement for archiving a design is to store the input data to a product model and the product model itself. Conventional requirements are to store the output data only. With KBE it is not necessary to store the design output, since it can be regenerated. In practice, parts of the output data are stored in the form of geometry generated for CAD, design reports, cost reports, NC files, and so on.

SMA.9.6 Implementation

Like any other technology, KBE requires proper commitment from management in order to succeed. Because the benefits and the costs are spread across a large part of an organization, it can be difficult to justify as a "point solution" to a local departmental problem. For instance, there would be very little interest from a design office in producing designs that cost less to make if there is no mechanism to recognize the design office for its efforts. The design office may be interested only in projects that increased its local productivity.

SMA.9.7 Pilot Projects

KBE tends to be *sold* within an organization as a corporate productivity tool. This requires the involvement of a number of different departments within the organization, as well as the involvement of senior management. KBE implementations usually start with a pilot project involving two to four engineers working with two KBE systems. The project should have clear milestones and targets with a project span of six months, maximum. Following a successful initial effort, the project team can then be expanded, and a broader range of projects tackled.

SMA.9.8 Integration

KBE systems provide a number of integration tools to a product model developer. For major SM systems this integration can be transparent and automatic. Integration with less common systems can be accomplished using tool-kit products supplied as part of the KBE system. These provide ready-made template converters to translate KBE geometry into a chosen format.

The creation of more generalized geometric data files for finite element modeling systems, other analysis programs, and nongeometric engineering report outputs can be accomplished using similar tool kits. Database read/write tool kits are also available.

Parametric modeling was out of reach for many designers.

Introducing AutoCAD® Designer for the PC.

Now you can create parametric, feature-based solid models right on your trusty PC. New AutoCAD® Designer lets you build "intelligent" 3D models dynamically, as your ideas take shape. By performing "what if" scenarios, you can explore dozens of design possibilities in minutes.

AutoCAD Designer software also brings breakthrough features to the everyday task of 2D drafting. Now you can automatically generate as many drawing views as you need, directly from the model.

Bidirectional associativity makes revisions effortless. So you can make changes at will, in any mode.

So we moved it to a more convenient location.

Both model and drawing update simultaneously.

Best of all, you can take advantage of this technology immediately — because AutoCAD Designer works right inside AutoCAD® Release 12. AutoCAD users can get up and running in a matter of hours. And, at $1,500,° price isn't even an issue.

All this makes AutoCAD Designer the cornerstone of the Autodesk mechanical design family. To see how it fits in with other Autodesk mechanical solutions, call your Authorized Autodesk Dealer for a demonstration. Or call 1-800-964-6432, ext. 586 for a free demo disk. Outside of U.S., just fax 1-415-491-8311.

Autodesk®

Chapter 10

Viewing and Displaying Solid Models

Joel N. Orr
President
Orr Associates International

The unequivocal portrayal of three-dimensional (3D) objects is the central concern of mechanical drawing. This activity has a long history. The Babylonian engineer Gudea, in about 2000 B.C., created a stone engraving of a fortress plan that endures to this day. It is astonishingly similar to modern-day plan-view drawings.

Vitruvius, a Roman architect circa 27 B.C., wrote the first textbook of engineering drawing. In it, he emphasized that the architect should know something about drawing in order to show the work that is to be built.

But it was Gaspard Monge who first laid out the principles of engineering drawing as they are used today. *La Geometrie Descriptive,* published in 1801, was the first complete treatise on the topic. The process of projecting views of an object onto three mutually perpendicular planes, and then revolving the top and side views into the same plane as the front, was first enunciated in that work. Of course, the accuracy and mutual consistency of these views is the responsibility of the drafter. While drafting conventions provide helpful guidelines, there is nothing to prevent the drafter from producing inconsistent views. Additional views require additional drawing, of course.

One of the great benefits of Solid Modeling (SM) in an engineering world accustomed to drawings is that solids can be used to produce drawings in which the consistency of the views with one another is assured. Moreover, different views can be produced quickly and easily by simply describing the desired viewing angle and projection. When you wish to view a model, the system can show it in different ways for your convenience: smooth color-shaded images for overall impressions; faceted-shaded and wireframe views for fast display; sections for analysis.

10.1 Hardware and Display

Generating smooth color-shaded images places great demands on both the computer and the display system. Many of the display techniques in use today were developed to circumvent the limitations of early hardware. For example, early high-end graphic displays plotted lines directly on the CRT screen, and were limited in the number of flicker-free lines they could display simultaneously. Display techniques were therefore developed to minimize the number of lines needed to show a model, such as representing smooth curves as sequences of straight-line segments and masking out text.

As display hardware improved, more and more of the display functions began to be accomplished in hardware, enhancing display speed and quality. The coming of age of raster displays in the late 1970s made it possible to separate model complexity from electronic considerations such as refresh rate. In today's computers, graphic performance has increased by orders of magnitude over what it was then, and cost has come down considerably. But processor speed and memory costs have always been constraints of even the high-end systems, and continue to be so.

For many applications, routing the output of the modeler to videotape is useful. Due to the generally lower resolution of video media, care must be taken to get nice-looking results (see Sec. 10.5).

Virtual reality (VR) systems, with their head- and boom-mounted displays, have raised the threshold for what is considered acceptable in terms of resolution and refresh rates. Display manufacturers are being spurred to design and manufacture more and more realistic display devices, at lower and lower cost.

Three-dimensional output from SM systems is now also available, and is another way in which models can be viewed. Rapid prototyping technologies (see Chap. 19) make it possible to create a physical version of the solid model at the push of a button, in tens of minutes. For many applications, the physical model conveys much more information than even the nicest color-shaded, dynamically rotated screen image.

10.2   Wireframe Display

The simplest way to display a solid model is as a wireframe. The wireframe is an abstraction of the solid; it is a 3D model that consists of the lines representing the edges of the model. In the case of curved surfaces, additional lines (isolines) running along the surfaces are generally added to make them visible.

In models of any complexity, wireframes can be visually confusing. The viewer may not be able to tell which part of the model is in front of other parts. Nonetheless, there are situations in which wireframe models can be helpful for the very reason that they show front, back, top, and bottom of the object simultaneously.

Older display systems (strokewriting or vector displays) often had a hardware feature called *depth cuing,* which dimmed the lines of the display in proportion to their distance from the viewer. This helped clarify the wireframe image for the viewer.

10.2.1   Hidden-Line Removal

The first step in reducing the abstraction of a wireframe and increasing its clarity is usually hidden-line removal, in which the definitions of the bounding surfaces of the model are used to determine which edges would and would not be seen from the viewer's point of view, while the ones that would be hidden are not displayed.

Early systems used a technique called *haloing* to increase viewing clarity without paying the full computational penalty of hidden-line removal. Each line crossing was computationally examined to determine which of the lines was closer to the viewer; the line "in back" would then be erased for a short distance on either side of the crossing point, as if the line "in front" had a halo around it that obscured a portion of the line "in back." This technique was visually very effective, but never caught on commercially.

10.2.3   2D on 3D Displays

It is sometimes useful to see features that would normally be visible only on a 2D drawing within the 3D model—dimensions and notes, for example. But there are no standard conventions for displaying these. Generally, it is most convenient to portray them in the plane to which they refer. Some SM systems, however, can keep the characters and dimensions parallel to the viewing plane, regardless of the rotation of the model.

10.3   Color-Shading Techniques

In order to display a solid model as a color-shaded image, the program must determine which parts of the model will be visible to the viewer and create the display in such a manner that only those are showing. Then it must determine the visual characteristics of the display as defined by lighting and texture parameters. The solid model is then displayed accordingly. Figures 10.1 through 10.6 (see color insert) illustrate many of the techniques that follow.

Shading

SMA.10.1   Always Plan Ahead

The key to creating a successful display of a solid model is to plan ahead. Visualize in your mind and write down what you would ideally like to see happen on the screen as a result of your efforts.

Overlooking this fundamental, simple, and yet crucial, step could cost a significant amount of wasted effort once you have immersed in the myriad details of actually creating views and displays, whether they be animated or even static.

What does your intended audience (not you) really want? Here are some things to consider:

1. The basic model(s)
2. Enhancements
3. The surrounding environment (if any)
4. Color scheme
5. Animation (yes or no)
6. The audience's audience (if any)
7. Desired angles and perspectives to be viewed
8. Program(s') capabilities and limitations
9. Multiple/simultaneous views on screen
10. Text integration (yes or no)
11. Sound integration (yes or no)
12. Final display hardware

Once you have committed your skill to making it all happen, you will find the above premeditated considerations invaluable. Further, you will invariably be stimulated by new revelations and possibilities as you work—however, because of the background work you've laid out, the technical details will not now cause you to be mired and led astray from the grand scheme of your work.

Keith Campbell, Engineer, VP Marketing
American Small Business Computers, Pryor, Okla.

10.3.1   CPU Time

Most SM systems offer a variety of shading techniques—quick ones for use during the design process whose results are of limited quality, and slower ones that produce high-quality images for final output and presentation. The larger the number of colors and the higher the resolution of the output, the longer it will take to compute an image.

10.3.2   Lighting

Depending on the SM system, there are five basic types of lighting which can be applied to a solid or surface model scene. Some of these may be distance-attenuated. These are listed below and illustrated in Fig. 10.7.

1. Omnidirectional light
2. Directional cosine light
3. Spotlight
4. Infinite light
5. Area light

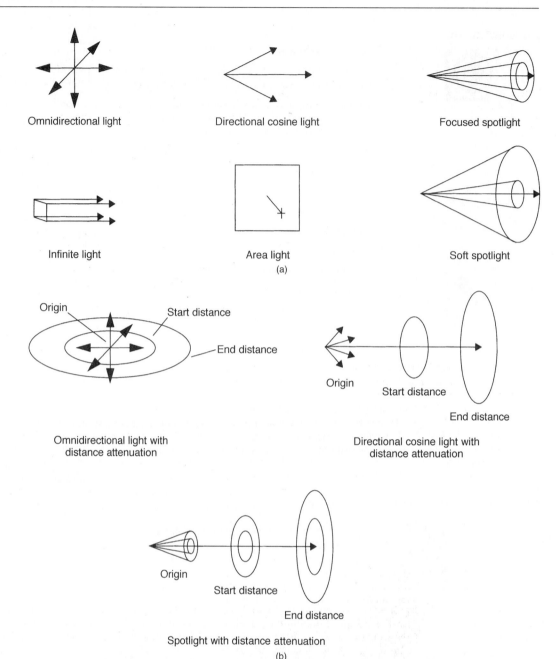

FIGURE 10.7 Sample icons for directional lighting. (*a*) Unattenuated lighting; (*b*) with distance attenuation. (*Courtesy of Wavefront Technologies.*)

10.3.3 Polygon Sort Shading

The simplest approach to creating a color-shaded image is called *polygon sort shading*. The model is approximated as an aggregate of polyhedra. Each polygonal face is examined for visibility—generally, by examining the dot product of the surface normal and the viewing vector. Faces that are determined to be visible are then sorted by their distance from the assumed viewer's eye position, then drawn in farthest-to-nearest order.

Polygon sort shading is fast and low in resource consumption, but can give imperfect results. Sometimes SM systems cannot determine which of two polygonal faces is closer to the eye position.

A shading model is then used to determine the color of each face by computing the effect of the light source on the face based on its position relative to the eye of the viewer. Of course, this yields a faceted view, in which each facet has a uniform shade; not a very realistic picture, but one that can be produced

FIGURE 8.3 Example of general surface enclosure. This general surface enclosure was constructed by using a set of sculptured surfaces which were designed to meet at their intersections. In those places where the surfaces did not meet exactly at intersections, they were either truncated or extended to a common boundary so as to form one continuous, smooth, solid enclosure. (*Courtesy of Manufacturing and Consulting Services, Inc.*)

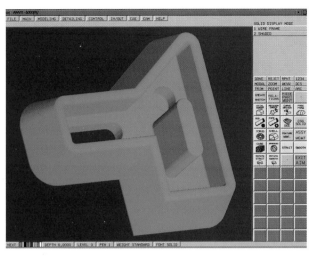

FIGURE 8.23 Example parametric/relational design process. Step 12, the final part. (*Courtesy of Manufacturing and Consulting Services, Inc.*)

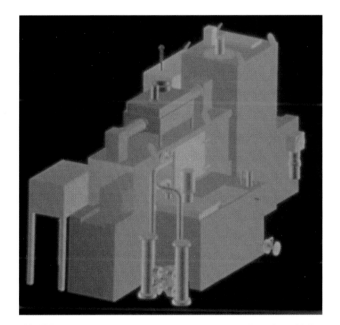

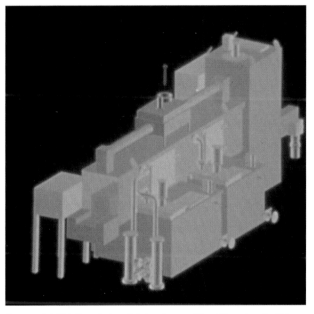

FIGURE 9.8 Two solid-model topologies from a single, real-world KBE product model. This is an industrial cleaning machine. Changing the *"cleaning cycle"* produces a visibly different design; there are also many less visible differences. (*Courtesy of Concentra Corporation.*)

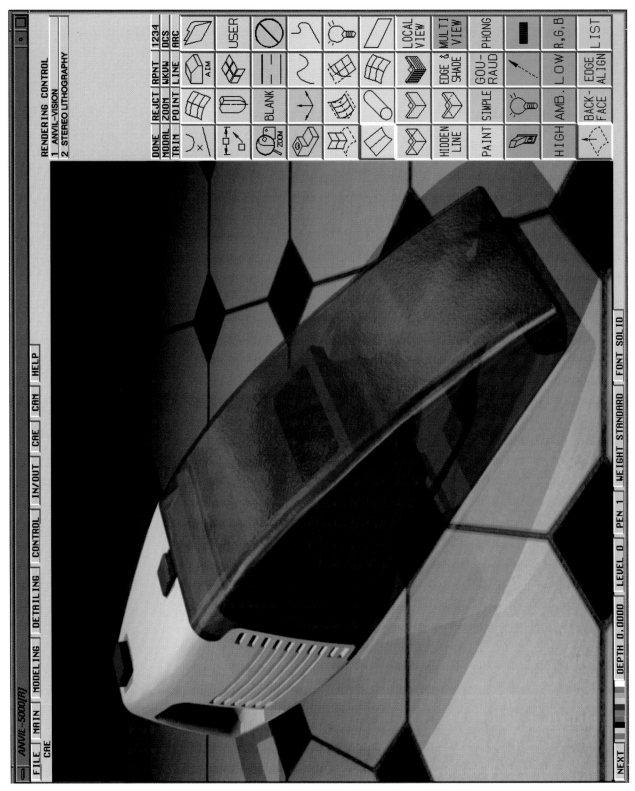

FIGURE 10.1 The ANVIL-Vision™ rendering package allows photorealistic images to be generated directly from ANVIL-5000® design data. Materials and textures can be assigned to geometric entities as the product is designed, and their properties will automatically be incorporated into the ANVIL-Vision image. Notice the use of tiling, texture mapping, shadow casting, and translucency. *(Courtesy of Manufacturing and Consulting Services, Inc., and The Hoover Company.)*

FIGURE 10.2 Rendered image from AutoCAD Designer®. *(Courtesy of Autodesk, Inc.)*

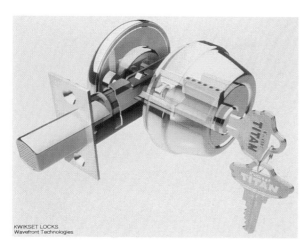

FIGURE 10.3 Image produced by Kwikset Locks for their fall 1993 catalog using Wavefront® visualization software and Parametric Technologies Pro/ENGINEER® SM package. Notice the translucency, reflectivity, and materials-coloring techniques. *(Courtesy of Wavefront Technologies and Kwikset Locks.)*

FIGURE 10.4 This image was rendered with ModelView®. Notice the use of refraction, reflection of the glass and toothbrush, and pattern mapping to present a photorealistic, ray-traced image of the design. *(Courtesy of Intergraph Corporation.)*

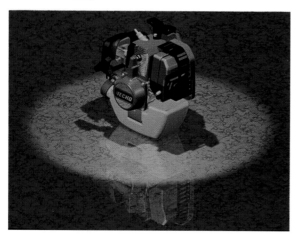

FIGURE 10.5 This portable motor for lawn mowers was modeled with EUCLID® and rendered with its integrated Lightworks® application. Notice the use of spotlighting, reflectivity, and shadow casting to highlight the product's design. *(Courtesy of Matra Datavision.)*

FIGURE 10.6 CATIA Image Design® showing application of 3D textures. Note that the cat has the look of marble while the teapot has a texture more associated with a rough casting. The depth and extent of the roughness are both under user control. *(Courtesy of IBM Corporation and Dassault Systèmes.)*

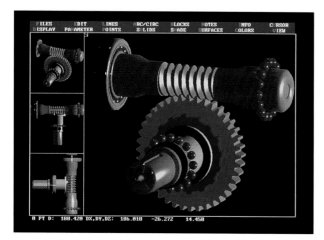

FIGURE 10.8 Chrome worm gear spindle modeled and rendered with DesignCAD 3D®. Eight light sources were positioned to produce the desired lighting and shininess. *(Courtesy of American Small Business Computers.)*

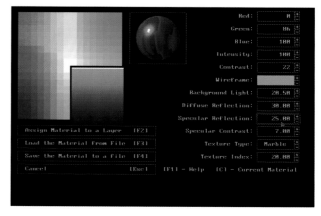

FIGURE 10.9 Sample Specular Lighting control panel from DesignCAD 3D®. Notice that there are over 14 different parametes for controlling the look of a material. *(Courtesy of American Small Business Computers.)*

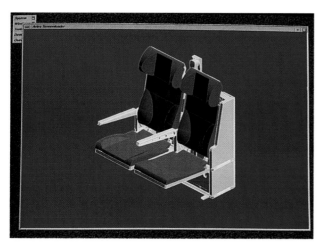

FIGURE 11.1 Solid model of an aircraft crew seat assembly. *(Courtesy of The MacNeal-Schwendler Corporation and AMI Industries.)*

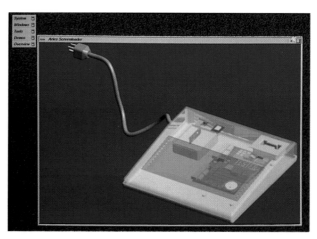

FIGURE 11.4 The use of enhanced display techniques such as translucency aid in visualizing complex assemblies. Here, the external packaging of a piece of medical diagnostic equipment is made translucent to allow the visual display of internal components. *(Courtesy of The Mac-Neal-Schwendler Corporation.)*

FIGURE 11.5 Solid model of an automobile rear suspension assembly that would require static detection consideration. *(Courtesy of The Mac-Neal-Schwendler Corporation and Ford Motor Company.)*

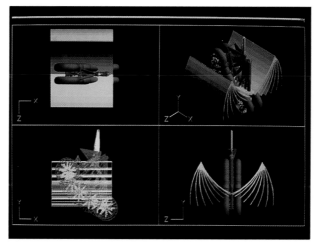

FIGURE 11.6 Solid model of an aircraft landing gear assembly. Several views of the assembly are displayed as a fan diagram to illustrate range of motion. *(Courtesy of The MacNeal-Schwendler Corporation.)*

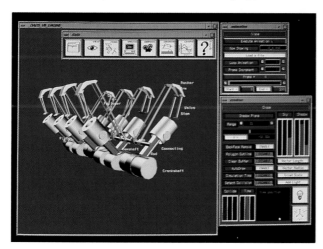

FIGURE 13.1 Model of V-8 engine for analysis. *(Courtesy of Computer-Aided Design Software, Inc., CADSI.)*

FIGURE 13.3 Model of vehicle suspension system. *(Courtesy of Computer-Aided Design Software, Inc., CADSI.)*

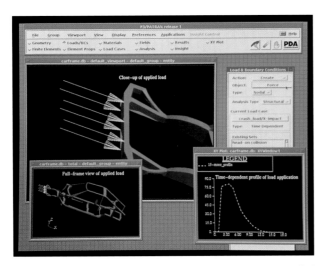

FIGURE 14.8 Case loads and boundary conditions can be applied directly to a solid model. *(Courtesy of PDA Engineering.)*

FIGURE 14.9 Postprocessing results can be displayed in color directly on the solid model. *(Courtesy of The MacNeal-Schwendler Corporation.)*

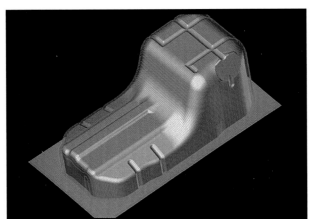

FIGURE 15.2 Die for stamping automotive oil pans from steel sheets. The die is machined directly and designed to produce the desired part shape. This die tool is then used to produce the final oil pan. *(Courtesy of Varimetrix Corporation.)*

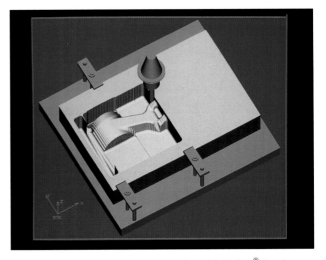

FIGURE 15.11 Solid material verification with Vericut®. Proving out tool paths prior to actual machining is a cost-effective method for avoiding mistakes on the shop floor. *(Courtesy of CGTech.)*

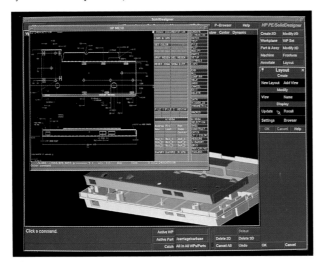

FIGURE 17.3 Bidirectional associativity. Solid models and details drawing can be associated bidirectionally where dimensional changes in either can be made to automatically update the other. *(Courtesy of Hewlett Packard Company.)*

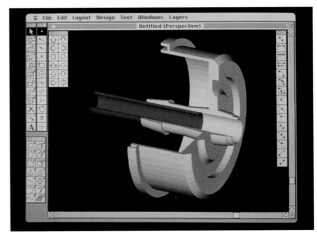

FIGURE 18.1 DesignCAD® operating on the Apple Macintosh® GUI. Single or multiple windows can be moved and resized. Toolboxes and dialogues can also be placed where needed. Cursor icons automatically change as required. *(Courtesy of DesignCAD, Inc.)*

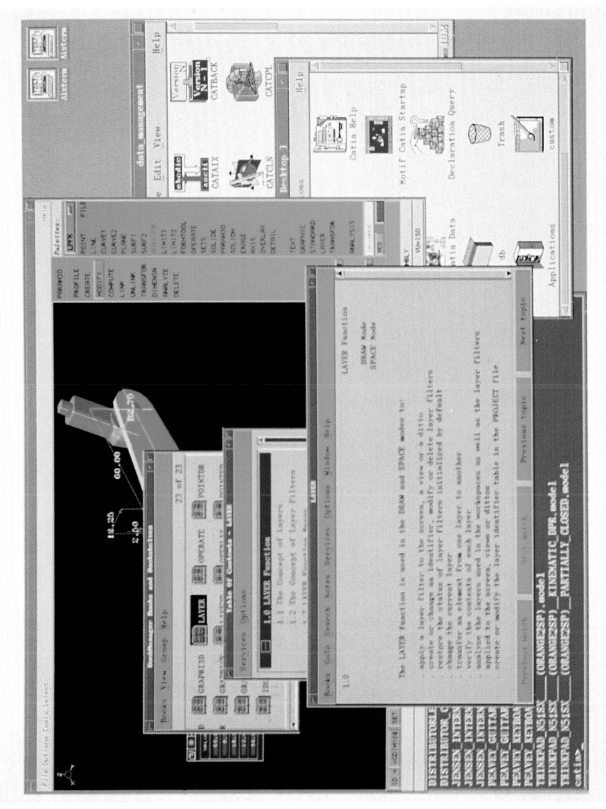

FIGURE 18.2 The GUI is a key area of solids design. Here we see CATIA® using a Motif-based interface. On the screen are several open windows which show on-line help, file management, a CATIA® parametric solid modeling session, and icons. Selecting an icon can launch a background task. A new model file can be opened by selecting a CATIA® data file icon and dragging it to the CATIA® modeling window. Because the interface is consistent throughout CATIA® applications as well as across hardware platforms, switching between platforms is easy and training is simplified. *(Courtesy of IBM Corporation and Dassault Systèmes.)*

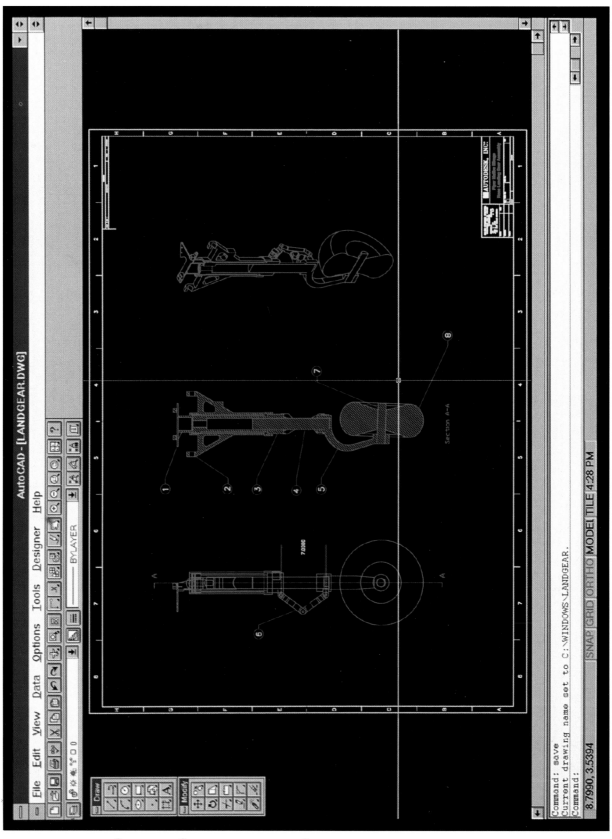

FIGURE 18.3 AutoCAD® and Designer® features a Microsoft Office®-compliant graphical user interface. Features include: drawing preview, floating toolbars, dialog-box control with visual feedback, and object linking and embedding. *(Courtesy of Autodesk, Inc.)*

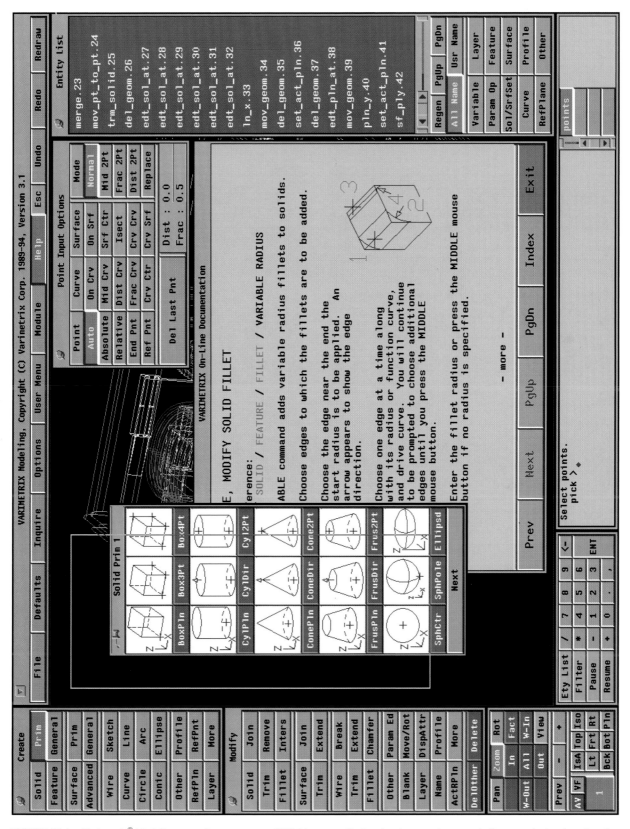

FIGURE 18.4 Varimetrix® Modeling operating on a custom GUI. Menus are displayed and removed automatically as required and can be relocated as shown. Pinned menus can remain on screen for repeated selection. On-line documentation provides help in mid-operation and allows quick cross-reference to highlighted subjects and key words. Appropriate menus also incorporate horizontal and vertical slider bars for viewing information. *(Courtesy of Varimetrix Corporation.)*

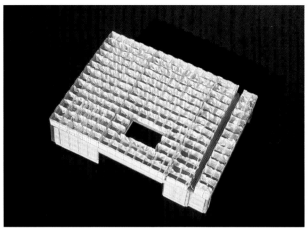

FIGURE 19.3 The bottom view of an SLA part with the support structure still attached. Support structures are removed by cutting and sanding. *(Courtesy of Protogenic, Inc., and EFI Electronics Corporation.)*

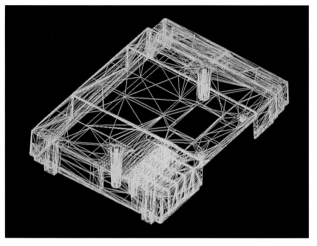

FIGURE 19.5 Looking at the STL file with the 3D Viewer® from 3D Systems. *(Courtesy of Protogenic, Inc., and EFI Electronics Corporation.)*

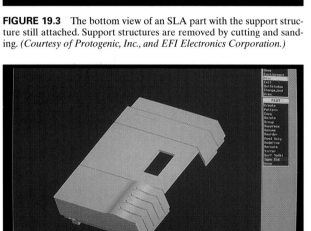

FIGURE 19.6 The original solid model created with Pro/ENGINEER® from Parametric Technology Corporation. The part is a 5 × 4 × 1 inch housing for an electronic device. *(Courtesy of Protogenic, Inc., and EFI Electronics Corporation.)*

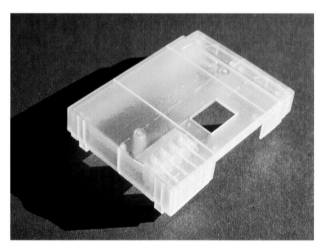

FIGURE 19.7 The finished SLA prototype part. *(Courtesy of Protogenic, Inc., and EFI Electronics Corporation.)*

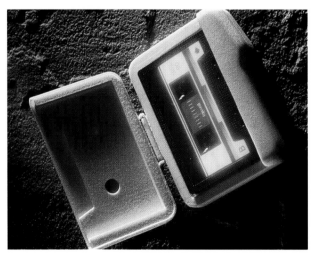

FIGURE 19.11 Sample prototype part used for design and concept verification produced by the SLS process. *(Courtesy of DTM Corporation and Structural Dynamics Research Corporation, SDRC.)*

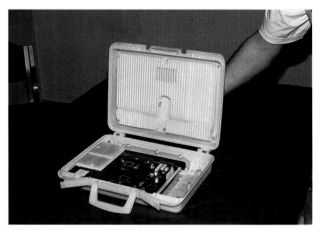

FIGURE 19.14 Sample SGC design prototype. Developers were able to take the mechanical components (including both shells) of the ABB Nera Inmarsat mobile satellite briefcase-phone, built using a Cubital Solider 5600, and immediately assemble them into a prototype of the completed briefcase. *(Courtesy of Cubital America, Inc., and ABB Nera, Norway.)*

FIGURE 19.17 Sample LOM prototype parts. Notice the look and feel of wood. *(Courtesy of Helisys, Inc.)*

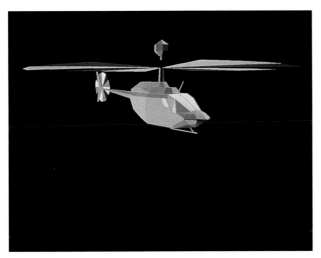

FIGURE 24.1 Solid model example produced by Project 2851. *(Courtesy of Interactive Computer Modeling, Inc. and PRC.)*

FIGURE 19.20 Sample FDM prototype parts. Notice the look of injection and blow molded plastics. *(Courtesy of Stratasys, Inc.)*

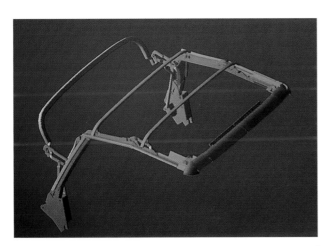

FIGURE 24.2a Convertable top stack design, stage 1. *(Courtesy of Interactive Computer Modeling, Inc. and Dura Convertable Systems.)*

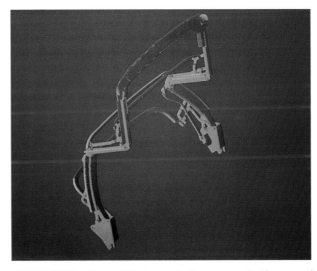

FIGURE 24.2b Convertable top stack design, stage 2. *(Courtesy of Interactive Computer Modeling, Inc. and Dura Convertable Systems.)*

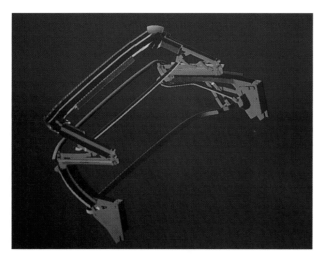

FIGURE 24.2c Convertable top stack design, stage 3. *(Courtesy of Interactive Computer Modeling, Inc. and Dura Convertable Systems.)*

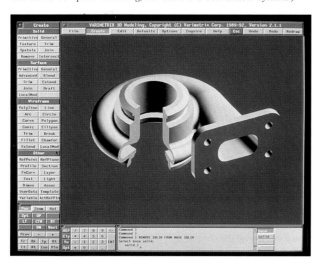

FIGURE 25.14a SM and rapid prototyping (RP). Screen image of turbo housing solid model. *(Courtesy of Varimetrix Corporation.)*

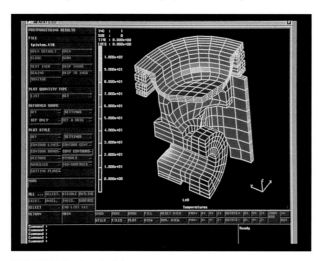

FIGURE 26.3 Sample finite element mesh illustrating an irregular volumetric array. This particular example uses such an array to analyze and display temperature distributions in a piston. *(Courtesy of MARC Analysis Research Corporation.)*

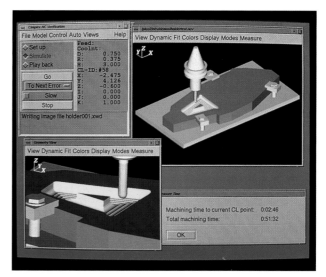

FIGURE 25.11 NC verification showing stock, clamps, and partially cut part. Errors (including fixture cuts, tool-holder collisions, and rapid cuts) are detected and reported. The scallops left between cuts are clearly visible. *(Courtesy of CIMPLEX Corporation.)*

FIGURE 25.14b Rapid prototype (RP) part produced from solid model utilizing the stereolithography process developed by 3D Systems, Inc. *(Courtesy of Varimetrix Corporation.)*

FIGURE 27.3 SM makes it easier for designers and potential customers to communicate new design ideas prior to prototyping or production. *(Courtesy of Structural Dynamics Research Corporation, SDRC, and Dalkin Clutch.)*

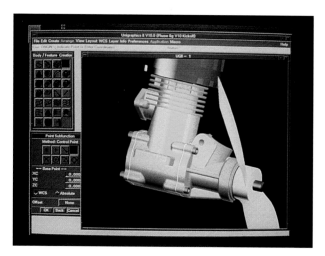

FIGURE 27.4 Visualization. Current generation SM systems, such as Unigraphics®, employ enhanced visualization techniques. This allows better communication between designers and customers. *(Courtesy of Electronic Data Systems, Inc., EDS.)*

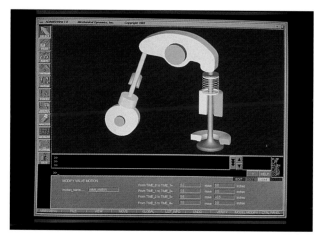

FIGURE 27.7 Kinematic analysis of component-design with Adams®. SM empowers a wide range of analysis applications, including structural, thermal, ergonomic, as well as kinematics and dynamics. *(Courtesy of Mechanical Dynamics, Inc.)*

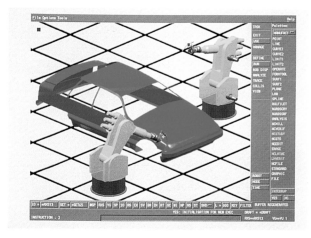

FIGURE 27.8 Rendering of robot simulation with CATIA®. SM allows advance planning of automated manufacturing processes. *(Courtesy of Aleph Technologies, IBM Corporation, and Dassault Systèmes.)*

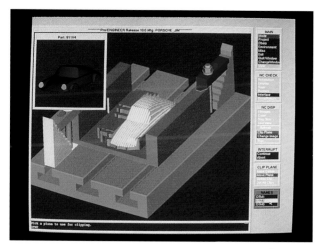

FIGURE 27.9 SM and NC verification with Pro/ENGINEER®. SM provides the geometric definition to perform a variety of fabrication simulation techniques. *(Courtesy of Parametric Technology Corporation, PTC.)*

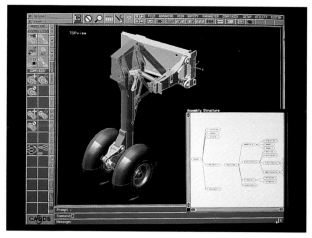

FIGURE 27.10 Solid assembly modeling with CADDS5®. SM provides many benefits for assembly modeling, such as tolerance analysis, static and dynamic interference detection, and part instancing. *(Courtesy of Computervision Corporation.)*

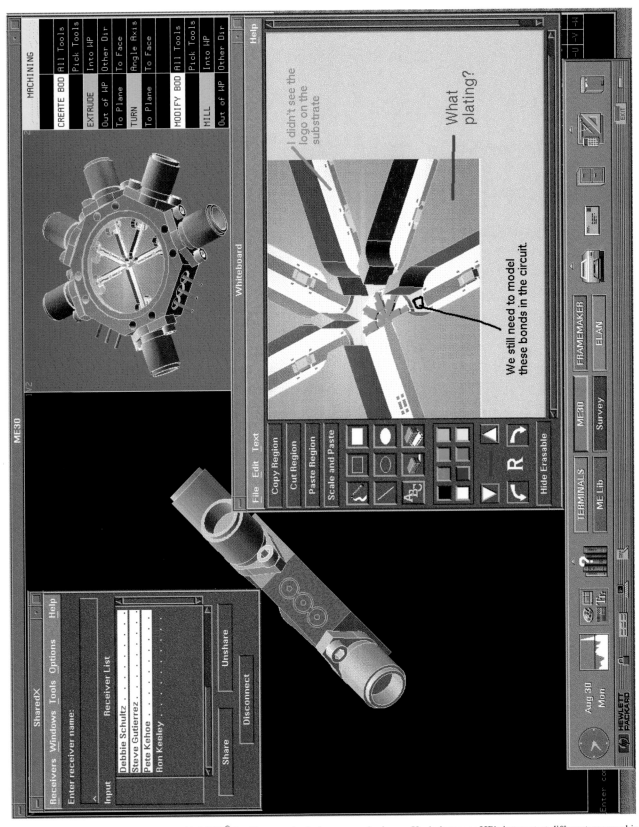

FIGURE 27.11 SM and virtual teams with ME30®. In this example, designers are sharing an X window over HP's internet at different geographic locations. The SM design application is in the background. The shared image appears in the foreground (lower right). Notice that each active virtual team member has a different pen color for markup during phone conversations. *(Courtesy of Hewlett-Packard Company.)*

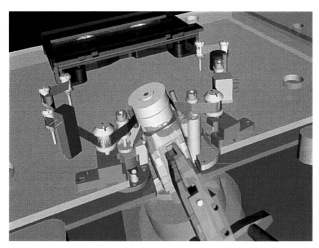

FIGURE 29.2 Typical solid model at Sony created with I-DEAS® from Structural Dynamics Research Corp., SDRC. Shown is the design outline of the *"Rotating Drum Characteristic Evaluation System"* mechanism by SM. It shows the *"rotating drum"* mechanism, its periphery, the loading of the tape, the high-density arrangement of *"tape path configuration elements,"* and the efficiency of SM to avoid interferences. *(Courtesy of Sony Corporation, Japan.)*

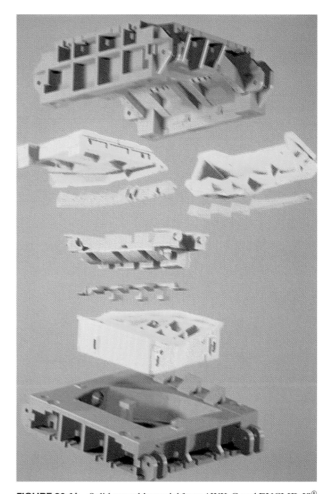

FIGURE 30.1*b* Solid assembly model from AWK-G and EUCLID-IS® from Matra Datavision. *(Courtesy of Volkswagen Automotive Group, Germany.)*

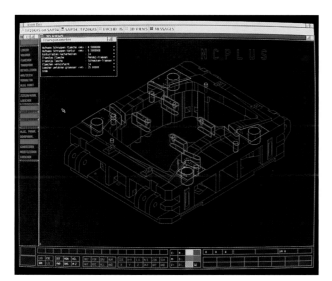

FIGURE 30.6 NC visualization. A visual survey of the die cast by the NC programmer is aided by the use of varying colors based on manufacturing elements. *(Courtesy of Volkswagen Automotive Group, Germany.)*

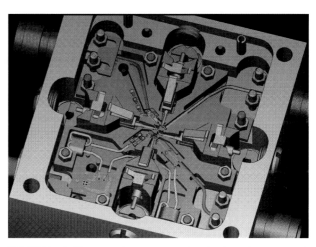

FIGURE 31.1 SM example showing a microcircuit package assembly modeled with ME30®. *(Courtesy of Hewlett-Packard Company.)*

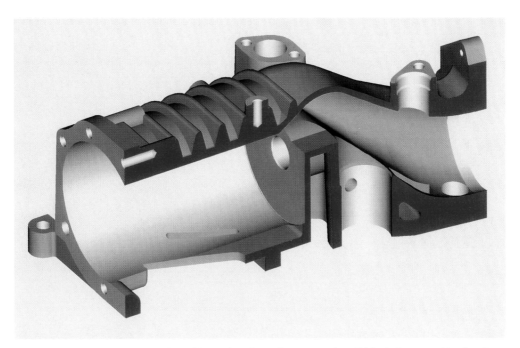

FIGURE 32.1 SM makes possible the quick creation of complex cross sections. White indicates machined surfaces, blue indicates cast features, and red indicates the temporary cross-section plane. *(Courtesy of Eaton Corporation, Supercharger Division.)*

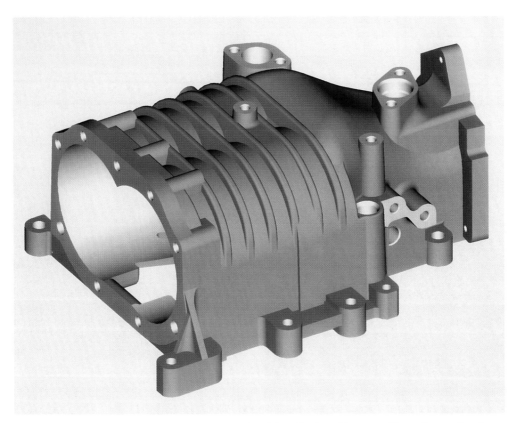

FIGURE 32.2 Solid model of supercharger cover casting, V-6 application. *(Courtesy of Eaton Corporation, Supercharger Division.)*

quickly and with relatively few resources. The lack of realism is especially pronounced when the model contains curved surfaces.

10.3.4   Antialiasing

Antialiasing is widely employed within graphical rendering systems to make shaded images appear smoother than they really are. Along the boundary at which different-colored surfaces meet, the "stair-steps" of the raster display can be annoyingly evident—especially if the boundary is neither vertical nor horizontal. If the display has the capacity to generate a sufficient number of shades, spreading the color difference over a number of pixels adjacent to the boundary tricks the eye of the viewer into thinking that the image is smooth and continuous.

10.3.5   Dithering

Antialiasing is sometimes accomplished through dithering, which refers to the creation of colors that are not directly available on a given display or printer by alternating the pixels of the component colors. Dithered images are not as smooth and aesthetically pleasing as nondithered ones, but use of dithering offers a wider range of colors than is otherwise available.

10.3.6   Translucency

Translucency, the quality of allowing light to pass through, can be simulated in color-shaded images by mixing in each pixel, or picture element, color from the background. This technique can be very effective for portraying complex objects, even when modeling materials that are not naturally translucent. Being able to "peer inside" complex mechanisms, while retaining a sense of the overall object, is helpful to viewers. *Transparency* is defined as complete translucency.

10.3.7   Reflectivity

Two kinds of reflectivity are commonly simulated: specular and diffuse. Specular, or "mirrorlike," reflectivity is very impressive when modeling shiny surfaces. The effects of diffuse reflectivity on the viewer are more subtle, but can be very effective.

10.3.8   Phong and Gouraud Shading

Phong and Gouraud shading are methods for interpolating the shading of adjacent polygons across each polygon, yielding smooth-appearing images. This smoothness can be geometrically deceptive, for the shaded image is no more precise than the underlying polyhedra. Nevertheless, it is much more visually attractive than flat shading, and often serves the purposes at hand. Gouraud shading is somewhat less compute-intensive, and somewhat less effective, than Phong. Phong shading yields superior highlights and transparency effects.

10.3.9   Ray-Tracing

Ray-tracing is a shading technique in which the path of a ray of light from the source to the viewer's eye position is traced for each pixel of a display. The full path of the ray is computed, yielding secondary and tertiary reflective effects. This approach can produce extremely realistic images, including shadows, specular reflections, transparency, and other optical effects. However, it consumes enormous quantities of computational resources, and can take a long time, even on very powerful computers.

10.3.10 Radiosity

Radiosity is a technique developed at Cornell University. Certain aspects of a scene's reflective characteristics can be computed for a given 3D model; then, when the point of view is moved, these do not need to be recomputed—making it possible to quickly compute the shading of successive frames of a movie with much less computational power than would be needed for, say, ray-tracing. Radiosity does not handle specular reflectivity as nicely as does ray-tracing, however.

10.3.11 Texture Mapping

Texture mapping is the process of "painting" a surface with a "texture" image (which could be as simple as a flat color or as complex as a photograph). If the texture has depth, as in the case of a 3D surface, it is called a *bump map*. For example, a window in a solid wall can be simulated by texture-mapping the image of a window onto the wall. Geometrically, there is no hole in the wall; visually, the wall appears to have a window in it.

A slightly more complex example: A realistic orange can be created by mapping a bumpy orange texture onto the surface of a sphere. The underlying solid retains its abstract geometric shape; the texture alters the appearance of the object, but not its geometry or topology. SM systems vary widely in the extent to which they incorporate texture mapping.

10.4 Comparison of Shading Performance

The display of color-shaded images of 3D models is an extremely complex matter, involving dozens of processes and components. The shading algorithms move into and out of hardware, into and out of different layers of the operating system/application continuum.

Workstation and software vendors have attempted over the years to establish metrics for shading performance, but with little success; competitors always challenge both the units and the measurement practices. One vendor will claim to be able to display so many millions of Gouraud-shaded polygons per second; another will point out that the first vendor is using polygons that are minimal—triangles, actually. A particular workstation vendor began expressing its performance in terms of shaded triangles per second; this was challenged by its leading competitor, who pointed out that the numbers did not correlate with real-example benchmarks.

The only way to determine the shading performance of a given combination of hardware and software is to shade a relevant selection of images on it and time the processes.

10.5 Computers, Video, and Film[1]

With the use of SM and electronic animation systems, the desire to link computers to commercial video- and film-recording equipment is greater than ever. Yet the interface between computers and video/film recorders remains somewhat complex. This section explains that interface so modelers and animators everywhere can get the most out of the work they do on-screen.

Linking computers to film- and video-recording equipment is important because it allows users to record computer animations onto videotape or film, and display them using video and film projection systems. The benefits work in the other direction as well. A two-way interface between a computer and video/film systems makes it possible to import still or full-motion sequences for display on the computer screen and for image processing with software applications.

Someday, the interface between computers and video/film recording equipment may be as simple as running cable between the two types of systems. Today, however, the interface is more complex.

10.5.1   Computers to Videotape

Recording a computer animation onto videotape is complicated by the fact that computers and video-tape recorders (VTRs) are incompatible in several significant ways. When connecting a computer workstation to a standard VTR, for example, the following incompatibilities must be addressed.

Signal Standards

Workstation display systems use video timing standards which are very different from the common television standards used by broadcast and home-quality VTRs. Part of this is due to the higher resolution of the workstation display. Many workstations are capable of displaying 1024 horizontal lines of information. The National Television Standards Committee (NTSC) standard (American and Japanese television) for composite video, on the other hand, specifies only 525 lines of video information; PAL (European and most other television) systems use 625.

Interlacing

Another timing-related complication arises from the fact that most workstations' display systems are noninterlaced, meaning that each refresh of the workstation monitor contains a complete frame of video information. In contrast, NTSC/PAL composite video contains two separate "fields"—one field of odd scan lines and one field of even scan lines, each interlaced and displayed separately. This large difference in resolution and interlacing is the major reason why the outputs from workstation display systems cannot be directly recorded onto videotape.

Display Speed

Display speed is also a big factor. A typical NTSC resolution image, stored digitally on the workstation, is roughly 1 megabyte of data. In order to achieve full-speed playback (30 frames per second for NTSC), the workstation's hard disk drives need to be able to sustain 30 megabytes per second throughput. Commonly available technology allows for only 5 to 6 megabytes per second, clearly under the requisite bandwidth.

10.5.2   Making the Connection

There are a number of ways to link computers and VTRs, and they range greatly in price and complexity.

Video/Film

SMA.10.2   Contacts

Following are some companies to contact if you are interested in connecting computers to video and/or film. They specialize in this technology and can provide valuable assistance.

Sierra Video Systems
P.O. Box 2462
Grass Valley, CA 95945
(916) 478-1000

Snader and Associates
P.O. Box 5916
Sausalito, CA 94966-5916
(415) 332-7070

VMI Inc.
211 Weddell Drive
Sunnyvale, CA 94089
(408) 745-1700

Jay Cole
Wavefront Technologies, Santa Barbara, Calif.

The easiest, yet most expensive, solution for converting high-resolution workstation output to video-tape is a scan converter. Scan converters are dedicated image processors which use filtering algorithms to compress or average high-resolution video signals from workstations into a TV-resolution video signal which may be recorded directly onto videotape. Most scan converters are capable of "real-time" conversion. That is, they are capable of converting the workstation image to video "on the fly."

This real-time conversion feature makes these converters ideal for recording activity from the entire workstation screen onto videotape in real time. However, many animators stay away from scan converters because they often lessen the quality of the original renderings. For this reason (and for cost), the preferred solution for recording computer animations onto videotape is a video frame buffer.

Video Frame Buffer

Typically installed in the workstation, a video frame buffer is a hardware device with video memory capable of holding and storing one or more frames of video information for display. Unlike a scan converter, which works in real time, a video frame buffer is loaded with individual images by the host computer. Because video frame buffers display video directly, they solve the problem of incompatibility between the high resolution of workstation displays and the lower resolution of videotape. Video frame buffers generate output compatible with VTR equipment in terms of resolution, timing rates, and interlacing. For those who choose to go the frame-buffer route, the computer/VTR interface may require up to two additional pieces of equipment: an encoder or a transcoder and a means of controlling the VTR.

Encoders

An encoder converts the component (RGB) video signals from the workstation's frame buffer to the composite signal used by most video systems. High-quality encoders can be expensive, but image quality varies significantly between low-end and high-end encoders. For this reason, the cost and quality of the encoder must be weighed against the image quality desired.

Transcoder

A transcoder converts the RGB information from the frame buffer to the video signal used by BETACAM-type devices. Many frame buffers have built-in functionality for generating BETACAM output directly, making a separate transcoder unnecessary. Likewise, VTRs capable of RGB input do not require a transcoder.

VTR Control System

Although it is possible to send commands directly from a workstation to a VTR, accurate recordings of animations require the use of an intermediate piece of equipment called a *VTR control system* or *animation controller*. This device receives commands from the host workstation, then issues the commands to the VTR.

This intervening step is needed for two reasons:

1. Since the images to be recorded cannot be loaded into the frame buffer in real time, each frame must be recorded one frame at a time. Furthermore, most VTRs require that the videotape be moving at full speed in order to record properly. Therefore, the VTR controller manages a cyclic process of pre-rolling the VTR a few seconds, bringing the tape up to full speed, and instructing the VTR to momentarily enter record mode just as the desired position on the tape is reached. UNIX workstations cannot provide the dedicated attention needed for a frame-accurate recording on a VTR.

2. Most workstations generate RS-232 output commands, while most VTRs accept RS-422 commands. A VTR control system provides the conversion between these different forms of communication.

Other Components

For specific applications, other components may be required for the computer/video link. These include:

1. A video "sync" generator which provides the required video timing signals to the overall subsystem

2. A SMPTE (Society of Motion Picture and Television Engineers) standard time-code generator which generates the time-code signal that can be recorded onto videotape

3. A time-based corrector for stabilizing images retrieved from a VTR for editing/compositing purposes

4. A switchable RGB/composite monitor for observing both the component output from the frame buffer and the composite signal to be recorded onto videotape

Digital Disk Recorder (DDR)

Generally considered to be the highest-quality and most expensive approach to video recording, the DDR can also be the simplest to use. The DDR is computer-designed for video and oftentimes connects to the workstation via the commonly understood network. Most of the computer animation videotape complexities disappear, and simple workstation software can transfer images digitally to the DDR. In most organizations, all the video-recording equipment is attached to one particular workstation. A network can give animators at other workstations access to this equipment, assuming appropriate software is available.

10.5.3   Computers to Film

Interfacing computers to film is much simpler than that for computers to videotape, thanks to the availability of digital film recorders (VTRs, in contrast, are analog devices). Whether the output is a single high-resolution print or a moving picture of an animation, when using a digital film recorder the entire computer-to-film interface consists of a workstation, the film recorder, a camera, and assorted cables and connectors.

Early "digital" film recorders contained some analog circuits which were affected by temperature, making early models unreliable for precise recording. However, reliable, all-digital film recorders are available, greatly simplifying the task of recording computer animation onto film.

Digital film recorders operate at fixed horizontal resolutions of 2408, 4096, or 8192 lines. Images must be rendered at those resolutions to fill the screen. A film recorder takes 45 seconds to 3 minutes to record a frame of animation.

For professional recordings of animations onto film, a 35mm or 60mm camera is needed. Typically, this is an Oxberry, pin-registered, cine-movement camera. For those who have a specific need for 16mm film, it is best to record onto 35mm film initially and get a duplicate print in 16mm format from a film laboratory.

Reference

1. Adapted from "Connecting Computers to Video and Film Equipment," background information, white paper, Wavefront Technologies, revised 1994. Reprinted with permission.

Isometric Viewing

SMA.10.3   What's Wrong with Isometric Viewing?

Many intricate models lose detail when viewed improperly. If possible, avoid viewing from a true isometric view or where two sides are equal angles from the eye point. A slightly skewed angle will result in differing shades for each side, making the model more clear. Where software allows, add more light sources to enhance background detail, but avoid overlighting the model.

John R. Gowans, Applications Support Specialist
CRS Sirrine Engineers, Greenville, S.C.

Isometric Viewing
(*Continued*)

SMA.10.4   Explore Alternatives

A good SM system provides not only isometric and standard views (sometimes referred to as *canned views*), but any other view in 3D space as well. A wireframe view that looks good at a certain set of angles may not look good at all from the same view once you apply hidden-line removal, shading, lighting, specular highlighting, etc. Therefore, views other than strictly isometric may be necessary.

SMA.10.5   Getting It Right

Iso means equal. An isometric view is a view of equal angles. Depending on the control-command set a given 3D program may give you, it may not be easy to approximate such a view on your screen or hardcopy device. Check your program's capabilities for this. For instance, if you have control simply to specify angles (or even specify isometric), first be sure the program cares which angle your object is to start with. That is, does it work properly only when you begin from an orthogonal view? Or will the program calculate it from any view?

Also, if the program allows for specifying only horizontal and vertical angles (as opposed to specifying all three), then specifying 45° for both angles will not give you the desired isometric view but, rather, a skewed view. You may have to experiment to obtain a truly isometric view.

Keith Campbell, Engineer, VP Marketing
American Small Business Computers, Pryor, Okla.

Hidden Lines

SMA.10.6   A Creative Balance

A key to producing a wireframe display is thinking of it at first as a very basic conflict you will invariably encounter in a solid model of any complexity: the battle between the quantity of lines which will display balanced against quality of view for sake of the viewing audience.

Take into account the size and resolution in which the scene will be displayed. For instance, suppose a cylinder is made up of so many lines that, when hidden lines are removed, it will look virtually black. Fewer lines (though yielding less polygonal accuracy) may look far better—once the lines are actually hidden.

Caution: *Never wait till you've completed the entire model scene before hiding lines!* It is better to check each object in the scene as you go, so you can correct it right then, before the model scene gets more complicated.

SMA.10.7   Line Densities

When used correctly, different line densities on different objects within a scene can be extremely effective, both artistically and aesthetically.

SMA.10.8   Think Hidden-Line Removal

The model (or scene) should actually be created with the thought firmly fixed in one's mind that the end-result display is to be one with hidden lines removed—and not shaded. This cannot be overstressed.

SMA.10.9   Wireframe Display

Wireframe displays can look very confusing to the viewing audience. Often, it is easy for you (the creator) to visually lose track of the orientation. The object may look upside down or turned inside out or even flipped. You can only imagine the problem of a viewer who did not create and work with the object trying to decipher your work. Always strive to step back and look at it from the eyes of the viewer, your audience.

Keith Campbell, Engineer, VP Marketing
American Small Business Computers, Pryor, Okla.

SMA.10.10   Interactive Hidden-Line Removal

SM systems should provide automatic and interactive hidden-line removal. Hidden-line views should be "usable" and "zoomable" views of the project, and not a separate representation or plot

(*Continued*)

Hidden Lines
(Continued)

image. Additional end-user editing should not be required. As designs are added, changed, or deleted, only the affected view areas should be rerendered, rather than regenerating the entire view.

Brian Ruuska, CAD/CAE Applications Engineer
3M Company, St. Paul, Minn.

SMA.10.11   Not a Panacea

One may think that the process of hidden-line removal itself will take care of many problems. However, a hidden-line rendition with too many lines, in the case of polygonal modelers and displays, can look almost as messy as before they were hidden. The same model which, when shaded, looks fantastic may look like a horrible thickness of lines when lines are hidden.

SMA.10.12   Dual Models

In some circumstances, it can be necessary to have two separate, though similar-looking, models: one made up of fewer lines for hidden-line display and another for shading purposes which may need the extra lines.

Keith Campbell, Engineer, VP Marketing
American Small Business Computers, Pryor, Okla.

Light Source Shading

SMA.10.13   Time for Perfection

Shading that takes light sources into account can be a key to making or breaking a high-quality—and particularly visually appealing—image of your model. I once spent two weeks on a model of a chrome worm gear spindle suspended on shiny red ball bearings (in turn, floating in space), which was meshing with a circular gear turning another spindle at 90° with a key slot in it (see color insert, Fig. 10.8 on p. ■■).

I also spent another week working on getting just the right lighting effect by using eight different light sources to strike the worm gear spirals at just such an angle so they would be very shiny and highlighted—while at the same time allowing the rest of the worm spindle to be rather dark and unreflective, yet highlighting the ball bearings and the other 90° spindle.

SMA.10.14   Persistence Can Pay Off

Struggle to learn, experiment, and understand your system's light-source functions. Once you do, it still may take awhile to apply them to a given model; however, if their use is important, you can make the difference between a mediocre rendering and a masterpiece worthy of entering into contests.

Keith Campbell, Engineer, VP Marketing
American Small Business Computers, Pryor, Okla.

Translucency

SMA.10.15   Final View Angle

One of the tricks in a design for translucent exhibition is to adjust the final view angle so the audience will gain the best understanding of its contents. Some views with translucency can be confusing, particularly if the SM system does not allow you to pick what you do and do not want to be translucent.

SMA.10.16   Internal Components

If you can choose which objects may be translucent, make the outside of an object translucent and internal objects opaque so they may be easily discerned.

Keith Campbell, Engineer, VP Marketing
American Small Business Computers, Pryor, Okla.

Specular Lighting

SMA.10.17   Positioning Light Source

In a static (or single view, as opposed to an animation), the direction the spotlight is coming from will be critical. If it is in the wrong place, the audience will not be able to tell there is any specular lighting at all. This would be like a fountain with the water turned off. When the spotlight is used in the optimum place, the results can be brilliant, like fireworks bursting onto a night sky. Experiment, experiment!

SMA.10.18   Material Selection

Consider carefully the appropriateness of materials on which specular lighting is used! A shag carpet, for example, should have no specular reflection at all (unless for surrealistic or other reasons of artistic license). Depending on reality or artistic reasons (or a mixture of both), it can be important to either observe or recall from experience the true effect of specular lighting on different materials, surface textures, etc., when applying specular reflection. Concrete is a poor specular reflector, whereas chrome is an excellent one.

SMA.10.19   For Good Results

Keys to good results with specular lighting are:

1. Understanding the definitions of the components of specular lighting.

2. Actual experimentation with specular lighting functions on-screen. This part cannot be overemphasized. All the reading in the world cannot replace this.

SMA.10.20   Controls, Controls

Specular lighting can be difficult to control unless your SM system's manual has a good explanation of its parameters. Even in inexpensive programs, there can be over 14 different parameters (on one screen) which control the look of a material (see color insert, Fig. 10.9).

Such controls can include: color-selection box; amount of red, green, or blue color; overall intensity of all colors; contrast; wireframe color; color globe; background (ambient) light; diffuse reflection; specular reflection; specular contrast; texture type; and texture index.

It is amazing when working with specular reflection and specular contrast how much other parameters can have a bearing on these two. For instance, changing the ambient light can change the perceived amount of specular reflection. Therefore, do not proceed with the mind-set that specular values can be set independently of other parameters.

SMA.10.21   Specular Reflection

The specular reflection value (from 0 to 100 percent) is the amount of light (25 from a flashlight or spotlight) that is striking a surface. This is as opposed to the ambient (or all-around/background) light that is coming from everywhere.

If specular reflection is set to 0, you will see no spot of light. The higher the percentage, the larger/brighter the spot will get. Specular contrast is like the focusing of the spotlight (specular reflection). With a specular contrast of 0, specular reflection would be the same as the diffuse reflection: the spotlight wants to diffuse out over the entire object (i.e., it is not contrasting with the material around it). The higher the specular contrast percentage, the more focused the light beam becomes on the object.

SMA.10.22   Curved versus Flat Surfaces

A curved or spherical surface is necessary to reveal the effects of specular lighting. The flatter a surface, the more it tends to spread out the beam, because the flat surface tries to evenly reflect the light projected onto it. So, trying to get good results from a flat surface will be difficult or impossible. However, if you have curved or spherical surfaces in your model, some very striking effects from specular lighting can be obtained.

Keith Campbell, Engineer, VP Marketing
American Small Business Computers, Pryor, Okla.

Static and Animated Views

SMA.10.23 Static versus Animation

If the display is to be static (i.e., a single snapshot of your model), then view angle, all lighting parameters, etc., are far more critical than in an animation. Why? An animation, with your object moving around, will display an entire panorama of many effects on many surfaces from many angles. You cover practically all the bases by default of the motion of the objects.

However, in a static shot, this is not so. You will get one chance upon release to present your model to your audience. Your model has only one chance, one view, one lighting set, one everything, and therefore must be given the advantages of the best of all possible combinations at once.

SMA.10.24 A Static Selection

With a static view, pay close attention to bringing all lighting parameters and settings to perfection. This should be done even if you get to display multiple shots that are not animated, although at least you will have a few more opportunities. Also, in this case, experiment in showing the contrast of the different effects to your audience. They may find them very revealing. Even if you get a chance to exhibit multiple shots, the preceding advice will still apply because they are static.

Keith Campbell, Engineer, VP Marketing
American Small Business Computers, Pryor, Okla.

Note: What follows are recommended settings for displaying various types of materials. Although SM and display programs will vary, this advice can be generally applied to all applications.

Material Settings Nonmetallic

SMA.10.25 Color

Set color and ambient to the same color. To create an illusion of shadowy areas without casting shadows, make ambient a darker shade than color.

SMA.10.26 Highlight

Highlight color should be a shade of gray, depending on how shiny the object is. A gray highlight reflects the color of the light source. The more white in the light source, the shinier the object will appear.

Shininess values control the size of the highlight as it appears on the object, depending on how close the light source is or how flared the light is. For example, a shininess value of 100 might produce a smooth, highly polished surface like a billiard ball.

SMA.10.27 Texture

Initially, set the color and ambient to white. Then, after rendering, if you need to correct the color, adjust the color and ambient accordingly. You would normally map a texture to the color and ambient, but not to the highlight.

SMA.10.28 Reflection Map

To create a mirrorlike material using reflection maps, set the color and ambient to black, the highlight to white, and the background type to checkered. Sharpness controls how clearly the material reflects the reflection map. For example, a sharpness control of 200 might look like a mirror. A value of 30 might look more like brushed metal.

Reflection maps can emulate the colors in the environment. Start by adjusting the highlight to gray and the color and ambient to black. Then add the color of the material to the color, ambient, and highlight. Brass, for example, would have a yellowish color applied. Highlights on metals are usually the color of the metal.

Mike Wilson, Product Marketing Manager
Wavefront Technologies, Santa Barbara, Calif.

Material Settings Other

SMA.10.29   Shiny Plastic

Set the color and ambient to the color of the material. Set the highlight color to white to get the true reflection of the color of the environment. The higher the shininess value, the more reflective the material will look. For textured plastics, apply a bump texture. For highly reflective plastics, apply a reflection map. For transparent plastic, use dissolve instead of refraction, because most plastics have a low refraction index.

SMA.10.30   Cloth or Dull Wood

The color comes from the color of the texture, not from the color of the material. Set the color, ambient, and highlight to white. Apply a color texture to the color and ambient.

SMA.10.31   Glass

Set the dissolve to .75 and the background type to checkered. For refraction, set color, ambient, and highlight to black, set density to 1.2, and set the background type to checkered. When using refraction, apply the refractive material to a closed object, such as a cube, rather than a single polygon. Light must pass through two surfaces in order for it to bend.

FIGURE 10.10   Refraction. When light passes from one medium to another, it is reflected by an amount dependent on the optical density of the two media. The appearance of a pencil bending in a glass of water is a function of the optical density of the two elements air and water. Figure 10.3 illustrates an application for this technique. *(Courtesy of Wavefront Technologies.)*

Mike Wilson, Product Marketing Manager
Wavefront Technologies, Santa Barbara, Calif.

Caution

SMA.10.32   Perspective Views

With or without clipping, be careful in the use of perspective—or your distance from your object or scene. For example, some programs can handle being able to look on the other side of a wall if the perspective (or viewing distance) is too close. If they can't, you will find yourself staring at a solid wall upon rendering. Also, in some programs, the image can actually become inverted or otherwise distorted.

Keith Campbell, Engineer, VP Marketing
American Small Business Computers, Pryor, Okla.

SMA.10.33   Tiling

Tiling places a grid over an object and creates new elements on the grid lines. When displayed together, the tiled elements represent the same area as the original elements. For the visual results of tiling, see color insert, Figs. 10.3 and 10.6.

 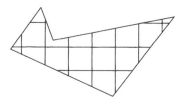

FIGURE 10.11   Creating a tiled element. *(Courtesy of Wavefront Technologies.)*

Important! Tiling can use considerable amounts of memory. If the system slows down while the tiled element is being created, it may have run out of virtual memory. This may be because you are

(Continued)

Caution
(Continued)

using a fine tiling resolution on a large object. If you need to use the fine resolution, subdivide the object into parts and tile each part separately. This avoids creating too many tiles at one time.

SMA.10.34   Sharpness

High sharpness values may introduce aliasing (jagged edges) effects in flat surfaces that are viewed at a sharp angle.

Mike Wilson, Product Marketing Manager
Wavefront Technologies, Santa Barbara, Calif.

Recommended

SMA.10.35   Shadows and Ray-Tracing

Shadow-casting and ray-tracing are two techniques that add realistic effects to rendered images. Shadow-casting directs an object to cast a shadow of itself. The shadow object is invisible, except for its shadow. Ray-tracing creates realistic reflections and refractions on reflective surfaces. Ray-tracing is a high-quality alternative to reflection mapping.

It is best to use a simplified version of the original object as the shadow or trace object since shadow-casting and ray-tracing greatly increase rendering time.

Mike Wilson, Product Marketing Manager
Wavefront Technologies, Santa Barbara, Calif.

SMA.10.36   Texture Mapping

Texture mapping potentially presents a multitude of problems, depending on the control your program gives you over it and your understanding and mastery of that control. Pray your program has a good Undo command and, if not, be sure to keep a backup copy of your work in stages along the way.

Keith Campbell, Engineer, VP Marketing
American Small Business Computers, Pryor, Okla.

SMA.10.37   For Video or TV Format

If the final product of a solid model is to go to video or television format, subtle colors may be desired to avoid color bleed or "dot-crawl." Stark colors may lose edge definition on some displays and are not truly realistic. Many paint manufacturers supply free color fans or samples which can be used for quick color selection or client approval when no computer is available. Observing colors with a computer modeler's eye makes one appreciate the subtle differences of color in real life.

John R. Gowans, Applications Support Specialist
CRS Sirrine Engineers, Greenville, S.C.

SMA.10.38   SM and Video Training

Consider the use of SM to develop interactive video computer simulations for assembly and training programs. Depending on the product and processes involved, using SM could overcome many physical limitations of conventional video production.

Brian Ruuska, CAD/CAE Applications Engineer
3M Company, St. Paul, Minn.

Recommended
(Continued)

SMA.10.39   Using Special Effects

Initially, a solid can be displayed using special effects during the construction phase. Although this is nice for the designer, special effects become an important advantage when the solid is complete. Special effects can be utilized if information about the solid needs to be presented or explained. The closer the solid is to reality in display, the easier it becomes to understand. The disadvantage of special effects is added cost due to the requirement of enhanced hardware in many cases. The cost of this hardware must be justified against the usage of the display.

David E. Schaeg, Designer
Emerson Motor Co., St. Louis, Mo.

SMA.10.40   User-Defined Views

SM programs usually allow you to create (or set the parameters for) a specific view, including the perspective and several other parameters. This can be very helpful, especially if you can save that set of view parameters—either as a named file and/or with a particular drawing.

This way, you never have to strive to re-create a particularly striking view of a model: it will either automatically be retrieved with the model—or at least you may retrieve the view after retrieving the model.

In the case that it can be saved as a separate file, the view parameters may be used on other models as well. This is particularly important because, depending on the purpose and use of the model, one can spend days just getting the view correct—after the model is created.

Keith Campbell, Engineer, VP Marketing
American Small Business Computers, Pryor, Okla.

SMA.10.41   Get What You Need

SM products vary along with their display capabilities. Some have extensive display controls as part of the base modeling package, while others offer add-on modules which specialize in advanced display techniques. Always define what your needs are prior to evaluating SM products based on their display capability. This will assist in limiting the field to those products which are neither under- or overqualified and are in the price range you can afford.

Don LaCourse, President
The Solid Modeling ExChange, Algood, Tenn.

SMA.10.42   Automatic Silhouette Lines

Cylinders and other regularly curved surfaces should be displayed without tabulation lines. All SM systems should strive to add the capability of generating silhouette lines on demand. This will allow the exterior curvature of a surface to be viewed automatically from any angle.

Brian Ruuska, CAD/CAE Applications Engineer
3M Company, St. Paul, Minn.

Section 3
Applications

Chapter 11
Solid Modeling for Assemblies

Graham A. Rae
Director, MSC/Aries Product Management
The MacNeal-Schwendler Corporation

Darrel J. Hamlet
Senior Sales Engineer
Rand Technologies

This chapter describes how individual solids can be used to represent and design complex assemblies as a logical hierarchy that relates to the packaging of the physical assembly itself. Very often, designers must be concerned with the spatial relationship of a single part to other parts that make up the total design. For example, a design may have to maintain not only certain center-of-gravity limits but also minimum clearance between adjacent parts within the assembly. Figure 11.1 (see color insert) shows a typical solid assembly model.

11.1   Assembly Modeling

Effective assembly modeling requires an understanding of the fundamentals and semantics involved. This section reviews basic assembly components, how to work with solid models of these components, and related computer hardware and software issues.

11.1.1   Assembly Components

As with any field of endeavor, there are certain terms that have become the working language for assembly modeling. Discussion of these terms follows.

Part.   A part is the most fundamental element of an assembly model. In practical terms it usually corresponds to a discrete component of the assembly. As an example, consider an automobile engine assembly. In this case, some parts that would constitute the assembly would be the crankshaft, connecting rod, and camshaft. Each part would typically be represented as a single solid, but could in addition contain wireframe geometry, text, and surfaces.

Subassembly.   A subassembly is a grouping of parts and/or other subassemblies to form an entity that can be manipulated and referenced as one item. Normally, designers create a subassembly structure for convenience in managing the total assembly. In practice, a subassembly is a logical grouping of parts that corresponds to the physical unit itself.

For example, an automobile oil pump can be a subassembly of the engine assembly. This allows the designer to relocate the oil pump by referencing it as a single entity rather than its constituent parts. The engine would typically be created as a collection of subassemblies (oil pump, water pump, alternator, etc.) in addition to discrete parts such as bolts and gaskets.

Assembly.   An assembly is a grouping of subassemblies and parts that, when taken together, constitutes the total design. Following the automobile example, this would be the total vehicle.

11.1.2   Building the Assembly Hierarchy

Using solid models to create or represent an existing assembly requires an outline plan for the grouping of components into subassemblies. The hierarchy can be thought of as a tree diagram that defines a logical grouping of subassemblies and individual parts. An assembly tree is similar to, but not the same as, a CSG tree (discussed in Chap. 4). Figure 11.2 illustrates the assembly-tree structure.

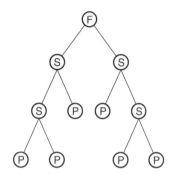

Ⓕ Final assembly

Ⓢ Subassembly

Ⓟ Part

FIGURE 11.2   The assembly hierarchy can be thought of as a tree structure that defines a logical grouping of subassemblies and individual parts. The assembly tree is similar to but not the same as a CSG tree.

For example, it would not be logical to group a subassembly of front suspension parts with individual parts of the oil pump, because then moving the suspension subassembly would cause a corresponding movement of the oil pump, which in all probability is not desired.

Another important reason for planning this hierarchy at the outset is to provide the flexibility to organize the total task into subtasks that can be assigned to individual designers or subcontractors who are then responsible for particular discrete subassemblies or parts.

Essentially, there are two approaches to creating assembly models: the top-down approach and the bottom-up approach. Referring to the assembly tree in Fig. 11.2 will aid in understanding these two approaches. Chapter 6 also provides additional insight into top-down and bottom-up design.

Top-Down Approach

In the top-down approach to assembly modeling, the organization or individual responsible for the overall assembly establishes the logical hierarchy of subassemblies and parts and assigns creation of actual geometry to others. Individual designers need not be concerned with the organization of all the subassemblies in the final assembly.

Typically, each part and subassembly are positioned and oriented within a coordinate system such that when the geometry is created it will be in the correct location within the assembly. (See Chap. 3 for more on coordinate systems.)

Bottom-Up Approach

If one person is responsible for the entire design, it is usually more appropriate to use the bottom-up approach to assembly modeling. Here the designer creates the part geometry as the first step, then combines parts into appropriate subassemblies and the final assembly.

Once the assembly structure begins to take shape, it is very useful to create the geometry for each part while viewing its associated assembly. In this way, as more part geometry is added to the assembly, one can immediately see how it relates to the geometry of other parts. In addition, most systems that support this concept allow the geometry of one part in the assembly to serve as reference geometry to aid in the construction of other parts. This concept lends itself to the use of standard part models or component libraries.

11.1.3 Component Libraries

The old adage, "Don't reinvent the wheel," is highly applicable to assembly modeling. In other words, the SM user shouldn't have to create from scratch a "wheel" (or any other common component) every time it is needed in an assembly model. For example, if there are six #10 shoulder screws in a specific assembly, the designer need only create *one* solid model of the screw, which can then be referenced or instanced into the assembly any number of times.

This concept of common parts and subassemblies leads to component libraries. A component library is simply a collection of frequently used components, often stored in an easily accessible location for all SM designers to use. The major benefit of having component libraries is that parts and subassemblies have to be modeled only once, and can be referenced from then on. The use of multiple component libraries can save companies lots of time and money!

There are two primary methods of establishing component libraries. These are: (1) purchase the component libraries from another company or vendor, or (2) create them yourself. To purchase a component library implies that someone else has created a library of components and is willing to make that library available either in general or under certain conditions. It also implies that the model data is in a format that can be used by your particular SM software.

Most companies establish their own component libraries by creating a separate database into which SM operators "deposit" finished solid model components. For example, a BEARING database can be set up on a computer that will be the central location for all bearing assemblies modeled. Then, if a certain bearing is needed for an assembly, it can simply be instanced into the assembly model from the BEARING database. To be *instanced* means that the bearing will appear on the display of the new assembly while the bearing's geometric database remains in the component library. The productivity of this concept is apparent. Figure 11.3 illustrates the component library concept.

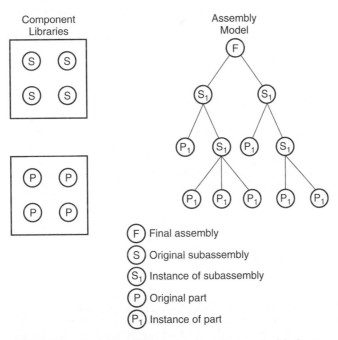

FIGURE 11.3 Component libraries allow the collection of original component models so that they need to be modeled only once. Assembly models display an instance of the original components in their assembled position. Updating the library component models will automatically update all instances of the components.

Not only do component libraries eliminate redundant effort in creating solid models, but they also permit automatic updating of assemblies that incorporate a particular component when that component is modified in the library. So, for example, if an SM operator alters the original model of a standard motor mounting plate in the component library and this component is used by seven different assembly models, then all seven assemblies will get updated with the new library entry.

11.1.4   Performance Issues

The computer hardware used for assembly modeling can greatly impact the interactive performance or usability of the SM software. With proper consideration of memory (RAM), hard disk (storage), and graphics (display) hardware requirements, future problems, and physical restrictions can be alleviated. These issues are discussed here.

Memory Requirements (RAM)

On most SM systems, assembly-modeling data structures do not require large amounts of memory or disk space. Note that we are referring only to assembly-modeling capability. Other SM capabilities require more memory. Parts in the assembly merely refer or point to the actual part geometry file which, in most cases, is located in a component library. For example, if there are four wheels in an automobile assembly, then there is one full definition of the geometry of the wheel and four pointers to that definition in the assembly model.

When working with the assembly, most SM systems load only the part geometry required for a particular operation into memory. For example, even when checking for interferences between every combination of parts in an assembly, the system would load only two sets of part geometry into memory at a time.

Hard-Disk Requirements (Storage)

It is the part geometry itself that dictates the amount of hard-disk space required to store the complete assembly. The amount of space required should be governed by the size of the component libraries. For example, five assemblies that require the same part will require the necessary hard-disk space to store only one of the parts. The assembly model file itself should require very little hard-disk space, assuming that each of the individual parts are library components.

Graphics Requirements (Display)

When working with assembly models that contain a large number of parts, consider using a hardware graphics accelerator supported by your particular software package. A large amount of solids data on the screen can slow the system down for viewing operations such as rotation, panning, and zooming. Allowing the graphics accelerator hardware rather than the system CPU (central processing unit) to perform the necessary display processing will result in a substantial performance increase, and will allow dynamic viewing operations in real time.

11.1.5   Visualization Issues

Assemblies, by their very nature, include a large amount of visual data. Consider the case of a solid model of a complete aircraft. It would be virtually impossible to make any sense of the display using a simple wireframe graphics representation of the solid. Images with hidden lines removed are better, but by far the best type of display is shaded color, which provides excellent realistic images and far less visual ambiguity.

Depending on the SM system, graphics images can be further enhanced through use of features such as translucency, specularity, reflectivity, and multiple light sources. Translucency, for example, allows viewing through the outside skin of the solid so that hidden assembly features are made visible. In Fig. 11.4 (see color insert) the packaging of a piece of medical diagnostic equipment has been made translucent to allow one to see into the equipment to check the positioning of internal components. (Refer to Chap. 10 for more on viewing and displaying solid models.)

An additional display technique that is very useful in large assemblies is the ability to perform a graphical section view to show an internal cross section of the geometry. In addition, some SM software supports the concept of a dynamic section plane that allows the operator to step through a series of internal cross sections of the assembly in real time. This is especially useful for interference studies and viewing of analysis results.

11.1.6   Additional Advantages

Other than those previously mentioned, assembly modeling offers additional advantages to the SM operator and manager. These can include bill-of-materials (BOM) generation, where-used queries, and coordinate systems.

Bill of Materials

For any assembly, it is important to know the quantity of each part used. This information is necessary for cost estimating and ordering purposes.

Most SM assembly modelers can automatically create a tabulated bill of materials and diagram that shows the assembly hierarchy, the number of occurrences of each part in each subassembly, and the number of occurrences of each subassembly in the overall assembly.

Where-Used Queries

Imagine the case where a standard part referenced in an assembly is obsoleted by the manufacturer. A "where-used" query option is typically available with SM assembly modelers that will search through designated assemblies and give notification of where and how many times the obsoleted part is referenced.

Coordinate Systems

Many designs make extensive use of coordinate systems. For example, there are most likely several hundred coordinate systems used in the design of an aircraft. A wing assembly, for example, would have its own coordinate system, and each structural rib may also have its own coordinate system. This allows designers to work with a coordinate system positioned and aligned for convenient input of design data for each subtask.

When creating or modifying a part in an assembly, it is normal to use a coordinate system local to that part, simplifying creation or interrogation of the part. Matching of coordinate systems is often used as a means of mating parts and subassemblies together: two parts or subassemblies are brought together such the coordinate systems are aligned and colocated with respect to each other. (See Chap. 3 for more on coordinate systems.)

Some SM assembly modelers offer an alternative means of positioning parts and subassemblies by making use of geometric features on the solid. For example, a motor housing can be positioned with respect to its mounting base by matching a face on the base of the motor to a face on the mounting base. This would give the relative alignment. A further requirement may be to position the centerline of a hole with the centerline of the motor shaft.

11.2   Interference Detection

An interference which goes undetected until the hardware prototype stage can prove very costly and delay product introduction. An important benefit of SM is the ability to determine interference problems. This can range from a simple "yes" or "no" type of output to calculating and displaying the interference volume or volumes.

Interference between parts can be thought of as *common volume*. If two solids share common space or volume, then they interfere with one another. If they share common faces and/or edges, then they are in contact with one another. Many SM systems will automatically search through an assembly and perform automatic boolean intersection calculations between each pair of solids. Static and dynamic are two types of interference detection.

11.2.1   Static Detection

Static (fixed position) interference detection is generally used to investigate the final configuration of the assembly for potential interference problems. However, it can also be used to check out intermediate configurations of the assembly. The key feature of either case is that nothing in the assembly is moving. The SM operator must position all assembly components within the context of the assembled state and then perform the static detection. Figure 11.5 (see color insert) illustrates an assembly model that would require static detection consideration.

11.2.2   Dynamic Detection

Dynamic (moving position) interference detection is generally used to determine if any *collisions* will occur as the assembly moves through its range of motion. It may be helpful to think of the dynamic case as nothing more than a series of static cases over some time interval. The boolean interference checks are calculated at various increments, which means that dynamic interference checking will take much longer than static interference checking. Complex motion for large assemblies can require considerable time and computer hardware resources. Figure 11.6 (see color insert) illustrates an assembly model that would require dynamic detection consideration.

Most SM systems offer macro programming capabilities, which can be used to increment the relative positions of components in an assembly model to achieve pseudo-dynamic interference checking. This approach might be useful, for example, for checking an assembly process for possible interferences (design for assembly). The motion paths that an assembly person or robot might follow could be traced in 3D and automated via a macro. (See Chap. 16 for more on programming with SM and Chap. 25 for more on SM and manufacturing.)

11.2.3   Tolerance Analysis

If one or more parts are manufactured at their maximum dimensional tolerance, there will be a ripple effect that may cause collisions or interferences downstream. Within the manufacturing tolerances of all the components of the assembly, there can often be many situations where parts may not assemble properly. Problems may arise by having one or more parts out of specification. A tolerance buildup may gradually creep into the assembly by having many parts involved, each within their respective manufacturing tolerances, but when taken as a whole simply out of tolerance at the assembly level.

As the complexity of the assembly model increases, so do the total number of possible permutations of tolerance-related part and subassembly problems. There are specific programs to address tolerance issues, including *Design for Manufacturability* by Boothroyd & Dewhurst[1] and *Variation Simulation Analysis* (VSA) by Applied Computer Solutions.[2]

11.3   Applications

By now one might ask, "When does it make sense to build assembly models?" or "How can I apply an assembly model in such a way that it can explicitly help me accomplish my job better?" The following applications offer insight to some uses of assembly modeling.

11.3.1   Ease of Assembly (Fit and Form)

Perhaps the most obvious benefit of SM assembly modeling is having the ability to check spatial relationship(s) between components. In addition, the designer can often foresee manufacturing (assembly process) problems with dynamic explosion techniques, as illustrated in Fig. 11.7.

FIGURE 11.7   Solid model of a washing machine pump assembly shown dynamically exploded to evaluate fit and function of components. *(Courtesy of The MacNeal-Schwendler Corporation.)*

Dynamic explosion refers to the ability to dynamically *explode out* the components of an assembly, and then to dynamically reassemble them. Also, *off-the-shelf* manufacturing requires management of many original equipment manufactured (OEM) parts and subassemblies. Often, there is a need to know how much space a supplier's component will occupy in the overall assembly. In this instance, design envelopes (e.g., surface enclosures) can be used.

11.3.2   Mass Properties

Inherent in the solid assembly is a distribution of mass. In many applications, aerospace for example, the total mass, center of gravity, and moments of inertia (both area and mass) must not only be known but controlled. Accurate calculation of assembly mass properties is directly related to the "accuracy" of the solid models. In general, precise solid models are more accurate than faceted models (especially coarsely faceted models). The level of preciseness is based on the numerical accuracy of the mathematics involved in defining the solid(s). Figure 11.8 shows the graphical display of mass-properties information on an SM assembly.

There are times, however, when the designer may know some of the mass-property information associated with certain parts or subassemblies and wish to include this in the overall assembly model. Designers do not have to take the time to construct a detailed solid model. Most systems offer the capability to assign mass properties to components, usually via a dialogue box or on-screen table. This can save much time, considering that mass-property information can usually be tagged to most entities (wireframe entities, surfaces, solids, etc.). In this way, the designer can maintain a high level of understanding of the mass distribution in the product, without spending too much time creating a model of an off-the-shelf component.

For example, assume that a product engineer is using an industry standard DC motor in an assembly. Midway through the design cycle, there is a requirement to provide a fairly accurate estimate of the total shipping weight of the product along with the center-of-gravity (CG) location. In the overall solid assembly model, a simple box can be inserted that represents the motor's physical space. Then, because

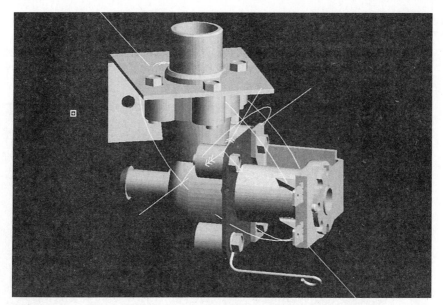

FIGURE 11.8   Solid model of a washing machine pump assembly with graphic symbols showing center of gravity and ellipsoids of inertia. *(Courtesy of The MacNeal-Schwendler Corporation.)*

it is already known, the weight and center of gravity can be assigned such that it will be taken into account in the overall assembly mass-property calculation.

11.3.3   Documentation

Should the solid assembly model be recorded with words and/or pictures? The answer depends primarily on the available computer hardware. If there is a color Postscript® printer available, then most design documentation can be graphically captured in full color. This is probably the most common means of communicating solid models graphically on paper. After all, a color hardcopy is worth a thousand words.

Most SM systems offer the capability to not only capture the screen in full color and send it to a printer, but also to capture the screen as a file (in a variety of standard graphic formats) that can be exported to various desktop publishing packages. Figure 11.9 illustrates this capability. (Refer to Chap. 17 for more on SM and documentation.)

Of course, there are more basic documentation requirements, such as bill of materials information, 2D detail drawings, process sheets, etc. These are usually stored electronically (for archival and concurrent use by others) as well as printed or plotted on paper.

In addition, there may be a need to photograph and/or videotape design work. Photographs can be taken directly of a high-resolution monitor by a professional, or even a practiced amateur photographer. There are also slide-making systems that can be attached directly to computers. Video images can be captured directly from the screen as well, but are usually extracted from the computer through video interface hardware to avoid scan lines associated with differences in scan rates between camera and monitor (see Chap. 10, Sec. 10.5). Either way, most solid assembly packages offer view dynamics (moving, rotating, exploding, slicing, etc.) as a means of communicating with others.

11.3.4   Rapid Prototyping

Rapid prototyping (RP) can be thought of as another form of documentation. Today, there are many RP methods available, but regardless of the method used, the solid assembly model will, at some time, need to be verified. This verification can consist of many forms. For example, it may be necessary to

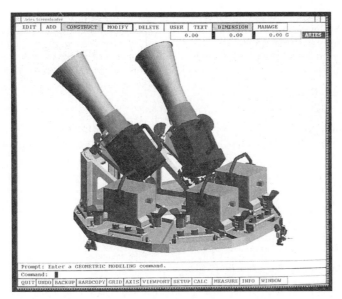

FIGURE 11.9 This solid model assembly image of the Space Station navigational platform was captured in an electronic format and used to produce a 35mm slide. *(Courtesy of The MacNeal-Schwendler Corporation and Honeywell Space and Strategic Operations Division.)*

physically verify that part A can be inserted into the assembly with subassembly B in place and bolted down. There is a certain amount of confidence-building required in modeling before engineers trust their SM assembly model data.

Another benefit of applying RP technology to SM assembly models has to do with the ability to simulate a production run by making molds directly from the RP prototypes. This might give insight into production variations and tolerances attainable through the manufacturing methods proposed for a particular part or assembly.

In addition, purchasing, sales, and marketing groups can show prospective customers and suppliers what the future part or product will look like (and sometimes how it will function) by showing 3D RP copies to them. These models can be built with fairly tight tolerances and, with some paint and polish, can secure a contract or reduce bids before the product is even made. (See Chap. 19 for more on SM and RP.)

11.3.5 Mechanism Modeling and Manufacturing Processes

Mechanism modeling is the use of assembly models to simulate mechanism behavior. If a product's function is kinematic or dynamic in nature, one can simulate the relative interaction between components. Design considerations such as determining the maximum reaction forces and moments for the entire range of motion, or visualization of how the assembly works, can be addressed.

If a design is static (does not move), then there is usually no need to simulate relative motion between components. However, it might still be of interest to simulate the manufacturing or assembly process of some or all of the components. Some of the manufacturing benefits of mechanism modeling are, but are not limited to, the following:

1. Determine clamping forces needed to hold the part for certain operations.
2. Synchronize various manufacturing processes (e.g., cam-driven machinery).
3. Visualize how specific points move in space during an operation.
4. Determine velocities and/or accelerations of certain components.
5. Determine torque requirements to rotate a component (e.g., motor-sizing estimates).

In any case, building mechanism models from the solid assembly model can be very straightforward. Generally, all that is required is to define the relative behavior between mating components (sliding, rotating, etc.), apply forces and/or moments, and prescribe motion generators. In most cases, the components of the assembly model are treated as rigid bodies (extremely stiff) and will behave as such. If the flexibility of the components needs to be taken into account, there is analysis software available to address these issues as well. The mechanical response of the assembly is then solved (kinematically or dynamically) and the results can be made available for graphical postprocessing.

Within the postprocessing phase, there are many ways of viewing results. Among the most popular are:

1. Shaded solid animation
2. *X-Y* plotting of displacements, velocities, accelerations, forces, etc.
3. Automatic interference-detection displays where the "instant in time of intersection" is captured and displayed
4. Trajectory curves superimposed on the assembly to highlight precise motion of certain points over time

(See Chap. 13 for more on SM for kinematic and dynamic analysis.)

11.3.6 Finite Element Analysis (FEA)

FEA technology is used in assembly modeling to calculate structural response from static and/or dynamic loads (both structural and thermal) imposed on the assembly. The objective is to answer questions such as the following:

1. What are the stresses and displacements resulting from bolting two parts together?
2. What are the contact stresses as two mating parts move with respect to one another?
3. What will the temperature contours in a printed circuit board be if it is positioned directly above the power supply and the cooling fan stops working?

Contact and noncontact types of component interaction are usually modeled with gap elements. In other words, as two or more parts move within their spatial envelopes and eventually come in contact with one another, the structural response can be determined.

Shipping and packaging concerns can be addressed with FEA as well. One can easily create a hypothetical shipping environment, usually a worst-case study with maximum expected loads applied. A designer could use FEA, for example, to determine what would happen if a package were dropped on its corner from a height of 36 inches, or to find out whether a component of the assembly would be damaged if it is subjected to a broad-based random excitation (such as a truck driving down a bumpy road).

Finite element models are normally built from solid models. There are very robust automatic mesh generators that greatly simplify the task of approximating geometry. Loading and boundary environment(s) that are to be simulated can be obtained from the results of a mechanism's analysis (as mentioned previously), experimental or historical data, or conservatively estimated for a worst-case type of analysis (as in the example of the cooling fan stopping and subjecting the electronic package to a free-convection environment).

In any event, SM assembly models can provide the basis for FEA. There are many benefits to predicting the behavior of an assembly *prior* to actually building a prototype. (See Chap. 14 for more on SM for FEA.)

Assembly Modeling

SMA.11.1 Component Libraries

Create and promote the use of multiple component libraries. This will save modeling time, reduce assembly model database size, and will in many cases increase performance. (See Sec. 11.1.3 for more on component libraries.)

Careful inspection of assembly models affected by a change to a component library model should be made. Possible misalignment of downstream components within each individual assembly model may result. It should be noted that the SM operator making the change to the component library model may not necessarily know of the implications of the change(s) with respect to all of the assembly models that have incorporated the component.

(Continued)

Assembly Modeling
(Continued)

SMA.11.2 Assembly Model Objectives

A lot of time can be saved in building an assembly model if the final objective or application is kept in mind. For example, if the sole purpose is to create a finite element mesh, then very often the fine details (small fillets, holes, etc.) can be ignored during creation, removed, or blanked afterward to save time and effort. It is prudent to always keep in mind the objectives for building the assembly model.

SMA.11.3 Hard-Disk-Space Requirements

It is important when purchasing decisions are being made concerning SM hardware and software requirements to take into account the projected size of assemblies and parts to be designed and then to add a factor of safety into your calculations to allow for expansion.

The size of the SM software package itself must also be factored in, as it is a fact of life that, as vendors add more functionality into their SM software products, disk-space requirements will increase. It is prudent to assume a 10 to 20 percent growth per year for most typical solids-based packages.

SMA.11.4 Assembly Model Management

Implement a proper database management system that will keep track of changes and downstream effects (e.g., a changed part may adversely impact other assembly models).

SMA.11.5 Visual Feedback

In assembly modeling, visual feedback is very important. If possible, work in a shaded solid display at all times. This helps keep the image from seeming to "pop in and out," creating optical illusions of depth which are typical of wireframe displays. The use of graphics accelerators, as mentioned in Sec. 11.1.4, will provide the response times necessary for shaded assembly modeling.

SMA.11.6 Share Your Knowledge

Encourage all SM operators to share their experiences in assembly modeling techniques. Formal user groups are often formed for this purpose.

SMA.11.7 Model Representations

Use simplified representations of OEM products in your assembly models. For example, if an off-the-shelf DC motor is incorporated into an assembly model, and knowing the assembly's mass properties is important, then model the motor as a box and assign actual mass properties to the simplified representation.

If, on the other hand, the concern is interferences of the motor with neighboring components, then create a simplified surface envelope of the motor. The point is to always keep in mind the desired goal of the assembly model and then determine how best to utilize operating time in SM assemblies.

SMA.11.8 Exploded Assembly Views

When an assembly model contains a large number of parts, it is often very useful to create an exploded view. This operation takes each part and either physically or graphically moves it radially outward from some center point. Exploded views are often used as graphics images in various technical publications such as repair manuals or assembly instructions (see Chap. 17).

SMA.11.9 Graphics Accelerators

Use graphics accelerator hardware with assembly modeling whenever possible. Your hardware costs will increase initially—but try to think ahead. If your interactive display performance is increased by 200 percent, you will spend much less time waiting. The increased productivity will justify the costs over a very short time.

(Continued)

Assembly Modeling
(Continued)

SMA.11.10   Purchasing Hard-Disk Space

It should be noted that the cost per megabyte of hard-disk storage will greatly decrease when purchasing larger hard disks. It is typically less expensive to buy a larger single hard disk now than to add additional hard disks later. Also, if one of the SM workstations must be a server as well, then it is recommended that multiple hard drives be installed and that one be dedicated to server activity.

Don LaCourse, President
The Solid Modeling ExChange, Algood, Tenn.

Interference Detection

SMA.11.11   Model Accuracy

In order for any type of interference detection to report accurate results, the models being analyzed must be true and accurate representations. Simplified versions of component parts as mentioned in Sec. 11.4.1 will not suffice.

SMA.11.12   Tolerance Considerations

Tolerance analysis can be considered a form of static detection. Maximum material conditions (MMC) should be considered when performing any static detection analysis. Parts that initially show no interference may contact or interfere when manufacturing tolerances are taken into account.

Don LaCourse, President
The Solid Modeling ExChange, Algood, Tenn.

SMA.11.13   Sole Reliance

Design as you normally would and use interference checking for the fine details. Don't become reliant solely on interference checking, or your instinctive design abilities may get sloppy!

Mason Deever, Consultant
Jamm Computer Services, Mesa, Ariz.

SMA.11.14   Dynamic Detection

Remember to consider all possible positions of assembly parts during interference detection analysis. It is prudent to assume that if parts can interfere, they will.

SMA.11.15   Reducing Calculation Time

When possible, reduce the calculation time required by limiting the solids to be checked. For example, when there are obviously pairs of solids that do not interfere, do not include them in the interference calculation. Most SM systems allow the user to *hide* or blank those solids not desired as part of the calculation.

SMA.11.16   Useful Interference Checking Procedures

Besides the traditional interference check to determine whether solid A overlaps the same space as solid B, it is also useful to get visual cues on which solids overlap and what the volume of overlap is.

(Continued)

**Interference
Detection**
(*Continued*)

In assembly environments, for convenience and accuracy, it is useful to have the ability to choose a volume in which to test all components for overlap. Similarly, it is useful to have the ability to check every component in the entire assembly without having to interactively pick or in some other way identify them.

Mark J. Silvestri
Life Cycle Solutions, Inc., Avon, Mass.

References

1. Design for Manufacturability, Boothroyd & Dewhurst, Wakefield, R.I.
2. Variation Simulation Analysis (VSA), Applied Computer Solutions, Inc., St. Clair Shores, Mich.

Chapter 12

Solid Modeling and Mass-Properties Analysis

Victor E. Wright, P.E.
Design and Engineering Consultant

A key feature of a solid model is that its database includes information which can determine the mass properties of the physical objects being modeled. Thus, it is possible to analyze the mass properties of actual physical objects by analyzing equivalent solid models of those objects. The advantages of determining a solid model's mass properties may range from predicting an object's weight to predicting the dynamic behavior of a complex mechanism.

Matter has mass and occupies volume. These two properties, mass and volume, distinguish matter from empty space and form the basis for Solid Modeling–related mass-properties analysis. This chapter reviews the functional process of SM and mass-properties analysis as well as the various types of analysis results.

12.1 Operational Approach

The operational approach to mass-properties analysis on a solid model may vary from system to system. However, all systems require information on an object's material characteristics and environmental conditions. Typically, this information can either be entered at the time of the analysis request or stored permanently in the model's database. Material density will be a required input.

After entering the requested information, the SM system calculates the solid's mass properties and displays the results either alphanumerically, graphically, or both. Results can typically be displayed on the solid, in a window, or sent directly to a data file or printer. Depending on the SM system, mass-properties results can also be assigned to a parametric/relational variable to capture or influence design intent. Figure 12.1 shows a window containing the results of a typical mass-properties request.

12.2 Mass

Mass is a measure of the basic property of matter—inertia, which is the tendency of an object to remain at rest or in motion in the absence of external forces. Matter has inertia, and therefore mass, whereas empty space has neither. For a given kind of matter and state of that matter, the mass is proportional to the amount of matter present. Because matter has mass, it exhibits other properties that are of immediate interest, such as weight, for example. Additional properties are also proportional to the amount of matter present.

Depending upon the system of units in use, the unit used to measure mass may be a fundamental unit or a derived unit. Mass is related to the units of force, length, and time by the following relation:

$$F = m \frac{dv}{dt} = ma$$

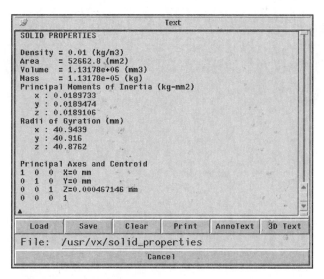

```
                              Text
SOLID PROPERTIES

Density = 0.01 (kg/m3)
Area    = 52662.8 (mm2)
Volume  = 1.13178e+06 (mm3)
Mass    = 1.13178e-05 (kg)
Principal Moments of Inertia (kg-mm2)
    x : 0.0189733
    y : 0.0189474
    z : 0.0189106
Radii of Gyration (mm)
    x : 40.9439
    y : 40.916
    z : 40.8762

Principal Axes and Centroid
1  0  0  X=0 mm
0  1  0  Y=0 mm
0  0  1  Z=0.000467146 mm
0  0  0  1

  Load      Save      Clear     Print    AnnoText   3D Text

File:   /usr/vx/solid_properties
                        Cancel
```

FIGURE 12.1 Sample results of a mass properties analysis request. *(Courtesy of Varimetrix Corporation.)*

It is obvious that the electronic data structures that make up solid models do not themselves have mass. The mass of a solid model is simply a number that is assigned to and stored in the data structure that describes each solid entity in the model. Alternatively, the mass of a solid may be calculated at will from volume and density values.

12.3   Volume

Matter occupies space and has volume. An SM system represents a solid object by specifying the volume it occupies. Although there are several database structures for representing solid objects, such as constructive solid geometry (CSG) and boundary representation (B-Rep), all distinguish the solid object from the empty space surrounding it. This involves specifying surface boundaries between the solid and surrounding space. The volume enclosed by this boundary is the volume of the solid.

Volume is measured in linear (length) units raised to the third power, inches^3, feet^3, meters^3, etc. SM systems, like the CAD systems to which they are related, measure distance in generic units that have no intrinsic meanings. However, the generic units of the SM system can be assigned meanings that correspond to the units used to measure physical objects.

Solid Modeling systems need not store the volume of a solid entity in that entity's data structure, as the volume can be calculated from the solid's boundary when required. Indeed, it is wasteful of resources to store volume in the data structure because volume changes with each modification of the boundary.

12.4   Materials and Densities

A given amount of a specific kind of matter, at a given temperature and pressure, has a certain amount of mass and occupies a certain volume. The amount of matter in a unit volume (a cube measuring one unit on a side) is a measure of the material's density. Specifically, density is a measure of the mass of the material in a unit volume.

Solid Modeling systems can calculate the volume enclosed by the surfaces of a solid model. Material specifications can be associated with a solid model or a component of a solid model by including an attribute in the portion of the database that describes the model or component. If the component is defined by a database record, the material assignment is contained in a field of that record. If the component is defined by a group of records, the material assignment may be contained in one of the records. A material assignment will typically consist of the type of material (such as steel or copper) and conditions (such as temperature and gravitational forces).

Density and other properties may be stored with the material assignment or in a separate lookup table. Given a material density and a calculated volume, the SM system can calculate the mass of a solid model or component. To accommodate additional analyses such as finite element analysis (FEA), a solid model may include other material properties, such as the coefficient of thermal expansion and modulus of elasticity. (Refer to Chap. 14 for more on SM and FEA.)

12.5 Surface Area

Solid models may be defined by surfaces, as in B-Rep models, or by solid objects, as in CSG models. In either case, or in the case of a hybrid approach, surfaces are associated with the spatial boundaries of the solid model.

A solid model is typically assembled from primitive elements, each one of which has an associated bounding surface, usually of regular form. In turn, the composite solid model is bounded by a complex surface group. This complex surface group is comprised of portions of the surfaces that bound the various primitive solids. That is, portions of many of the elemental surfaces lie inside the solids bounded by other surfaces. To calculate the surface area of the composite solid, the system must determine the intersections of the elemental surfaces and tally only the surface area that divides the composite solid from empty space.

Some SM systems display solids by default in a wireframe format. The wireframe consists of edges which are the intersections of adjacent surfaces and tessellation lines which are intermediate contours added as visualization aids (see Fig. 12.2*a*). These are sometimes called *isolines*. That is, the database contains information about the bounding surfaces, but does not display them explicitly.

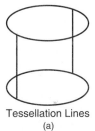

Tessellation Lines
(a)

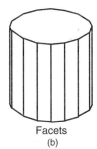

Facets
(b)

FIGURE 12.2 In a wireframe display, the difference between tesselation lines and facets. (*a*) Tesselation lines; (*b*) facets.

Some SM systems approximate surfaces with planar polygons (see Fig. 12.2*b*). The smaller the polygons, the smoother the surface. By the same token, it takes less time to calculate the display of a surface that is approximated with a smaller number of large polygons.

Solid Modeling systems can calculate the surface area of a solid, if required. First, the system calculates all of the edges or surface intersections. Then it determines which portion of each surface is a boundary between the solid model and the surrounding empty space. Finally, it tallies the areas of the exposed surfaces.

12.6 Moments of Inertia

If couple, or moment, is applied to a system consisting of a rigid body of mass *m,* an axis of rotation, and a connecting rod of negligible mass and length *r,* the mass *m* will begin to rotate around the axis of rotation (see Fig. 12.3). The time required to bring the body to a given speed depends upon both the mass of the body and the length of the connecting rod. As either the mass of the body or the length of the rod increases, so does the time required to bring the speed of the rotation to the given value.

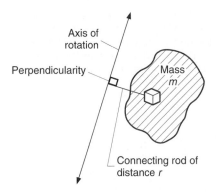

Axis of
rotation

Perpendicularity

Mass
m

Connecting rod of
distance r

FIGURE 12.3 Moment of inertia. The moment of inertia of the mass m with regard to an axis of rotation at a distance r is r^2m. That is, it is proportional to the mass and the square of the distance to the axis of rotation.

Just as the inertia of a mass indicates its resistance to changes in velocity, the moment of inertia indicates the resistance of a mass to changes in speed of rotation around a given axis. The moment of inertia of the mass m with regard to an axis at a distance r is r^2m. That is, it is proportional to the mass and the square of the distance to the axis of rotation.

For a body of finite dimensions, the moment of inertia must be found by subdividing the body into small elements and calculating the moment of inertia for each element. That is:

$$I = \int r^2 dm$$

As noted, a solid model does not define mass explicitly, so the calculation of the moment of inertia of a solid model is essentially:

$$I = \int r^2 dV$$

multiplied by the density value assigned to the model or component.

It is generally not feasible to calculate the moment of inertia analytically, because solid models of real-world objects have complex shapes. Instead, numerical methods must be used. An SM system incorporates the algorithms required to perform such calculations. The system subdivides a solid object into small elements (the number can usually be specified by the designer), calculates the moment of inertia of each element, and sums the elemental results to arrive at a value for the moment of inertia of the model or a component of the model.

Because numerical methods are used to calculate the moment of inertia of a solid object, the result is approximate. Specifying a small number of elements causes the system to use larger elements in the calculation, which leads to less accurate results. There is a trade-off between accuracy and speed of calculation.

12.7   Centroid

If a force is applied to a body of finite dimensions, the body will tend to translate and rotate simultaneously. If the force is applied at a certain location, however, the body has no tendency to rotate. Such a force passes through the centroid of the body, or the center of mass. If the density is uniform, the center of mass is also the centroid of the volume. The body behaves as if all the mass were concentrated at the centroid. The centroid is located at the intersection of two axes, about each of which the moment of inertia is zero.

12.8   Radii of Gyration

The radius of gyration of a solid object is calculated with respect to a particular axis of rotation. It is the distance from the center of mass, or centroid, of the solid to the projection of the centroid on the axis of rotation. The distance is measured along a perpendicular from the centroid to the axis of rotation.

The radius of gyration, k, with respect to a given axis of rotation can be calculated from the moment of inertia with respect to the same axis of rotation with the following relation:

$$I = k^2m \qquad \text{or} \qquad k = \sqrt{\frac{I}{m}}$$

Three radii of gyration, calculated with respect to three antiparallel axes of rotation, locate the centroid or center of mass. Each radius of gyration defines a cylindrical surface which passes through the center of mass. Two of the surfaces intersect to form a curve. The third surface intersects with the curve in a single point. Generally, these calculations will be made with respect to the mutually perpendicular axes of a cartesian coordinate system.

12.9   Products of Inertia

The product of inertia of an element is calculated with respect to two axes, and is defined by relations of the form:

$$P_{xy} = \int xy \cdot dm$$

$$P_{yz} = \int yz \cdot dm$$

$$P_{zx} = \int zx \cdot dm$$

When the moment of inertia of a solid is calculated with respect to an arbitrary axis passing through the origin of the coordinate system, the result consists of the moments of inertia with respect to the three coordinate axes, and products of inertia with respect to the three pairs of axes.

12.10   Principal Axes

The moment of inertia of a solid can be calculated with respect to an arbitrary number of axes passing through a given reference point. In general, the moment of inertia will consist of moments of inertia with respect to a coordinate system with its origin at the reference point, and products of inertia with respect to the same coordinate system. If the coordinate system is rotated about the origin, both the moments of inertia and the products of inertia will change.

Consideration of all possible coordinate systems reveals that for one system, the products of inertia are zero, and moments of inertia with respect to the coordinate system axes are at maximums or minimums. When the coordinate system has been oriented so that the products of inertia with respect to it are zero, then the axes of that coordinate system are the principal axes of the solid.

If the centroid of the solid is used as the reference point, then the principal axes so located are the principal centroidal axes.

12.11   Principal Moments

The principal moments of inertia are the moments of inertia calculated with respect to the principal axes. Again, the principal moments will be either maximums or minimums with respect to a given axis of the coordinate system. As the coordinate system is rotated about the given origin, the moment of inertia with respect to a given axis increases or decreases.

In fact, the moment of inertia with respect to the given origin of the coordinate system does not change, because it is determined by the amount of mass in the body and the manner in which the mass is distributed. As the moment-of-inertia components change, so do the products of inertia, as noted previously. When the products of inertia are zero, the moments of inertia are principal moments.

12.12   Cautions and Needed Improvements

While the underlying mathematics of mass-properties analysis in SM are sound, there are areas for improvement. Error reporting and validity checks are two such areas.

The results of any analysis are only as good as the geometric and input data. In the case of SM, this is the solid model itself. Improvement is needed in providing sufficient feedback that the solid model under consideration is valid—all geometry is in a form acceptable for accurate analysis and that any in-process errors are duly reported, noted, and logged.

Designers will rely heavily on the results of their SM systems mass-properties analysis for many and varied reasons. They expect and deserve accurate results from accurate models. While both designers and SM systems' developers have a responsibility to being accurate, each can do more. Developers can design added intelligence into their SM systems to safeguard against designer and system errors. Designers can provide more feedback to developers about their results (good and bad) in the field.

Application

SMA.12.1   Details for Weight

When checking a part for mass properties, especially in the case of a die casting, it is usually necessary to put draft on the surfaces, but not necessarily the fillets or radii. The best way to check this is to build a part completely and check the mass properties. Then suppress the radii and see what kind of difference it makes. You'll find that some of the larger radii might need to be put in. Once you get a good idea of what is needed and what isn't, this will save some time if you are just concerned with weight.

Philip Johnson, Development Engineer
Emerson Electric Company, St. Louis, Mo.

SMA.12.2   Modeling Containers

Many manufacturers specialize in the design of consumer- and industrial-related containers such as milk bottles, shampoo bottles, and automotive fluid reservoirs. Next to manufacturability, volume is perhaps the most critical design criteria for these products. With SM, volume is easily determined as needed.

SMA.12.3   Material Cost and Requirements

Volume can be used to determine the amount of material required to produce a given part. For example, by knowing a part's volume, one can determine exactly how much base material is required to injection-mold a plastic part. This information can be used to purchase only the amount of material required to complete a given production run. Exact material costs per unit can also be determined.

SMA.12.4   Weight by Volume

By determining volume and material, weight is easily calculated. In the case of modeling containers mentioned in SMA.12.2, one may now determine how much the container weighs after it is filled with its appropriate contents, including the material used to manufacture the container.

SMA.12.5   Surface Area

Knowing the amount of surface area of a given solid can be very useful. When modeling a large structure that will require multiple finishes, such information can be used to determine how much primer, paint, or other exterior materials are required. The added weight and material costs of such external finishes can also be determined. Surface area can also assist in determining the effects of surface friction or drag on a given component.

Don LaCourse, President
The Solid Modeling ExChange, Algood, Tenn.

Technical

SMA.12.6   Check Surface Normals

When performing mass-property calculations on solids, it is important to keep all surface normals pointing in the same direction (usually outward; see Fig. 12.4). Programs used to calculate volume and centroids could actually subtract surface area when it should have been added, resulting in incorrect values. This is most noticeable when joining IGES and other surface data into a solid. Visually inspecting a shaded solid model can reveal inverted surface normals (the back side of a surface will not shade).

(Continued)

Technical
(*Continued*)

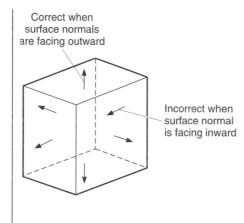

Correct when surface normals are facing outward

Incorrect when surface normal is facing inward

FIGURE 12.4 Surface normals and analysis results. The surface normals of a comprised solid should always face toward the exterior of the part. Inverted surface normals will not shade properly and may cause errors in analysis results.

Wally Fredrick, Director Customer Support
Varimetrix Corp., Palm Bay, Fla.

SMA.12.7 Which Mathematical Definition?

Mass-properties analysis algorithms for faceted solids can be based on either the exact mathematical definition or the faceted representation. Be sure you know before you perform any analyses, especially where precision and accuracy are important.

Brian Moriarty, Senior Engineer
Hamilton Standard Space & Sea Systems,
Windsor Locks, Conn.

SMA.12.8 Maintain Closure

Mass-properties analysis is based on solid objects of closed volume; there are no cracks or missing surfaces. Most SM systems will not allow nonclosure conditions to occur, or will at least flag the condition if present. Errors in function or results may occur if mass-properties analysis is performed on solids which are lacking surface definition.

SMA.12.9 Accuracy Checks

In the case of volume, simple accuracy checks can be performed to boost confidence in your SM system's mass-properties analysis results. A basic check can be to model a simple cube and check the SM system's results with the actual known value. A more advanced check would be to ask for the volume of two complex solids. Subtract one of the solids from the other and ask for the volume of the result. This value should equal the actual subtraction of the two previous values.

When possible, compare the volume of the solid model with that of the actual manufactured part. This can be performed by submersing the part in a volume of water and noting the difference in water level. The results of such tests should fall within your SM system's tolerance values. Note that in most SM systems the tolerance for mass-properties analysis results can be changed independently of the system's display or modeling tolerances.

Don LaCourse, President
The Solid Modeling ExChange, Algood, Tenn.

SMA.12.10 Moments of Inertia Caution

The moments of inertia of a complex solid can be obtained by summing the moments of inertia of its various components taken with respect to a particular coordinate system. However, care must be taken in regard to a solid built from overlapping components with boolean operations. The SM sys-

(Continued)

Technical
(*Continued*)

tem can place an arbitrary number of solids in the same place, whereas only one real solid object can occupy a given elemental volume of space at a time.

Solids formed by union or intersection of two overlapping solids must be analyzed as composite objects. As an alternative, a union can be analyzed as two separate objects; then the moment of inertia of the intersection of the two objects can be subtracted from the sum of the moments of the two component objects. Of course, no time is likely to be saved.

A subtraction can be analyzed as two separate objects if the "hole" object is completely contained in the solid object. That is, if a cylinder is subtracted from a slab to make a hole, the cylinder's moment of inertia can be subtracted from the solid slab's moment of inertia as long as the cylinder is completely contained in the slab and is the same height and width as the slab.

SMA.12.11   Volume Caution

Some SM systems calculate volumes by firing random rays through the solid, rather than by exhaustive numerical analysis. The rays may miss small features, which can lead to substantial errors, because the moment arm in the expression for moment of inertia is squared. Results should not be taken for granted.

SMA.12.12   Is There Enough Detail?

When using the mass-properties analysis capabilities of your SM system, be sure your model contains enough detail to provide accurate output data, without causing unnecessary time delays, to process the information with marginal changes in the results.

Kevin P. Alexander, CAD/CAM/CAE System Administrator
Littleford Day, Inc., Florence, Ky.

Chapter 13

Solid Modeling for Kinematic and Dynamic Analysis

Edward J. Haug, Ph.D.
Director, Center for Computer Aided Design
The University of Iowa

Rexford L. Smith
President
Computer Aided Design Software, Inc.

Author's Note: Because of the limited space available in this chapter and the advanced techniques involved in kinematic and dynamic analysis, many technical terms are used here without a full and complete explanation of their meanings. Refer to "Suggestions for Further Reading" at the end of this chapter for additional sources of information and the Glossary for assistance on terminology.

The objective of this chapter is to assist engineers and modelers in using Solid Modeling (SM) for computer formulation and solution of kinematic and dynamic models of mechanical systems that have emerged over the past decade. Emphasis is placed on the important role played by SM in defining mechanical system models and visualizing results of computer simulations.

The contribution of computers in all fields of science and engineering is already significant, and is becoming pivotal to many disciplines. Computer software has revolutionized the analysis of structures and electronic circuits and is now having a major impact on the kinematic and dynamic analysis of mechanical systems.

Historically, SM in mechanical system design has been restricted to cumbersome batch-oriented programs. The process then evolved to include interactive interfaces with limited graphics. Today, with ease of use a concern, SM systems are completely integrated and offer advanced 3D geometric construction capabilities, analysis, and animation. Such an integrated analysis and visualization process is vital in kinematic and dynamic analysis, since the interpretation of motion predicted over time is one of the most important phases of the mechanical design process. In the past, this required mock-ups or prototype equipment. Today, it can be done with computer animation of solid models. SM visualization thus allows insight into design performance prior to the physical prototype stage. One can evaluate the effect of components on other areas of the model early in the design process, which can contribute to a shorter design cycle.

With SM and kinematic and dynamic analysis tools, problems can be isolated and adjustments made to the design until the desired results are achieved. Realistic simulations of the behavior of any number of alternative designs, as well as performance "trade-off" studies can be performed, reducing the expense of building and testing.

13.1 Defining Kinematic and Dynamic Analysis

For the purposes of this chapter, a *mechanical system* is defined as a collection of rigid bodies that are connected by joints that limit relative motion of pairs of bodies. The motion of a mechanical system is defined by the time history of the position and orientation of the bodies that make up the system. Kinematics and dynamics of mechanical systems are characterized by large amplitude motion, which leads to geometric nonlinearity in the kinematic equations and the differential equations of motion.

The definitions of three types of analysis typically involved in the design of mechanical systems will now follow.[1]

13.1.1   Kinematic Analysis

Kinematic analysis of a mechanical system is the study of motion of the system, independent of forces that produce motion. Typically, the time history of the position or relative position of one or more bodies in the system is specified. The position, velocity, and acceleration of all bodies in the system over some specified interval of time are then determined by solving systems of nonlinear algebraic equations for position and linear algebraic equations for velocity and acceleration. The resulting motion is then visualized using animation of all bodies making up the system.

13.1.2   Dynamic Analysis

Dynamic analysis of a mechanical system determines the motion of the system due to the action of applied forces. A special case of dynamic analysis, known as *static analysis,* is the determination of an equilibrium position of the system under the action of forces that are independent of time. The motion of the system, under the action of applied forces, is required to be consistent with kinematic relations imposed on the system by the joints that connect bodies in the system. The equations involved in dynamic analysis are differential equations or a combination of differential and algebraic equations.

13.1.3   Inverse Dynamic Analysis

Inverse dynamic analysis is a hybrid form of kinematic and dynamic analysis in which the time history of positions or relative positions of one or more bodies in the system is defined. This allows complete determination of position, velocity, and acceleration of the system from the equations of kinematics.

For dynamic analysis, these results are used in the equations of motion of the system to determine the applied forces and torques that are required to generate the specified motion. These forces and torques determine the capacity of actuators that are required to generate the desired motion.

13.1.4   Force

The source of forces that act on a mechanical system is an important consideration, particularly when some form of control is applied. Forces due to electrical and hydraulic control subsystems such as electric and hydraulic motors play a crucial role in the dynamics of modern mechanical systems. The scope of mechanical system dynamics is, therefore, heavily dependent on the classes of force systems that act on the mechanical system.

Gravitational Force

The most elementary form of force that acts on a mechanical system is gravitational force, which is normally taken as constant and acting perpendicular to the surface of the earth. Other forces act on bodies in a system due to interaction with their environment. These include aerodynamic, friction, and damping forces that act due to the relative motion of the components of the system.

Compliant Element Force

An important group of forces acting in a mechanical system is associated with compliant elements such as coil springs, leaf springs, torsion bars, tires, and shock absorbers. Forces due to compliant elements act between bodies in the system and are functions of their relative position and velocity.

13.2 Methods of Kinematic and Dynamic Analysis

A revolution occurred during the 1970s and 1980s in computer-aided kinematic and dynamic analysis of mechanical systems. Large-scale computer programs appeared that have replaced manual graphical analysis with computer analysis and visualization using SM. Both conventional and computer-aided approaches to kinematic and dynamic analysis are discussed following.

13.2.1 Conventional Approach

The mechanism designer has traditionally resorted to graphical techniques and physical models for the kinematic analysis of mechanical systems, due to the highly nonlinear nature of large displacement kinematics.[2,3] These methods are limited in generality and rely heavily on the designer's intuition. Contemporary mathematical treatments of mechanism and machine dynamics provide a more systematic approach to analysis.[1,4–7]

The conventional approach to the dynamic analysis of mechanical systems is to use lagrangian methods[8–10] for formulating the equations of motion of the system. Numerous texts on basic dynamics[5,8–10] provide the fundamentals that are needed for mechanical system dynamic analysis.

Mathematical models of kinematic and dynamic systems have traditionally been determined by ad hoc formulations. These formulations take advantage of the properties of a specific system to obtain simplified forms of the equations of kinematics and dynamics. A creative selection of position and orientation variables can occasionally lead to a formulation of the kinematic and dynamic equations of motion that allows manual derivation, but rarely analytical solution, of the equations of motion.

More often, analysis of systems with even three or four degrees of freedom leads to massive algebraic manipulation in constructing the equations of motion. The ad hoc formulation approach is, therefore, limited to relatively simple mechanical systems. Some extension has been achieved using computer algebra,[11] in which a computer performs differentiation and algebraic manipulation, determining terms that are required in the equations of motion.

After the governing equations of motion have been derived by manual or symbolic computation methods, one is still faced with the problem of obtaining a solution of the differential and algebraic equations of motion. Since these equations are highly nonlinear, the prospect of obtaining analytical solutions is remote, except in very simple cases. Advances in computer technology have allowed engineers to use the computer and available numerical methods to solve the equations of motion. This still involved a substantial amount of time and specialized personnel for deriving equations of motion and writing ad hoc computer programs to perform the numerical integration.

In contrast to the traditional ad hoc approach that has been employed in mechanical system kinematics and dynamics, an extensive literature has evolved in finite element structural analysis[12,13] and the analysis of electronic circuits.[14,15] These fields are characterized by the same technical approach. Rather than relying on arduous ad hoc formulations, a systematic approach is taken, and computers are used for both the formulation and solution of the governing equations.

13.2.2 Computer-Aided Approach

Through the systematic formulation and selection of numerical techniques, operator-oriented software is currently available that is capable of simulating a broad range of structures and circuits. The overwhelming success of finite element structural and electronic circuit analysis software in the 1980s has led to the development of general-purpose software for mechanical system kinematic and dynamic analysis.

Beyond analysis, another challenge facing the design engineer is how to guarantee an effective and efficient design without going through numerous iterations of physical prototypes. Even after a product is designed, it still must be subjected to costly testing. It is difficult to physically prototype and realistically test some designs. The inability to produce physical prototypes greatly increases the complications in proving design viability.

The traditional method of testing designs falls into the "design-build-test-redesign-rebuild-retest" cycle. This process can be very long and expensive. With current methods, this process can now be reduced, and in some cases eliminated, with software prototyping and computer-aided engineering tools that allow design verification throughout the production cycle. The goal here is a concurrent engineering (CE) environment in which a master product definition database (master model) serves all stages of design, analysis, testing, and manufacturing. (See Chap. 27 for more on Solid Modeling and Concurrent Engineering.)

The emergence of technologies that allow engineers and analysts to incorporate multidisciplinary concepts and simulate design performance are making major contributions to the design process. Engineers are now able to safely and efficiently verify design performance, without the high cost or endangerment to human lives.

13.3   Computer-Aided Kinematic and Dynamic Analysis

The objective of computer-aided kinematic and dynamic analysis is to create a formulation of the underlying laws and to implement them with computer software that allows one to:

1. Input data that defines mechanical systems of interest and automate the formulation of governing equations of kinematics and dynamics.
2. Automate the solving of nonlinear equations for kinematic and dynamic response.
3. Provide animated computer graphics output of simulations, based on solid models, to communicate results.

The essence of this objective is to make maximum use of digital computer power for rapid and accurate data manipulation, numerical computation, and visualization of results. This relieves the engineer of the historic process of tedious and error-prone manual calculation and ad hoc creation of computer programs.

Advances in computer-aided finite element structural and electronic circuit analysis suggest that a systematic approach to the formulation and solution of the equations of kinematics and dynamics of mechanical systems is required to implement computations in an operator-oriented computer program. There are numerous alternatives available to achieve this objective. We will now discuss, in more detail, computer-aided kinematic and dynamic analysis integration issues, their operational approach, and the need for further improvements.

13.3.1   Solid Modeling Integration

The effective utilization of kinematic and dynamic analysis hinges upon its integration with established CAD and SM tools for model generation and visualization of results. While results in graphical form help to understand the behavior of the system, the full power of computer-aided kinematic and dynamic analysis is realized only when animated output is provided, much as a videotape of an actual experiment with a real vehicle is required to fully understand the intricacies of vehicle motion.

Using body position and orientation variables, with kinematic constraints selected from a library, motion analysis can be applied to permit the definition of a mechanism in an SM environment. The application of kinematic and dynamic analysis software allows one to automate the process of formulating and solving the equations of kinematics and dynamics.[1]

Interfaces with other mechanical computer-aided engineering (MCAE) programs make kinematic and dynamic analysis software an important component of a total design system. Such software complements finite element analysis (FEA) and computer-aided design (CAD) by mathematically simulating the dynamic performance of mechanical systems. This is made possible through database translators that communicate with many major FEA and CAD programs. This integration eliminates manual transfers with two-way data exchange.

Mode shape information created from FEA can be used in dynamic simulation to add realism. Alternatively, the loads from dynamic analysis can be returned to the finite element model to perform stress analysis. In addition, the FEA program will provide the dynamic analysis program with applicable information about the properties of components. Once FEA has analyzed the model, the results can be returned to dynamic analysis to be postprocessed and displayed.

Solid Modeling geometry can be used as a starting point for model building. The solid model can be combined with analysis results from the postprocessor to generate animation. The kinematic and dynamic modeling capabilities can often be operated from within the SM system and the model then transferred to the dynamic analysis software. The necessary interfaces and analysis software can be embedded in the SM program, allowing operation from within a familiar environment. This process can increase design accuracy and eliminate data transfer errors. Results can be returned to the SM database to display all part component displacements at any point in time. This integration with SM utilizes and enhances the SM database.

13.3.2 Kinematic Analysis

For kinematic analysis (the motion of the system, independent of the forces that produce the motion), one must determine the number of degrees of freedom[1,4,5] in the system and define drivers,[1] which are time-dependent constraint equations that specify the absolute motion of an individual body or the relative motion of pairs of bodies to determine the motion of the entire system. The kinematic analysis software then solves the equations of kinematics on a specified time grid and reports position, velocity, and acceleration results in tabular, graphical, and animated form.

13.3.3 Dynamic Analysis

Dynamic analysis (the motion of the system due to the action of applied forces) is performed with force and torques that are applied to individual bodies or between bodies. The analysis software forms and solves the differential and algebraic equations of motion to predict performance of the mechanical system under consideration. Positions, velocities, and accelerations of all bodies in the system, as well as forces acting between bodies at joints, are determined on an assigned time grid and reported in tabular, graphical, and animated form.

13.3.4 Operational Approach

The computer-aided operational approach to kinematic and dynamic analysis includes defining the system model, selecting control elements, analysis, and reviewing results.

The System Model

In the initial design of a mechanism, one might use a simplified solid model of the assembly and determine input parameters. In the case of an automobile suspension, these parameters might be the speed of the vehicle and the characteristics of the terrain. A preprocessor serves for this data entry function, allowing one to accurately build and edit a model for analysis. Information such as mass properties, the location of the center of gravity, and joint locations are entered in the preprocessor or through integration with the SM database.

Model Elements

A library of planar and spatial mechanical constraint, force, and control elements is accessed, allowing the simulation of a variety of mechanical systems or components. Each model element defined may be initialized with a set of default values for most variables, saving time and reducing the amount of operator input required.

Hydraulic, digital, or analog control systems may also be modeled and analyzed. On-line libraries of standard control elements may be accessed, allowing one to model signal inputs, transfer functions, and feedback, and apply the results as forces and torques acting on the mechanical components.

Analysis

With all data entered, the dynamic, kinematic, inverse dynamic, static, or assembly analysis stage can begin. The equations of motion for all bodies within the model are automatically generated and numerically solved during this stage. The system calculates reaction forces, positions, velocities, and accelerations for the individual parts and the assembly as a whole.

Reviewing Results

The postprocessor of the kinematic and dynamic analysis software allows the designer to quickly examine and evaluate results of the analysis. Any variable within the model can be graphically plotted or listed in tabular form. These variables can include body positions, velocities, accelerations, force element data, total and potential energy, and joint reaction forces. The full visual effect of a model in motion is made possible through animation capabilities. Animation controls allow the designer to use simple construction commands to build or import geometry. This geometry is then assembled and linked with position data from the analysis results to create a realistic animation.

Animation controls also allow the point-of-view and viewing perspectives to be manipulated. This allows one to focus on specific areas of the model, or to view it from a selected position. Animation features can also include definable light sources for full shadowing effects. The visual display of components can be rendered in wireframe, transparent, and solid forms. Solid surfaces can be further defined as FLAT, for faceted shading, or GOURAUD, for smooth, interpolated shading.

Final Note

Historically, kinematic and dynamic analysis has been restricted to rigid bodies. Flexibility effects are often important as well, since mechanical systems are becoming lightweight and operate at higher speeds. Modal synthesis techniques can be applied which have been widely used by the automotive and aerospace industries for many years. This approach combines finite element vibration and static modes with rigid body motion. The result is a fully coupled representation of flexibility of a mechanical system.

13.3.5   Cautions and Needed Improvements

1. Designers need ways to find mass and inertia properties of "lumped" parts, as described previously. This allows rigid body models to be made directly from the solid model database of detailed parts in a machine.
2. Designers need a way to locate and orient coordinate systems on the solid relative to the main part reference frame for attaching joint and force elements between rigid bodies. This has been a major shortcoming of some SM systems because it precluded any entity that was not conceptually a solid. Fortunately, most SM systems today have the ability to effectively locate points and/or coordinate systems on or in the solid model.

13.4   Analysis Examples

To illustrate the complex nature of mechanical systems it is helpful to review a few typical engineering models to which kinematic and dynamic analysis can be applied. These complex mechanisms are broken into components for analysis purposes. Three analysis examples follow.

13.4.1   The V-8 Engine

The V-8 engine shown in Fig. 13.1 (see color insert) contains many moving parts and illustrates a number of the most common mechanisms employed in machine design.

The crankshaft of the engine rotates in lubricated bearings and contains eccentric rotational bearings with connecting rods, which are subsequently coupled through rotational bearings to translating pistons that move in combustion cylinders. The crankshaft, connecting rod, and piston assembly comprises what is commonly called a *slider-crank mechanism,* which is used in this and many other machine components.

The basic purpose of this mechanism is to transfer forces that are induced by combustion of fuel on the pistons into torque that acts about the axis of rotation of the crankshaft. This induces the rotational motion that is used to propel a vehicle or to drive rotating machinery. Cams are typically used to induce precisely timed motion of the cam-follower, which controls the position of the valve stem through a rocker arm, to open and close the intake and exhaust valves during engine operation. To close a valve and to maintain contact between the cam and follower, valve springs are used, as shown.

13.4.2   Windshield Wiper Mechanism

The windshield wiper mechanism shown schematically in Fig. 13.2 is a linkage that transmits motor-driven rotation of the crank to reciprocating motion of windshield wipers. The crank and left rocker arm are pivoted in the vehicle frame at points A and B. The crank coupler is pivoted in the crank at point C and in the left rocker arm at point D. Since the distance from B to D is greater than the distance from A to C, a full rotation of the crank causes only a partial rotation of the left rocker arm, leading to the desired reciprocating motion of the left windshield wiper. The dimensions of the various links are carefully selected to generate the desired range of motion.

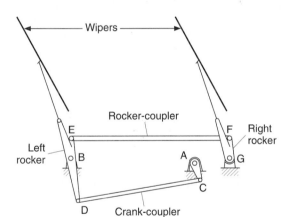

FIGURE 13.2 Schematic of windshield wiper mechanism.

A second linkage is formed by the right rocker arm that is pivoted in the frame of the vehicle at point G and the rocker coupler that is pivoted in the left and right rocker arms at points E and F. This second linkage transmits reciprocating motion from the left rocker arm to the right rocker arm, hence driving the right windshield wiper.

13.4.3   Vehicle Suspension System

A final example that illustrates the scope of kinematics and dynamics is the vehicle suspension system shown in Fig. 13.3 (see color insert). This common vehicle suspension consists of a McPherson strut front suspension and a trailing arm rear suspension. Each front wheel assembly is attached to the chassis of the vehicle through a lower control arm and a telescoping strut assembly, as shown in Fig. 13.4.

Concentric with the strut assembly, but not shown, are suspension and shock absorber components. The spherical joints at the top and bottom of the strut assembly permit steering rotation of the wheel

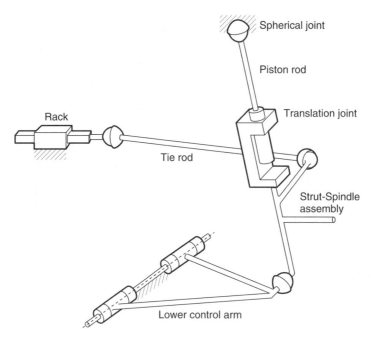

FIGURE 13.4 McPherson strut front suspension.

assembly about the strut. The more elementary rear suspension shown in Fig. 13.3 is simply a pair of control arms that are pivoted in the chassis to permit the rear wheel assembly to move relative to the chassis. Spring and damping components attached between the rear control arm and chassis provide for support of the chassis and cushioning of extreme tire and road forces.

The Analysis Model

A tire-force model that calculates tire deflection and lateral slip is used to determine forces on the wheel as a result of tire–roadway interaction.[1] Including translation of the steering rack and two roll stabilizing bars, this model is made up of eight bodies that move relative to one another and in space. A total of 44 algebraic constraint equations involving 56 variables are formed. The motion of the vehicle is determined by specifying rack displacements due to steering, and by solving 100 differential and algebraic equations at every time step while numerically integrating the resulting equations of motion.

This computation can be performed without ever having to write an equation of motion, using only precoded kinematic constraint equations, tire-force equations, spring-damper force equations, and equations of motion. This complex mechanism model can be formed and solved on virtually any modern engineering workstation in a modest amount of time.

The Analysis Results

This vehicle model and its analysis show that relatively complex mechanical systems can be modeled using the methodology outlined here. Such models can be used to investigate design alternatives and different uses of mechanical systems prior to fabrication and test of hardware. This is indicative of the power offered by using computer-aided kinematic and dynamic analysis tools as an integral part of the mechanical system design process.

The vehicle trajectories shown in Fig. 13.5, as a result of the steer-and-hold input at three different automobile speeds, show distinctly different results. The dotted curve, representing the slowest speed, yields an almost precisely circular trajectory.

The dashed curve, at the intermediate speed, yields a curve that is not exactly circular, suggesting that some lateral slipping has occurred between the tires and the road surface. The solid curve, representing the highest speed, suggests that the vehicle has spun out and slowed substantially before it recovers and

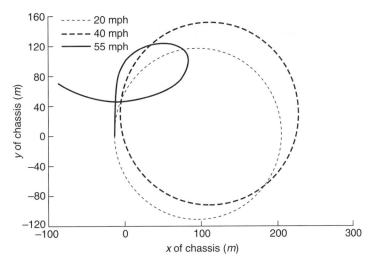

FIGURE 13.5 Vehicle trajectories as a result of steer-and-hold input at three different automobile speeds.

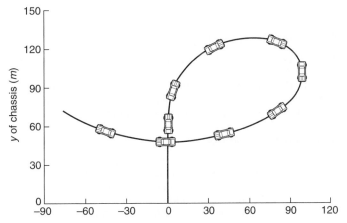

FIGURE 13.6 Vehicle orientation in circular steer maneuver (55 mph).

follows a new circular path. The latter behavior is confirmed by the sequence of vehicle positions shown in Fig. 13.6, concluding that substantial slipping and dissipation of energy occurs before the vehicle slows and recovers to undertake a circular path.

Effective utilization of these tools hinges upon the visualization of results. While the graphical form of results shown in Figs. 13.5 and 13.6 aid in understanding the behavior of the system, the full power of computer-aided kinematic and dynamic analysis tools is realized only when animated output is provided.

13.4.4 Conclusions

These examples represent typical mechanisms that are encountered in mechanical system motion analysis and design. The breadth of applications is extensive and includes automotive, aerospace, robotics, machine design, heavy equipment, materials-handling systems, off-road vehicles, consumer products, and medical devices. While applications and environments differ greatly, many technical similarities permit the development of a uniform approach to computer-aided kinematic and dynamic analysis.

Guidelines

SMA.13.1   Keys to Real SM Benefits

There are two keys to capturing real design benefits from the use of motion simulation in an SM environment:

1. Make sure the simulation software is tightly integrated with your solid modeling system.

2. Apply the appropriate level of simulation technology to the task at hand. (Stated another way, "Don't try to needlessly turn your designers and design engineers into analysts.")

James D. Price, Vice President, Marketing
Mechanical Dynamics, Inc., Ann Arbor, Mich.

SMA.13.2   Realistic but Simple

Keep the geometry realistic, but simple if possible. This will achieve desired results while keeping modeling and processing times to a minimum.

SMA.13.3   Model Reference Frame

The reference frame for the solid model must be easy to identify so users can see how the geometry is laid out. The center of gravity must also be located relative to this main part reference frame.

Recommended

SMA.13.4   One Solid Per Rigid Body

For dynamic analysis, the solid model should be organized such that one solid exists for each rigid body in the dynamic model. Some users create detailed solid models of each bolt, screw, and washer in an assembly. This is fine for the drawing database and manufacturing applications. This is not very useful in dynamics simulations because there is too much detail, and the only thing of interest is the proper mass and inertia of the rigid group of components.

SMA.13.5   Part Instancing

Some SM programs allow the use of instanced parts where the original (generic) part can be inserted into the assembly multiple times, or even scaled and inserted. Utilizing instances is fine from a motion analysis standpoint if unique names and property information is given to each resulting part, but it is not useful if a complex sequence of relationships must be processed to find the desired result. It is usually best to copy the generic part to another part with a unique name. Then the new part can be inserted into the assembly.

SMA.13.6   Joint and Force Identification

To locate the joint and force connections for motion analysis, it is essential that the solid model have points or coordinate systems that represent the required data. The points and coordinate systems should be visible and labeled in a way that will facilitate their use. For example, a revolute (or pin) joint between two bodies requires the origins of the two coordinate systems to be coincident and one each of their axes to be aligned. Names like *body A* and *revolute B* can help to identify which joint a given coordinate system is used with. Other times, generic names like *Csys 1* (coordinate system 1) are more useful if one coordinate system is used in many places.

SMA.13.7   Model Files

When developing solid models for kinematic and dynamic analysis, operators should create solid representations of each rigid body separately and not put them all in one model or file.

Good to Know

SMA.13.8   Model Detail

SM data can be useful for surface geometry information that is used in rendering and animation programs. Motion analysis is best understood when viewed as animated geometry. The solid model

(Continued)

can provide the basis for triangulated surface polygon geometry. Too much detail in the solid model geometry can be a drawback if it results in so many polygons that the computer hardware cannot achieve animation display rates that give users meaningful feedback.

SMA.13.9   Solid Modeling

To most designers the term *Solid Modeling* refers to the process of creating geometry with mass properties. In addition, solid models provide mass and inertia properties that are essential for creating the equations of motion used in dynamic analysis. It is impractical to calculate the mass and inertia properties by hand for almost any modern mechanical system. The geometry is generally too complex and users now expect more accurate simulation results.

SMA.13.10   Animation Alternatives

Many of today's engineering workstations can animate fairly complex parts made up of thousands of polygons (not necessarily triangulated) at a high frame rate. However, as the number of polygons approaches the millions, the frame rate slows down—even with the best hardware. The best that can be done in these cases is to resort to "frame at a time" recording on videotape or optical disk. This involves more hardware to control turning on recorders when one frame has been rendered, and generally takes much longer. Most simulation problems mandate quicker turnaround time than this allows. See Chap. 10 for more on linking computers to video.

SMA.13.11   What Can SM Designers Do?

The great majority of SM systems on the market today offer optional modules for mechanism modeling and simulation that, generally speaking, enable SM designers to do three things:

1. Model mechanical systems (mechanisms) from within the SM GUI environment by connecting parts in an assembly with joints from a standard library.

2. Simulate 3D system motion, using an embedded kinematic motion solver to test the feasibility of various configurations, detect collisions, establish work-space envelopes, evaluate motion paths, etc.

3. Output a complete, preformatted model easily and transparently for the analysts to perform more sophisticated, dynamic studies with third-party analysis software.

SMA.13.12   Optionally Integrated SM Analysis

A key benefit of optionally integrated SM mechanism/kinematics packages is that they provide 20 percent of motion simulation capability required 80 percent of the time by designers and design engineers. For straightforward 2D or 3D motion studies, there should be no need to learn a foreign user interface or command syntax, and the complexity of the analysis "solver" is masked from the designer.

SMA.13.13   Integrating Motion Simulation

Integrating motion simulation with SM adds important capabilities for both design engineers and analysts. SM provides the mass and inertia properties, positions and orientations, and almost everything necessary to conduct accurate kinematic and dynamic analysis. The automated model creation and review is easily accomplished through integration with the simulation program.

SM now provides the best starting point for motion analysis and studies of design alternatives. Integrated simulation allows design engineers to become more efficient and proficient in their ability to produce quality designs. Analysts benefit from a new means of exchanging model information with designers and are allowed to concentrate their efforts on only the most difficult problems.

Richard Kading, Manager of Engineering and Development
Computer Aided Design Software, Inc., Coralville, Iowa

References

1. Haug, E. J., *Computer Aided Kinematics and Dynamics of Mechanical Systems, Part I: Basic Methods,* Allyn and Bacon, Boston, 1989.

2. Beyer, R., *The Kinematic Synthesis of Mechanisms,* McGraw-Hill, New York, 1963.

3. Hirschhorn, J., *Kinematics and Dynamics of Plane Mechanisms,* McGraw-Hill, New York, 1962.

4. Paul, B., *Kinematics and Dynamics of Planar Machinery,* Prentice-Hall, Englewood Cliffs, N.J., 1979.

5. Wittenburg, J., *Dynamics of Systems of Rigid Bodies,* Teubner, Stuttgart, 1977.

6. Soni, A. H., *Mechanism Synthesis and Analysis,* McGraw-Hill, New York, 1974.

7. Suh, C. H., and Radcliffe, C. W., *Kinematics and Mechanisms Design,* Wiley, New York, 1978.

8. Greenwood, D. T., *Principles of Dynamics,* 2d ed., Prentice-Hall, Englewood Cliffs, N.J., 1988.

9. Kane, T. R., and Levinson, D. A., *Dynamics: Theory and Applications,* McGraw-Hill, New York, 1985.

10. Haug, E. J., *Intermediate Dynamics,* Prentice-Hall, Englewood Cliffs, N.J., 1992.

11. Noble, B., and Hussain, M. A., "Applications of MACSYMA to Calculations in Dynamics," *Computer Aided Analysis and Optimization of Mechanical System Dynamics,* E. J. Haug (ed.), Springer-Verlag, Heidelberg, 1984.

12. Zienkiewiez, O., *The Finite Element Method,* McGraw-Hill, New York, 1977.

13. Gallagher, R. H., *Finite Element Analysis: Fundamentals,* Prentice-Hall, Englewood Cliffs, N.J., 1975.

14. Chua, L. O., and Lin, P.-M., *Computer Aided Analysis of Electronic Circuits,* Prentice-Hall, Englewood Cliffs, N.J., 1975.

15. Calahan, D. A., *Computer Aided Network Design,* McGraw-Hill, New York, 1972.

Suggestions for Further Reading

Paul, B., and Krajcinovic, D., "Computer Analysis of Machines with Planar Motion—Part I: Kinematics; Part II: Dynamics," *Journal of Applied Mechanics,* vol. 37, 1970, pp. 697–712.

Chace, M. A., and Smith, D. A., "DAMN—A Digital Computer Program for the Dynamic Analysis of Generalized Mechanical Systems," SAE paper 710244, January 1971.

Sheth, P. N., and Uicker, J. J., Jr., "IMP (Integrated Mechanisms Program), A Computer Aided Design Analysis System for Mechanisms and Linkages," *Journal of Engineering for Industry,* vol. 94, 1972, pp. 454–464.

Orlandea, N., Chace, M. A., and Calahan, D. A., "A Sparsity-Oriented Approach to the Dynamic Analysis and Design of Mechanical Systems, Parts I and II," *Journal of Engineering for Industry,* vol. 99, 1977, pp. 773–784.

Wehage, R. A., and Haug, E. J., "Generalized Coordinate Partitioning for Dimension Reduction in Analysis of Constrained Dynamic Systems," *Journal of Mechanical Design,* vol. 104, no. 1, 1982, pp. 247–255.

Chapter 14

Solid Modeling for Finite Element Analysis (FEA)

Richard D. Lowrey, Ph.D.
Mechanical Engineering Consultant
Lowrey Consulting

Solids-based analysis frees engineers to perform more engineering with greater accuracy. Solid Modeling (SM) systems offer automatic finite element meshing and interactive loads and boundary condition definition. Up to 90 percent of interactive mesh generation time can be saved, with greater accuracy, automatic mesh checking, and good mesh density control. Up to 80 percent of interactive load and boundary condition definition time can be saved, with far greater accuracy, especially on curved geometry. Intelligent meshes are possible because the optimal mesh density variation is principally a function of loads, restraints, topology, and changes in topology. Properly used automatic mesh generators can produce meshes which yield higher accuracy results than an analyst can produce interactively. The software never forgets the rules with which it is programmed; an analyst often forgets at least one rule, and wishes to regenerate and analyze the mesh if only more budget were available. Better mesh control and more intelligence continue to advance automatic mesh generators.

Meshes can be automatically generated on two- and three-dimensional structures. The topology and geometry of the boundary object are used. If bidirectional associativity is implemented, geometry changes are automatically incorporated in the mesh. However, topology changes, such as additional solid model edges, will require remeshing.

Each mesh and load case is associated to the solid on which it was generated. An analysis is defined in minutes for a particular solid by selecting a mesh and load case created for it, the element type, the analysis type, the solver, and other variables. The load case becomes associated to the mesh upon analysis execution. The loads specified on the solid are now converted to the finite element mesh. Pressures on complex surfaces are converted without error to nodal or element forces, using minuscule CPU time. Restraints on surfaces are converted to nodal restraints with proper orientation to the surface.

14.1   Operational Approach

The solid model contains all geometrical and topological information required to create a finite element mesh, load, or restraint. The geometry can be quickly integrated, differentiated, and applied as required by mesh logic.

Many meshes, loads, and restraints may be created on a solid. An early analysis might use a coarse mesh, a load case consisting of two times gravity plus pressure on a particular surface, and fixed restraints at the base of the structure. Later analyses typically use finer meshes, more detailed load cases, and refined restraints.

14.2 FEA Basics

A finite element is like a single block in a concrete block wall, as shown in Fig. 14.1. The element models the load-response behavior of that single block. The material properties of the block measure how stiff the block is. The finite element mesh is the accumulation of all of the blocks. The mesh models the interconnectivity of these blocks. The response at every point on the wall can be determined for a load applied at any point on the wall.

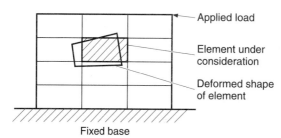

Applied load

Element under consideration

Deformed shape of element

Fixed base

FIGURE 14.1 FEA basics of a concrete block wall. Each block is like a finite element. A load can be applied at any point, and deformations computed at all points. Strains and stresses are computed from the displacements.

The element is finite in that it represents a finite piece of the entire wall, and it can deform in a finite number of modes or ways. Each axial or shear deformation accounted for in the element is called a *degree of freedom*. The actual block has a particular hollowed shape. We know that it will not deform as would a solid, homogeneous block. The true shape of the block could be modeled more accurately with more finite elements, and better analysis results would result. Ultimately, every molecule could be modeled, and nearly exact results would be obtained, but at an enormous computational cost. The block actually has an infinite number of degrees of freedom.

As the finite element model of the wall is refined, the analysis results of that model more closely approximate reality. Deformations and stresses generally increase. That is, an analysis typically computes lower bounds on these quantities.

14.3 Preprocessing

Preprocessing is the stage during which the entire finite element analysis is defined. This includes definition of the finite element mesh, element types and properties, material properties, loads, constraints, load cases, and the type of analysis.

Before graphical displays existed, all analysis data was defined manually—one node, element, load, or constraint at a time. Models were created via batch execution without mesh plots.

Interactive preprocessing became possible with the advent of graphical displays and real-time execution. The result of each command could be seen immediately. The input device (mouse) later enabled graphical selection of data to speed generation. Low-level entities such as a vertex, node, or element could be selected.

Automation extends interactive capability by graphical selection of higher-level entities such as model edges, surfaces, or volumes; intelligence to generate mesh entities on these objects; and associativity of the solid and the analysis data. For example, a complex model surface can be selected and in a single operation all finite element nodes that will reside on this surface may be restrained normal to the surface, tangent to the surface, or both. If the mesh is changed, the nodes restrained are still just those that reside on the specified surface.

Generation of the finite element mesh was previously the most time-consuming phase. Automation allows the operator to select model entities (such as vertices, edges, surfaces) and specify mesh density criteria. In a single operation, the entire mesh might then be generated. Simple changes in the mesh density criteria allow creation of a new mesh of different density.

14.4 The Finite Element Mesh (FEM)

A finite element mesh is a collection of finite elements that model the structure. The mesh identifies the following for each finite element: (1) the nodes to which it connects, (2) its element type (linear solid, etc.), (3) its material properties, and (4) its physical properties (such as thickness). (See Table 14.1.)

TABLE 14.1 Mesh Elements

Typical mesh elements are shown here indicating element dimension, degree, shape, and element type. Notice that the element dimensions are 1D for lines, 2D for areas, and 3D for volumes. Also notice that the number of nodes between vertices per edge are: none for linear, one for quadratic, and two for cubic elements.

Dimensions	Element degree	Element shape	Element type
1D (line)	Linear		Beam, truss
	Quadratic		Beam
	Cubic		Beam
2D (area)	Linear		Plane stress Plane strain Plate, shell*
	Quadratic		
	Cubic		
3D (volume)	Linear		
	Quadratic		

*A shell element is not required to lie on a plane.

14.4.1 Mesh Elements

Mesh elements are simplified states of stress and displacement. For example, in a state of plane stress, all stresses, strains, and displacements exist in a single plane. Values normal to this plane are zero. The complete set of equations of state from the theory of elasticity are hence simplified dramatically by eliminating the proper zero terms. These reduced equations for strain displacement and stress-strain are utilized to reduce analysis expense.

14.4.2 Automatic Mesh Generation

Automatic mesh generators produce meshes for a surface, solid, or surface/solid structure. A model will be automatically meshed with shell elements only on a surface model; or solid elements only on a solid model; or shell elements in thin regions and solid elements in thick regions of surface/solid structures. Connecting solids and shells together at interface regions requires operator interaction.

Surface models can be two-dimensional (planar) or three-dimensional structures. Solid models are three-dimensional structures (i.e., they occupy three-dimensional space, and loads cause responses, in all three dimensions). Solids can also be used to represent two-dimensional structures, but at greater analysis expense. Examples of stress states are given in Table 14.2, and the loads and stresses for each stress state are given in Table 14.3.

TABLE 14.2 Examples of Stress States

State	Example
Truss	Pin-ended member of a truss-bridge
Plane stress	Membrane (2D); tent (3D)
Plane strain	Long, straight, constant cross-section tunnel
Plate	Wall; thick plate in bending
Shell	Thin general structure
Solid	Thick general structure
Axisymmetric	Revolved solid or shell

TABLE 14.3 Loads and Stresses of Stress States

State	Loads	Stresses
Truss	Axial only	Axial only
Plane stress	In-plane force only	In-plane normal + shear
Plane strain	In-plane force only	All normal + in plane shear
Plate	Normal forces, moments	Bending
Shell	All forces, moments	All
Solid	All forces	All
Axisymmetric	All	All

14.4.3 Model Types

Each finite element type has a specified set of degrees of freedom for representing a specific stress state. For example, a truss element carries only axial force, and deforms axially. The change in cross-section shape and stresses can be ignored because the significant stresses are all axial. The accuracy of the analysis is virtually unchanged, while the cost of the analysis is reduced tremendously. (See Table 14.4 for categories of structures and states of stress.)

TABLE 14.4 Categories of Structures and States of Stress

Structures transmit loads primarily in certain directions. The idealized deformations, strains, and stresses act in these same directions. This table shows primary load directions and general states of stress for various structure types.

Structure type		Load direction	Stress direction
Solid		Loads in any direction	General stress state
Axisymmetric	Thick	Loads asymmetric	
	Thin shell	Loads axisymmetric	
	Body of revolution	General loads	
Plane stress membrane		Loads in-plane only	Zero normal stress thru thickness
Plane strain (slice)			Constant normal stress thru thickness
Plate bending		Loads out of plane only	Zero normal stress thru thickness
Shell (membrane and bending)		Loads any direction	Zero normal stress thru thickness

Plane Stress Models

Plane stress models can be created from a solid model if a surface model is not available. A minimum element length of two times the structure thickness usually limits the mesh to the desired one element through the thickness.

Plane Strain Models

Plane strain models can be created from a solid model and meshed the same way. Constrain all displacements normal to the thickness.

Axisymmetric Solid Models

Axisymmetric solid models without axial torsion can be created from a solid model by using a small sector of the solid, perhaps a 1° slice. The thickness across the sector should be small compared to every dimension on the revolved profile. Constrain all displacements normal to the sector planes. Use a minimum element length of two times the maximum sector thickness for a mesh one quadratic solid element thick.

Shell Models

Shell models must be well conditioned to obtain the correct mesh. For example, parallel ribs normal to the shell on opposite sides of the shell, but intersecting the shell slightly offset from each other, often yield an automatic mesh of nonnormal ribs that meet the shell at a common intersection.

Where the shell geometry is complex, a solid mesh in the region will produce better results, but at greater CPU and memory expense.

Tapered ribs may be automatically meshed as uniform thickness shell elements requiring the user to edit the thickness across the elements.

Shells with step thickness changes on just one side of the shell may not be meshed properly. The plane of the elements at the step thickness transition can lie partly outside the model.

Solid Models

Solid models are meshed with tetrahedron volume elements in most solid-based systems. The initial tetrahedron elements are linear formulations and have just four nodes, one at each vertex, and six straight edges connecting the vertices. The straight edges will violate the curved solid model surfaces. This mesh may be adequate for thermal and modal analyses. Analysis CPU cost is low.

Quadratic elements are computationally more efficient than linear elements for analyses where the field variables are quadratic or higher. For example, a prismatic cantilever beam subjected to an end moment or shear force deforms quadratically along its length. Quadratic elements approximate the quadratic deformation and linear stress variation accurately. Linear elements can deform only linearly, with slope discontinuities at element edges. The deformation is too stiff, underestimating the actual deformation.

A quadratic mesh is generated from a linear mesh by adding a node on the midlength of every element edge. Where an edge is on a curved solid model surface, this midlength position is on the curved surface.

14.5   Meshing the Solid Model

Automatic mesh generation can be performed using the default mesh density parameter values. This mesh may be adequate for a design engineer performing static load stress analysis of a concept design with linear elastic materials and small displacements. If the loads and boundary conditions are properly defined, the maximum displacements and stresses (von Mises, Tresca, principal, etc.) can be compared to those in other concept designs. Stresses displayed on the deflected shape may reveal how to improve load paths.

Product development teams should include the analyst at team inception so that valid result comparisons between concept designs can be obtained, thus including the analyst's knowledge in the design, rather than as part of a redesign effort. The controlling load case could require modal or dynamic (time-varying) analysis; a series of analyses; or combined-load cases which require a higher level of analysis expertise.

The task of producing and optimizing a finite element mesh of a solid model incorporates many functional and management issues. These issues range from creating and controlling the mesh to calculating mesh size, performing mesh checks, and detail removal. These and other issues are discussed below.

14.5.1 Mesh Density Controls

Proper mesh density controls can yield better analysis results at reduced analysis expense. These controls limit the maximum and minimum element edge lengths, the maximum angle each element subtends on curved surfaces, minimum corner angles of element faces, and maximum element face-aspect ratios. These criteria are shown in Fig. 14.2.

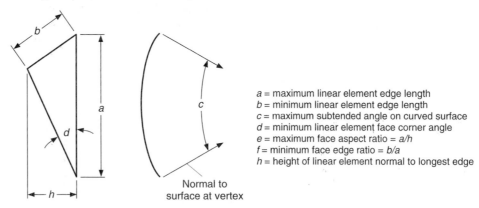

a = maximum linear element edge length
b = minimum linear element edge length
c = maximum subtended angle on curved surface
d = minimum linear element face corner angle
e = maximum face aspect ratio = a/h
f = minimum face edge ratio = b/a
h = height of linear element normal to longest edge

Normal to surface at vertex

FIGURE 14.2 Mesh density controls on a surface element or face of a volume element. The geometry and topology of finite elements are used to control the element shape for optimal analysis cost and quality of results.

Maximum Element Edge Length

Maximum element edge length is the longest acceptable straight-line distance between element corner nodes. It is used to continue mesh refinement until this criteria is met by every element edge on the solid model edges. This specification may also be applicable to all element edges on faces of the solid, or throughout the entire solid. If not specified, it usually remains unlimited, but may be computed relative to the maximum overall dimension (longest diagonal of a bounding box enclosing the model), or default to a multiple of the minimum element edge length.

Minimum Element Edge Length

Minimum element edge length is the shortest desired straight-line distance between the corner nodes of an element. It is used to end local mesh refinement. For example, the mesh on a face will be refined until all other mesh accuracy criteria are satisfied on this face, or the minimum element length is achieved everywhere on the face. This specification might apply only on solid edges, or faces, or throughout the solid. If not specified, it is set to a fraction of the maximum element edge length so that mesh refinement will always terminate.

Maximum Subtended Angle

Maximum subtended angle is used to limit the curvature of element edges on curved surfaces. This is the angle between surface normals at the ends of an element edge.

Minimum Element Face Corner Angle

Minimum element face corner angle is the minimum angle between the straight lines connecting the corner nodes of every element face.

Maximum Face-Aspect Ratio

Maximum face-aspect ratio is sometimes used instead of minimum element face corner angle. It is computed as the length of the longest edge divided by the height of the element face measured normal to the longest edge.

Minimum Face-Edge Ratio

Minimum face-edge ratio is sometimes used in place of minimum element face corner angle. It is the ratio of the shortest element edge to the longest element edge.

Edge Mesh Density

Edge mesh density is primarily controlled by minimum and maximum element edge lengths. These values are chosen for the level of accuracy desired, to control the mesh size and analysis cost, and often as a first effort to control the amount of disk space required for the analysis, and for results storage. Figure 14.3 provides an example.

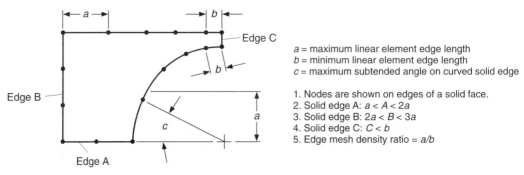

a = maximum linear element edge length
b = minimum linear element edge length
c = maximum subtended angle on curved solid edge

1. Nodes are shown on edges of a solid face.
2. Solid edge A: $a < A < 2a$
3. Solid edge B: $2a < B < 3a$
4. Solid edge C: $C < b$
5. Edge mesh density ratio = a/b

FIGURE 14.3   Example of edge mesh density on a solid face. The edges of a solid face are sometimes meshed before other solid entities. The distribution of nodes on the edges determine the shape of the face and volume elements which follow.

Surface Mesh Density

Surface mesh density is primarily controlled by minimum element face corner angle criteria. Figure 14.4 shows the surface mesh of the same solid face example shown in Fig. 14.3.

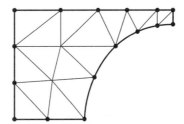

FIGURE 14.4   Example of surface mesh density on a solid face. The surface mesh is created from the edge mesh and other control criteria.

Volume Mesh Density

Volume mesh density may or may not use the surface mesh density criteria already specified, extended to all internal finite element edges and faces.

14.5.2   Relative Mesh Density

The mesh density must not be very fine in some area relative to the coarsest area. The ratio of maximum and minimum element lengths and angles on edges, surfaces, and through the volume should be well controlled, as adverse effects on bandwidth and accuracy can occur. Large ratios of maximum-to-minimum element size can increase the bandwidth by a quadratic function for a surface mesh, and by a cubic function for a solid mesh.

Once all element edges are less than the minimum element edge lengths specified, further mesh refinement generally does not measurably or cost effectively improve the analysis results, regardless of element shapes.

14.5.3 Editing the Mesh

The mesh can be edited globally or regionally by changing the mesh density parameters and regenerating the mesh. The mesh can be edited locally by the use of functions described as Add Edge Node and Add Face Node provided in most systems. These functions are best used as early in the mesh process as possible so that a smoother mesh results. They should be used in conjunction with changes in mesh density parameters when appropriate. Other functions such as Smooth Mesh and Improve Mesh are also usually available.

Add Edge Node

Add Edge Node can be used when the mesh is in any state from edge nodes on. The edge node distribution can be smoothed, or a node added to accommodate a load or restraint. This function is illustrated in Fig. 14.5.

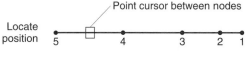

a = maximum linear element edge length
b = minimum linear element edge length

1. Nodes are shown on a solid edge.

FIGURE 14.5 Editing the mesh by adding an edge node and smoothing. A node may be added at a cursor-selected or keyed point on an edge and may be smoothed in adherence with user-specified criteria.

If the surface mesh already exists, then the surface elements on the two faces surrounding the added node will be updated. The number of nodes and elements can actually decrease slightly if the added node breaks up a group of poorly shaped elements.

Add Face Node

Add Face Node can be used in the face mesh and linear volume mesh stages, but usually not after the quadratic elements have been created. Nodes can be added to accommodate loads and environments or to improve the mesh. This function is illustrated in Fig. 14.6.

To improve the surface mesh, select a new node location in the center of long, narrow elements. Element edges will radiate from this new node to surrounding existing nodes. Local smoothing may be automatic.

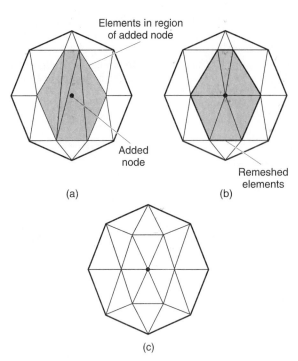

FIGURE 14.6 Editing the mesh by adding a surface node and smoothing. A node may be added at a cursor-selected or keyed point projected onto a surface and may be smoothed in adherence with user-specified criteria. Those elements whose vertices form a circumscribed circle (or sphere) which include the added node are remeshed. (*a*) Original mesh, (*b*) remeshed elements, (*c*) mesh after smoothing.

Smooth Mesh

Smooth Mesh is a function which moves nodes to locations which improve the element shapes, primarily minimum corner angles. Analysis results can improve with no increase in analysis cost.

Improve Mesh

Improve Mesh is a function which moves or adds nodes to create elements which are proportional in size to the strain energy density in the region. Strain energy density is the product of stress times strain. Lines of highest constant strain energy are relatively closer together than lines of highest constant stress.

14.5.4 Material Properties

Many SM systems only allow a single homogeneous material to be defined for the entire solid. Material properties typically provided for include Young's modulus of elasticity, shear modulus, Poisson's ratio, mass density, coefficient of thermal expansion, coefficient of thermal conductivity, specific heat, and hardness. New capabilities include specification of material properties for each region, and material property orientation control as required for grained materials and fiber-reinforced structures.

14.5.5 Bandwidth and Wavefront

Bandwidth (BW) and wavefront (WF) are two methods to measure the number of degrees of freedom (DOF) used while solving a matrix. A bandwidth solver holds the DOF of the nodes on the bandwidth in core while solving the stiffness matrix. A wavefront solver holds the DOF of the elements on the wavefront in core while solving the matrix.

The bandwidth or wavefront of the mesh is important because it strongly affects the cost of an analysis through the amount of computer memory and matrix solution time required. The matrix solution time is the greatest expense of analysis, and is a squared function of the root-mean-squared (rms) bandwidth or wavefront.

If memory is critical, then minimize the maximum bandwidth. Otherwise, minimize the maximum rms bandwidth or wavefront as follows:

Method	Memory	CPU time
Bandwidth	$a1 \cdot DOF \cdot BWmax$	$b1 \cdot DOF \cdot BWrms^2$
Wavefront	$a2 \cdot DOF \cdot BWmax$	$b2 \cdot DOF \cdot WFrms^2$

Constants $a1, a2, b1,$ and $b2$ are determined for a specific computer by performing analyses of different sizes and recording the variables DOF, BW, memory required, CPU time, etc. Then solve for values of $a1$, etc., using a best-fit method.

The bandwidth and wavefront of a mesh can be estimated for surface and volume meshes as a function of model type, the number of degrees of freedom (DOF), and dimensions length (L), width (W), and thickness (T) as follows:

Mesh type	Model type	Bandwidth est.	Idealized model
Surface	Long	$(DOF \cdot W/L)^{1/2}$	$W < L$
	Compact	$(DOF)^{1/2}$	Square: $W = L$
Volume	Compact	$(DOF)^{2/3}$	Cube
	Thin	$(DOF)^{1/2}$	Square: $T \ll W$
	Long	$(DOF \cdot W/L)^{1/2}$	$W < L, T = W$

14.5.6 Calculating Final Mesh Size

Euler's formula (see below) of topological invariance of surfaces[4] can be applied to calculate the number of nodes and elements of the quadratic surface mesh from topological quantities of the linear mesh. The quadratic mesh size is a function of the number of surface elements, element vertices, and holes in the surface. SM-based mesh generators have access to these parameters, and can display the number of nodes and elements, bandwidth or wavefront, memory size required, and analysis execution time, but most provide this information only for the completed mesh.

It is often important to calculate the final mesh size during early mesh stages so that the memory size and computational speed capabilities of the computer, the array size limitations of the analysis software, and budget constraints are not exceeded. A measurable amount of time and cost can be avoided by creating a mesh that will not be too large.

Surface Mesh

Leonhard Euler, 1707–1783, published what is known as the *Euler characteristic of simple* (no holes) *polygonal surfaces*. The surface can be divided into any mixture of three-or-more-sided polygons. The relationship between vertices, edges, and faces is invariant. The Euler characteristic is stated as:

$$V - E + F = 1 \qquad \text{(no holes in the surface)}$$

where $V =$ number of vertices or corners of linear 2D elements
$E =$ number of edges of the polygons or 2D elements
$F =$ number of faces or 2D elements

A quadratic mesh adds one node to each edge of the linear mesh. In Fig. 14.7, each vertex and each face is shown associated to an edge of a surface mesh with three to six edges per element. The number of quadratic nodes (QN) in terms of E and F, or V and F, is given by:

$$QN = V + E$$

$$= 2 \cdot E - F + 1$$

$$= 2 \cdot V + F - 1$$

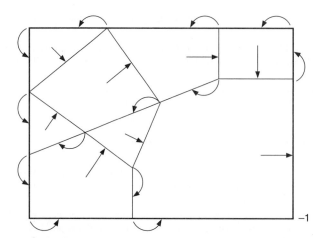

1. Each element vertex and element centroid point to an element edge.
2. An interior element may be replaced by a hole yielding one less F and one more H. Euler's equation still holds.

FIGURE 14.7 Euler's equation $E = V + F + H - 1$ applied to a variable edge surface mesh. The number of element edges is a function of the number of vertices, faces, and holes. A quadratic mesh will add one node on each edge; a cubic mesh will add two nodes on each edge.

A hole (H) in the surface eliminates one face (2D element). The quadratic node calculation is modified for holes as:

$$QN = 2 \cdot E - F + H + 1$$

$$= 2 \cdot V + F + H - 1$$

A cubic node (CN) mesh increases the E (edge) multiplier from 2 to 3; and similarly for higher-order finite element meshes.

$$CN = 3 \cdot E - F + H + 1$$

$$= 3 \cdot V + 2 \cdot F + 2 \cdot (H - 1)$$

Karl Friedrich Gauss, 1777–1855, determined that the Euler characteristic increases by 1 for simple polyhedra surfaces (i.e., closed surfaces with no holes). The quadratic and cubic node equation for a closed surface mesh with holes (and the surface mesh of a solid with holes!) becomes:

$$QN = 2 \cdot E - F + H + 2 = 2 \cdot V + F + H - 2$$

$$CN = 3 \cdot E - F + H + 2 = 3 \cdot V + 2 \cdot F + 2 \cdot (H - 2)$$

Solid Mesh

The Euler characteristic has been extended to solid finite element meshes as presented in Ref. 5. The elements must all be of one type—such as tetrahedra, pentahedra, or hexahedra. A topological hole in a solid intersects two surfaces, or else it is merely a surface depression. The surfaces intersected may be other holes.

The quadratic and cubic node equations are:

Tetrahedra:	$QN = S + V + 2 \cdot V_s + 3 \cdot (H - 1)$
	$CN = 2 \cdot S + 2 \cdot V + 3 \cdot V_s + 6 \cdot (H - 1)$
Pentahedra:	$QN = 3 \cdot S/2 + 2 \cdot V_s + F/2 + H - 1$
	$CN = 3 \cdot S + 3 \cdot V_s + F + 2 \cdot (H - 1)$
Hexahedra:	$QN = 2 \cdot S + 2 \cdot V_s + F/2 + H - 1$
	$CN = 4 \cdot S + 3 \cdot V_s + F + 2 \cdot (H - 1)$

where S = number of solid elements
  V_s = number of vertices of the linear solid mesh
  F = number of faces on exterior surface

Complex solid models can have intersecting holes, complicating the evaluation of the number of holes.[5] An error in the number of holes has a minor impact, unless a large number of holes are present.

The quadratic mesh size can also be estimated for solids and shells/surfaces during the edge mesh and surface mesh states.[5] These estimates can be in error by approximately ±30 percent and ±10 percent, respectively.

14.5.7 Mesh Checks

Automatic mesh generators check for some of the same criteria that individual analysis programs check. These include: (1) finite elements of zero area, length, volume, or stiffness; (2) distortion index or jacobian of the element stiffness matrix; (3) edge curvature angle or mid-edge node location to find highly distorted elements; (4) aspect ratio; (5) warp; or (6) skew.

Load cases are usually checked for obvious unconstrained rigid body motions.

14.5.8 Detail Removal

In some SM systems, detail not affecting critical analysis results can be removed from a solid model to reduce analysis execution time. For example, small holes away from high-result gradient regions (areas of high stress) often have little impact on displacements, static or dynamic stress, vibration, modal, or thermal results. Similarly, external corner radii, small cutouts, and small appendages may have limited impact on results.

Note that internal fillets may have a significant impact on results, especially when near high-result gradient regions. Include the fillets or other detail if extreme values or high-result gradients occur in the vicinity.

Controlling Mesh Density

SMA.14.1 Maximum Element Edge Length

Try a starting value of one-sixth of the maximum overall dimension of the part for compact solid models and thin solids. For a thin solid, this value should also be less than 10 thicknesses. Use one-tenth the maximum overall dimension for long shell or solid parts, and when a finer mesh is justified.

A smaller value of maximum element edge length usually produces more nodes. For complex geometry, a smaller value may reduce the total number of elements, bandwidth, analysis cost, and storage requirements. This results from a better balance of the maximum and minimum element edge length parameters.

SMA.14.2 Maximum Face-Aspect Ratio

A value less than 4 is desirable. A value of 1.1547 requires all equilateral triangle faces, which is impossible to attain for a general solid.

SMA.14.3 Minimum Face-Edge Ratio

A minimum ratio of 1.0 requires identical equilateral triangle element faces everywhere, which is impossible to achieve in a general solid. Start with a value around .5, and increase toward .7 as required. A minimum ratio of .7 will produce element edge lengths differing at most by 30 percent. Most element edges will differ by less than 20 percent. A minimum corner angle of 41° can occur. A ratio of .5 implies a minimum corner angle of 0° can occur, but few will be less than 20°.

Minimum Element Edge Length

SMA.14.4 Subdivision

Some mesh generators refine the mesh by subdividing the longest element edges by a factor of 2 in a region where a mesh accuracy criteria is violated. An element edge marginally longer than the

(Continued)

Minimum Element Edge Length
(*Continued*)

minimum element edge length can be subdivided by 2, becoming almost half as long as the minimum length specified. A small corner angle can result, but the two longer edges will also be short, and cause little error.

SMA.14.5   Typical Value

A typical value for minimum element edge length is 3 percent of the maximum model dimension, but not more than perhaps five times the minimum feature or edge size. Minimum element edge length strongly influences the mesh density at small features or detail. Increasing this value allows more nodes to be placed where they have a stronger influence on accuracy of analysis results.

SMA.14.6   If Set Too High

If minimum element edge length is set too high, then checking for minimum corner angle criteria, discussed later, may be prematurely terminated.

Maximum Subtended Angle

SMA.14.7   If Stress Is Important

When the stress value is important, limit this angle to 10 to 40°, depending on the level of accuracy required. Analysis solvers usually calculate this angle, and issue a warning or error message when 45° is exceeded.

SMA.14.8   If Stress Is Not Important

When stress value is not important, and the solver will allow a larger angle, then use one. This angle is ultimately limited by mesh generators to 90 or 120°. Curved geometry is easily violated, and poorly shaped elements created, for angles beyond 120°.

SMA.14.9   More Elements on Curvature

More elements will exist on curvature than this angle implies due to other accuracy criteria and round-off. For example, if 60° is specified on a cylindrical surface, then seven elements, not six, will predominate around the circumference.

SMA.14.10   Prevailing Edge Length

The smaller element edge length resulting from maximum subtended angle and maximum element edge length will prevail on curved geometry.

Minimum Element Face Corner Angle

SMA.14.11   Recommended Value

The minimum corner angle of each triangular face should be about 15°. A small corner angle will not look good, but accuracy will be maintained if the element edge lengths are small.

SMA.14.12   When to Use Higher Values

Set the minimum element corner angle higher on large faces, faces where high-result gradients or values are expected, or where higher result accuracy is needed. Set it lower on small faces, and faces where low-result gradients or values are expected.

SMA.14.13   Premature Termination

If unacceptable element shapes are created on a face, set both the maximum and minimum element edge lengths to lower values so that the minimum element corner angle criteria will not be prematurely terminated.

SMA.14.14   Dense and Coarse Regions

The mesh generator will transition away from dense and coarse regions while trying to maximize the minimum element face corner angle. Better element shapes are produced in this way.

Edge Mesh Density

SMA.14.15   On a Curved Solid Edge

The edge mesh density on a curved solid edge or surface will additionally be controlled by the element edge maximum subtended angle requirement. All straight element edges are controlled by maximum element length, while all curved edges are controlled by the minimum value of maximum element length and maximum subtended angle, so close attention should be paid to both values on curved solid model edges and surfaces. The ratio of these two values should generally not vary by more than a factor of 3.

SMA.14.16   Topology Issues

The edges of elements are never allowed to cross the edges of the solid. The faces of the solid may be smooth, continuous, and differentiable at an edge, but the elements will be aligned along this solid edge. If element edges should be allowed to cross this solid edge, then the solid model edge must be removed from the topology. If the radius of curvature of the two faces is significantly different in this vicinity, then do not remove the edge, or the mesh may be poor here.

SMA.14.17   Additional Control

The edge mesh will additionally be controlled during face mesh generation by the minimum corner angle requirements of all elements along the edge.

SMA.14.18   Aligning Elements

It is sometimes desired to align elements along a line where none exists in the solid model so that forces, restraints, etc., can be more easily specified. The user can sometimes add an edge or surface region local to analysis to accomplish this. Otherwise, the solid model must be modified. For example, a cylindrical bearing surface may be created with a segmented circle extruded to add edges where needed on the surface.

Surface Mesh Density

SMA.14.19   Extending to Face Elements

The minimum and maximum element edge lengths and maximum subtended angles specified during edge meshing may or may not be extended to all finite element edges on the solid face. If they are extended to the face elements on the interior of solid faces, then the values are usually larger by a factor of 1.1 to 1.4 because the geometry is changing less rapidly on the interior of faces. Theory of elasticity dictates that stress, strain, and strain energy gradients will be somewhat lower here than at SM edges unless concentrated loads or restraints exist on the interior of the face.[2]

SMA.14.20   Number of Edge Nodes

If the number of edge nodes is nearly equal to the number of surface nodes, then increase the minimum corner angle criteria. If recreation of the face mesh still produces few additional nodes on the surface, then also reduce the maximum element edge length.

Volume Mesh Density

SMA.14.21   Internal Volume Mesh

If maximum and minimum element edge length criteria are extended to the internal volume mesh, the values are usually increased by a factor of 2 from the values specified on edges.[3]

SMA.14.22   Changes in Topology

Since the changes in topology inside the solid are zero, theory of elasticity dictates that the optimal mesh will be coarsest internally, provided that concentrated internal loads (such as heating and cooling tubes) are not present; hence, the factor of 2 typically applied to the maximum and minimum element edge lengths internal to the solid. The mesh must be finest near surface topology changes. The largest element edges internally should be longer than the maximum element edge length on edges and surfaces.

(Continued)

Volume Mesh Density
(Continued)

SMA.14.23   Initial Volume Elements

Initial volume elements are linear, which will violate curved surfaces. When the linear volume element mesh exhibits the characteristic shapes and densities desired, the quadratic volume mesh can be created. A node is added at the midlength of each edge. If the element is on a curved surface, the midlength node is located to reside on the curved surface.

SMA.14.24   Internal Element Edges

All internal element edges will be straight, but must be shorter near surfaces. A poor mesh can result where straight internal edges are near curved solid model surfaces and rapid solid model topology changes. Very narrow sliver elements may be created.

Relative Mesh Density—Edges

SMA.14.25   Edge Ratio Values

The ratio of maximum-to-minimum element edge length on an edge should not exceed a factor of 3 unless very small detail or a short edge is adjacent.

SMA.14.26   Narrow Faces

If a face is very narrow, select the face and set the minimum element edge length to about three times the narrow dimension. Use a larger value if this value is less than one-tenth the maximum element length on this and immediately adjacent faces. It might be as large as the smallest minimum element length on adjacent faces.

SMA.14.27   Meshing Order

If minimum element edge length is defaulted or equal for all edges, then the mesh may proceed in the order that the faces were created during solid modeling. If minimum element edge length is set to different values on some edges or faces, then the mesh will probably proceed in the order of ascending minimum element length.

Relative Mesh Density—Faces

SMA.14.28   For Difficult Faces

If a particular face is difficult to mesh, set the minimum element length on all other edges larger than the value required on the difficult face. The difficult face will probably mesh first, providing insight on the mesh problem. When the problem is understood and the difficult face can be meshed easily, reset the minimum element lengths as required, and re-create the mesh.

SMA.14.29   Element Edge-Length Ratio for Faces

The ratio of maximum-to-minimum element edge length on a face should not exceed a factor of 4 except when a very small detail is adjacent.

Relative Mesh Density—Volumes

SMA.14.30   Element Edge-Length Ratio for Volumes

The ratio of maximum-to-minimum element edge length throughout the volume should not exceed a factor of 6 except when very small detail is present.

SMA.14.31   For a More Uniform Mesh

A more uniform mesh is always produced by setting maximum and minimum element edge length closer together. It is always better to raise the minimum element edge length by about twice the percentage that the maximum element edge length is lowered. For example, if the minimum element edge length is raised 20 percent, then lower the maximum element edge length just 10 percent. Pay close attention to how the bandwidth changes. If it decreases and the mesh improves, then proceed further.

Other Mesh Density Controls

SMA.14.32   Dense Nodes

Look for any edges with very dense nodes. There may be another edge very near by. Is this a modeling error? A very short edge adjacent to a long edge can cause dense nodes at the intersection of the edges.

SMA.14.33   Solid Model Problems

SM problems can become obvious with a coarse node mesh. Very short edges, small edge angles, and narrow faces will cause dense nodes. Changes or simplifications of the solid model may become necessary at this point.

SMA.14.34   Local Control

Each parameter that controls the mesh density might be applicable only on the solid model entity selected when specifying the parameter value. However, it may apply to higher-level entities as well. For example, element edge length might be specified on selected solid model edges. It may or may not apply to the finite element edges on the two solid model faces connected to this solid model edge, to the element edges inside the solid model connecting to this solid model edge, or to element edges in the vicinity of the edge length specification.

SMA.14.35   Global Control

If no solid model entities are selected when a parameter value is set, then the parameter may apply to all appropriate entities. For example, if element edge length is specified, but no edges or faces of the solid were selected, then this value may be applied to element edges on all solid edges, all solid faces, or both.

SMA.14.36   Available Parameters

If the mesh generator does not allow specification of a specific mesh density control parameter, then its logic might not utilize this parameter. Alternately, the parameter might be computed relative to another parameter.

SMA.14.37   Default Parameters

If the value of a mesh density control parameter is not specified by the user, then a default value related to geometry or another parameter is automatically computed. Default values usually provide for a coarse mesh.

SMA.14.38   Mesh Density Conversion

Mesh density parameters can be changed to produce a finer mesh, but not a coarser mesh. The mesh must revert to an earlier stage, or the initial stage, and the mesh regenerated.

SMA.14.39   Naming Conventions

Mesh generators use parameter names similar to those discussed in Sec. 14.5.1. Naming conventions may vary slightly from this text and also from system to system.

SMA.14.40   When Parameter Values Are Not Obvious

When proper values for mesh density parameters are not obvious, generate an initial coarse mesh, perhaps using defaults. A coarse mesh can be created quickly. An improved mesh strategy may become obvious, and better estimates of all mesh density parameters made. Consider total number of nodes (larger is better for results accuracy) and bandwidth (smaller is better for analysis execution time) to determine the ideal mesh parameter values.

SMA.14.41   Parameter Sensitivity Study

If ideal mesh parameters are still not clear, perform a parameter-sensitivity study by changing just one parameter at a time from the default values. One or more parameter values may be out of balance. Parameters that add nodes, reduce the bandwidth, and improve element shapes merit the most change. For example, if decreasing the maximum element edge length has little positive impact, then raising the minimum element edge length probably will!

14.6   Case Loads and Boundary Conditions

Loads and boundary conditions are created by selecting entities and specifying the necessary values. They can be specified on solid model entities (see color insert, Fig. 14.8) such as vertices, edges, surfaces, or the entire solid before or after the mesh is created. They are converted to definition on the mesh upon analysis execution only. The graphical select type can usually be set so that only a particular entity type is selected.

Loads and boundary conditions can also be specified on mesh entities such as nodes or elements. Changes in the mesh require redefining of these loads and boundary conditions.

Local coordinate systems are created so that the direction of loads and boundary conditions can be controlled, and analysis results interpreted easily. For example, the displacement normal to a complex surface can be automatically constrained to zero everywhere. A local coordinate system will be automatically created for each node on the surface. The analysis results on this surface can be obtained in the local coordinate systems, the global system, or some other local coordinate system.

Loads and boundary conditions are defined for specific analysis types such as mechanical, thermal, fluid, electromagnetic, etc. Each load defined will be recognized only by its appropriate analysis type. Only mechanical and thermal loads and boundary conditions are discussed here.

A load case is defined by selecting a group of loads and boundary conditions that represent an actual condition. Specific loads and boundary conditions may be included in any number of load cases.

14.6.1   Mechanical Loads

Acceleration

Acceleration is a linear force field applied to mass, such as gravity. Direction, magnitude, and material property mass density are required.

Angular Velocity

Angular velocity is the constant rate of rotation or spin of the structure about an arbitrary axis. The axis of motion need not be an axis of revolution of geometry. Constant radial forces proportional to mass and radius of motion are applied.

Angular Acceleration

Angular acceleration (or spin acceleration) is the rate of increase of spin about an axis of motion. Radial forces are created. For example, a bullet experiences an angular acceleration as it accelerates down the barrel, due to the riffling helix. Constant radial forces proportional to mass and radius of motion squared are applied.

Moments

Moments may be applied to shell elements at a single node, or at nodes on an edge. Moments must be applied to solid models as force couples (equal but opposite parallel forces separated by some distance) acting at nodes.

Point Forces

Point forces may be applied at a single node, at nodes along an edge, at nodes on a surface, or at nodes inside the solid. Forces on planes of symmetry need to be reduced by appropriate factors to reflect the fraction of the structure modeled.

Surface Pressure

Surface pressure may be uniform or nonuniform, varying as a function of the active local coordinate system on an edge or surface. Large-displacement (updated lagrangian) analyses ramp loads from zero up to their maximum value in several load steps, and the pressure remains normal (nonconservative) to the element. Flexible structures such as aircraft wings require this.

Temperature

Temperature is specified at a node, a face, or through the volume, or from a prior thermal analysis. The difference between a reference temperature when the structure was created and the current temperature distribution can be analyzed.

14.6.2   Mechanical Boundary Conditions

Node Displacement

Node displacement or restraint enforces a zero or nonzero translation and/or rotation at that location.

Symmetry and Antisymmetry Surface Restraint

Symmetry and antisymmetry surface-restraint boundary conditions apply only to structures that are symmetrical about the plane of symmetry. More than one plane of symmetry may exist. A surface model will have a vertex and/or an edge on the plane of symmetry, while a solid model will have a vertex, an edge, and/or surface of the solid on the plane of symmetry. Analysis costs can be greatly reduced because only an integer fraction of the entire structure is analyzed. Results for the entire structure can be obtained, but may require more user interaction.

Symmetry boundary conditions require constraint of the nodal displacements normal to the plane of symmetry. The nodes may move on the plane of symmetry.

Antisymmetry boundary conditions require constraint of the displacements on the plane of antisymmetry, but not normal to it.

Fixed Restraint

Fixed restraint boundary conditions on an edge or a surface constrain all nodal displacements and rotations. The specification of symmetry plus antisymmetry boundary conditions on a surface is identical to a fixed boundary condition.

14.6.3   Thermal Loads

Convection

Convection transmits heat from a node or surface by the movement of constant temperature gas or fluid over the surface. A heat convection coefficient is required.

Conduction

Conduction transmits heat through the solid, and is viewed more as a reaction than a load. Coefficient of thermal conductivity and specific heat material properties are required during thermal steady-state and transient analyses.

Heat Source

Heat source may be defined at a point, along a line, or through a volume to model heating or cooling devices. A body heat source might represent a chemical reaction releasing (or collecting) a distributed heat.

Radiation

Radiation transmits heat from molecules undergoing internal chemical change.

14.6.4 Thermal Boundary Conditions

Heat Flux

Heat flux or flow transmits heat from a surface at a specified rate.

Temperature

Temperature is specified at a node, a face, or through the volume as described in mechanical loads.

14.7 Analysis

Analysis types are typically mechanical, thermal, fluid, electromagnetic, etc. Loads might be static or dynamic (time-varying). Results from one analysis might be saved for use in a subsequent analysis. For example, a thermal transient analysis produces temperatures; the temperatures at a specific point in time might be passed to a static mechanical analysis. The temperatures and stresses might be passed to a dynamic mechanical analysis.

14.7.1 Estimating Time Requirements

The time estimate to analyze a load step is a function of the speed of the processor, the percentage of the processor available to the analysis solution, the number of degrees of freedom, and the bandwidth squared. The wall-clock time from a solution of a substantial model, with preferably no other users, should be obtained for the purpose of determining the constant a. When only 50 percent of the CPU is available to an analysis solution, then the wall-clock time will be twice as large as:

$$\text{Time} = a \cdot \text{DOF} \cdot \text{BW} \cdot \text{BW}$$

where DOF = degrees of freedom
     BW = bandwidth
      a = time constant for a specific CPU

14.7.2 Estimating Storage Requirements

Storage requirement estimates can be obtained for each analysis type. It is a function of the bandwidth, analysis type, and the block size used. A mechanical analysis typically stores about 72 pieces of data per element, while a thermal analysis only stores 8 pieces of data—hence the difference in analysis type factor (ATF).

Hard disks are formatted in different numbers of bytes per block, depending on the vendor, and on customer preference. Many workstations are formatted with a block size of 4096 bytes per block. Thus, for estimating storage requirements:

$$\text{Number\_Blocks} = b \cdot BW \cdot BW \cdot ATF/BLOCK\_SIZE$$

where b = storage constant for a specific CPU
ATF = analysis-type factor
ATF = 1 for thermal
ATF = 8 for stress analysis

14.7.3   Internal Solvers

SM systems that provide automatic finite element mesh generation also provide analysis solvers inside their software. Data management becomes very simple. Design engineers and other product development team members can perform concept design analysis very quickly as their product evolves. Product development becomes a much more intelligent process.

Internal solvers are usually limited to static stress and thermal analysis. Extensive analysis capabilities are available from software vendors who specialize in analysis. The mesh and environment created can be easily accessed by external solvers.

Internal solvers are found to be accurate and reliable. To gain confidence, compare the results obtained to analyses performed with solvers one is familiar with. Simple test cases with known solutions can also be used, but include shear deformation in theoretical results.

14.7.4   External Solvers

Extensive analysis capabilities required for detailed analysis are available from software vendors who specialize in analysis. Other analysis types, elements, loads, restraints, special features, training, consulting, etc., are available from these sources.

These analysis products undergo rigid testing to eliminate flaws and ensure accuracy. Most analysts have experience with one or more of these products and are confident of the results obtained. Detail analysis may require a special technique or feature available in a product in which they have confidence, and they may prefer not to qualify use of an unfamiliar product. Contracts may even require that the analysis product used meet stringent requirements.

Analysis files created by solid-based systems are large compared to files created by experienced analysts, as every load or restraint component is written as a separate command. Analysts generally use generation features to produce multiple loads, etc., with every command.

14.8   Postprocessing

Postprocessing must be very simple for rapid design evaluation during concept design, and also comprehensive for use during detail design. Extreme values can be reported in a menu, and/or displayed with colors on a shaded solid model (see color insert, Fig. 14.9). Extreme values will occur on the surface unless an internal load such as a heat source causes the extreme to occur inside the solid.

14.8.1   Concept Design

Concept design evaluation should ensure that maximum displacements and stresses are reasonable. For homogeneous ductile materials, the maximum von Mises stress must be less than the material's yield stress, and the maximum Tresca stress must be less than the material's shear strength. For homogeneous brittle materials, the largest principal stress must be less than the ultimate tensile strength of the material, per the maximum normal stress theory. As the design process continues, these checks remain the initial checks, and additional detailed evaluations of the analysis results are made.

14.8.2   Interactive Query

Interactive query of analysis results returns the extreme values of stresses and displacements regardless of location, or of all values at a single location. The stress components at a controlling stress location such as von Mises may be of special interest.

Interactive query of analysis results is performed by selecting a node and requesting results to be displayed in a table or listed in the session log. Query is limited to a requested type of data in some systems.

Stress values displayed on plots, displayed in a query menu, and tabulated in a report may differ because plots use stresses extrapolated to the surface; query values may be from a few Gauss points (where the finite element's stiffness is evaluated); and tabulated values may be nodal or gaussian values. Extreme values will exhibit the greatest differences.

14.8.3   Model Simulation

Result displays can be produced on deflected or undeflected geometry. The cause of the extreme result value is sometimes easier to understand on the displaced geometry. Display with element edges shown may also help.

Each result may be color shaded on the exterior of the solid, color shaded on a cross section of the solid, or displayed as several transparent, colored, iso-result surfaces. Each color is indicative of a certain level of the result being displayed. The display of the mesh may need to be turned off during results display if it makes the display too busy or if it solid-shades.

14.9   Cautions and Needed Improvements

In most programs the finite element mesh generation logic does not generally utilize the fundamental knowledge that an analyst uses when generating a mesh. That fundamental knowledge comes from the theory of elasticity and engineering mechanics. The accuracy of a well-distributed mesh can easily have less than half the error in primary results (such as displacements) as a uniform mesh or a poorly distributed mesh with the same number of degrees of freedom. The secondary results (such as stresses) often show even less error because derivatives of the primary results are used to compute the secondary results. The errors are amplified less. The mesh distribution at a minimum must be a function of geometry and change in geometry.

Mesh generation logic does not generally include utilization of the analysis type or the loads and restraints when creating the mesh. This is further complicated by the desire of the analyst to create a mesh that can accommodate more than one set of loads, and more than one analysis type.

Point loads create fictitious local errors because loads are never actually applied at an infinitesimal point, but rather are distributed somewhat. A distributed point load which distributes some of the load to nearby nodes with a cosine of similar function over a specified radius is needed. The mesh must of course have more than one node inside the radius specified.

Other loads such as contact loads between a shaft and its bearing are often not provided for or easily modeled by the analyst. Improvement is needed in this area.

Elements

SMA.14.42   Tetrahedron Elements

Tetrahedron elements have traditionally had an image problem, primarily because early formulations were linear, having an inadequate field variable for most analyses. They deform with slope discontinuities at the interelement boundaries, rather than in the smooth, continuous fashion needed and available with quadratic tetrahedrons. Operator manuals of commercial analysis products noted this early tetrahedron weakness. Most failed to update their manuals in a timely fashion when quadratic tetrahedrons became available, especially if they did not yet have an automatic mesh generator.

(Continued)

Elements
(*Continued*)

SMA.14.43   Analysis Convergence

Analysis convergence studies[1] of compact solid models with quadratic or higher displacements show that quadratic tetrahedrons and hexahedrons converge at approximately the same rate; linear hexahedrons converge more slowly; and linear tetrahedrons are the most inefficient. The quality of analysis results obtained is related to the number of nodes per element.

SMA.14.44   Incompatible Mode Linear Hexahedron Elements

Linear hexahedrons with incompatible modes can appear to converge the fastest. Incompatible mode elements add an extra function in the element that allows quadratic deformations inside the element, but the deformations are incompatible at the interelement boundaries. The incompatibility is less severe than that in simpler linear elements. A prismatic beam fixed at the base and subjected to end moment converges to the theoretical bending deformation with a coarse mesh. However, shear deformation must also be included in the theoretical deformation. Linear hexahedrons underestimate shear deformation and normal warping strains, and hence converge to slightly incorrect displacement values for short beams and compact solids.

SMA.14.45   Quadratic Hexahedron and Tetrahedron Elements

Quadratic hexahedrons converge slightly faster than quadratic tetrahedrons in models with primarily planar faces and simple geometry. Hexahedrons in such a model will have nearly ideal shapes, while tetrahedrons will have more distorted shapes. Where the geometry varies rapidly, a finer mesh is required. In high-stress gradient regions, the interior angles of hexahedrons should not deviate from 90° by more than 25°. Results diverge rapidly with greater deviation.

SMA.14.46   Number of Elements versus Nodes

There are about five times as many elements in a tetrahedron mesh with the same number of nodes and execution cost as in a hexahedron mesh. The tetrahedron mesh can be distributed better if adequate mesh density control is provided.

Mesh Process

SMA.14.47   Automatic versus Interactive

Cost comparisons of automatic versus interactive mesh generation systems must include the labor and CPU cost to produce results of comparable accuracy. An automatic mesh generator yields lower total cost, and the analyst has more time for engineering.

SMA.14.48   Local Mesh Modifications

If a different mesh is required at any stage, then it is best to modify the mesh before proceeding. A smoother mesh allowing higher results quality will be attained with the earliest changes in parameter values. For example, if a finer mesh is needed on a surface, refine the mesh during the surface mesh stage rather than waiting until the linear volume or quadratic volume mesh stage.

SMA.14.49   The Mesh Algorithm

Try to understand the general mesh algorithm so that better meshes can be created as experience grows. Understand which mesh commands, especially those of mesh density, are applicable at any time. Automatic checks should be made, noting where the ratio criteria for edges and faces are exceeded.

SMA.14.50   Uniform Element Edge Lengths

This usually requires that the minimum element edge length be about one-quarter of the maximum element edge length. If only a few faces have moderately short solid edges, then these faces can be set with the minimum element edge length as a function of the shortest edge length.

SMA.14.51   Coarse Mesh

Identify areas where the mesh may be coarse without loss of accuracy. If the load is low, restraints are not nearby, and the geometry is not changing, than a coarse mesh is probably acceptable here. Does the mesh generator logic automatically produce a coarse mesh here? Do additional loads cause a denser mesh upon re-creation of the mesh?

(*Continued*)

Mesh Process
(*Continued*)

SMA.14.52   Mesh Sequence

Automatic mesh generators typically mesh in this order: (1) nodes at vertices, (2) nodes on edges, (3) nodes and surface elements on surfaces, (4) linear volume elements, and (5) quadratic volume elements. The mesh density is controlled by specifying the mesh size on edges, surfaces, and through the volume at each step. Global values can be specified as well as values modified in selected areas. Additionally, nodes and associated elements can be added at specified locations to accommodate loads, restraints, and accuracy concerns.

SMA.14.53   Mesh Order

Are the edges or faces meshed in a particular order—such as when they were created in the solid, or as a function of the minimum element length? Knowledge of the mesh order can be used to advantage when debugging a mesh problem.

Geometry

SMA.14.54   Curved or Varied Geometry

Tetrahedrons can perform as well as hexahedrons when geometry is curved and/or varies rapidly. A simple example is an equilateral tetrahedron solid model with a pressure on one face and fixed at the base. All of the tetrahedrons will have nearly ideal shapes, while the hexahedrons will have fair to poor shapes in the high-stress gradient regions. Interior angles of tetrahedrons can deviate from 60° by up to 45° before errors are as large as hexahedrons at 25° deviation.

SMA.14.55   Faces with Very Short Edges

These will require that the minimum element edge length be set to at least three times the short edge length.

SMA.14.56   Small Features or Small Faces

These generally require face-aspect ratio to be set to a low value, perhaps 0.3 or lower. A few elements which may have relatively poor shapes are acceptable as long as the minimum element length is met.

SMA.14.57   Complex Solid Models

These may require that the minimum aspect ratio be set inversely proportional to the minimum element edge length. For example, where a small minimum element edge length is required, the minimum aspect ratio will be higher, and vice versa.

The largest maximum element length should not be greater than 50 times the smallest minimum element length for the entire solid. Excessively large bandwidths and execution costs can occur without measurable improvement in the stresses.

SMA.14.58   Fillets

If fillets are small relative to nearby geometry, and will be included in the mesh, set the local element length so that just one element spans the fillet radius. Angle control around the circumference of the fillet works best. Set ANGLE to 120° for a 90° fillet because all edges that are not precisely circumferential will subtend more than 90°. Set the minimum element length larger than the circumferential distance across the fillet, and maximum element length to about three times the minimum element length. Aspect ratio and corner angle criteria may also need to be set less stringently.

SMA.14.59   Large Faces

Large faces relative to adjacent faces must not have a single or small number of elements spanning the face. A large bandwidth and poor analysis accuracy usually result from this condition.

Analysis

SMA.14.60 Visual Inspection

Display the finite element mesh with solid shading prior to analysis to verify that the mesh is as desired. Also display each load and boundary condition prior to use.

SMA.14.61 Preanalysis Test

An initial analysis using a coarse linear mesh can be used to inexpensively test the loads, boundary conditions, and the final quadratic mesh before a time-consuming analysis is executed. The deformed shape must be intuitive before executing a lengthy analysis. The approximate levels of stress and magnitude and direction of deformation can be checked. Rigid body motions and missing or erroneous loads are frequently found. Loads may be off by an order of magnitude, or erroneous units conversions may occur for loads or material properties. Local loads that are not distributed over enough nodes can overwhelm all other stresses.

Good to Know

SMA.14.62 FEA Results

The results of FEA are only as good as the finite element modeling that was done. If loads, constraints, and forces are not calculated and applied accurately, then the results will not be of any significant use. It is also necessary to understand not only physical properties, but material properties for FEA to be effective. FEA can become complex very quickly.

Andrew Price, Manager Engineering Applications
Axis Technologies, Fairport, N.Y.

SMA.14.63 Program Overrides

Identify any program logic that overrides user-specified mesh variables. For example, the maximum element length on a surface may be limited to four times the minimum element length. Any variables that cannot be specified by the user are potentially being set by such logic.

SMA.14.64 System Capabilities

At present, no solid-based analysis system can handle every analysis. Capabilities that may be weak or missing are:

1. Adequate mesh density control
2. Some analysis types
3. Some loads and restraints
4. Interface between element types such as solid and shell
5. Interface between components of an assembly
6. Orientation of material or element properties

References

1. Lowrey, Richard D., "A Comparison of Quadratic and Linear Hexahedrons and Tetrahedrons," *ANSYS Users Conference Proceedings,* Pittsburgh, Pa., May, 1989.
2. Lowrey, Richard D., "Characteristics of Quality Finite Element Meshes," *ANSYS Users Conference Proceedings,* Pittsburgh, Pa., May, 1991.
3. Lowrey, Richard D., "Computing Relative Mesh Densities of Exterior Surfaces for Quality Finite Element Meshes," *ANSYS Users Conference Proceedings,* June, 1992.

4. Spivak, Michael, *Differential Geometry,* vol. II, *Publish or Perish,* 6 Beacon St., Boston, Mass., 02108, 1970.

5. Lowrey, Richard D., "Computation of Final Mesh Size Before Mesh Completion," *NASTRAN World User's Conference Proceedings,* Universal City, Ca., March, 1990.

Suggestions for Further Reading

S. P. Timoshenko and J. N. Goodier, *Theory of Elasticity,* 3d ed., New York, McGraw-Hill, 1970.

S. P. Timoshenko and S. Woinowsky-Krieger, *Theory of Plates and Shells,* 2d ed., New York, McGraw-Hill, 1959.

O. C. Zienkiewicz and Y. K. Cheung, *The Finite Element Method in Structural and Continuum Mechanics,* New York, McGraw-Hill, 1967.

C. S. Desai and J. F. Abel, *Introduction to the Finite Element Method,* New York, Van Nostrand Reinhold Co., 1972.

J. Robinson, *Integrated Theory of Finite Element Methods,* New York, John Wiley and Sons, 1973.

Market Leadership –
Engineered with EMS

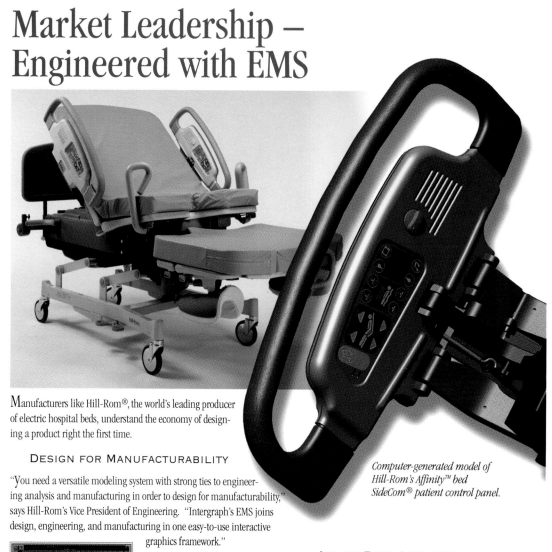

Manufacturers like Hill-Rom®, the world's leading producer of electric hospital beds, understand the economy of designing a product right the first time.

DESIGN FOR MANUFACTURABILITY

"You need a versatile modeling system with strong ties to engineering analysis and manufacturing in order to design for manufacturability," says Hill-Rom's Vice President of Engineering. "Intergraph's EMS joins design, engineering, and manufacturing in one easy-to-use interactive graphics framework."

Computer-generated model of Hill-Rom's Affinity™ bed SideCom® patient control panel.

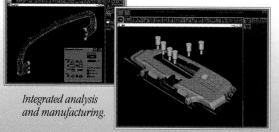

Integrated analysis and manufacturing.

ART-TO-PART AUTOMATION

With EMS, a single, intelligent data set defines a product from art to part – with no translation required. Complete variational and parametric design features are fully integrated with industrial design, engineering analysis, fabrication, NC programming, and more. Plus EMS merges easily into your existing environment, leveraging your investments in existing technology.

EXPLORE EMS, A SMARTER WAY TO MANUFACTURE
Call Intergraph today for more information: 800-345-4856

INTERGRAPH
Solutions for the Technical Desktop

Chapter 15

Solid Modeling for Numerical Control

Robert J. Byrnes
Vice President
Varimetrix Corporation

The critical path from Solid Modeling (SM) to manufactured part, with rare exception, passes through processes known as *numerical control* (NC). NC refers to a wide range of applications, but most directly refers to the control of machine tool motion through sequences of numbers and instructions. This is in contrast to manual or mechanical methods of machine tool control. The advantages of NC over manual or mechanical methods are reliability, precision, and flexibility.

Numerical control machine tools were originally programed at the NC machine by the direct entry of coordinates. The programmer computed tool position data on paper and keyed in the proper positions. Typically, these coordinate values and other machine instructions are now generated by CAD/CAM software. Geometry and other relevant data is analyzed under the control and guidance of the NC operator. The output is then sent to the NC machine in any of a number of formats.

15.1 Part Shape

The goal of the NC process is efficiently obtaining the desired part shape. Although there are many methods in which machine tools are used to shape material (see Chap. 25), this chapter will focus on shaping a part through material removal (chipping). Machine tools use NC data to control the speed and position of cutting tools in order to remove unwanted material. Figure 15.1 illustrates a few milling tool examples.

Cylindrical milling tool examples

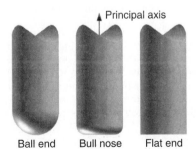

Ball end Bull nose Flat end

FIGURE 15.1 Side view of three milling tools. All are axially symmetric and remove material by spinning about the tool axis. The stock is chipped away, leaving the desired part shape. *(Courtesy of Varimetrix Corporation.)*

Essential information for computing correct tool motion begins with an accurate definition of the part shape, but also includes:

1. Machining characteristics of the part material
2. Shape and physical properties of the cutting tool
3. Critical dimensions and datum locations

4. Part accuracy and finish requirements (tolerances)

5. Shape of the stock (part material) at the start of machining

Tool motions are grouped into ordered sequences called *toolpaths*. Toolpaths and other machine instructions are grouped together into process plans which define the order of manufacturing operations needed to obtain the final part (see Chap. 25 for more on process plans).

In a broad sense, a part's shape more than anything else determines the difficulty and cost of manufacturing. This is because a part's shape is what most often determines the complexity of the manufacturing plan. Similarly, the detail and accuracy of the part geometry determines the ease or difficulty the NC operator will have in generating toolpaths. As testimony to the importance of these details, NC programmers often speak of the quality of the modeling data they are provided, both good and bad.

Although there is a great deal more information than part shape that must be communicated to the NC operator, this chapter will focus on the solid model itself. In some instances, such auxiliary manufacturing information will be discussed.

15.2 Solid Modeling and Numerical Control (NC)

Solid Modeling software provides the capability to create and modify solid geometry. It also provides a number of methods to create and modify nongeometric information. This nongeometric information should include that which is needed by NC operators. If the NC software is properly integrated within the SM system, it should be able to acquire and utilize this information as needed.

The majority of NC operators are using software tools which do not recognize or leverage any of the special properties of solids. Even if the NC software does not recognize solids directly, it may readily accept SM geometry as curves and trimmed surfaces. One of the most important benefits for manufacturing from a solid design is that the part shape is always valid—without conflicts in topology (see Chap. 3 for more on topology). Problems that might have been discovered only after the investment of manufacturing resources would not even be allowed within the SM system.

However, this alone does not necessarily justify the use of SM. There may be new inefficiencies introduced through SM; this technology is not a panacea. There are cases when a two-dimensional design is adequate. There are still other cases when the simpler geometry from a partially designed part may make manufacturing easier. For example, it may consume significant human and computer resources for the designer to create fillets throughout the design—whereas the NC operator might prefer obtaining a part's filleted shape with a toolpath.

Simple cases notwithstanding, only SM provides a complete definition of the design intent and complete information about the desired part shape. This information can also be used for verification of the NC process and for inspection to ensure the accuracy of the manufacturing process.

Numerical control software products which compute toolpath data from geometry have the following characteristics in common:

1. All analyze geometry.

2. All use manufacturing information.

3. All compute tool positioning information.

4. All output information in a format which can be provided to a machine controller or postprocessing software.

Many finished products are the direct result of NC machining. However, a vast number of products and components indirectly result from NC. Plastic parts are not machined, but the tooling to create them (molds) often are. This is an example of how NC is used to produce a tool for a part, yet not the part itself. The shape of the tool is based upon the final part shape, but also must include parameters to allow for plastic shrinkage and other manufacturing considerations. Figure 15.2 (see color insert) shows a die which is used to stamp sheet steel for automotive oil pans. Figure 15.3 shows a turbine blade which is machined directly.

15.3 Change Propagation

Constant change is the rule in product design and manufacturing. Changes are made to a part's design as it is refined into a product, and as current products are evolved into new products. Similarly,

Tool path for milling
face of turbine blade

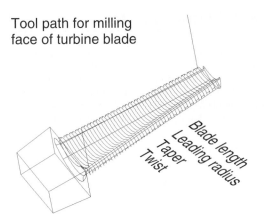

Blade length
Leading radius
Taper
Twist

FIGURE 15.3 Example of a turbine blade that is machined directly. The parameters listed are varied to provide the family of blades necessary to build the complete turbine assembly. Here, the tool path is applied to one side of the blade. The other side is cut in a subsequent operation. *(Courtesy of Varimetrix Corporation.)*

manufacturing plans and processes evolve to accommodate changes in part shape, material availability, and new production methods. To efficiently adapt to these changes there are a number of SM and NC systems which provide change management capabilities throughout the design and manufacturing database.

Managing Change

SMA.15.1   Propagation Control

Can changes be fed forward on demand from the manufacturing group? It is not uncommon for the NC operators to be creating toolpath information for one version of a part while the design group may be one or two versions ahead of them. The NC group may want to accept a new revision as soon as it becomes available, or they may need to cut a prototype of the previous version before accepting the changes.

SMA.15.2   Release/Revision Management

If change propagation will pass from design through NC, is there a mechanism for release/revision management? Rather than receive design changes as they appear, it is often more desirable for NC operators to receive updates when they are ready for them. Control of updates requires some form of revision management. When NC data is generated, the operators should be able to have confidence in which updates have been incorporated into their version of the part.

SMA.15.3   Constraining Modes of Operation

Is there a special mode of operation to ensure that the part design and the NC data can be synchronized after a change? Some SM systems require that designers perform all work in a special mode of operation in order for automated change propagation to work. If the design group follows these rules, are they sufficient to ensure that the CAM group can efficiently absorb the changes? Beware that special parametric modes can place rigid constraints on the SM operator, disallowing the ability to work efficiently.

SMA.15.4   Toolpaths and Process Plans

Will change propagation automatically update toolpaths and maintain process plans? Toolpaths should adapt to changes in geometry or manufacturing parameters. In general, they should update automatically. In some cases changes are significant enough to require changes in the manufacturing plan. If conflicts arise it will be very helpful if there are mechanisms in the NC software to warn the CAM operator of potential problems.

SMA.15.5   Database Access

It may be important to your organization to allow manufacturing information in the database to be accessible to your design staff. Because NC programmers sometimes need to modify geometry, you may want those modifications incorporated into the design group's version of the part. This may also include manufacturing constraints that might be useful for future designs.

15.4 Solid Modeling versus Numerical Control Features

A feature is a high-level construct which describes a region or shape on a part (see Chaps. 8 and 25 for more on SM features). A feature includes the geometric elements which comprise it (curves/edges and surfaces/faces) and perhaps attribute information (dimensions, tolerances, constraints). The real power found in a feature, as opposed to a group of geometric elements, is that it also describes functional intent. This allows other engineers as well as software to ascribe meaning to the contents of a feature. Examples of features are blind and through-holes, open and closed slots, necks, and flanges (see Fig. 15.4).

"Hole" type form features

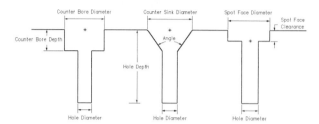

Manufacturing attributes: "Tolerance," "Finish," "Threads/Unit"

FIGURE 15.4 Common "hole" type form features and associated attributes. *(Courtesy of Varimetrix Corporation.)*

Features can be used by other operators and application software to make better and more sophisticated decisions. The primary reasons for this are (1) the geometry has been grouped together into a meaningful unit, and (2) the geometry has been assigned a functional classification.

The examples of features presented in Fig. 15.4 are equally valid in SM and in manufacturing. However, the contrast between a designer's viewpoint and a machinist's does lead to inevitable conflicts. For example, a rib is a natural description of a design feature that forms a web in a structure. However, a machinist is concerned with material to be removed, so the relevant features are the pockets (holes) on either side of the rib (see Fig. 15.5).

The prominent design features are the outer wall (with thickness applied) and the two ribs.

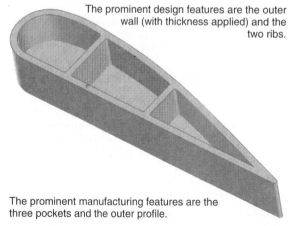

The prominent manufacturing features are the three pockets and the outer profile.

FIGURE 15.5 Design versus manufacturing features. The design features which define this part are the outer profile shape and the ribs. The manufacturing features include the outer profile and the pockets which are separated by the ribs. *(Courtesy of Varimetrix Corporation.)*

There are software tools which attempt to bridge the gap between different feature descriptions of the same final part. Yet, because different industries and different sites do not share feature types and because features can overlap on the part, it is not yet reasonable to expect software to always automate the conversion. This is especially so when the interpretation of the feature is also a function of the manufacturing methods that will be used.

In NC applications, features are a powerful way to group geometry into discrete regions to which operations can be applied in order to realize the part. Feature types can be associated to operation types, and data embedded in features can be used as parameters to guide those operations. NC software designed around this philosophy can take the greatest advantage of the data in your SM system.

15.5 Tolerances

Tolerances are any numerical constraints which describe the allowable error in design or manufacturing operations. There are tolerances which are used by the SM software to perform calculations, and there are other tolerances which are used by manufacturing operations to produce a physical part to a desired accuracy. These tolerances are related, but not identical. Tolerances eventually determine the accuracy, quality, and cost of the final product.

A few examples of tolerances used by SM systems are:

1. Proximity
2. Gap width between faces
3. Surface and curve intersection tolerances

Note that SM tolerances are used by the software to assist in the creation and modification of geometry.

A few examples of tolerances used by NC software are:

1. Surface sampling accuracy
2. Surface chord height accuracy
3. Gap widths between geometric elements
4. Finish smoothness
5. Flatness
6. Parallelism

Note that NC tolerances are largely dictated by a part's functional specifications.

Because SM tolerances affect the creation of geometry, they are likely to have an influence on the toolpaths generated. For example, surface intersection tolerance and gap width can affect the small, but real, distances between faces to be machined. CAM software must make decisions about how to control the tool when there are gaps between geometric elements. Sometimes the decisions made are good, and sometimes not.

A small gap tolerance will result in smaller spaces between faces and perhaps better tool control in the neighborhood of the edges. But small tolerances may also result in added overhead for the design as well as the NC software. This is because when edges are created to tighter tolerances more data is usually created.

There is a generally safe window wherein the tolerance is good enough and yet not so small that the result is unnecessarily expensive. The accuracy required for geometric design should be several times smaller than that required for the final product. Production costs can be reduced if the inaccuracy of the manufactured part is as large as possible while still satisfying the part's functional specifications.

Manufacturing tolerances are determined by how accurately the final product must be made so that it can perform its task. The required tolerances may affect the choice of materials, the manufacturing processes, cutting tools, tool feed rates, and speeds used during cutting.

There are products which provide tolerance analysis to optimize the costs involved in manufacturing. More information can be obtained about tolerance analysis from sources dedicated to this topic.

15.5.1 Tolerance Balancing

Software applications which analyze geometry often assume that the geometry is "optimal." That is, the shape provided accurately represents the intended part shape. If optimal geometry is provided, it should also have an associated tolerance to represent the allowed inaccuracy in the physical part. In this case the tolerance should be balanced (for example, ±0.15 as opposed to +0.2/−0.1). If the tolerance is not evenly balanced, then the geometry is not optimal; it is not centered within its allowed envelope. In order to create toolpaths, the optimal geometry is usually used. If the geometry is not in optimal form the NC operator will either use the offsetting capability built into the toolpath calculation software or actually offset individual geometry elements. The latter is equivalent to having the NC department perform redesign.

Tolerances

SMA.15.6   Tolerance Balancing

In the design phase, strive to optimize geometry by balancing uneven (±) tolerances whenever possible; otherwise, the NC operator will be called upon to balance them for you.

15.5.2   Gap Tolerance

Gaps are voids, or spaces, between surfaces. No data defines the part shape in these regions. These regions should be small, being about the size of the tolerance your modeler uses for solid or surface intersections. In places where there is no data, the NC software must make assumptions about how to control machining. If the gaps are small the NC software will probably perform well. If the gaps are large enough (with respect to the toolpath tolerance and tool size) the resultant toolpath may gouge the part. Gaps can appear between faces of a solid model as the result of the following types of modeling operations:

1. Solid creation through sewing surfaces together
2. Adding, intersecting, or subtracting solids
3. Adding features
4. Filleting operations

Some gaps are created as the result of software errors and others are the unavoidable results of the algorithms used by the SM system. The latter case is addressed here. These gaps should always be less than a user-specified tolerance (see Fig. 15.6).

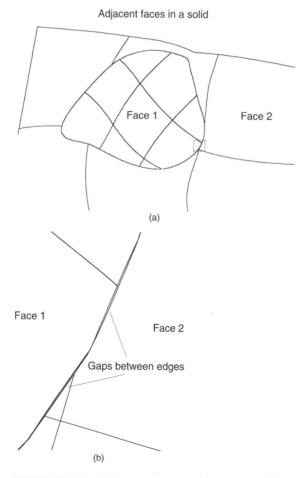

FIGURE 15.6   Gaps within a solid. (*a*) View of two adjacent faces of a solid. Remember that boolean and surface sewing operations are accurate within a specified system tolerance. (*b*) Close-up of adjacent edges. Gaps smaller than the system tolerance will remain in the solid. (*Courtesy of Varimetrix Corporation.*)

Beware that when solids are displayed on the screen, gaps that exist between edges may be invisible. Rather than displaying all edges of all faces in a solid, when edges are shared only one is usually displayed. No amount of "ZOOMing" in will show more than a single edge. However, depending on your manufacturing tolerances, that invisible gap may be significant.

Revealing Gaps

SMA.15.7 Investigative Methods

1. Investigate commands that will allow measurement of distances between edges in the solid.

2. Explode faces from the solid and then measure distances between surface edges (see Fig. 15.7).

3. Try cutting sections and measure distances between resulting curves. A section of a solid should form one or more closed loops. These loops will consist of one or more curves. Adjacent curves will either overlap, intersect, or have gaps between them. The distances involved should be acceptably small.

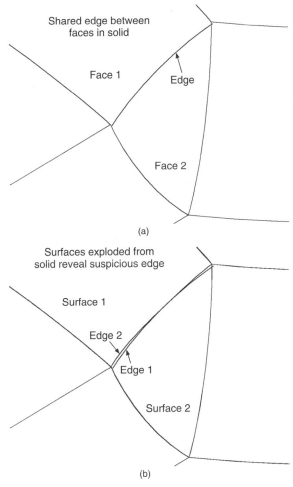

FIGURE 15.7 Example of exploding a solid to reveal gaps. (*a*) Faces within a solid may indicate a suspicious edge. (*b*) Exploding the solid into surfaces confirms the bad-edge definition. This example has been dramatized for clarity. (*Courtesy of Varimetrix Corporation.*)

SMA.15.8 Gaps May Be Masked

Compensating software within the SM system may successfully mask many gap problems. One example is the displaying of only one member of a set of shared edges within a solid as mentioned above. Another example is rendering software that can compensate for gaps and provide attractive displays. Unfortunately, the requirements for producing good toolpaths are often more difficult to satisfy than those for display.

(Continued)

Revealing Gaps
(Continued)

SMA.15.9   Translate Out and Back

Try writing the part out through a translator (such as IGES) and reading it back into your SM system. If the geometry will be sent to NC through such a translator, this is the most accurate way to inspect the geometry. Simply processing the data in this way may reveal problem areas. Also, translated data is often simpler (consisting of curves and surfaces) and may therefore be less difficult to inspect.

15.6   Dimensions

In the past, CAD/CAM implied that the only information that was shared between design and manufacturing was the part shape. Having a part shape alone does not give the NC operator enough information about how to create toolpaths to produce the part. Additional information may already be understood within the context of a given company. But, if a manufacturing group is given an entirely new part, additional information must be communicated.

One important factor in communicating design intent to manufacturing engineers is how the part is dimensioned. The manufacturing engineer needs to know which dimensions of the part are critical. That is, the engineer must understand which locations (datums) all geometry and measurements are based on.

Although design in many organizations begins with drafting (or sketching) and proceeds to 3D, it is now often easier to work entirely in 3D. Unless datums (three planes which define a reference frame) are identified during design, producing drawings for the part may lead to confusion. Simply documenting lengths and angles does not necessarily convey the critical dimensions of the part from a manufacturing standpoint.

Dimensioning

SMA.15.10   Datum Positions

Annotate the model to ensure that parts are machined to meet critical dimensions. Careful attention should be paid to ensure that not only are the critical design dimensions sufficient and not in conflict, but that they can be confirmed after machining. If datum positions are clearly identified, a correct manufacturing plan may be more directly obtained.

15.6.1   Reference Geometry

Reference geometry identifies for the machinist which operations should be performed in the same setup. The *setup* refers to the placement of the stock on the machine tool table. This, in turn, determines the direction from which the tool will approach the part. This is referred to as the *principal axis* (see Chap. 25). Each time the principal axis is changed to reach other features on the part, clamps may need to be removed and the part reoriented. This is a significant source of inaccuracy, errors, and manufacturing costs. For example, if there is a strict requirement that two holes be parallel, then they should be drilled in the same setup.

Sometimes the machinist can infer this information, but that is relying on chance, and mistakes can be made. If the NC process plan specifies the necessary information, then there is no ambiguity. A good NC planner will try to obtain the needed information from the designer. Ideally, this information would be built into the database as attributes of the solid or of the features used and would be readily identifiable from the part's dimensions.

15.7   Manufacturing Considerations

If the part's design requires multiple manufacturing operations to be performed, those programming the NC toolpaths should be made aware of any further downstream manufacturing. It is essential for them to be informed so that their work does not negatively affect further operations. The following considerations may apply:

1. A specific finish/scallop height (beyond the design requirement) may be necessary.

2. Sharp edges may need to be smoothed. This is very important, depending on how the part is to be handled.

3. Stock allowance may need to remain if the part or tool is to be textured (such as sandblasted) after machining.

4. If finish requirements are critical, certain manufacturing processes may be disallowed.

5. Heat from rapid material removal near the part surface may alter the hardness of the material.

15.7.1   Holes

If the part to be machined has holes, it is sometimes desirable for the NC operator to be able to temporarily remove them from the design. This capability is referred to as *feature suppression*. Although some methods for suppressing design features require that the part database be "regenerated," this can be avoided if the NC software can detect and selectively ignore features. The motivation for suppressing hole features is that the holes interrupt the tool motion as it is calculated across the part (see Fig. 15.8).

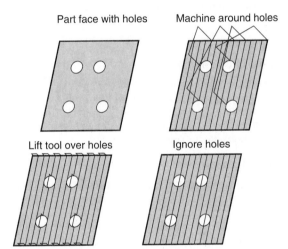

FIGURE 15.8 An example of feature suppression: (top left) part face with holes; (bottom left) same face with tool path lifting over the holes; (top right) tool path cutting regions interrupted by the holes; (bottom right) tool path ignoring the hole features. *(Courtesy of Varimetrix Corporation.)*

More specifically, many NC milling utilities treat all holes in surfaces similarly. Because it is occasionally desirable to machine around holes, this becomes the rule. If there are many holes to be drilled after milling, the resultant toolpath might carefully, and unnecessarily, avoid each of them while removing the rest of the material from the face. This results in unnecessary tool motion and, occasionally, spikes in exactly those places where holes will need to be placed.

15.7.2   Surfaces

If the SM system does not allow the editing of individual surfaces or the ability to sew surfaces together into a solid, the quality of the geometry is entirely controlled by the SM software. If the SM system does allow this flexibility, then the quality of the geometry will also depend upon how the surfaces are created and modified.

Surfacing

SMA.15.11   Difficult Areas

Try to avoid surface shapes that are unnatural. It is sometimes better to create a surface and trim it to fit than to find a way to awkwardly force one into place. A good rule of thumb is that if you are having a hard time working with a surface so will everyone else who has to deal with it.

15.7.3 Solids and Surfaces

As geometry is created it is added to the SM database, and usually some evaluation is performed to display it. As work with the part continues, the geometry is repeatedly evaluated. Sometimes, problems are found during the repetitive evaluation and are identified. Fortunately, most problematic geometry is identified during this design phase.

However, when models are sent to analysis software (in particular NC), the geometry is sometimes refined and analyzed to a much higher degree than ever before. Analysis software generally stresses the following conditions:

1. Strict tolerance refinement of each face and its edges

2. Subsequent calculations which rely on surface tangency and normal vectors

Caution:

Every point on a surface has a normal vector which is perpendicular to the surface at that point. This is not true for surfaces whose definition includes a crease. There is no unique surface normal for points on such a crease. The tangent plane to the surface at that point lies on that point and is perpendicular to the surface normal. Surface tangent vectors lie in this plane.

Problem Detection and Troubleshooting

SMA.15.12 Test for Hidden Problems

When problems are encountered during NC programming, their cause must be determined. If the quality of the part's underlying geometry is suspect there are a number of tests that can be performed within the SM software. The results of these tests may indicate problems which otherwise might pass through to other applications. Finding problems early in the design phase will prevent a possible cascade of difficulties downstream.

SMA.15.13 Display Tolerance

Try to decrease the display tolerance. If allowed, this can be a simple and cost-effective test. Look for surface display curves (edges and isolines) which appear strange. The edges may not meet up or they may overlap in the corners. This may be a bad surface, or it could simply be a characteristic of the display utilities. If all of your surfaces share this, you probably should not bother using this as an indicator.

Caution: After inspection don't forget to reset your display tolerance to its previous value.

SMA.15.14 Display Curves (Isolines)

Try increasing the number of display curves (isolines). This ensures that you are seeing a more comprehensive evaluation of the surface and can reveal abnormal surface areas.

SMA.15.15 Outside Offset

Try offsetting the solid toward its outer side. (Surfaces may also be offset individually if only a few faces are suspect.) With large offsets you are likely to see strange results. A small but visually significant offset should be used. You are interested only in seeing that the offset geometry is smooth and predictable. There should be no sudden, unexpected, or large variations in the display curves, nor should there be "ripple effects" along the edges. If the amount of offset is greater than the curvature of any concave regions, the geometry may fold. This is a reasonable result in many systems, and can be avoided with a smaller offset.

SMA.15.16 Shading or Rendering

Try shading or rendering the part. This can also reveal problem geometry. Surfaces that should appear smooth or change curvature in a uniform manner should not show sudden shading differences or isolated visual features. Shading can be useful because it is generally quick (compared to other evaluation techniques) and also uses the surface normal information. Decreasing the display tolerance will result in a more comprehensive test.

Warning: This can consume memory rapidly. Try to avoid using display tolerances so small that the test cannot be completed.

(Continued)

**Problem Detection
and Troubleshooting**
(Continued)

Caution: Don't forget to reset the display tolerance to its previous value.

The simpler the shading utility, the better in this case. Just as some modeling and NC software compensate for anomalies in the geometry, so do some rendering software.

SMA.15.17 Undetected Problems

If a part contains problematic geometry, the NC application may handle it masterfully, or toolpath generation may come to a halt. This is also an invitation for the NC operator to fit new geometry that has behavior which is more acceptable to the NC software, but does not necessarily fulfill the design intent.

Small trouble regions such as these in surfaces can sometimes slip through design only to be found while using an application which performs a more demanding analysis. Often the only work-around is to redefine the geometry. Figure 15.9 illustrates a similar problem condition.

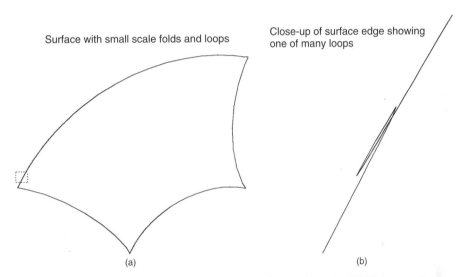

Surface with small scale folds and loops

Close-up of surface edge showing one of many loops

(a)

(b)

FIGURE 15.9   Problem surface regions. (*a*) Surface extracted from problematic solid; (*b*) close-up of surface edge showing folds and loops which are the source of the problem. *(Courtesy of Varimetrix Corporation.)*

15.8   Solid Modeling and Numerical Control Software Compatibility

The greatest benefits may be obtained when both SM and NC software are integrated. Shared database and terminology have always been important, but optimal use of resources requires reliance upon feature-based design and automated change management. All software involved must support similar data structures to facilitate communication of nongeometric information and data interdependencies. If any translators are used they must also support such data structures.

Obstacles between SM and manufacturing should be minimized when the SM and the NC products are provided by the same vendor. Unfortunately, this is no guarantee of a high level of compatibility. Also, different vendors may provide better individual solutions for different applications, compelling the use of software products of differing lineage.

Because of the widely varying capabilities of NC software in popular usage, it is helpful to consider several categories. The groupings below are based exclusively upon the level of compatibility between the SM and NC software.

15.8.1   Compatibility Group I

The first level of compatibility can be defined as being those NC utilities which do not use solids. It is probable that this group of NC utilities is not integrated with the SM system. Unless a custom translator will convert data from SM to NC, IGES will probably be used. Using 2D sections and 3D edges as wireframe geometry are typical limitations and solid faces will become trimmed surfaces.

Higher-level data constructions, such as features, are unlikely to be usable by this compatibility group. This is because, by virtue of not supporting solid models, it is improbable that feature information or parametric relationships will be maintained.

15.8.2   Compatibility Group II

The second level of compatibility is NC software that can utilize solid geometry, but does not share the same database.

Translators that are generally available to industry (such as those using IGES) often do not address the translation of solids data, even when these standards include an effective definition for solid translation. This is because not all CAD/CAM vendors implement the full standard. You may then be compelled to look for a custom translator which is capable of communicating all desired information. Make sure that this information can be communicated bidirectionally if data created by the NC operators will be needed by your design group.

If solid models and design features cannot be communicated to the NC software it may be possible to re-create them. Capabilities vary greatly in this regard. Some NC software will automatically sew all translated surfaces into a solid, while others do not or they require a great deal of manual interaction. Highly interactive processes invite errors and are not cost-competitive.

If there are other data relationships that you would like to maintain, custom software may need to be written to ensure that this information is properly shared between design and manufacturing.

15.8.3   Compatibility Group III

The highest level of compatibility is achieved when the SM and NC software are fully integrated and share a common database.

The NC software should be able to accept all SM data without conversion or translation. Design features should be recognized by the manufacturing software. Ideally, all information attached to the SM constructions will be accessible to the manufacturing engineers. In short, all information entered into the database is communicable between the SM and NC software.

15.9   How Solid Modeling Benefits Numerical Control

There are a number of benefits directly obtainable by NC operators through SM. Solid Modeling and related technologies provide improvements in procedure and product quality as well as cost savings. The following is a brief outline of benefits available to NC engineers through SM technology:

1. Tooling design
   a. Silhouette lines and parting lines can be generated.
2. Toolpath setup
   a. The part is fully defined and valid.
   b. Shell or offset solid commands can be used to arrive at geometry representing the shape of castings and molds.
   c. Shaded, hidden-line, and wireframe rendering.
   d. Improved modeling of stock, clamps, and fixtures.
   e. Interference checking.
3. Toolpath creation
   a. Tool motion can be generated more intelligently because of the complete description of the part shape in the database.
   b. Some modelers allow faces and edges to be selected individually. This means that operations can address specific regions on the part without the need for exploding the solid. When an NC operation is applied to an entire solid, a single geometry select indicates all the geometry to be addressed. If the contents of the solid are changed, the NC software should be able to automatically respond to those changes with updated toolpaths.

c. SM software which uses NURBS or Bezier geometry should guarantee gouge-free toolpaths. This is because the NURBS family, which includes Bezier shapes, has properties which ensure accurate and complete analysis (see Chap. 5 for more on NURBS). Other free-form surface definitions do not.

d. Some SM software maintains primitive shape information. This means that the NC software is capable of identifying cylinders, arcs, and circles to properly insert circle records into toolpaths.

e. Because solids have a defined inside and outside, the NC software is capable of using this information to simplify the interaction necessary to create toolpaths.

f. Feature-based SM and NC software allows machining operations to be associated to specific features or feature classes. This promotes more efficient generation of manufacturing plans as well as more effective change management after part modification.

4. Toolpath inspection

   a. Rendering is useful for a visual inspection of toolpath coverage or suspicious tool motion. Some products allow toolpaths to be seen with the rendered part.

5. NC verification

   a. Solid material removal verification is a cost-effective method for ensuring toolpath accuracy and machining completeness prior to actual machining (see color insert, Fig. 15.11). If the utility is integrated with your NC and modeling database there are a number of added benefits which may include automatic marking or correction of suspicious motion in the NC database.

   b. SM operations can be used for preparing stock definitions for verification. If the original stock shape is known, subtracting the part shape from it shows all material to be removed.

15.10 Solid Modeling Improvements Needed for Numerical Control

NC relies upon information about both the product being manufactured and about the tools, machines, and materials in use on the shop floor. The impact of SM will continue to be in the communication of product information to the NC software—complementing the information provided to the NC operator.

The move toward information representation in higher-level constructs—such as features—will compel the development of superior NC software to utilize it. This will allow the NC operator to concentrate on the difficult decision making involved in manufacturing, as the software automates control of simple and repetitive tasks.

Finally, to support communication of this information to products from different vendors, improved translation standards and translators must continue to evolve. In this area, standards have often long preceded correct implementation by CAD/CAM vendors. However, recent trends support the coexistence of dissimilar products within corporations, and vendors are placing more emphasis on compliance with data communication standards.

Note: Before buying any NC software, make sure that it can do your job. Some allowance should be made for future growth in your NC capabilities, but you are unlikely to be satisfied unless it is immediately productive.

Preferred Capabilities Recommended Practices

SMA.15.18   Solid Support

NC software should support solids. If it cannot read them directly from your SM system, it should be able to import them or re-create them from translated surfaces.

SMA.15.19   Feature Support

NC software should support features. Manufacturing features provide many benefits: geometry is grouped into a meaningful unit; data useful to manufacturing can be attached. The NC software should be able to use the features created with your SM system. If it does not use them directly it should be able to translate them into feature types which are more useful to the NC application.

SMA.15.20   Gouge-Free Toolpaths

Toolpath generation utilities should be gouge-free. Gouge-free refers to toolpaths which do not gouge the part (see Fig. 15.10). Gouge-free toolpath utilities from different vendors define a range of sophistication and efficiency. The ability to ensure that the part will not be gouged is extremely valuable. The indirect benefit of gouge-free toolpaths is the reduction in interaction required from

(Continued)

the NC operator. The greater the amount of automation, the more likely that changes in the product design can be automatically propagated through to update manufacturing data.

Side view of surfaces to be milled

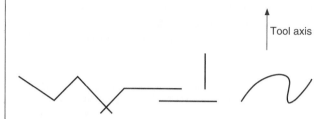

Tool axis

Conditions include:
  Slope discontinuities, gaps, intersections, vertical surfaces,
  overlaps, and surfaces with regions too small to fit tool
(a)

Tool path showing centerline of tool movement

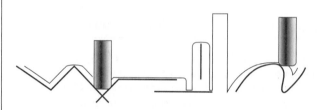

Bull-nose tool is shown tangent to the part geometry
(b)

FIGURE 15.10 Side view of a complex surface arrangement and gouge free tool path. (*a*) Most of these conditions (gaps and overlaps) should not occur within a single solid; (*b*) gouge-free tool path applied to the same surfaces. Note the two superimposed tool representations. (*Courtesy of Varimetrix Corporation.*)

SMA.15.21   Toolpath Verification

Material removal verification provides a means to check for gross gouging of the part or clamps on the machine's work table (see color insert, Fig. 15.11). Toolpath verification utilities can also verify whether sufficient material has been removed by the toolpaths. Such a utility can be stand-alone, using the NC output, or can be integrated with the SM database.

SMA.15.22   SM Integration

If the NC software is integrated within the SM system, the NC operator can efficiently create accurate representations of the stock, clamps, and fixtures used. These solids can be used for toolpath generation and verification, and stored for future use.

SMA.15.23   Associable Process Plans

Manufacturing plans and operations should be associable to part and feature types. These plans should be archivable so that they can be reused with future part designs. This can automate NC plan and toolpath generation.

SMA.15.24   Parametric Constraints

The NC software should support parametric constraints as does an SM system. If your site will share information between all applications, bidirectional communication of geometry, constraints, and other attributes are necessary.

Note: NC is primarily a downstream application with regard to SM, so the primary concern should be the flow of information from SM to NC. Whether or not the SM and NC software is provided by the same vendor, the following should be considered.

SMA.15.25   Primitive Preference

Use SM primitives whenever possible and appropriate to the design (see Chap. 6). This may significantly reduce computation for everything from display to toolpath generation and will reduce database size. Also, most NC machine controllers have built-in capabilities for machining specific shapes. Being able to take advantage of these capabilities can result in much shorter NC output and often better parts.

The most common of these special capabilities are known as *cycles.* Examples of cycles are making holes and cutting smooth arcs. A few NC controllers are capable of smoothly driving advanced shapes, such as conics, splines, and bicubic patches. Your NC site will likely be sufficiently pleased if you use axially symmetric primitives such as arcs, circles, cylinders, and spheres instead of similarly shaped splines or ruled, lofted, or meshed surfaces.

SMA.15.26   Information Availability

The effectiveness of product development is largely based on the quality and quantity of information that can be conveyed among the participants. Successful and cost-efficient product development provides NC operators with the information they need to machine good parts. Whenever possible, data should be contained within the SM database so that all applications have access to it.

SMA.15.27   Site Specific

There are many variables which are necessarily different from site to site. This compels the participants to investigate the best mechanisms for optimal efficiency for their location and application.

SMA.15.28   Determine and Identify

1. Identify which geometry types can be communicated and utilized by the NC software (2D, 3D, wireframe, surfaces, B-Rep solids, CSG solids, etc.).

2. Identify limitations on geometry positioning, curvature, and other shape parameters that will pose barriers for the NC software.

3. Identify what information other than geometry can be communicated and utilized by the NC software (for example, tolerances, dimensions, and other product specifications).

4. If design features are supported, determine if any can be communicated to and utilized by the NC software.

5. If you have policies against the conversion of geometry from one mathematical form to another, determine if a single mathematical form can be maintained throughout.

6. If NC operators add or modify geometry, determine if and how those changes should be communicated back to design for approval and incorporation into the design database.

7. Determine how part releases and revisions will be managed.

8. If change management is built into your SM system, determine if the NC software can manage changes and if special steps should be taken to support this. This capability can greatly reduce costs, especially if simultaneous design and manufacturing planning is desired or multiple prototypes are needed.

9. If more than one NC group is involved, determine if and how they should communicate data between each other.

10. In order to support design for manufacturing (DFM) procedures, investigate how manufacturing constraints can be communicated from the NC department to the design department.

11. If a tool must be machined in order to manufacture the part, determine if the design group or the manufacturing group is responsible for the design of the tool. Corporations often form committees using members of both groups for this purpose.

12. Conventions to make communication clearer should be defined (for example, the use of layers/levels, colors, rules for naming, attributes).

13. If individual components of the product are to be machined by different groups, NC operators will need to coordinate how fit and tolerance requirements will be met.

Chapter 16

Customizing the Solid Modeling System

Olaf Bellstedt
Senior Software Engineer
Varimetrix Corporation

Once familiar with a particular Solid Modeling (SM) system, you will most likely find a few things that it will not do, or does differently than expected. At this point you can do one of two things: either look for another system that completely satisfies your needs or customize your existing one. Customization is likely to be the most cost-effective choice. Once the decision is made to customize, there are several more choices to make. First analyze your needs and then decide on how best to meet those needs. Depending on your SM system, you may customize by either writing a simple macro, a user program, or an entire third-party application. Of course, if none of these methods satisfy your needs, with the proper amount of planning, time, and effort you can always write your own SM program.

16.1   Needs Analysis

It is recommended that you always analyze your needs prior to embarking on any customization effort. Ask yourself what specifically you wish to achieve. Once you know exactly what you want to do, find out if and how you can accomplish it. In most cases, your SM system will provide the necessary tools to achieve your customization goals.

Next, ask yourself what it is you want to customize:

1. Do you need only to change some program settings?
2. Do you want a given command to behave differently?
3. Do you want to add new functionality?

Depending on your system, if a change in settings is required, then in most cases all you need to do is edit a start-up file, create a default model, or both. If you want to change the behavior of an existing command, you can most likely create a macro or user program to re-create the command. If you want to add new functionality, plan on writing your own programs. Adding new commands can be easier than you may think. In most cases, a simple macro will do. Remember that you are limited only by your imagination as long as the proper tools, knowledge, and motivation are available.

16.2   Macros

The easiest way to customize is by writing macros (sometimes referred to as *scripts*). These are generally ASCII text files containing commands that are specific to your SM system. Macros are read by the system and the commands are then interpreted one at a time. Some systems allow you to compile macros into binary form, which will increase their processing speed. The functionality that can be achieved varies widely between different systems. Some allow only program-specific commands, while others provide programming languages along with the capability to create or add new commands to menu structures as desired.

A macro is typically created with a text editor that can generate ASCII output. Some systems provide built-in editors that allow the creation of macros without having to exit the SM program. There are systems that allow for an existing solid to be saved in macro format, which greatly simplifies the creation of macros that develop or modify solid geometry.

Macros are sometimes thought of as being good only for simple tasks. However, they can be used to create very complex and powerful applications. If the capability exists within the macro to call other macros and programs, then there is no limit to their capability. A good macro language will provide access to most, if not all, commands of the SM program, including access to the database. With database access, it is possible to extract desired data, call another program to process the data, and then return the results to the SM database. Another powerful feature of a macro language is the ability to create, modify, and interact with the SM program's graphic user interface (GUI), as shown in Fig. 16.1. This example shows that macros can be fully integrated into an SM program.

Macros can be used to automate the task of modeling components such as fasteners (see Fig. 16.2). Macros can also be used to create speed-key combinations for quickly executing a series of SM commands from the computer keyboard (see Table 16.1). All of these examples illustrate the power and flexibility of creating and executing custom macros.

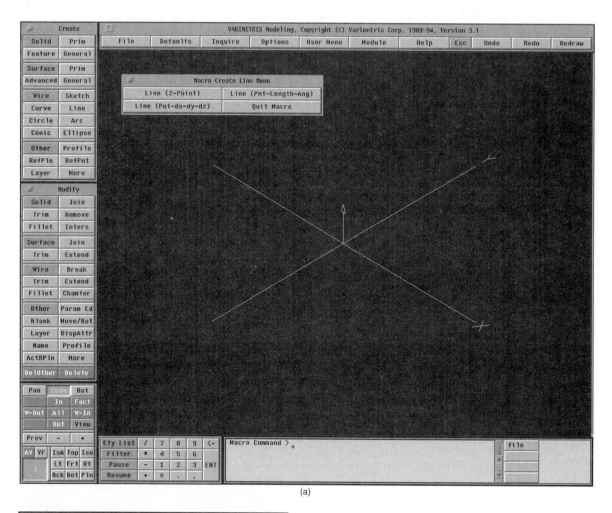

(a)

(b)

FIGURE 16.1 Creating custom menus with macros. (*a*) A full graphics screen view with custom menu displayed. The custom macro can be executed from the command line or selected from a customizable user menu. (*b*) View of custom menu generated by the macro. The source macro for this example is shown in Fig. 16.1*c* on p. 16.3.

```
Set_task TASK_UIF;

# Create new menu that is used by this macro;
Win_create 10,500,50,400,1,3,3,200,100,0,0,5,0,2,1,"screen-bold-14","Macro
Create Line Menu";

# Add 4 buttons (2 x 2) to menu;
Win_add_btns
500,1,1,3,2,2,1,0,0,0,0,0,25,200,3,0,0,16,17,18,19,26,24,0,"screen-bold-12";
Btn_set_text 500,1,1,0,0,0,2,201,"Line (2-Point)";
Btn_set_text 500,1,2,0,0,0,2,202,"Line (Pnt-Length-Ang)";
Btn_set_text 500,1,3,0,0,0,2,203,"Line (Pnt-dx-dy-dz)";
Btn_set_text 500,1,4,0,0,0,2,204,"Quit Macro";

# Display the just created menu;
Win_show 500,1;

cmd = 0;

# Loop until the exit command is received;
while cmd <> 204;

Set_task TASK_APP3D;

        # Wait for input from the menu;
        print "Macro Command > ";
        cmd = panel_input;

        # Now process the input from the menu;

        # Line 1;
        if cmd = 201
                print "Create a line by picking the two end points.\n";
                print "Pick first line point : \n";
                pt1 = input_pnt;
                print "Pick second line point : \n";
                pt2 = input_pnt;
                ln_2pt ABS,pt1[1],pt1[2],pt1[3],ABS,pt2[1],pt2[2],pt2[3];
        endif;

        # Line 2;
        if cmd = 202
                print "Create a line by picking the first end point and by
                specifying\n";
                print "the length of the line and the angle in the x-y
                plane.\n";
                print "Pick first line point : \n";
                pt1 = input_pnt;
                print "Enter length of line : \n";
                distance = input_dst;
                print "Enter angle in the x-y plane : \n";
                angle = input_ang;
                x = pt1[1] + distance[1] * cos(angle[1]);
                y = pt1[2] + distance[1] * sin(angle[1]);
                z = pt1[3];
                ln_2pt ABS,pt1[1],pt1[2],pt1[3],ABS,x,y,z;
        endif;

        # Line 3;
        if cmd = 203
                print "Create a line by picking the first end point and by
                specifying\n";
                print "the delta x, y, and z values.\n";
                print "Pick first line point : \n";
                pt1 = input_pnt;
                print "Enter delta x : \n";
                dx = input_num;
                print "Enter delta y : \n";
                dy = input_num;
                print "Enter delta z : \n";
                dz = input_num;
                x = pt1[1] + dx;
                y = pt1[1] + dy;
                z = pt1[1] + dz;
                ln_2pt ABS,pt1[1],pt1[2],pt1[3],ABS,x,y,z;
        endif;

endwhile;

Set_task TASK_UIF;

# Remove menu from display;
Win_show 500,2;

# Remove menu from memory;
Win_destroy 500;

# Exit macro;
exit;
```

(c)

FIGURE 16.1c Source macro for the custom menu and its selections shown on the previous page. The custom menu is created by and gathers input for the source macro which provides three methods to create a line and an option to quit the macro. Each method uses different inputs to create the line, but ultimately the macro calls the same SM program command (ln_2pt) each time. *(Courtesy of Varimetrix Corporation.)*

16.3

```
macrodef screwthd1($panel,$item)
$pitch=$(screws.pitch.value)
$nd=$(screws.nd.value)
$turns=$(screws.turns.value)
$shlngth=$(screws.shlngth.value)

$vindex=log($(screws.degincr.value))/log(2)
$inc_degree=atof($(screws.degincr.CHOICEITEM.$vindex.string))
fprintf($journal,"%f",$inc_degree)

axis fix
;
setup coordsystem axis
;
quit
add locator at_axis
;
axis move to_point
digitize exact
0 0 $shlngth v 1
;
view show front
;
$n = $turns
$p =   $pitch
$i = $p / ( 360.0 / $inc_degree )
$d = .86603*$p/8
$h = .86603*$p
$thd1 = $p*$turns+$p/2
$md1 = $nd/2-$h+$d/4
/*$md2 = $nd/2-$h+3*$d/2*/
$md2 = $nd/2-17*.86603*$p/24

$rad = $nd / 2.0
$total_angle = $turns * 360.0

$z = 0.0
$angle = 0.0

add spline through

while ( $angle <= $total_angle)
        digitize
        $xval = $rad * cosd($angle)
        $yval = $rad * sind($angle)
        $xval $yval $z v 1
        printf("z = %f, max = %f\n",$z,$len)
        /* Bump incrementers */
        $z = $z + $i
        $angle = $angle + $inc_degree
end_while
;
view show top
;
quit
modify visibility
blank
pick
spline
$nd/2 0 0 v 1
;
quit
add curve
digitize exact
$nd/2 0 .0625*$p v 1
lineseg
$nd/2 0 -.0625*$p v 1
$nd/2-17*.86603*$p/24-.05*$p/tand(30) 0 -.0625*$p-(17*.86603*$p/24)*tand(30)-
.05*$p v 1
$nd/2-17*.86603*$p/24-.05*$p/tand(30) 0 .0625*$p+(17*.86603*$p/24)*tand(3
0)+.05*$p v 1
$nd/2 0 .0625*$p v 1
;
modify visibility
unblank
spline
;
view zoom prezoom
;
quit
add solid sweep
name "thread"
section_curve
```

(Continued)

FIGURE 16.2 Sample macro for creating threaded fasteners. A family of fasteners can be created from a single macro based on a designer's input parameters. (*Courtesy of The MacNeal-Schwendler Corporation.*)

```
curve
$nd/2 0 .0625*$p v 1
;
path_curve
spline
$nd/2 0 0 v 1
;
axis_fix
vector_x 0
vector_y 0
vector_z 1
;
quit
add solid cylinder
name "minor_dia"
tolerance .001
line
diameter
2*$md2
pick
0 0 -$p v 1

0 0 $thdl v 1
;
view fit all_geom
;
quit
construct union
name "Threaded"
tool1 "thread"
tool2 "minor_dia"
;
quit
add curve
digitize exact
0 0 ($n-.5)*$p v 1
lineseg
$nd/2-(.5*$p)/tand(30)+$d 0 ($n-.5)*$p v 1
$nd/2-(.5*$p)/tand(30)+$d+2*$p 0 ($n-.5)*$p-2*$p v 1
$nd/2-(.5*$p)/tand(30)+$d+2*$p 0 ($n-.5)*$p+2*$p v 1
0 0 ($n-.5)*$p+2*$p v 1
0 0 ($n-.5)*$p v 1
;
quit
add solid revolution
name "end_cham"
angle 360
tolerance .001
pick curve
$nd/2-(.5*$p)/tand(30)+2*$p 0 ($n-.5)*$p+2*$p v 1
;
centerline
0 0 0 v 1

0 0 1 v 1
;
quit
construct subtraction
name "threads"
tool1 "Threaded"
tool2 "end_cham"
;
quit
modify visibility blank
pick solid
0 0 0 v 1
;
quit
add solid cylinder
name "shank1"
tolerance .001
line
diameter $nd
pick
0 0 .0625*$p +(17*.86603*$p/24)*tand(30) v 1
0 0 -$shlngth v 1
;
view show isometric
;
view fit all_geom
;
quit
construct chamfer
solid
name "shank"
```

(Continued)

FIGURE 16.2   (Continued)

16.5

```
angle 30
offset
/*.5*$p/tand(30)*/
17*.86603*$p/24
loop
$nd/2 0 .0625*$p+(17*.86603*$p/24)*tand(30) v 1
;
0 0 .0625*$p+(17*.86603*$p /24)*tand(30) v 1
;
quit
modify visibility unblank
solid
;
quit
construct union
name "THREAD_AND_SHANK"
tool1 "threads"
tool2 "shank"
```

FIGURE 16.2 (*Continued*)

TABLE 16.1 Typical Pro/ENGINEER Mapkey Macros

*By typing the following keyboard inputs (mapkey macros), the respective series of commands will be performed, achieving the described task. Mapkeys can be completely customized to a designer's environment. (*Courtesy of Parametric Technology Corporation.)

Mapkey	Series of commands executed
sd	#view;#cosmetic;#shade;#display;#done-return; (Shades the object on the screen)
ef	#environment;#datums off;#axes off;#csys off;#done-return; (Turns off datum planes, axes and coordinate systems)
vr	#view;#repaint;#done-return; (Repaints the screen)
mp	#info;#mass props;#part_mp; (Gets mass property information for a part)
st	#dbms;#store; (Stores the current object)

16.3 Intelligent Programming

The next step beyond macros would be to write your own program that hooks into the SM program through a defined application programming interface (API). The API provides a functional interface to the SM program's capabilities. With an API you can:

1. Access SM functions from within your custom program.

2. Have the SM functions executed.

3. Have the resulting information returned to your custom program.

Such capabilities allow almost unlimited customization. The disadvantage is that more development time and effort is required than with a macro. Such intelligent programs are typically called *third-party applications* and are usually written in the same programming language that was used to create the SM program. The most widely used programming languages today are C, C++, Assembler, Fortran, and Pascal.

16.4 Adding Functionality

Customizing will add functionality to your SM program and will typically take three forms:

1. Adding commands

2. Adding menus

3. Adding programs

16.4.1 Adding Commands

The easiest customization method is to add your own commands. Such commands can be entirely new or a combination of existing commands. Some SM systems provide a built-in mechanism to add user commands, while others allow the interactive execution of macros. Macros are usually more flexible. If the system provides sufficient interaction tools from within the macro, this method can be very powerful and easy to implement.

16.4.2 Adding Menus

The capability to add new menus to the menu structure can make macros look like commercial third-party applications and allows for total integration of user commands into the SM program (see Fig. 16.1).

16.4.3 Adding Programs

Most SM systems will allow you to run user-defined programs from the command line or from a special menu. Some allow you to fully integrate your programs into their menu structure. In the latter case, you can tie your program to one of the buttons in the menus and your program in turn can create new menus with new commands. This type of interfacing allows seamless and unlimited extension of the system's capabilities.

16.5 Customization Techniques

Relatively simple customization techniques can be used to achieve a lasting impression on those not intimately familiar with the SM system, such as customers or executive-level management. Such techniques can also be used to assist in actual design efforts. These techniques include:

1. Presentations
2. Simulations
3. Animations
4. Automation

16.5.1 Presentations

The ability to save and recall screen images can create very impressive presentations. Usually only a very simple macro is required to put together a very stunning slide show of a design process once all the necessary images are saved.

16.5.2 Simulations

Simulations can be created in several ways. Interactive or self-running simulations using macros or user programs can be developed. An interactive simulation could consist of a macro that prompts for an angle and then rotates some part about a joint by the entered angle. A self-running simulation would simply show the part going through a specific range of angles without any required input.

16.5.3 Animations

Animations can be either real-time or simulated. A real-time animation would consist of a macro actually executing commands to modify or move geometry. A simulated animation would simply be a slide show of captured images depicting movement.

16.5.4 Automation

Macros are ideal for automating tasks. The simplest form of automation is to combine a specific sequence of commands into a macro. Instead of repeating the same commands over and over, just run the macro and see the results. Of course, you can add interaction to convert a very specific automated sequence into a generic tool that works in a variety of situations.

16.6 Cautions and Needed Improvements

A word of caution to the beginning programmer: Don't try to write your own SM program all at once. Commercial programs are developed over the course of years by staffs of programmers. Planning and research are the most important issues. Investigate all possibilities before you start, and watch out for incompatibilities between different libraries that you intend to use.

Customization aside, there is room for improvement. Current commercial SM systems can benefit from improved user interfaces. This is one area which should be continuously refined and improved as needs and desires change. SM systems should help you be productive. This can be accomplished only if the task of learning it is made as easy as possible.

Also, further integration of products is necessary. The use of several programs to complete a design should not be required. One integrated product should take you from drawing sketches to creating solids to creating a toolpath or some other output, all with the same geometry. Most customization today is done in the areas of interfaces and integration.

Interface concerns range from user interaction with the program to exchanging data with other programs. Integration is how well the different parts of a program work together. Unless SM systems evolve into more complete solutions that satisfy a variety of needs, there is a strong need for advanced customization tools that allow more intimate access to the system than is currently available.

16.7 Conclusions

Since there is no such thing as a perfect SM system, customization will always play a very important role. Everyone has different needs to be addressed, and who better to address those needs than the end user. With the necessary tools and documentation you can customize your SM program to fit your needs. If necessary, you can write your own third-party program or even an entire SM program, but plan carefully and make sure you understand what is involved. Writing your own SM program can be very rewarding but also very frustrating. Future versions of SM programs will better address the needs of a variety of users, and therefore reduce the need for extensive customization. However, since it may not be possible to satisfy every user, we can only hope that SM vendors continue to provide advanced customization tools.

Customizing

SMA.16.1   Debugging Macros

Depending on the tools provided, debugging macros can be very easy or quite cumbersome. If there are no specific debugging tools, the easiest method would be to add print statements at crucial steps in the macro to display the status and contents of important variables at these points.

(Continued)

Customizing
(*Continued*)

SMA.16.2   Small Adjustments

Sometimes the smallest adjustments can make a big difference. It is possible that relatively minor system variables or settings can achieve your desired goal. Think small first. You may save time and effort.

SMA.16.3   Start-Up Files

Many SM systems provide some form of start-up or initialization file that can be modified to suit your needs (see Fig. 16.3). This method can provide extensive customization. The most common settings available will be system units, data backup, and program behavior such as menu locations. Your system may provide additional capability.

SMA.16.4   Default Models

Some SM systems provide the capability to create a default model. This model would be loaded into memory every time a new model is started. The objective here is to automatically load a predefined system environment which includes all desired user settings. Default models can be used instead of or in addition to start-up files. Default models are usually more user friendly since all settings can be entered through the program's GUI and not with a text editor as in the case of the start-up file. Default models also, in general, provide much greater flexibility and more detailed customization.

```
############################################################;
#        Startup Command File For Varimetrix Modeler.       #;
############################################################;

# set menu side (0-left, 1-right);
Set_uif_side 0;

# set auto backup flag;
Set_auto_backup 0;

# set auto backup interval (sec);
Set_backup_interval 600;

# set name of startup model;
Set_dflt_mdl "default.mdl";

# set path of default directory;
Set_dflt_dir "/usr/models";

# set button highlighting, 0-off, 1-on;
Set_btn_hi 1;

# set command echoing on or off (0-no echo, 1-echo);
Set_cmd_echo 1;

# set undo-redo on or off;
Set_undo_redo 1;

# set name of startup macro for new models;
Set_startup_macro "start.mac";

# define command string used to print file (% locates filename);
Set_print_cmd "pr % | lpr";

# set linear/angular units, resolution, size, scale for new models;
# linear units (0-mic,1-mm,2-cm,3-m,4-km,5-mil,6-in,7-ft,8-yd,9-mi);
# angular units (0-rad, 1-deg);
Set_model_units 1,1,0.1,300.0,1.0;

# set pick aperture as fraction of view extent (.001-0.5);
Set_pick_aper .015;
```

FIGURE 16.3   A sample start-up file. Notice that there are options to specify a start-up or default model as well as a start-up macro. Three independent customization options are available here: (1) the start-up file itself, (2) the default model, and (3) the start-up macro. (*Courtesy of Varimetrix Corporation.*)

SMA.16.5 Batch Mode Processing

Operations must be executable in "batch" modes for time-consuming functions. For example, removing hidden lines from a process plant with dozens of pieces of equipment and hundreds of pipelines can take many hours of CPU time, and may be more effectively executed overnight in an unattended batch process.

Brian Ruuska, CAD/CAE Applications Engineer
3M Co., St. Paul, Minn.

**Writing Your Own
SM Program**

SMA.16.6 Planning Checklist

Planning is the most important first step in writing your own SM program. Here is a planning checklist to help organize your thoughts.

1. What is it that you want to achieve?

2. Create a specification for your program. Write down exactly what kind of functionality you expect.

3. What kind of SM engine do you need or want?

4. What kind of graphics do you want to support?

5. What kind of user interface do you want?

6. How do you plan to integrate all components?

SMA.16.7 Planning Action

Be as specific as you can in defining your own SM program. Once you have a clear idea of where you are going, start looking for individual pieces. Check on what is currently available. Software technology changes fast. State-of-the-art technology can become obsolete within months. Try to find component libraries that match your specification, but watch out for incompatibilities. In the end, everything must work together, one way or another.

SMA.16.8 SM Engines

There are several SM engines commercially available. Functionality can vary greatly. Some engines provide only the tools to create and modify geometry but not a database to store geometry. Others provide a more complete solution. Determine which combination provides the tools you need. Don't try to find everything in one place. You may have to shop around for a while before you find everything you need. Create a list of features that different engines provide along with what they are missing, and do a side-by-side comparison to find the best match for your specifications.

SMA.16.9 Graphics Libraries

Today, good graphics are extremely important in SM. There are a few good libraries available that provide a variety of tools. Most SM-related graphics libraries use display lists. A display list is basically a second database that contains all of your geometry in a form that is optimized for display purposes. Hardware issues can become very complex, depending on the hardware and operating system with which you wish to be compatible. Here are some things to consider in a graphics library:

1. Look for up-to-date hardware support.

2. What type of graphics hardware does the library support?

3. Does the developer of the library keep up with the rapidly evolving display hardware?

4. Does the graphics library take advantage of the hardware? This includes the graphics coprocessor or any hardware implementations of graphics functions.

SMA.16.10 The Graphic User Interface (GUI)

There are many GUI tool kits available today. Make sure that the tool kit you choose supports a widely accepted standard such as Windows, X11, or Motif. If possible, choose a tool kit that supports multiple standards so that you can move your program to another platform. Also refer to Chap. 18 for advice on developing and evaluating GUIs.

(Continued)

**Writing Your Own
SM Program**
(*Continued*)

SMA.16.11   Start Small

Always start small and never overextend your efforts. This can lead to frustration and delays. Look at as many examples as you can to get an idea of what it takes to achieve your goals and then take it one step at a time.

SMA.16.12   Integration

Integration of different tool kits and libraries is always left up to you, the programmer. Although many kits provide user-friendly integration tools, when it comes down to the details of your application, it's your creativity and programming skills that will achieve your desired level of integration.

Good to Know

SMA.16.13   Productivity Aids

Develop and use as many automated programs as possible to accomplish reoccurring operations such as drawing tapped holes, bills of material, drawing notes, standard hardware, drawing symbols, folding/unfolding sheet metal, etc. SM designers should not have to construct a screw, nut, or bolt more than once. At our facility we have in use over 200 of these time-saving productive applications.

Richard A. St. Arnauld, Sr. Tool Design Engineer
Pratt & Whitney Aircraft Div. of UTC, West Palm Beach, Fla.

SMA.16.14   Tutorial Sources

The best source for programming tutorials and examples would be a bookstore with a good computer-related section. You can find complete manuals for specific applications, as well as programming manuals that include diskettes with source code. Also talk with current SM vendors. Programming manuals are sometimes included with a basic SM package. Most SM vendors provide a developer's kit or can point you in the right direction.

SMA.16.15   Off-the-Shelf Code

Current SM vendors are typically the best place to find out more about the availability of existing programs and code specific to their applications. For more general information check your local bookstore, software store, or dealer.

SMA.16.16   Available Tool Kits

A good source for available tool kits are various programmers catalogs that include large selections of programming libraries for many applications. You can find graphics libraries, databases, GUIs, interprocess communication libraries, and others, all in one place. Here are two sources to check:

1. The Programmer's Shop Buyer's Guide

> The Software Developer's Company, Inc.
> 90 Industrial Park Road
> Hingham, MA 02043
> Tel: 800-421-8006

2. Programmer's Paradise

> A Division of Voyager Software
> 1163 Shrewsbury Avenue
> Shrewsbury, NJ 07702
> Tel: 800-445-7899

Chapter 17

Solid Modeling and Documentation

Olaf Bellstedt
Senior Software Engineer
Varimetrix Corporation

Once a solid model has been created, there is still an issue to be addressed: documentation. Documenting a solid model can be a complex or a simple matter, depending on one's needs and requirements at various stages in a product's life cycle. Through automation and the nature of products and processes, some organizations may require very few paper drawings during early stages of design and manufacturing. Although others may require more detailed documentation, they may communicate it electronically and thus may not require extensive hardcopy prints. Others still may require extensive detail and the need to communicate and distribute traditional drawings.

Solid Modeling (SM), if exploited to its fullest extent, can provide the basis for all of a product's documentation needs from concept through to design, manufacturing, distribution, and the needs of the customer as well. This chapter is intended to highlight some of the documentation concerns particular to SM applications as well as ways of exploiting the descriptive qualities of a solid model for various documentation needs.

17.1 Detail Drawings

Detail drawings are the result of extracting information from a solid model and presenting that information in the form of a two-dimensional document. The amount of detail required can vary from extensive views, dimensioning, and notes, to a single view and a few critical dimensions and tolerances.

The level of detail required is in direct proportion to the extent to which the solid model is used in its electronic form (see Fig. 17.1). The traditional detail drawing's functional purpose is to convey information for a product's manufacture. In some organizations this step is no longer required or is greatly reduced.

There are various methods of extracting the information required for a detail drawing. Also, the relationship between 3D and 2D entities in the solid and the drawing are to be considered. These methods and relationships include levels of associativity and integration.

17.1.1 Levels of Associativity

There are three possible levels of associativity between a solid model and a resulting detail drawing: (1) no-way, (2) one-way, and (3) two-way associativity (see Fig. 17.2). Each of these levels is discussed here.

Nonassociative Detailing (No-Way)

Nonassociative detailing provides no direct link between the solid and the detail drawing. The drawing can be based on the actual solid geometry by exporting data via DXF or IGES translators to a separate drawing package, or the drawing can be created from scratch.

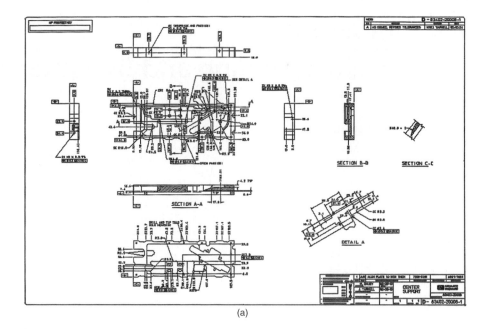

(a)

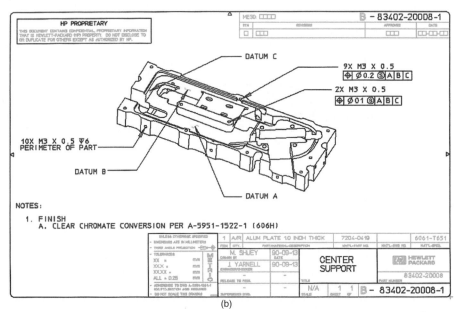

(b)

FIGURE 17.1 Levels of detail required in an SM detail drawing. (*a*) Traditional detail drawing when the solid model is not used in its electronic form; (*b*) the same detail drawing when the electronic form of the solid model is used to its fullest extent. *(Courtesy of Hewlett-Packard Company.)*

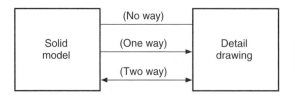

FIGURE 17.2 Levels of associativity. There are three levels of associativity between a solid model and a detail drawing.

Either method provides no way to easily update the detail drawing if any changes are made to the solid. There is also no method of changing the solid by modifying the drawing. Since these detail drawings are often drawn from scratch, there are opportunities to introduce errors. Also, nonassociative detailing does not provide a way to check for errors, except for manual methods of comparing all dimensions and details with the original solid model.

Unidirectional Detailing (One-Way)

Unidirectional detailing usually provides a link from the solid model to the detail drawing, but not from the drawing to the solid. This method provides some means of automating the required updates to the drawing if the solid model changes.

Many SM systems provide a drafting or detailing module that allows the importation of actual solid geometry. Once imported, the solid can be rotated, sectioned, or different display modes such as silhouette or hidden line can be selected. Once the right view has been achieved, it can be saved into the detail drawing. This graphical interactive method is the easiest and most powerful way to create detail drawings. Also, since the detail views are created directly from the solid, there are no geometric errors and the detail will update with any changes to the solid. Supplementary information such as dimensions and notes are usually added manually.

Bidirectional Detailing (Two-Way)

In bidirectional detailing the associativity goes both ways, from the solid to the drawing and from the drawing back to the solid. In this case, if the solid changes, the drawing can or will be updated. However, the solid can also be modified by changing certain dimensions on the detail drawing (see color insert, Fig. 17.3).

This method is the most powerful but also the most dangerous. It may not always be desirable to allow the solid to be changed from the detail drawing. If people outside the design group have access to these detail drawings, it is possible for someone to inadvertently change a parameter, which then propagates back to the solid model, which in turn, if not detected, could be disastrous. With the proper control, however, bidirectional associativity can be a very powerful design tool for engineers who are more comfortable working with detail drawings than with a solid model.

Associativity

SMA.17.1 Solid Errors and Cleanup

Although the use of SM geometry to automate the creation of detail drawings eliminates the possibility of errors, detail views will be only as reliable as the solid from which they are extracted. Errors in the solid can and will show up in the detail views. Also, the use of solid views may not be as clean as expected. Manually cleaning up views may be required.

SMA.17.2 Detailing Associativity

Be aware of the amount of associativity available between views generated from a solid and added 2D information (dimensions, notes, or cleanup). Prior to completion, views may be moved, rotated, or resized many times. Make sure associativity exists as soon as the view is imported; otherwise, added detail may be lost or misplaced on the drawing.

Don LaCourse, President
The Solid Modeling ExChange, Algood, Tenn.

17.1.2   Space Relationships

There can be many relationships between 2D and 3D geometry. Two-dimensional geometry is usually referred to as a *drawing,* and three-dimensional geometry as a *model* or *solid model.* Be aware of the integration of 2D and various forms of 3D data as well as how entities relate to each other.

Integration

Being integrated means that two products such as drafting and modeling either share the same database or can exchange data directly, without having to go through a neutral file format such as IGES. Also, if, for example, a drawing contained several profiles that were sufficient to define a solid, they could be loaded into the solid modeler and then a solid created from them without having to reconstruct the profiles. Ideally, though, detail drawings (if required) are a by-product of the solid model.

Nonintegration

Solid Modeling and drafting modules that are not integrated must use a neutral file format to exchange data. The disadvantage of this is that information is almost always lost in the transfer. The type of information lost is usually constraints or particular methods of geometry creation. For example, if a three-point circle is created, with each point tangent to a line of a square box, then this information can be maintained in the SM database. Each time the box is changed, the circle will automatically adjust to maintain its constraints (tangent to three sides of the box).

However, if this data is exported via a neutral file format, only a square box with a circle that is defined by a center point and a radius tangent to the box may result. The method of creating the circle, as well as the constraints, may be lost in the conversion because the selected file format may not have the capability to store this information in any shape or form.

Entities

Be aware of what types of entities exist or are created when 2D and 3D geometry are integrated. What happens when a solid model is imported into the drafting package? Since a solid has three dimensions, when it is viewed in a 2D program there will be entities on top of entities. How does the drafting package handle these overlapping entities?

One way is to leave all the entities where they are. The disadvantage here is that, when you add geometry to this drawing and you want to select an endpoint of a given entity, you cannot be sure if you picked the correct entity, or the one below it, or the one below that. One solution is for the drafting package to depth-sort the 3D entities and filter out the undesired ones. Another solution is for the drafting package to actually create a 2D view of the solid that references the 3D geometry consisting of valid 2D geometry. Be aware of how your application handles these relationships.

The Sketcher

The sketcher is basically a complete set of drafting tools that can be accessed directly from within a solid modeling session. The nature of SM requires the creation of 2D entities on many and varying construction planes. Since many SM systems do not provide all of the drafting tools that a drafting package does, the sketcher becomes very useful for integrating this capability as needed (see Chap. 8).

17.2 Desktop Publishing

Desktop publishing (DP) is playing an ever-increasing role in documentation. Given the right software, images of the solid model or detail drawings can be directly integrated into various documents. The need to electronically scan drawings or graphic images into documents can be avoided if the DP software can read one of the output formats of the SM or drawing package. In some cases there can be a uni- and bidirectional associativity between the solid model, the detail drawing, and the DP document. In this case, any time the solid is modified, the DP documentation can be automatically updated and needs only to be reprinted.

17.2.1 Graphic Formats

There are two basic types of graphic formats: *raster* and *vector*. Raster formats are based on pixels (individual picture elements), whereas vector formats are based on vectors (a straight, directional line

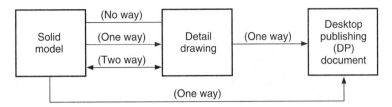

FIGURE 17.4 Levels of associativity with DP documentation. In most cases, one way associativity can be established between the SM geometry portion of DT documentation and either the SM-associated detail drawing or the solid model itself.

between two points). There are many different formats within these two groups. Following are lists of the more commonly used formats.

Raster Formats

PCX	PC Paintbrush®
GIF	Compuserve®
TIF	Tagged Image Format
BMP	MS Windows®
WPG	WordPerfect® Graphics File

Vector Formats

DXF	AutoCAD®
EPS	Encapsulated PostScript®
IGES	Initial Graphics Exchange Specification
HPGL and HPGL/2	Hewlett Packard Graphics Language

Raster formats are mainly used by paint packages and graphics programs. Vector formats are mainly used by software that creates geometry such as SM and drafting programs.

Desktop Publishing

SMA.17.3   Graphics Conversion

Although raster and vector graphics formats are different in form and function, there are utilities available to convert graphic files from one format to another with varying degrees of success. Formats within the same graphic type, raster, or vector tend to convert at a higher rate of success. One such conversion utility is HiJaak® by Inset Systems, (203) 740-2400.

Don LaCourse, President
The Solid Modeling ExChange, Algood, Tenn.

17.2.2   Applications

There are many and varied applications for the use of solid models in documentation. Some of these applications are discussed here, while others are to be explored and discovered.

Assembly Drawings

With the use of SM, various levels of assembly can be documented to show a finished product, including all of its components (see Fig. 17.5). Assembly drawings are rarely used to modify the actual solids. Varying levels of associativity to the solid model or some of its detail drawings are available. The same issues as mentioned in Sec. 17.1.1 also apply here. The preferred method of creating an assembly drawing from solids is with uni- or bidirectional associativity. This allows the assembly drawing to automatically update if any of its associated subdrawings or models are modified. Utilizing component libraries and instances of parts will achieve associativity with the assembly model and/or drawing. (Also see Chap. 11.)

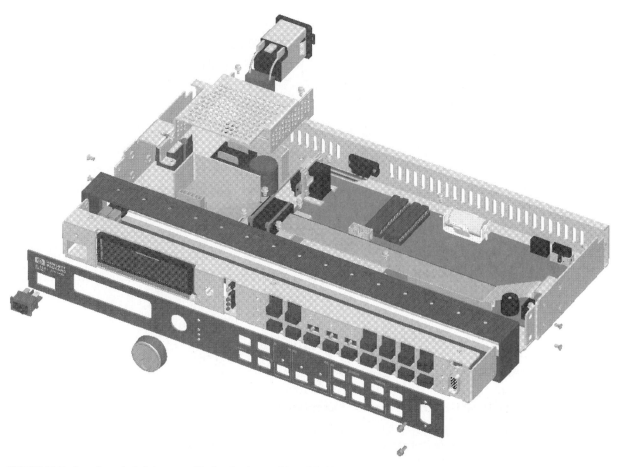

FIGURE 17.5   Sample exploded view assembly drawing from solid models. *(Courtesy of Hewlett-Packard Company.)*

QC Instruction Sheets

As a function of quality control (QC), many manufacturing facilities post instructional material on the manufacturing floor for use by assembly workers and supervisors (see Fig. 17.6). Such documents usually contain product specific geometry along with special and cautionary assembly instructions. This practice is an ideal opportunity to allow solid models to maintain the geometric portion of these documents.

In the ideal environment, instruction sheets are maintained by the QC portion of a plant wide engineering network. QC terminals are positioned at locations throughout the manufacturing floor for access by assembly workers and supervisors. Instruction sheets would be viewed, printed, and posted as modifications are made to products or processes. Graphic portions of the instruction sheets are associated directly with active SM geometry.

Service Manuals

Many industrial and consumer products are shipped with some form of service-related documentation. With SM, the time required to graphically illustrate service manuals with geometric views and assemblies is greatly reduced (see Fig. 17.7). If the production of service-related documentation is incorporated into the engineering network, an associativity can exist. This associativity can allow certain views used in service documentation to remain current as products are updated.

Internal Documentation

The preceding methods used for QC instruction sheets and service manuals can be applied to various forms of internal and external documentation such as memos, letters, reports, and proposals (see Fig.

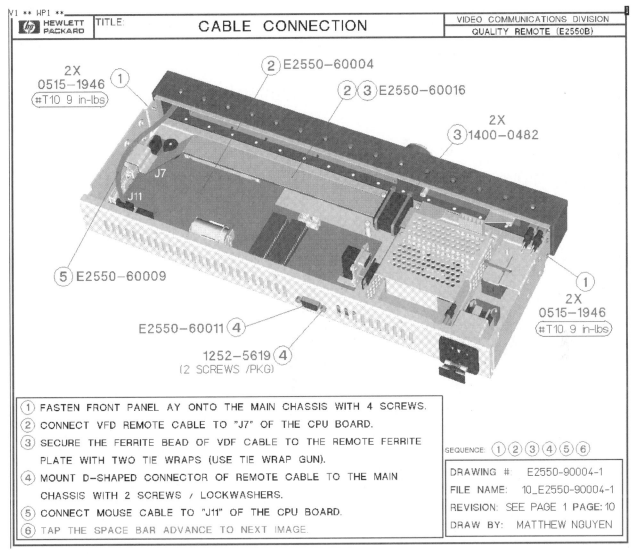

FIGURE 17.6 Sample quality control instruction sheet from solid models. Instruction sheets can be produced from and associated with solid models to guide manufacturing during actual product assembly. The preferred application is where instruction sheets such as this are accessed by assembly personal from networked graphics terminals located in production areas, thus eliminating the need to distribute paper documents. *(Courtesy of Hewlett-Packard Company.)*

17.8). Although associativity with product geometry may not be required, the easy access and integration of such geometry in this documentation can and will have a significant impact both internally and externally to one's organization.

17.2.3 Integrated Databases

As illustrated previously, if your DP software can read at least one of the output formats of your SM system, then it becomes easy to create very impressive and easily updatable documents. Any time the solid model changes, the file that was loaded into the document can be updated, which in turn keeps the document up to date. One should note, however, that this associativity would not extend to automatically creating additional views that may be required by a given change. This would require manual preparation. Once created, however, these additional views could then become associative.

Depending on your operating system, there are other, more advanced options to integrate two databases. Under MS Windows® for example, one could use DDE (dynamic data exchange) or OLE (object

HP Quality Advisor QA 100

Obtaining the Replacement Assembly/Part

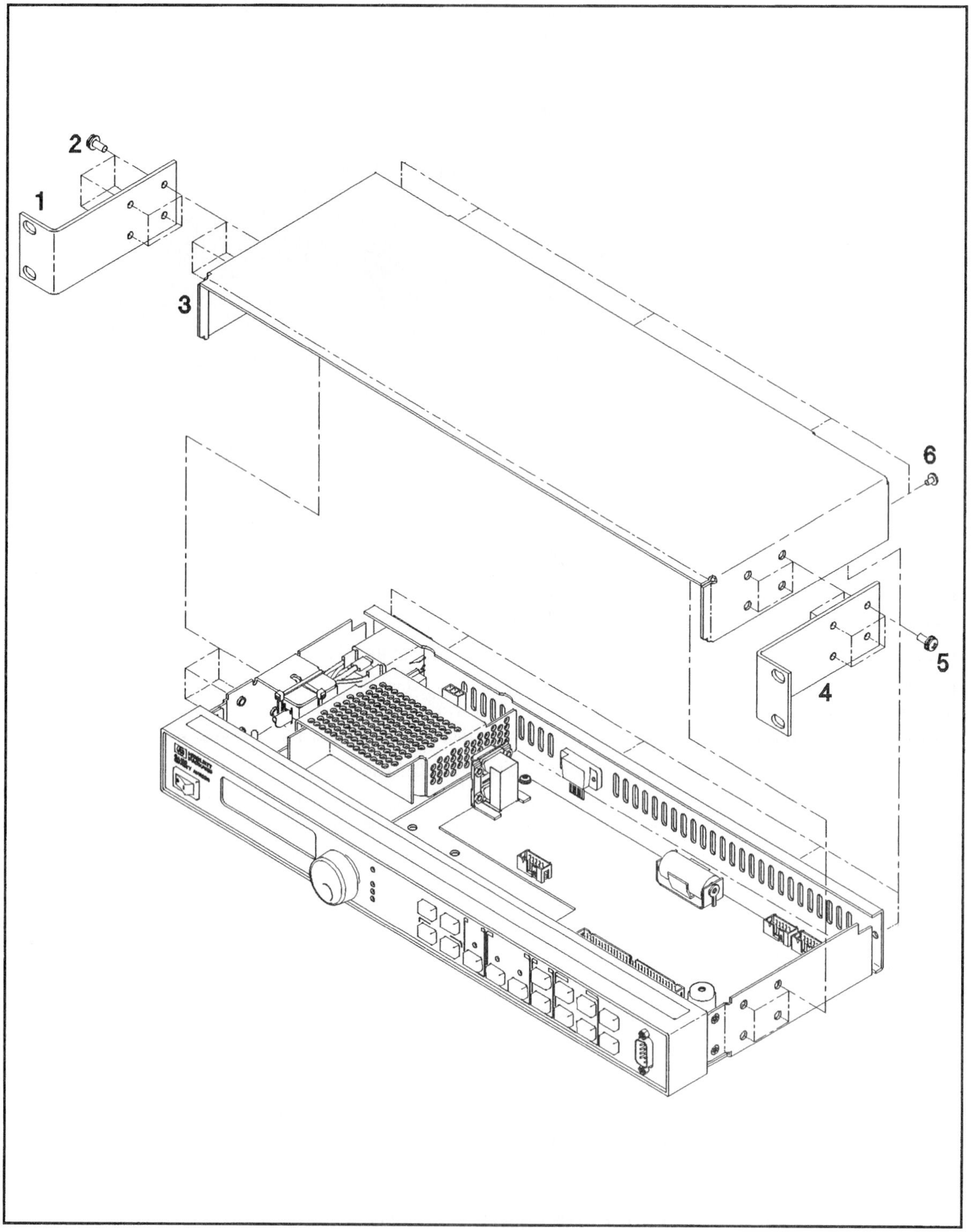

Figure 4-3. Cover Illustrated Parts Breakdown—HP Remote Front Panel

FIGURE 17.7 Sample page of service manual from solid models. One of the downstream benefits of SM is the extraction of 3D geometry for related documentation. This example shows a page from a product service manual whose product geometry is derived from and can be associated with a solid model. *(Courtesy of Hewlett-Packard Company.)*

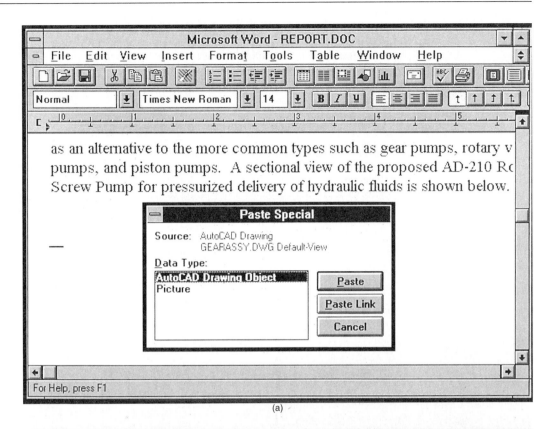

(a)

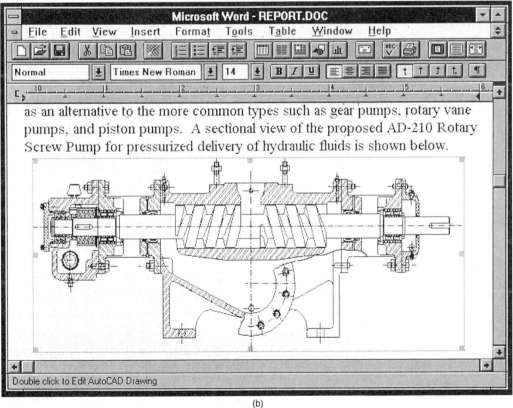

(b)

FIGURE 17.8 Internal documentation. Geometry and text generated from SM applications can be easily captured and imported into various forms of internal documentation. (*a*) Here, a geometry file is selected for import into a Microsoft Word® document; (*b*) shows imported graphic originating from an AutoCAD® detail drawing. *(Courtesy of Autodesk, Inc.)*

linking and embedding). The DDE protocol allows the creation of links between two applications. OLE takes this one step further, and allows the insertion of an entire object such as a graphics file. There are similar tools available on most advanced operating systems.

17.2.4 Screen Shots

A screen shot is a graphic image of all or a portion of the computer screen. Such images are usually created with one of many screen capture programs that allows one to specify a portion of the screen and then create an image file of this region. The graphic files created are usually raster- or pixel-based. Once a screen shot is created, the resulting graphics file can be used in a multitude of applications. Figure 17.9 shows examples of graphic screen shots. Others are seen throughout this handbook.

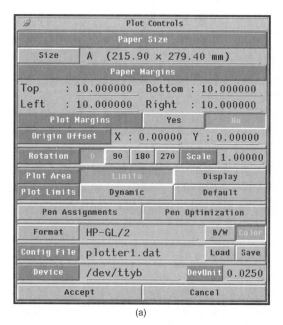

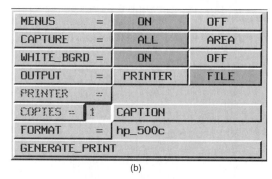

(a)
(b)
(c)

FIGURE 17.9 Sample screen shots of SM print/plot control menus. (*a*) Varimetrix® Modeling; (*b*) Aries ConceptStation®; (*c*) Pro/ENGINEER®. *(Courtesy of Varimetrix Corporation, The MacNeal-Schwendler Corporation, and Parametric Technology Corporation, respectively.)*

Image Recording

There are other ways to create images from a computer screen, such as photo or video. Taking a photo of an image on a computer screen can be tricky. The camera has to be perfectly parallel to the face of the screen in order to avoid distortion. The speed of the film and the exposure time are also crucial.

Video is also a popular media to produce very impressive presentations. There are basically two ways to get a screen image onto videotape: set up a video camera or use a video capture board with video output to go directly to tape. Using a standard video camera usually yields poor results since the monitor scan lines are clearly visible. Using video hardware that can convert the output of the computer's video board to a standard video or TV signal will achieve higher-quality results. (Also see Chap. 10.)

Desktop Publishing

SMA.17.4 Screen Images to Film

Graphic screen capturing is much preferred over traditional photographic methods. The graphic files generated can be easily converted to traditional 35mm slides, transparencies, overheads, or prints. Producing photographic material directly from graphic files eliminates distortion and other undesirable effects. There are numerous service centers that can convert graphic files to print within days and at a reasonable cost. One such facility is: The Image Center, Roanoke, Virginia, (703) 343-8243.

Don LaCourse, President
The Solid Modeling ExChange, Algood, Tenn.

Image Media

There are many forms of image media in use today. The oldest, of course, is the photograph. There are a variety of different films available, with specialty films for just about any purpose. For videotape, VHS produces reasonable quality. Professionals, however, tend to prefer the BETA system which provides better picture quality. There are also smaller formats like VHS-C and 8mm. The newest media being used to distribute images as well as video is CD-ROM.

Desktop Publishing

SMA.17.5 The HPGL Format

HPGL is a very good choice for a file transfer format because it is supported by most software on the market today. Most SM programs create HPGL files. Many DP programs can directly read HPGL files. If they cannot, there are many conversion utilities available that will allow you to convert HPGL to just about any format needed.

SMA.17.6 Image Processing

Screen capture programs are a great tool for image processing. Such programs allow you to grab just the right screen area and then save it to a graphics file. Once you have a graphics file you can do a variety of things with it. You can combine several images into a slide show or you can transfer them to other media such as photo, video, slides, or CD-ROM.

SMA.17.7 SM, CE, and Desktop Publishing

Beyond detail drawings, concurrent engineering (CE) includes the production of other types of documentation through computer-aided or desktop publishing (DP). Shop manuals, assembly manuals, user manuals, and other documentation required to complete the design cycle can be generated from the master solid model via an integrated publishing system. Associativity with the model allows documentation to be created in parallel with confidence that any changes to the geometric definition of the design will be automatically reflected in any document created during the process.

Keith Campbell, Engineer, VP Marketing
American Small Business Computers, Pryor, Okla.

17.3 Hardcopies

Even today in our quest to perfect the paperless design and manufacturing environment, there is still a need for quality hardcopy output. In both printing and plotting, there are many SM-related concerns, such as hardware and software controls, paper size, color, and resolution.

17.3.1 Printing Concerns

Hardware Controls

There are several issues to consider when dealing with printers. First of all, what type of interface is required? Most printers today connect to either a parallel or a serial port. Depending on the hardware to which you connect, one could be preferable over the other. In general, a parallel port is faster and easier to use than a serial port. Serial ports need to be configured to ensure proper communication with the printer. This configuration can be done either by the software from which you want to print or by the operating system. You can either print directly from your SM software or create an output file which can in turn be printed with an operating system utility.

In MS DOS® the *mode* and *print* commands are used to configure and print to each port. In most UNIX systems the equivalent commands are the *printcap* file and the *lpr* command. The printcap file is a configuration file that defines a printer with its required settings. There are several settings that must be set, such as baud rate, parity, number of data and stop bits, handshake protocol, and timeout value.

Printers usually have an on-board control panel that allows direct input for configuration. However, there are printers that can be configured only through software or by sending a print file containing configuration commands to them. Some printers can be connected to both a serial and parallel port simultaneously. Such printers will automatically handle the switching between the different ports. This can be very useful, for example, if you need to connect the printer to a workstation and to a network at the same time, assuming that the workstation is not networked.

Software Controls

The SM software that generates the print data must also be configured properly. The software must know which type of printer you have, which interface it uses, to which port it is connected, and any additional settings that are required. Some of these additional settings may include paper size, the number of lines per page, margins, the type font to use, or font size and spacing. If configuring a network print server, there will be additional settings to inform the SM software how to access the network. Figure 17.9 shows a few examples of printer/plotter control menus in actual SM systems.

Screen Dumps

If your SM software does not support printers at all, or if your software and printer are not compatible, there is still a way to generate hardcopy output. A screen dump could be the solution to this problem. There are many utilities available that can capture a screen image and then either print it directly or save it in a variety of image file formats. If the utility does not support printing, then you should be able to convert to an image format that can be read into another software package to which you have access, and then print from there (also see Sec. 17.2.4).

Halftones

What do you do if you have an SM color image but not a color printer? The answer is to convert your image to gray scale. Some printers can automatically convert a color image to gray-scale, but in most cases you may have to do it yourself. Most paint software packages do support image conversion from color to gray-scale, and most likely they will also support your printer.

Color Considerations

In computer graphics there are many different types of color images, differentiated by their color depth. The minimum color depth today is 8 bits, which provides for 256 colors at reduced quality. A high-quality image equal to a photograph, for example, requires a color depth of 24 bits. The most common color depths used today are 8 bits (256 colors), 16 bits (65,536 colors), and 24 bits (16,777,216 colors).

What do all these numbers have to do with printing? Well, most color printers are not capable of printing a 24-bit color image. Know what your printer is capable of and then generate images that adhere to that limitation. There are printers that can produce high-quality color prints, but they carry a higher price tag. The majority of printers today use one of these methods: dot matrix, ink jet, led, laser, thermal transfer, or dye sublimation. The price and quality of the output increase accordingly. A color dot matrix printer is fairly inexpensive but the quality is typically unacceptable for SM applications. The color ink jet, led, and laser printers can produce very good color prints, but the quality does vary from one manufacturer to the next. The top end in price and quality are thermal transfer and dye sublimation printers. The latter can produce true color prints.

17.3.2   Plotting Concerns

Hardware Controls

Hardware concerns for plotters are similar to those of printers, but with some additions. Most plotters today connect via both serial and parallel ports and the same aforementioned issues apply as for printers. In fact there is becoming less of a distinction between printer and plotter technology today. Laser printers now have serial ports and plotter emulation modes which will accept standard plot files. Plotters are now using ink jet technology traditionally employed in printers for years.

There are a variety of plotters on the market today. Many are pen plotters, which means they use a carousel of pens to plot the drawing. Some do not use pens but use a thermal transfer process instead. Thermal transfer plotters usually require special paper which can be quite expensive, but they produce better-quality plots, especially if the plot contains filled areas. A pen plotter can use less expensive paper but with added concern over pen maintenance. Always make sure all pens are maintained in good working order to prevent sloppy or smudged plots. Also, if a pen traces a particular path too many times, it can very well cut through the paper and render the plot unusable.

Software Controls

Again, all of the preceding printing concerns also apply to plotters. Any software including SM requires more information about a plotter than a printer. Settings such as pen color, pen velocity, pen pressure, and those for optimization are required. There are several methods to optimize pen plots. One method is to sort the plotting instructions by physical location on the paper to minimize the distance between successive drawing moves. Another is to sort the instructions by color to minimize the number of times the pen needs to be changed. The effectiveness of the latter method is greatly affected by the value of the maximum pen distance.

The type of paper used is another software concern. Plotters can use single sheets or continuous-feed paper. If continuous-feed paper is used, the software should advance to the next page when a plot is complete. Some controls even optimize the location of multiple-sized plots on continuous-feed paper.

Supported Plotters

Today, most plotters are HPGL (Hewlett Packard Graphics Language)-compatible. There are currently two versions, HPGL and HPGL/2. These graphics languages have a standard core format complemented by several extensions. An HPGL file that uses only the core commands should plot on just about any plotter on the market today. Only after you implement the graphics language extensions and specific plotter features do you need to worry about compatibility. Most plotters today are compatible with a specific HP-model plotter.

17.4   Network Considerations

If you have more than one computer but only one printer or plotter, then your best alternative is to make the device available across a network. There are several ways to accomplish this. If your computers are already networked, then you could make the one with the printer a print server. All the other computers would then send their print jobs to this server where they would be queued and then printed on a first-in, first-out basis. Some printers can be directly attached to the network and act as their own servers. In this case you don't need to worry about setting up a print server.

If you don't have an existing network, you can create a printer-sharing network. This is a simple way of connecting multiple computers to the same printer. The easiest and least expensive method is to get an automatic printer switch. Such a device manages the access to the printer by the connected computers. The disadvantage of such a device is that it usually only supports up to four computers. An alternative is to set up an actual print network using a receiver and job manager connected to the printer, and transmitters connected to each computer.

One other important factor to consider when printing on a network is the paper supply. Is your printer or plotter capable of using form-feed paper and does it have a sufficiently large paper tray? It doesn't make sense to use a printer or plotter that can output only one page at a time unattended.

17.4.1 Remote Plotting

There are several issues to consider when using remote plotters. If your remote plotter is a pen plotter, there is the issue of it having the correct color pens in the expected slots. Since remote plotters are usually used by more than one person, there should be a standard set of colors in the plotter that everyone uses. Another concern regarding pens is their frequency of use. Someone should be designated to make sure that the pens are always in good working order.

The paper supply also plays an important role. It is preferable to have a plotter with continuous-feed paper instead of single sheets. Since a remote plotter is usually some distance away from the computer, it is inefficient to have a plotter that requires the user to insert the paper and to check that everything is working before plotting, then walk back to the computer to start the plot, and then have to come back to pick up the plot. This setup might work efficiently if every user would always prepare the plotter for the next user; but, realistically, someone at some time will forget, and then you are back to walking to the plotter twice.

17.4.2 Queue Management

Queue management is the most important issue when one printer or plotter serves multiple computers. It is possible that if two users send a print job to the printer at the same time, then the first job to reach the printer will be printed and the second job will most likely be lost. If the operating system has a print spooler, the operator who sends a print job can continue working immediately. In systems like MS DOS, where there is no print spooler, operators have to wait until the printer is done printing before work can continue. There are, however, add-on DOS utilities to perform this function.

A print spooler is an important part of queue management. A print queue basically stores all incoming print jobs and then sends them to the printer on a first-come, first-served basis. Of course, a print queue makes sense only if you have a printer or plotter that can operate unattended.

17.5 Conclusions

Documentation can take many forms. Depending on the tools available, it can be quite easy and powerful or very difficult and work-intensive. However, given the right tools, you are limited only by your imagination.

Detail Drawings

SMA.17.8 What You Model Is What You Get

Designers must realize that the detailing method in today's 3D SM systems actually uses the 3D solid model in a 2D viewing format. Processes for suppressing or creating hidden edges may vary from vendor to vendor. One constant is that the detail will be only as accurate as the original solid model.

Kevin P. Alexander, CAD/CAM/CAE System Administrator
Littleford Day, Inc., Florence, Ky.

Detail Drawings
(Continued)

SMA.17.9   Control Drawings

An SM part file describes the shape and dimensions of all the features on a part, eliminating the need for a fully dimensioned part drawing. However, nongeometric information is difficult to convey in the SM file and typically must be communicated via a drawing. This simplified fabrication drawing should contain the following as a minimum:

1. Title block with part number, dash, revision, and part name

2. Material, finish, etc.

3. Hardware callouts

4. Tolerance callouts (GD&T)

5. An isometric view (minimum)

6. Critical dimensions

7. Revision history

SMA.17.10   Understanding Less Documentation

Solid Modeling allows parts and tooling to be built directly from the SM database. This is a new process for most companies and the concept must be explained to everyone in the company who previously worked with drawings (engineering, documentation, purchasing, quality, etc.)

Howard W. Stolz, Product Designer
Sun Microsystems, Mountain View, Calif.

SMA.17.11   SM Start to Finish for Die Castings

We build die castings from start to finish, using SM without creating a 2D drawing or any paperwork. The problem is that eventually a drawing has to be made so that the plant can check the parts to see if they are dimensionally correct. It would be nice to avoid the step of creating a 2D drawing completely. We have heard some talk of using lasers to create a solid model representation of a part and comparing it to the original model to see where differences occur. If true, this sounds like a solution we would want to know about.

Philip Johnson, Development Engineer
Emerson Electric Co., St. Louis, Mo.

SMA.17.12   HPGL as a Translator

There is a way to translate 2D views from any SM system to a drafting package that you feel is absolutely incompatible. Every SM system should be able to generate an HPGL plot. Capture this HPGL plot file and use a utility to convert it to DXF format. A file in DXF format can be read by almost all 2D and some 3D CAD systems. When all else fails, try HPGL.

Don LaCourse, President
The Solid Modeling ExChange, Algood, Tenn.

SMA.17.13   Cleaning Up

In detail drawings there is always something to clean up. Depending on your needs, there will always be some little detail that is just not quite right. If you have the right tools and software, this should not be a problem. Many integrated SM systems allow changes to detail drawings and still maintain full associativity to the solid model.

(Continued)

Detail Drawings
(Continued)

SMA.17.14   Zero Deviations

The bottom line is: Never change an SM detail drawing unless you are absolutely sure of what you are doing or unless you have bidirectional associativity to the solid and know what the result will be. Also, never manually change (with pencil and eraser) a detail drawing hardcopy plot no matter how much of a hurry you are in. The electronic file should always maintain *complete* control over hardcopies of any form.

SMA.17.15   Tesselation Lines

Depending on how your drafting program handles the display of 3D geometry, you could see any number of tesselation lines (also known as *isolines* or *flow lines*). Of course, if you don't want them but they show up, they need to be cleaned up. In cases where indicating the flow of a surface is more important than its boundaries alone, tesselation lines can be very beneficial.

SMA.17.16   Overlapping Entities

Any time you are dealing with 2D views of a 3D model, watch out for overlapping entities. Since you are looking at a solid in two dimensions, there will be lines on top of lines. This fact is very important if you add new geometry to the views and you would like to create constraints to the original 3D entities. How can you be sure that you are selecting the right entity?

These overlapping entities also are very noticeable when you create a plot on a pen plotter. Since each entity is plotted, if there are many entities overlapping, you will end up with too much ink on the paper, which can smudge, or the pen could cut through the paper.

Hardcopy

SMA.17.17   Long Plots

Special concern should be taken when attempting to plot a drawing that exceeds a standard E-size format. Check to see which plotter your SM software is supporting. If the indicated plotter supports only up to E-size formats, then some of the plot may be lost. Try to contain plots within the E-size format. If you must go longer, check compatibility. Some programs have special utilities that will splice multiple E-size plot files together to plot a longer drawing.

Don LaCourse, President
The Solid Modeling ExChange, Algood, Tenn.

SMA.17.18   Patterns and Plots

Sometimes, plot files are used to actually cut material patterns with a plotterlike machine. In these cases, the plotter pen is replaced with a type of cutting tool such as a laser.

SMA.17.19   Resolution

Any time you create hardcopy output, make sure that the resolution of your image matches the resolution of the hardcopy device. A high-resolution image printed on a low-resolution printer will look like a low-resolution image.

SMA.17.20   Troubleshooting Checklist

What to do if your printer or plotter just won't work anymore:

1. Check the obvious, make sure that the power cord is plugged in and you have some indication that the printer/plotter is on.

(Continued)

Hardcopy
(*Continued*)

2. Make sure that the data cable is connected properly to both the printer/plotter and the computer or network.

3. Verify which port the printer/plotter is connected to and make sure it matches the configuration of your software.

4. Make sure that your SM software is configured for your type of printer or platter.

5. Go through the troubleshooting list that should be included in your printer/plotter manual.

6. Go through the troubleshooting list that should be included in your SM software documentation.

7. If all else fails, call for technical assistance from either your printer/plotter or your SM vendor. Part of their job is to help you get back on track.

Section 4
Interfaces

Reduce product design time.
Improve product quality.

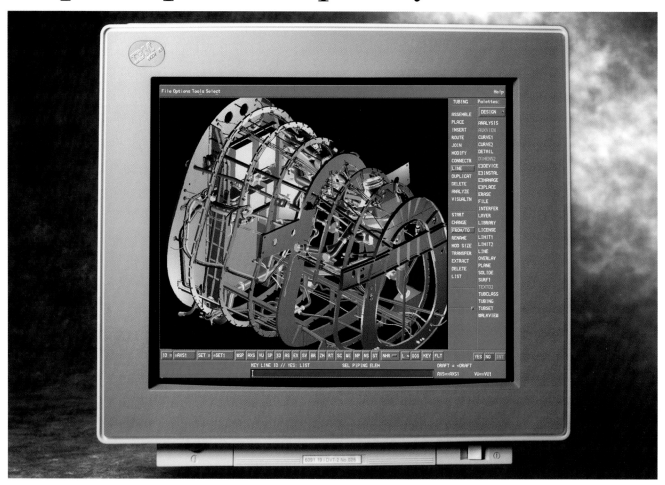

CATIA™ helps you gain the competitive edge in product design and manufacturing.

Whether you design and manufacture aircraft or screwdrivers, CATIA can help you improve productivity dramatically. With CATIA, the world's premier CAD/CAM/CAE system offered by IBM, you'll be able to reduce design time, improve product quality and lower development costs.

CATIA offers a full range of design capabilities—from 2D to 3D to parametric and variational modeling. It's totally integrated, too. From mechanical design to analysis and simulation through manufacturing, CATIA's solutions allow you to create a seamless—and paperless—environment for product design and manufacturing.

Ultimately, your design and build teams communicate better, solving problems faster. And you increase design accuracy and precision.

Installed in thousands of design and manufacturing companies around the globe, CATIA has proven that designing in 3D enhances competitiveness in virtually any industry. And CATIA users are realizing the value of being supported by IBM, with its full complement of on-going consulting and service programs.

To learn more about how CATIA Solutions and IBM can help you in your product design and manufacturing applications, call 1 800 395-3339.

IBM

Chapter 18

Graphical User Interfaces (GUIs)*

Aaron Marcus
President
Aaron Marcus and Associates, Inc.
Emeryville, California

Human-to-computer communication and interaction in previous decades has been a limited exchange of alphanumeric characters. Today, advanced graphical user interfaces (GUIs) present sophisticated displays and interaction paradigms that enable novice, intermediate, and expert users to work more productively. Many of these GUIs use windows, icons, menus, and pointing devices (WIMPs) to achieve their communication and interaction goals. In particular, many GUIs simulate a "desktop" environment in the display.

To be successful, the GUI must provide effective metaphors (as in the preceding desktop metaphor), organization, navigation of the data and functions, and an appealing look and feel. Users can appreciate and take advantage of quality in each of these areas. Good organization of contents, economical means to express key components, and effective use of visual elements all lead to more usable and friendlier Solid Modeling (SM) systems.

This chapter discusses various aspects of GUI environments focusing primarily on windowing systems, user-interface components, and window management. Many tips and suggestions are provided at the end of the chapter that will aid in the understanding, evaluation, and development of GUI applications, including SM.

18.1 Solid Modeling and GUIs

Solid Modeling presents designers with a special challenge: large collections of functions that act upon large amounts of data in complex ways. Many SM programs have converted to one or more commercial GUI paradigms such as Macintosh, Motif, Windows, etc., many of which are discussed individually in this chapter.

Solid Modeling operators should be especially sensitive to how clearly the menu hierarchy is organized and to how clearly dialogue boxes are labeled and laid out, because much of the designer's mental work takes place in these GUI components. Many products have moved to the use of icons to represent objects, structures, or processes. Again, users should examine how clearly icons are designed and labeled.

Current GUI building tools enable developers to construct SM applications more quickly than ever before. However, the tools do not ensure that the applications are automatically well designed. To provide some background, this chapter discusses some of the GUI paradigms and principles of good GUI design.

The GUI windowing system is similar to an operating system. Instead of file systems or CPU cycles, however, the windowing system manages resources such as screen space and input devices. In GUIs, the windowing system acts as a front end to the operating system by shielding operators from the abstract and often confusing syntax and vocabulary of a keyboard-oriented command language.

---

*This chapter is based on Aaron Marcus's book *Graphic Design for Electronic Documents and User Interfaces*[1] and a three-part article series, "Designing Graphical User Interfaces," that appeared in *UnixWorld*.[2]

18.2   Windowing Systems

Each of the windowing systems discussed briefly in the following sections has unique features and a place in the history of GUIs. Figures 18.1 through 18.4 (see color insert) show SM applications operating within a few of these GUI paradigms.

18.2.1   Macintosh

The Apple Macintosh® was introduced in 1984 as the first mass-marketed computer to feature a high-resolution, bit-mapped graphic display and a direct-manipulation interaction style. Its windowing system is built on top of a proprietary library of operating system and user-interface tool-kit routines in the Macintosh read-only memory (ROM).

The classic Macintosh GUI was a single-tasking system with a high level of responsiveness and a very simple model of the designer's tasks. Current versions permit multiple applications to be opened and operated. Apple Computer has succeeded in creating widespread acceptance among third-party software developers for their standard GUI components. As a result, knowledge about familiar Macintosh applications can ease the task of learning new ones.

The Macintosh was the first computer system with a GUI to gain widespread market acceptance and experience significant commercial success. Its popularity, particularly in nontechnical market segments traditionally unreceptive toward computing, can be attributed in large part to Apple's commitment to the creation of a consistent and user-supportive human interface.

Because of its historical precedence and market penetration, the Macintosh has established the standard of interaction by which GUIs are judged. The degree of responsiveness to the actions of the operator demonstrates the quality of interaction that is possible when the windowing system is integrated tightly with a particular hardware and software environment.

18.2.2   NextStep

The NextStep® GUI provides a windowing system and graphical desktop environment originally intended for the NeXT® Computer, which began shipping in 1988, but which ceased production in 1993. Nevertheless, the NextStep GUI has survived and is being made available on several types of workstations. The four component modules of the NextStep GUI are (1) Window Server, (2) Workspace Manager, (3) Application Kit, and (4) Interface Builder.

NextStep was the first in a series of products to adopt a simulated 3D appearance for its standard components. The Window Server uses Display PostScript® to create high-quality gray-scale screen displays providing graphics that can be output on any PostScript-compatible printer.

The Application Kit provides a standard set of object-oriented components that can be customized by application developers. The Interface Builder is an end-user-oriented tool that allows operators to link these objects to system- and application-level functions with no additional programming. With this tool, standard human-interface components can be used to automate tasks.

Like the Macintosh human interface, NextStep is oriented toward the needs of the nontechnical. A straightforward mental model (i.e., an organization of data and functions), a simple set of controls, and a well-developed collection of software tools shield the user from the complexity of the operating system and increases the suitability of the system for the initially targeted market (students and scholars) in higher education. Although the sophisticated UNIX-based operating system makes some degree of complexity inevitable, the design of the NextStep human interface makes the system accessible even for completely UNIX-naive users.

18.2.3   Open Look

The Open Look® GUI was developed jointly by Sun Microsystems and AT&T as the standard operating environment for UNIX System V.4. Open Look exists as a layer on top of a base windowing system that provides the imaging model (management of how graphical parts are displayed) and network communication services. Versions of Open Look have been implemented on top of both the X Window System (the base-level set of windowing functions developed by a consortium of computer companies and

MIT) and Sun's Network-extensible Window System (NeWS). Recently, further Open Look development was discontinued, and many applications providers are converting to other GUIs; however, many Open Look applications continue to exist.

Guidance for Open Look developers is provided by an exemplary functional specification and style guide. An explicit goal of the Open Look designers was to avoid potential legal challenges by creating innovative appearance and behavior characteristics. As a result, many of the conventions adopted deviate from the industry norm.

Open Look has adopted a contrasting appearance and approach to usability. Open Look was one of the earliest GUI conventions to propose muted color schemes for more effective display of complex screens. The layout of dialogue boxes and other content-full areas is often more "open" than in other approaches because of the design of the individual pieces. Open Look's orientation toward maximum functionality is evident in the numerous context-sensitive and mode-specific operations it provides. While it, too, makes the UNIX world relatively accessible even for inexperienced users, the extended functionality of Open Look itself introduces an additional layer of complexity that is not seen in NextStep or the Macintosh human interface.

18.2.4 OSF/Motif

OSF/Motif® is a window manager and GUI tool kit developed by Digital Equipment Corporation and the Hewlett-Packard Company for the Open Software Foundation (OSF). Motif provides a 3D, visually dense, and often more sophisticated-looking alternative to Open Look that is linked to the OSF version of standard UNIX.

Like Open Look, the Motif Window Manager exists as a software layer atop the network-oriented X Window System. Appearance can be modified independently of the functional characteristics of the resulting system, and individual vendors are encouraged to customize the functional shell with their own proprietary widget sets.

OSF/Motif provides a GUI for a high-end, network-based computing environment whose appearance and behavior is consistent with that of Microsoft Windows and the OS/2 Presentation Manager. Because of their de facto standardization on IBM and compatible platforms, these operating environments are likely to dominate the movement toward GUIs for PC-based systems. OSF anticipates that knowledge of Windows and the Presentation Manager will transfer easily to Motif, making it the windowing system of choice when PC users upgrade to workstation platforms.

The implementation of Motif on top of the network-transparent X Window System allows it to leverage an emerging standard in the workstation environment as well. Motif provides a windowing system that can serve as a bridge between the PC and workstation environments. Its potential for easing this transition will increase the attractiveness of Motif for organizations integrating high-performance workstations with existing PC networks.

18.2.5 Microsoft Windows and OS/2 Presentation Manager

Microsoft Windows® was created in 1985 as a multitasking, graphics-oriented alternative to the character-based environment provided by MS-DOS on PC-compatible systems. The bit-mapped displays and mouse-driven menus provided by Windows first opened the door to graphics-oriented software on the PC.

Initially, Windows was limited by many of the design characteristics (640K address space, low-quality display, etc.) of the DOS environment on which it was built. Recent enhancements, however, have increased the responsiveness and graphical quality of Windows, particularly on 80386- and 80486-based machines. Microsoft's Windows NT® environment is positioned to take advantage of window's general approach, but with added networking and multitasking capabilities. Windows NT provides a GUI for high-performance PCs and workstations.

The OS/2 Presentation Manager® was developed jointly by Microsoft and IBM in 1987 and is favored by IBM and some compatible microcomputer manufacturers. The appearance and behavior of Presentation Manager are derived primarily from Windows, which will eventually provide an identical set of functions for operators in the MS-DOS environment.

Microsoft Windows and the OS/2 Presentation Manager must satisfy a very different market, consisting largely of existing MS-DOS users in business and technical environments. The extensive support for keyboard-based control provided by these products reflects the heritage of the character-based DOS interface, which has historically relied heavily on keystroke combinations for selecting from menus and dialogue boxes.

18.2.6   Custom GUIs

Although most industry applications are moving toward one or more commercial GUIs using the aforementioned windowing systems, some previous and current products utilize custom approaches. For example, touch-screen versions may use nonstandard layouts, or standard GUIs may continue to include holdover function keys or buttons from the earlier text-oriented user interfaces.

In addition, few GUI building tools prevent developers from incorporating custom deviations from standard practice. Consequently, nonstandard, semicustomized versions of commercial GUIs may be encountered.

18.3   Windowing System Architectures

Windowing systems divide the display screen into multiple functional areas that provide a means of monitoring and controlling multiple application programs or manipulating multiple data objects in a graphical environment. The windows in which documents and applications are presented provide a set of well-defined visual and functional contexts that allow multiple processes to time-share a single set of input devices (mouse, keyboard, etc.) and a limited amount of physical display space. The windowing code (software architecture), the method of window management, and the base window system's method of displaying an image (image model) can have noticeable effects on the quality of the displays and the level of interaction experienced by the user.

There are two types of windowing system architectures. These are kernel- and client-server-based in design.

18.3.1   Kernel-Based Architecture

The location and organization of the software that implements the windowing system can influence the responsiveness, device dependence, and resource requirements of the resulting system. Kernel-based architectures provide high levels of interactivity but are dependent on the architecture and available resources of a single machine.

In kernel-based systems, windowing services are provided by some portion of the operating system itself or by a standard add-on module that resides along with the operating system in RAM (random access memory) or ROM (read-only memory)-based libraries. Kernel-based windowing codes and operating systems share the same physical memory space and are accessed in essentially the same way.

18.3.2   Client-Server-Based Architecture

Client-server-based architectures allow a single instance of the windowing system software to be shared across entire networks of heterogeneous machines, but response times may be limited by the communication bandwidth of the network. A *server* is a computer-running software that provides a particular capability to an entire network of interconnected machines. A *client* is a piece of software on the same network that requests and uses the capabilities provided by the server.

Even the best client-server implementations incur significant communication overhead that can lead to noticeable performance degradation compared to kernel-based windowing systems. Kernel-based systems achieve higher performance at the cost of device dependence and the need to redundantly execute the same code on each machine.

18.4 Window Management

Window management facilities allow the system to maintain spatial relationships between windows as they are moved, sized, and depth-arranged. Several options are available in window control menus that feature automatic arrangement of windows. Of particular importance are tiled, overlapping, and cascading windows. While the historical controversy over the relative merits of tiled and overlapping windows continues, industry practice has favored overlapping window management; however, tiled windows may still be useful in large or high-resolution displays. These window management styles are discussed in more detail.

18.4.1 Tiled Windows

Tiled windows are arranged automatically by the windowing system to completely fill the available display space (which may be either the entire display screen or an entire content area of a window). Windows are prevented from overlapping. When any window is resized, other windows must be sized in the opposing direction to compensate.

18.4.2 Overlapping Windows

Overlapping windows have associated depth values that represent their distances from the viewer. At each displayed location of a visual point or pixel, only the contents of the nearest window covering that portion of the display are presented. The window with the nearest (to the viewer) depth value thus obscures the contents of any other windows occupying the same display space, creating an illusion of physical overlapping. The resulting window stack is comparable to a pile of papers on a desk, and allows the designer to take advantage of existing spatial management skills.

18.4.3 Cascading Windows

Cascading windows are a special case of overlapping window management in which the windows are arranged automatically in a regular progression that prevents any window from being completely obscured. The origin (i.e., the upper-left corner) of each successive window is offset slightly in both the horizontal and vertical directions to conserve display space while simplifying the task of bringing any window to the front of the stack.

18.5 Windowing System Components

The appearance and behavior of the windowing system as experienced by the user is determined by a small group of standard components. GUIs make use of essentially the same set of interface components, while the names by which these components are identified vary significantly among vendors. The following set of terms and a discussion of each will streamline cross-product comparisons by identifying standard components consistently and unambiguously.

1. Windows
2. Menus
3. Controls
4. Dialogue boxes
5. Modeless dialogues

6. Modal dialogues
7. Control panels
8. Query boxes
9. Message boxes
10. Mouse and keyboard interface

18.5.1   Windows

From the viewpoint of the window manager, a window is any discrete area of the visual display that can be moved, sized, and rendered independently on the display screen. Even though most of the components are actually implemented and managed as windows by the system, it is appropriate to consider windows from the operator's point of view. The definition employed will therefore include only those display areas that allow one to change the view of their contents using techniques such as sizing, scrolling, or editing.

18.5.2   Menus

Menus provide a means of command retrieval that enables a user to see and point instead of remembering and typing. The menu system greatly reduces problems caused by the limitations of human memory, but does so at the expense of motor performance. The benefits are substantial, particularly when the number and complexity of commonly used applications limits the operator's expertise with individual command sets.

18.5.3   Controls

Any visually represented window component that can be manipulated directly with the mouse or keyboard is a *control*. Each of the windowing systems defines standard sets of controls that can be incorporated by applications to provide consistent interaction protocols across products.

18.5.4   Dialogue Boxes

Dialogue boxes provide a visual and functional context for presenting options from which the user can select. Any interactive exchange of information between the user and the system that takes place in a limited spatial context is considered a dialogue.

Although three distinct classes of dialogue boxes are described here (control panels, query boxes, and message boxes), there may be considerable overlap between classes. Any dialogue box can be characterized by a clearly defined scope that determines the effect on the state of the system and the subsequent operations permitted.

18.5.5   Modeless Dialogues

Modeless dialogue boxes are limited in scope and do not restrict the subsequent actions of the user. Modeless dialogues may incorporate some basic window functions such as sizing and positioning. Users can continue to work without responding, if necessary, and may be allowed to keep the modeless dialogue on display even after a response has been made.

18.5.6   Modal Dialogues

Modal dialogue boxes require the user to respond before any other action can be taken. Application modal dialogues prevent the user from invoking any application functions until the dialogue has been satisfied, while system modal dialogs prevent the user from performing any operations anywhere in the system.

18.5.7 Control Panels

Control panels appear at the implicit or explicit request of the user and provide information reflecting the current state of a number of related system parameters, any of which can be changed interactively while the panel remains on display. Changes to the system state do not take effect until the user explicitly accepts the new settings.

18.5.8 Query Boxes

Query boxes appear in response to user actions, but are not requested explicitly. Query boxes prompt for a single piece of information, such as a yes-or-no answer to a single question, and offer a context in which the necessary information can be provided. Like control panels, query boxes allow the user to cancel the action that led to the query.

18.5.9 Message Boxes

Providing critical information to the user is the primary function of message boxes, which are not requested and typically appear only when the system has entered, or is about to enter, an unrecoverable and potentially dangerous state. The user's response options are typically limited to a simple yes-or-no decision or, in irreversible system states, simple acknowledgment of the message.

18.5.10 Mouse and Keyboard Interface

GUI systems use a mouse and keyboard as the primary interaction devices. Each device is well suited to certain types of interaction tasks. The mouse provides an efficient means of accomplishing tasks that require spatial manipulation, such as menu navigation and window sizing and positioning. The keyboard is more efficient for sequential tasks, such as text entry and changing the relative depth location of windows by bringing one of them to the top.

18.6 Conclusions

This chapter introduces the major GUI/window manager paradigms and provides guidance for good GUI design. GUIs present many simultaneous, complex challenges to achieving successful visual communication. What follows is a basic set of recommendations that can help you get started in using layout, typography, symbolism, and color more effectively. After these guidelines have been incorporated, consider establishing product or companywide style guides, templates, and color palettes so that others may adapt and benefit from previous work. Developing better communication is an important part of developing SM applications that communicate through graphic design.

Note: The following advice is intended to aid in evaluating GUIs implemented with various SM software packages and can be generically applied to all computer-based GUIs. If an SM package allows designer customization of the GUI, this advice may assist in this process as well.

Design Principles

SMA.18.1   Leverage Known Design Techniques

The GUI of an SM system should be designed as closely as possible to leverage known design techniques rather than to force designers to understand SM techniques. This will make the SM system more intuitive and user-friendly.

Design Principles
(*Continued*)

SMA.18.2   Design Characteristics

A GUI design must account for the following characteristics:

1. *Metaphor:*   Comprehensible images, concepts, or terms

2. *Mental model:*   Appropriate organization of data, functions, tasks, and roles

3. *Navigation:*   Efficient movement among the data, functions, tasks, and roles via windows, menus, and dialogue boxes

4. *Look:*   Quality presentation characteristics

5. *Feel:*   Effective interaction sequencing

SMA.18.3   Design Guidelines

Three key principles guide GUI design, and are just as applicable when customizing a GUI. They are:

1. *Organize:*   Provide the designer with a clear and consistent conceptual structure.

2. *Economize:*   Maximize the effectiveness of a minimal set of cues.

3. *Communicate:*   Match the presentation to the capabilities of the designer.

Organization

SMA.18.4   Order and Chaos

Organization lends order to a GUI, making it easier for the designer to understand and navigate. Without visual and cognitive organization, the GUI becomes chaotic and therefore difficult to learn and use. Figure 18.5 shows an example of the trade-off between order and chaos. Organization can best be understood by examining key components such as consistency, screen layout, relationships, and navigability.

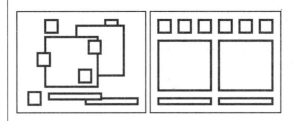

FIGURE 18.5   Chaotic and ordered screens. The examples illustrate the difference between a disorganized and organized screen layout.

SMA.18.5   Consistency

The principle of internal consistency says: Observe the same conventions and rules for all elements of the GUI. Figure 18.6 provides an example. Without a strong motivating reason, casual differences cause the viewer to work harder to understand the essential message of the display. The GUI should deviate from existing conventions only when doing so provides a clear benefit to the designer. In other words, the GUI should have a good reason for being inconsistent. GUI researcher Jonathan Grudin[3] has shown that sometimes it is impossible to avoid inconsistency, and that inconsistency can even be beneficial under certain circumstances. However, as a general rule, strive for consistency while still maintaining originality.

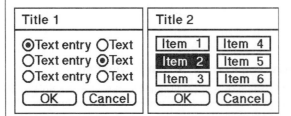

FIGURE 18.6   Internal consistency in dialogue boxes. The examples illustrate a consistent location and appearance for titles, main contents, and action buttons.

(Continued)

Organization
(*Continued*)

SMA.18.6   GUI Screen Layout

There are three primary means of achieving an organized screen layout: (1) using a grid structure, (2) standardizing the screen layout, and (3) grouping related elements. Figure 18.7 shows examples of dialogue boxes based on a grid structure.

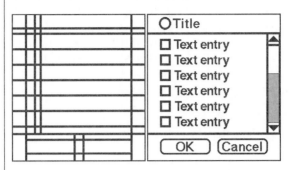

FIGURE 18.7   Grid and dialogue box. The examples illustrate a layout grid of lines that can be used to locate all visual elements of the dialogue box.

SMA.18.7   Relationships

Another technique helpful in achieving visual organization is to establish clear relationships by linking related elements and disassociating unrelated elements. Examples of elements grouped by relationships appear in Fig. 18.8.

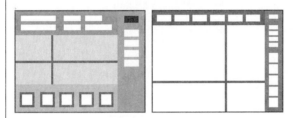

FIGURE 18.8   Relationships between grouped items. The examples illustrate confusing and clear use of color, locations, shape, and size to visually group components of screen displays.

SMA.18.8   Navigability

An organized GUI provides an initial focus for the viewer's attention, directs attention to important, secondary, or peripheral items, and assists in navigation throughout the material. Figure 18.9 provides an example of a screen layout redesigned for improved navigability.

FIGURE 18.9   Navigability. A viewer looking at the screen on the left wouldn't know where to begin; the redesigned screen on the right provides clear entry points into the screen via a visual reinforcement of the elements hierarchy.

Economy

SMA.18.9   Economic Guidelines

Economy is an important aspect of GUI design and modification. Simplicity suggests that we include only those elements that are essential for communication. In addition, the design should be as unobtrusive as possible. Here are some economic rules to follow:

(*Continued*)

Economy
(*Continued*)

1. *Modesty:*   In general, GUI components should be modest and inconspicuous. Designers should be almost unconscious of the GUI working to convey meaning.

2. *Clarity:*   Clarity is equally as important as modesty. Components should be designed with unambiguous meanings. Figure 18.10 provides an example of ambiguous and clearly designed icons.

3. *Distinctiveness:*   The third technique for achieving economy is distinctiveness. Distinguish the important properties of essential elements. Figure 18.11 illustrates this technique.

4. *Emphasis:*   The final technique for economizing is emphasis. In general, make the most important elements salient (i.e., easily perceived). Deemphasize noncritical elements and minimize clutter so that critical information is not hidden. Figure 18.12 illustrates this point.

Zoom

Help

FIGURE 18.10   Clarity. Ambiguous icons confuse and frustrate viewers; clearly designed icons help them to understand the application.

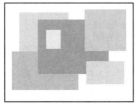 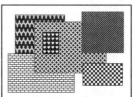

FIGURE 18.11   Distinctiveness. Too little (at left) gives the screen a bland uninformative look; too much is chaotic and yields no information about how the items relate to each other.

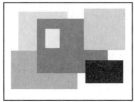 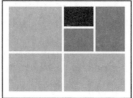

FIGURE 18.12   Emphasis. Because every element in the figure at left is emphasized, the overall effectiveness is reduced; the viewer doesn't know what is most important. The figure at right corrects this situation, giving appropriate emphasis to each element.

Communication

SMA.18.10   Achieve a Balance

To communicate successfully, a GUI must balance many factors. Well-designed GUIs achieve this balance through the use of information-oriented, systematic graphic design. This refers to the use of layout, typography, symbols, color, and other static and dynamic graphics to convey facts, concepts, and emotions.

SMA.18.11   Layout

The starting point for a well-designed GUI is its layout. Layout refers to the spatial organization of all dialogue boxes and windows according to an underlying grid of horizontal and vertical lines. In general, the visual field should be governed by 7 ± 2 major lines in each orientation. These lines will regularize the appearance of all other elements, including typography, icons, charts, etc.

SMA.18.12   Legibility

Any GUI should be legible. Legibility refers to the design of individual characters, symbols, and graphic elements to be easily noticeable and distinguishable. Figure 18.13 shows some examples of legibility based on typeface (font) and size.

(*Continued*)

Communication
(Continued)

SMA.18.13 Screen Backgrounds

Remember that dark screen backgrounds in brightly lit rooms may cause distracting reflections that can diminish screen legibility. In contrast, brightly lit screens in dark rooms may be too glaring and difficult to see.

𝕿𝖊𝖝𝖙 𝖘𝖊𝖙 𝖎𝖓 𝕺𝖑𝖉 𝕰𝖓𝖌𝖑𝖎𝖘𝖍

Text set in Univers

Large
Medium
Small

Large
Medium
Small

FIGURE 18.13 Legibility. The decorative typeface on the left is less legible than the clean sans serif type on the right. Size variations in text (lower left) aren't distinct enough, while the text on the right clearly establishes a type hierarchy.

SMA.18.14 Readability

Readability refers to a display that is comprehensible (i.e., easy to identify and interpret) as well as inviting and attractive. Figure 18.14 presents an example of contrast in readability of texts.

SMA.18.15 Typography

Individual GUI elements (typefaces, such as Times Roman or Helvetica, and type styles, such as bold roman or regular italic) and their arrangement (typesetting techniques, such as line spacing) should be optimized for effective communication. Here are some guidelines to consider:

1. Within menus, dialogue boxes, control panels, forms, and other window components, adjust the point size, word spacing, paragraph indentation, and line spacing to enhance readability and to emphasize critical information.

2. Limit selections to a maximum of one to three typefaces in one to three sizes, no matter what the SM application. Lines of text should have 40 to 60 characters maximum, and words should be spaced correctly (usually the width of a lowercase *r* for variable-width text).

Unreadable: Design components to
be easy to interpret and
understand. Design components to
be inviting and attractive.

Readable

Design components to be easy to interpret and understand.

Design components to be inviting and attractive.

FIGURE 18.14 Readability. Centered text (top) is not as easy to interpret or as enjoyable to read as the left-justified, well-spaced text below.

3. Text should be set in appropriate formats (e.g., set text flush left, set columns of numbers flush right, avoid centered text in lists, and avoid short justified lines of text). For fixed-width fonts, justified lines of text can slow reading speed by 12 percent.

4. Use upper- and lowercase characters whenever possible (i.e., avoid all-capital lines of text, which can also slow reading speed by 12 percent).

SMA.18.16 Symbolism

GUI symbolism refers to signs, icons, and symbols that can help to communicate complex information and make the display more appealing. In general, keep in mind the following:

(Continued)

Communication
(Continued)

1. Use symbols or icons that are clear and unambiguous.

2. Use familiar references when possible.

3. Be consistent in the size, angles, weights, and visual density of all the signs.

SMA.18.17   Multiple Views

One important technique for improving communication with the GUI is to provide multiple views of the display of complex structures and processes. Figure 18.15 gives an example of how to present multiple views. Good GUI design makes use of these different perspectives:

1. Multiple forms of representation

2. Multiple levels of abstraction

3. Simultaneous alternative views

4. Links and cross-references

 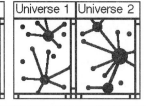

FIGURE 18.15   Multiple views (visual and verbal). The examples illustrate how graphic and textual GUI components can present the viewer with different views of a single object or multiple views of different objects in order to communicate complex information effectively.

Color and Texture

SMA.18.18   What Is Color?

Color, including texture, is a powerful communication tool—so powerful, in fact, that color is easy to misuse or overuse. GUI designers must therefore understand color's functions so as to use color with proper skill and sophistication. Color refers to these dimensions: *hue* (combinations of wavelength), *value* (degree of lightness or darkness), and *chroma* (degree of purity or vividness). In addition, *brightness* refers to the amount of radiant energy in the display of color.

SMA.18.19   Accomplishments

Color plays a significant role in communicating with a designer. Here are some of the most important tasks color can accomplish:

1. Emphasizes important information

2. Identifies subsystems or structures

3. Portrays natural objects realistically

4. Portrays time and progress

5. Reduces errors of interpretation

6. Adds coding dimensions

7. Increases comprehensiveness

8. Increases believability and appeal

SMA.18.20   Similarity

In general, similar colors imply a relation among objects. A viewer can sense the relatedness by color over space and over time in sequences of images. Therefore, color should be used to group related items, and a consistent color code should be used for screen displays, documentation, etc. Also, use similar background colors for related areas. This color coding can subtly reinforce the conceptual link among these areas in the designer's mind.

(Continued)

Color and Texture
(Continued)

SMA.18.21   Consistency

Be complete and consistent in color groupings. For example, command and control colors in menus should not be used for information coding within a work area unless a specific connection is intended.

Once color coding is established, the same colors should be used throughout the GUI and all related publications. This color continuity may require designing colors to appear in different media: CRT screens use additive color mixtures, while most hardcopy devices use subtractive color mixtures. The color gamuts (that is, available color ranges) of these two media usually are not identical.

Color Economy

SMA.18.22   Principles and Redundancy

The principle of color economy suggests using a maximum of 5 ± 2 colors where the meaning must be remembered. Note that this maximum is even less than Miller's number[4] of 7 ± 2, which refers to our cognitive functioning limit with short-term memory. If appropriate, use redundant coding based on shape as well as color.

SMA.18.23   Enhancement

The basic idea is to use color to enhance black-and-white information; that is, design the display to work well first in black and white.

For documentation tasks and for the use of color to portray an object, the maximum number of colors needed is dependent on the application. For aesthetic purposes (such as design style, emotional expression, or realism), many more colors may be required.

A set of 5 ± 2 colors may include a few grays and some strongly different hues, or the set may use only different values for a given hue.

SMA.18.24   Sequencing

To code a large set of colors, use the spectral sequence: red, orange, yellow, green, blue, and violet. Francine Frome,[5] a human-factors researcher, has shown that viewers see a spectral order as a natural one and would select red, green, and blue as intuitive choices for the front, middle, and back layers, respectively, when viewing a multilayer display.

Note, however, that brightness can change a viewer's perception of depth. If the colors are balanced, then red seems to come forward. Use redundant coding of shape as well as color. This aids those with color-deficient vision and makes the display more resilient to color distortions caused by ambient light changes or by converting a color display from one medium to another, such as from a CRT to slides.

Ambient light can cause changes in all dimensions of color. Conversion from one medium to another can cause unforeseen and sometimes uncontrollable changes. Remember that among Caucasian viewers, approximately 8 percent of males have some form of color-deficient vision.

Color Emphasis

SMA.18.25   Suggested Emphasis

Color emphasis suggests using strong contrast in value and chroma to focus the viewer's attention on critical information. The use of bright colors for danger signals, attention-getters, reminders, and cursors is entirely appropriate. High-chroma red alerts seem to aid faster response than yellow or yellow-orange if brightness is equal, but of course this also depends upon the background colors. When too many figures or background fields compete for the viewer's attention, confusion arises, as can happen in the approach to color design that makes displays look appropriate for Las Vegas (the use of many high-chroma colors).

SMA.18.26   Hierarchy

The hierarchy of highlighted, neutral, and low-lighted states for all areas of the visual display must be carefully designed to maximize simplicity and clarity. Here again we find the basic maxim: Simplicity, clarity, and consistency are especially important for color design.

(Continued)

Color Emphasis
(*Continued*)

SMA.18.27 Viewer Differences

Older viewers may be less able to distinguish blue from white and blue-green from bluish-white light due to natural aging and change of color in the lens of the eye.[6] Those who have viewed displays for very long periods of time may require more saturated or high-chroma colors because of changes in their visual system. Bear in mind that frequent, short-term viewing can benefit from low-chroma displays, and that very bright displays of letters, symbols or lines tend to bloom; that is, the light spreads out against the background.

Color Communication

SMA.18.28 Central and Peripheral Colors

Select colors appropriate to the central and peripheral areas of the visual field. The outer edges of the retina are not particularly sensitive to colors in general. Thus, red or green should be used in the center of the visual field, not in the periphery. If they are used at the periphery, some signal to the viewer must be given to capture attention (e.g., size change or blinking). Use blue, black, white, and yellow near the periphery of the visual field, where the retina remains sensitive.

SMA.18.29 Combinations

Use color combinations whose color contrasts are influenced least by the relative area of each color. Use blue for large areas, not for text type, thin lines, or small shapes. Blue-sensitive color receptors are the least numerous in the retina (approximately 5 percent), and are especially infrequent in the eye's central focusing area, the fovea. Blue is good for screen backgrounds.

SMA.18.30 Area

If the same colors appear in objects that vary greatly in size, bear in mind that as color areas decrease in size they appear to change their value and chroma.

SMA.18.31 High-Chroma and Spectrally Extreme Colors

Choose colors that are not simultaneously high in chroma and located at the extreme ends of the visual spectrum (e.g., red and blue).

SMA.18.32 Chroma and Value

Use colors that differ both in chroma and value (lightness). Do not use adjacent colors that differ only in the amount of pure blue, because the edge between the two colors will appear to be fuzzy. To avoid this effect, it is helpful to use other combinations, such as a dark blue and a light blue.

SMA.18.33 Combinations to Avoid

Colors of simultaneously high-chroma, spectral extremes, and strong contrasts of red/green, blue/yellow, green/blue, and red/blue can create vibrations or illusions of shadows and after-images. Unless special visual effects are needed, avoid these combinations.

SMA.18.34 For Dark Viewing

In general, use light text, thin lines, and small shapes (white, yellow, or red) on medium-to-dark backgrounds (blue, green, or dark gray) for dark viewing situations. Typical low ambient-light viewing situations are those for slide presentations, workstations, and video. Video displays produce colors that are lower in chroma.

SMA.18.35 For Light Viewing

Use dark (blue or black) text, thin lines, and small shapes on light (light yellow, magenta, blue, or white) backgrounds for light viewing situations. Typical viewing situations are those for overhead transparencies and paper. Reserve for text type the highest contrast between a figure and its background field.

(Continued)

Color Communication
(Continued)

SMA.18.36 Interactions

The interaction of color is a very complex subject that cannot be meaningfully covered in this limited space. The basic text on the subject is Albers' book, *The Interaction of Color.*[7] GUI designers need to become familiar with this topic, which students of art and design often study.

Color Symbolism

SMA.18.37 Using Color Codes

Remember the importance of symbolism in communication; use color codes that respect existing cultural and professional usage.

SMA.18.38 Connotations

Evoke color connotations with great care. Connotations vary strongly among different kinds of viewers, especially from different cultures. The correct use of color requires careful analysis of the experience and expectations of the viewers.

For example, mailboxes are blue in the United States, bright red in England, and bright yellow in Greece. If color is used in an electronic mail icon on the screen, this suggests that color sets might be changed for different countries to allow for differences in international markets.

Good to Know

SMA.18.39 Shortcutting the GUI

In many situations there may be direct keyboard combinations that invoke commands or a series of operations quicker than from the GUI or command line. Many of these shortcuts may not be documented.

Remember that a GUI is developed to shield you and to expedite direct command-line input. The SM system programmers embed keyboard combinations to expedite software development. If your vendor will allow it, find out what some of these direct keyboard input combinations are.

Caution: This direct input may bypass safeguards built into a GUI. Caution is advised until you are well aware of your system's actions and input requirements.

Don LaCourse, President
The Solid Modeling ExChange, Algood, Tenn.

SMA.18.40 For the Occasional User

The highest priority when evaluating or customizing an SM-related GUI is the consideration of the occasional user. The occasional user will be more productive if the GUI is simple and user-friendly. A GUI can become second nature to an experienced everyday user. It is the occasional user who will become frustrated and distracted if the GUI is not easy to use and understand.

David E. Schaeg, Designer
Emerson Motor Co., St. Louis, Mo.

References

1. Marcus, Aaron, *Graphic Design for Electronic Documents and User Interfaces,* ACM Press, New York, 1992.

2. Marcus, Aaron, "Designing Graphical User Interfaces, Parts 1–3," *UnixWorld,* vol. 7, nos. 8–10, August–October 1990, pp. 107–116, 121–127, 135–138.

3. Grudin, Jonathan, "The Case Against User Interface Consistency," *Communications of the ACM,* vol. 32, no. 10, October 1989, pp. 1164–1173.

4. Miller, G. A., "The Magical Number Seven Plus or Minus Two: Some Limits on Our Capacity for Processing Information," *Psych. Rev.,* vol. 63, 1956, pp. 81–97.

5. Frome, Francine, "Incorporating the Human Factor in Color CAD Systems," *IEEE Proceedings, 20th Design Automation Conference,* 1983, pp. 189–195.

6. Thorrell, L. G., and W. J. Smith, *Using Computer Color Effectively: An Illustrated Reference,* Prentice-Hall, Englewood Cliffs, N.J., 1990.

7. Albers, Josef, *Interaction of Color,* Yale University Press, New Haven, 1975.

Suggestions for Further Reading

Baecker, Ronald, and Aaron Marcus, *Human Factors and Typography for More Readable Programs,* Addison-Wesley, Reading, Mass., 1990.

Bertin, Jacques, *Semiology of Graphics,* University of Wisconsin Press, Madison, 1983.

Bliss, C. K., *Semantography,* Semantography Publications, Sydney, Australia, 1965.

Hofmann, Armin, *Graphic Design Manual,* Reinhold Publishing Corp., New York, 1965.

Marcus, Aaron, "Color: A Tool for Computer Graphics Communication," in Greenberg, Donald, et al., *The Computer Image,* Addison-Wesley, Reading, 1982, pp. 76–90.

Mueller-Brockman, Josef, *Grid Systems,* Verlag Arthur Niggli, Niederteufen, Switzerland, 1981.

Ota, Yuko, *Pictogram Design,* Kawashi Shobo Publishers, Tokyo, Japan, 1987.

Tufte, Edward R., *The Visual Display of Quantitative Information,* Graphics Press, Cheshire, Conn., 1983.

Rapid Prototyping for Rapid Products

Some time ago, engineers at Chrysler faced a formidable challenge: to design, test and put into production a new

exhaust manifold for the Viper car V-10 aluminum engine — in only 5 weeks. Because the Viper's tubular frame rails are located very close to the side of the engine, packaging the exhaust headers presented a particular challenge. The Chrysler engineers used stereolithography (SL), 3D Systems computer-based rapid prototyping system, to quickly develop prototypes which were used to verify an extremely tight fit within the engine compartment. Once the design was established, SL patterns were used to create the production tooling for the exhaust manifold. This rapid prototyping technology proved instrumental to meeting the deadline for the Viper's introduction as the pace car for the 1991 Indianapolis 500. What's more, Chrysler saved 18 weeks time and $64,000 in tooling costs on the manifold alone.

As a designer challenged with creating innovative products, meeting aggressive deadlines and staying within budget, you're constantly on the lookout for tools to support your productivity. Stereolithography by 3D Systems, leader in rapid prototyping technology, has proven time and again to be an invaluable tool for achieving product development success.

Imagine having the power to

- review physical concept models within hours after their design
- attend a critical design review meeting with prototype in hand
- rapidly verify form, fit and function of a new design
- catch errors in assembly connections, configuration angles or interferences with other components before tooling up for production
- generate patterns for soft and hard tooling overnight
- provide vendors with physical models to support bid requests
- save thousands of dollars in product development
- slash months off your product development cycle
- get your design to market ahead of your competition

These many advantages are instantly available through the line of stereolithography products and Technology Center prototyping services of 3D Systems. Hundreds of companies across the globe are testament to the powerful benefits of this proven technology. Engineering success stories span the range of industries and applications.

Allied Signal - Used stereolithography patterns to investment cast prototypes of a titanium anti-ice bleed valve. The engineering group saved 44 weeks and $100,000 in casting tool costs on this single project.

AMP - The stereolithography concept model of a 16 position, two-part connector with nine circuits demonstrated the erroneous lineup to seven circuits. Costs and time savings were estimated to be $80,000 and four months.

3D's QuickCast™ process enables investment casting directly from stereolithography patterns

Chrysler - Quickly revised the design of a transmission shift handle to improve aesthetics and "feel". A single iteration model saved over $40,000 and 18 weeks to arrive at the approved design.

Key Tronics - Created 36 small stereolithography prototypes for a fiber-optic cable system. The "usual" prototyping method using a single cavity aluminum tool would cost $4000 with a lead time of six to eight weeks, plus additional time for blueprints and fabrication of the mold itself. Using SL, the parts were created in nine hours and the entire project finished in two days at negligible cost.

Molex - Used SL to prototype more than 50 products for their new "Smart House" product line in time for introduction at a major trade show. Photographs of the stereolithography parts were used in their advertising and product brochures, allowing marketing to get a jump start on promoting the new line before production was completed.

Logitech - Won a major OEM contract for a unique two-button mouse by including a high quality SL prototype in the bid presentation, completing the entire prototype assembly in one week's time. They now produce more than one million of these devices per year.

These few examples illustrate what is fast becoming the mainstay of competitive product development in the U.S. From concept modeling to prototyping and pattern making, stereolithography continues to provide fast and effective design solutions which allow companies to speed their products to market in record time.

3D Systems Worldwide Corporate Headquarters
  and Technology Center
26081 Avenue Hall
Valencia, CA 91355
805/295-5600
805/295-0249 FAX

Chapter 19

Solid Modeling and Rapid Prototyping

Terry T. Wohlers
President
Wohlers Associates

Rapid Prototyping (RP) systems are machines that input 3D surface data from surface or Solid Modeling (SM) CAD systems for fabricating physical models and prototype parts. Unlike CNC machines, which subtract material to form a shape, RP systems are additive in nature. They use successive layers of material to form the part's shape.

To date, about 950 RP systems are currently installed and operating around the world. Organizations use RP systems for conceptual modeling, design review, fit, and function testing. In addition, RP parts can be shown to potential customers and sent with requests for bids. This can result in more accurate cost estimates. Also, RP technology can be used to produce patterns for molded tooling and investment casting.

Rapid prototyping can save organizations both time and money. For example, Mack Industries (Troy, Michigan) has cut in half the time it takes to build wood patterns using Helisys' Laminated Object Manufacturing (LOM) system.[1] AMP's Automotive/Consumer Business Group (Harrisburg, Pennsylvania) saved four months and $80,000 on one project using 3D Systems' StereoLithography Apparatus (SLA).[2] Biomet (Warsaw, Indiana) builds custom patella implants in 2 hours using Stratasys' Fused Deposition Modeling (FDM) system[3] when conventional (non-RP) techniques would take 8 to 12 hours. Using Cubital's Solid Ground Curing (SGC) system,[4] Stature Machining (Warren, Michigan) saved Whirlpool $22,000 and 3 weeks of time on a blower-housing project. Hewlett-Packard (San Diego, California) estimates they have saved $20,000 and weeks on one project using DTM's Selective Laser Sintering (SLS) system.[5]

Before you can produce a part using an RP system, you must first produce a fully closed 3D surface or solid model as input. Creating a solid model is, by far, the easiest way to ensure a closed and "watertight" model. Thus, most CAD operators use SM when they want to produce an RP part.

In this chapter we will discuss how most RP systems work. Also, we will provide insight into the STL and other interface file formats, discuss specific RP systems in detail, offer advice, and sources of additional information.

19.1 How Most Rapid Prototyping Systems Work

Rapid Prototyping systems operate using a layer-building technique by inputing horizontal cross-section data from a 3D surface or solid CAD model. Beginning with the bottommost cross section of the CAD model, RP systems create a thin layer of material [as thin as 0.004 in (0.102 mm)] equal to the dimensions of the CAD model cross section. The RP system then creates an additional layer on top of the first, based on the next-higher cross section. This process repeats itself until the part is complete.

19.2 The StereoLithography Apparatus (SLA)

SLA from 3D Systems is the most widely installed and used RP system in the world and produces parts from thin layers of liquid photopolymer (see Figs. 19.1 and 19.2). SLA production includes the following sequence of events:

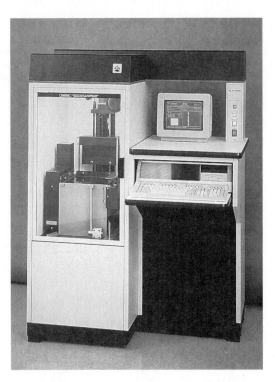

FIGURE 19.1 The StereoLithography Apparatus SLA-250 system. *(Courtesy of 3D Systems, Inc.)*

1. Part modeling
2. Support structure modeling
3. The STL interface
4. Processing
5. Production
6. Finishing

19.2.1   Part Modeling

The source information for any RP system is a 3D surface or solid model. Consideration of the SLA process may be required during part modeling, depending on the part's geometric characteristics and the resulting prototype's intended usage. Limitations and special considerations may influence part modeling preparations. Such considerations are necessary for any manufacturing process. (Refer to the SM Adviser for possible considerations.)

19.2.2   Support-Structure Modeling

The preparation of the CAD model may require the creation of one or more support structures. The shape and location of the supports depend entirely on the shape of the part. The support structure anchors the part to the SLA elevator platform and provides support during production. If you are using an outside SLA service bureau or in-house SLA center, these providers usually prefer to create the support structures for you since they are more familiar with the characteristics of their SLA equipment. Send them an STL file of the CAD model, without supports, and they can take care of the rest. If you choose to model SLA support structures yourself, by either automatic or manual methods, refer to the SM Adviser for some assistance. The support structures are removed when the part is complete. Figure 19.3 (see color insert) shows the bottom of a part with the supports still attached.

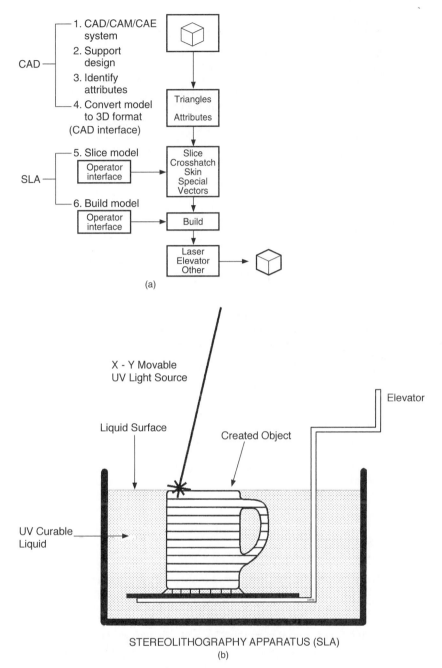

FIGURE 19.2 The SLA process. (*a*) Procedural diagram; (*b*) building the SLA part. *(Courtesy of 3D Systems, Inc.)*

19.2.3 The STL Interface

When the surface or solid model of the part (including all support structures) is complete, the CAD operator stores the model data in an STL file format. The STL file format is a de facto standard RP interface developed by 3D Systems. Nearly all RP systems either support or require the STL file format as input to begin the RP process. 3D Systems developed and published the STL format in 1987 for moving 3D CAD models to their SLA. Most 3D CAD vendors today offer STL file conversion as standard equipment or as an add-on system option.

19.2.4   Processing

SLA operators use 3D Systems' Slice software to slice the model contained within the STL file into thin cross sections. With Slice, the cross-sectional thickness can be adjusted between 0.002 and 0.030 in (0.0254 and 0.254 mm). A thinner slice creates a smoother and more accurate surface, but also requires more time to process, both at the slice computer and during actual building of the part. The sliced data contains contours that define the shape of the CAD model.

The process of slicing the STL file produces additional files. The data resulting from the merging of these files controls the movement of the SLA laser and elevator mechanism. Many process variables are available prior to SLA part production. SLA operators agree that the adjustment of these variables is the key to making good parts. This is why practice and experimentation with the SLA are so important.

19.2.5   Production

The SLA control computer contains a controller circuit board connected to the SLA unit. Driven by vectors determined by the STL file cross sections, a galvanometer mirror x-y scanner controls the exact movement of a laser beam. Beginning with the bottommost cross section, the laser beam prints and solidifies the first cross section on the surface of the liquid polymer. The solidified polymer adheres to the elevator platform located just under the surface of the polymer.

The elevator mechanism then lowers the platform a distance well in excess of the next desired layer thickness. This is done so that the viscous resin will flow inward rapidly. Next, the elevator mechanism moves upward, stopping at the point where the top of the previously cured layer is now exactly one layer thickness below the free resin surface. At this point, a wiper blade passes over the liquid resin surface, moving the excess resin from above the cured cross section of the part back into the vat. A "Z-Wait" interval then allows tiny surface imperfections to relax. The system then prints the next cross section that adheres to the hardened layer under it. Successive printing of cross sections, each adhering to the preceding layer, creates the part.

The amount of production time varies widely depending on the specified layer thickness, the size of the part, the type of resin, the laser power, and many other factors and parameters. On average, 3 hours of continuous processing can cure approximately 1 cubic inch on an SLA-250 or about 3 cubic inches on an SLA-500.

19.2.6   Finishing

After removing the part from the SLA vat of liquid polymer, excess resin surrounding the part must be cleaned away. Cleaning by agitation in tripropylene glycol monomethyl ether (TPM) or isopropyl alcohol (IPA) is a popular method because it reaches into small crevices and openings. After removing the excess resin, a technician must cut and remove the support structure from the part.

When first removed from the SLA tank, the part is not fully cured. Using the postcuring apparatus (PCA) completes the curing process. The PCA is a chamber that applies long-wavelength UV radiation (325 to 390 nm). Also, sunlight will cure SLA parts. This often results in a more uniform cure, but it takes longer. The part can be removed from the PCA after about 45 minutes, depending on the shape of the part and wall thicknesses. If necessary, the part can be sand- or bead-blasted, finished by hand, and painted to provide a desirable surface finish.

Surface-finish decisions depend on how the SLA part will be used. If it is to be a pattern for producing a molded tool, for instance, a smooth finish is desirable. This can take many hours. Surface finish is less important if you plan to use the SLA part for conceptual modeling and design evaluations only.

19.3   The CAD Interface

Although your organization may not own an RP system or have plans to purchase one any time soon, it may be beneficial to interface with one. Such an interface would give you the option of sending your

Two days ago, Michael's prototype was just a sketch on a napkin

Right after a lunchtime brainstorming session, Michael faxed his sketch to 3D Systems Technology Center. Within two days Michael had a detailed 3-dimensional model to present at a critical design review meeting.

Now, thanks to 3D's rapid prototyping technology, Michael's project is six months ahead of schedule and under budget. And, he's also cut his product's time-to-market dramatically. Stereolithography by 3D Systems has given Michael and his company the edge over the competition.

3D's Tech Center is the world's leading resource for solid imaging technology. The Tech Center transforms your ideas into 3-dimensional objects using any design documentation, from napkin sketches to CAD files.

3D's QuickCast™ produces investment castings in such metals as steel, aluminum, copper-beryllium and titanium.

The Center's solid imaging technology specialists have the experience and resources to produce concept models, patterns for soft and hard tooling, and preproduction parts in plastics or metals. In fact, through 3D's QuickCast™ rapid tooling technology, the Tech Center gives you investment castings in record time.

The Tech Center is not just for the Fortune 100 either. Every day small, dynamic companies who want to power products to market faster than their competitors are taking advantage of 3D Technology Center's capabilities. The Tech Center has become their vital, strategic partner in transforming ideas into marketable products.

Put rapid prototyping and rapid tooling to work for you. For more information and free brochures on 3D Systems Tech Center, or solid imaging equipment, call today:

3D SYSTEMS

3D Systems Technology Center
26081 Avenue Hall
Valencia, CA 91355 USA
Telephone: (805) 295-5600 Ext.174
Fax: (805) 295-0249

Telephone Design by Derek Rosen

© 3D Systems, Inc.

(CIRCLE READER SERVICE NO. 211)

3D models to an RP service bureau for prototype part production. Most service bureaus can build parts in a few days, depending on their current backlog of work.

If you have a 3D surface or SM CAD system, there is a good chance you have the capability to create an STL file. Third-party software developers also offer STL translator products. For example, C-TAD Systems (Ann Arbor, Michigan)[6] offers an IGES-to-STL file translator that is part of a product line called "The Integrator." This translator inputs an IGES file from any CAD system and converts it into STL format. In addition, it supports all IGES surface entities, including trimmed surfaces or faces. The product also offers color rendering, dynamic rotation, and basic editing of STL files. This allows the ability to verify the integrity of the part and make minor corrections before sending it to an RP machine. Brock Rooney & Associates (Birmingham, Michigan)[7] also offers an IGES-to-STL file translator.

MasterGraphics[9] (Waukesha, Wisconsin) offers a product called FacetPro® by Cramer Coil that reads and writes STL files using AutoCad Designer®.

19.4 Inside an STL File

STL translators create a file with an STL file extension such as "PART.STL". Most STL translators create either ASCII or binary files. ASCII (American Standard Code for Information Interchange) files contain standard text, numbers, and special characters produced by a computer keyboard. Binary files consist of the standard two-digit (0s and 1s) system that forms the basis for all arithmetic calculations in computers.

Binary files are usually several times smaller than ASCII files. If you look at, display, or print an ASCII STL file, you will see groups of three x, y, z coordinates, as shown in Fig. 19.4. Each coordinate group defines a single triangle vertex. Together, the groups define a connected set of triangular facets that describes the entire surface (inside and out) of the CAD model. A graphical representation of an STL file, pictured in Fig. 19.5 (see color insert), looks very similar to the original CAD model shown in Fig. 19.6 (see color insert). Software from RP system vendors is available to view STL files graphically. The final part, shown in Fig. 19.7 (see color insert), closely resembles the CAD and STL representations.

Many who manufacture RP parts view the facets as a limitation of the STL file format because they approximate the surface of the CAD model. In fact, you can often see the facets on the surface of an RP part prior to sanding and polishing. The facet approach of the STL format was chosen because it is possible to create a faceted representation of a 3D model from most CAD systems that offer surfacing and SM capabilities. Refer to the SM Advisor for additional STL assistance.

19.5 STL Alternatives

The STL format has been a topic at RP meetings and conferences. RP systems operators have been urging developers to improve or develop an alternative to the STL format. CAD operators who can create smooth, precise surfaces, such as Bezier or nonuniform rational B-spline (NURBS) surfaces, want to build RP parts that reflect this smooth surface data.

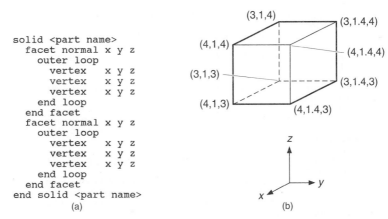

FIGURE 19.4 The .STL ASCII file. (*a*) File format; (*b*) orientation of a sample part. (*Continued*).

```
solid ascii
    facet normal 0.000000e+000 1.000000e+000 2.634149e-009
        outer loop
            vertex    3.000000e+000 1.400000e+000 4.000000e+000
            vertex    4.000000e+000 1.400000e+000 4.000000e+000
            vertex    4.000000e+000 1.400000e+000 3.000000e+000
        end loop
    end facet
    facet normal 0.000000e+000 1.000000e+000 2.634149e-009
        outer loop
            vertex    4.000000e+000 1.400000e+000 3.000000e+000
            vertex    3.000000e+000 1.400000e+000 3.000000e+000
            vertex    3.000000e+000 1.400000e+000 4.000000e+000
        end loop
    end facet
    facet normal -6.585373e-009 0.000000e+000 1.000000e+000
        outer loop
            vertex    4.000000e+000 1.400000e+000 4.000000e+000
            vertex    3.000000e+000 1.400000e+000 4.000000e+000
            vertex    3.000000e+000 1.000000e-001 4.000000e+000
        end loop
    end facet
    facet normal -6.585373e-009 0.000000e+000 1.000000e+000
        outer loop
            vertex    3.000000e+000 1.000000e-001 4.000000e+000
            vertex    4.000000e+000 1.000000e-001 4.000000e+000
            vertex    4.000000e+000 1.400000e+000 4.000000e+000
        end loop
    end facet
    facet normal 1.000000e+000 4.035481e-008 0.000000e+000
        outer loop
            vertex    4.000000e+000 1.000000e-001 4.000000e+000
            vertex    4.000000e+000 1.000000e-001 3.000000e+000
            vertex    4.000000e+000 1.400000e+000 3.000000e+000
        end loop
    end facet
    facet normal 1.000000e+000 4.035481e-008 0.000000e+000
        outer loop
            vertex    4.000000e+000 1.400000e+000 3.000000e+000
            vertex    4.000000e+000 1.400000e+000 4.000000e+000
            vertex    4.000000e+000 1.000000e-001 4.000000e+000
        end loop
    end facet
    facet normal -6.585373e-009 0.000000e+000 -1.000000e+000
        outer loop
            vertex    3.000000e+000 1.000000e-001 3.000000e+000
            vertex    3.000000e+000 1.400000e+000 3.000000e+000
            vertex    4.000000e+000 1.400000e+000 3.000000e+000
        end loop
    end facet
    facet normal -6.585373e-009 0.000000e+000 -1.000000e+000
        outer loop
            vertex    4.000000e+000 1.400000e+000 3.000000e+000
            vertex    4.000000e+000 1.000000e-001 3.000000e+000
            vertex    3.000000e+000 1.000000e-001 3.000000e+000
        end loop
    end facet
    facet normal -1.000000e+000 4.035481e-008 0.000000e+000
        outer loop
            vertex    3.000000e+000 1.400000e+000 3.000000e+000
            vertex    3.000000e+000 1.000000e-001 3.000000e+000
            vertex    3.000000e+000 1.000000e-001 4.000000e+000
        end loop
    end facet
    facet normal -1.000000e+000 4.035481e-008 0.000000e+000
        outer loop
            vertex    3.000000e+000 1.000000e-001 4.000000e+000
            vertex    3.000000e+000 1.400000e+000 4.000000e+000
            vertex    3.000000e+000 1.400000e+000 3.000000e+000
        end loop
    end facet
    facet normal 0.000000e+000 -1.000000e+000 2.634149e-009
        outer loop
            vertex    4.000000e+000 1.000000e-001 3.000000e+000
            vertex    4.000000e+000 1.000000e-001 4.000000e+000
            vertex    3.000000e+000 1.000000e-001 4.000000e+000
        end loop
    end facet
    facet normal 0.000000e+000 -1.000000e+000 2.634149e-009
        outer loop
            vertex    3.000000e+000 1.000000e-001 4.000000e+000
            vertex    3.000000e+000 1.000000e-001 3.000000e+000
            vertex    4.000000e+000 1.000000e-001 3.000000e+000
        end loop
    end facet
end solid
```

FIGURE 19.4 *(Continued) (c)* ASCII .STL file of sample part. *(Courtesy of 3D Systems, Inc.)*

Also, an STL file is often larger than the original CAD file. The actual file size depends on the size of the facets used and the shape of the part. An STL file containing many planar surfaces can be smaller in size. A rectangular plane requires only two triangular facets to describe it. CAD models with many curved surfaces require a large number of triangular facets and can result in an STL file 1.5 to 3 times larger than the CAD model file. Two alternatives to the STL file format are discussed below.

19.5.1 The Cubital Facet List (CFL)

Cubital Ltd. has developed an alternative format called the Cubital Facet List (CFL). This format also uses facets to describe the model, yet the files are smaller than equivalent STL files. This reduction in file size occurs because the CFL format, shown in Fig. 19.8, records facet descriptions without storing redundant information. An STL file repeats information, such as sets of coordinates and strings of text, unnecessarily.

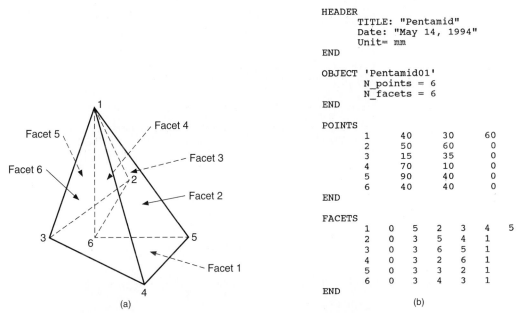

```
HEADER
        TITLE: "Pentamid"
        Date: "May 14, 1994"
        Unit= mm
END

OBJECT  'Pentamid01'
        N_points = 6
        N_facets = 6
END

POINTS
        1       40      30      60
        2       50      60      0
        3       15      35      0
        4       70      10      0
        5       90      40      0
        6       40      40      0
END

FACETS
        1   0   5   2   3   4   5
        2   0   3   5   4   1
        3   0   3   6   5   1
        4   0   3   2   6   1
        5   0   3   3   2   1
        6   0   3   4   3   1
END
```

(a)   (b)

FIGURE 19.8 Example of a Cubital CFL file in ASCII format. (*a*) Pentamid facet layout; (*b*) pentamid CFL file. Note the simplified format for the four main components of the CFL file (HEADER, OBJECT, POINTS, and FACETS). *(Courtesy of Cubital America, Inc.)*

CFL files also contain information not found in STL files. For example, a file header can include a description of the file, the date, and a brief description of the CAD system used to create the file. Also, it can include any comments the creator of the file wishes to include, including name, address, phone, and fax numbers. This practice is similar to that used in the IGES neutral file format. The CFL file sets aside special fields for the name and version of the operating system used to create the file and the unit of measure (inches, millimeters, etc.). STL files do not contain any of this information. Cubital's Solider system will input STL files and includes utilities for converting them to the CFL format.

19.5.2 StereoLithography Contour Format (SLC)

3D Systems also offers an alternative to the STL format called the StereoLithography Contour Format (SLC). This format, tailored to a specific CAD system, allows the sending of native model files directly to the SLA without first creating an STL file. From the native file, the SLC software creates a stack of contours needed to drive the movement of the laser beam. If the surfaces in the source file are smooth, the contours and final part will also be smooth (no triangulated facets). Note, however, that the final part will be only as smooth as the stairsteps caused by the individual layers.

19.6 Selective Laser Sintering (SLS)

The Sinterstation SLS system developed by DTM Corporation (see Fig. 19.9) operates on the same basic layer-by-layer concept as the SLA. However, it uses powder material instead of liquid. A leveling mechanism spreads a layer of powder material on a platform and the machine sinters the powder. The sintering process uses a CO_2 laser to raise the temperature of the powder to the point of fusing (see Fig. 19.10).

FIGURE 19.9 The Sinterstation SLS system. *(Courtesy of DTM Corporation.)*

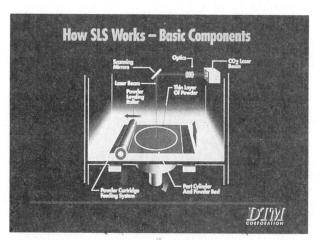

FIGURE 19.10 The SLS process. *(Courtesy of DTM Corporation.)*

To reduce the laser energy needed to sinter the powder, the system preheats the powder in the build chamber. For example, the system raises the temperature to about 365°F for nylon powder. This also helps to reduce thermal shrinkage of the layers, thus reducing part distortion during production. A half-ton air-conditioning unit cools the system. Preheating can take 45 minutes.

The SLS process can produce parts in several materials, including polycarbonate, investment casting wax, and nylon. Polycarbonate parts can reach a density of 75 to 95 percent. This means that 5 to 25 percent of the part is air. Parts made from DTM's nylon material approach a density of 96 percent. Parts of lower density are usually weaker than solid parts. (See color insert, Fig. 19.11.)

The SLS process can produce parts at a rate of about 0.25 in (6.35 mm) to better than 1.0 in (25.4 mm) per hour, depending on the size and layer thickness of the part. Therefore, you can build a 4-inch tall part in 4 to 16 hours.

19.7 Solid Ground Curing (SGC)

The Solider SGC system developed by Cubital Ltd. (see Figs. 19.12 and 19.13) does not require support structures because a wax material surrounds and supports the part as the machine builds it. The Solider 5600 is large and complex, but can simultaneously build as many parts as you can position in a $20 \times 14 \times 20$ in ($508 \times 356 \times 508$ mm) volume. The Solider system irradiates and solidifies a whole layer in a few seconds, regardless of size, complexity, and number of parts.

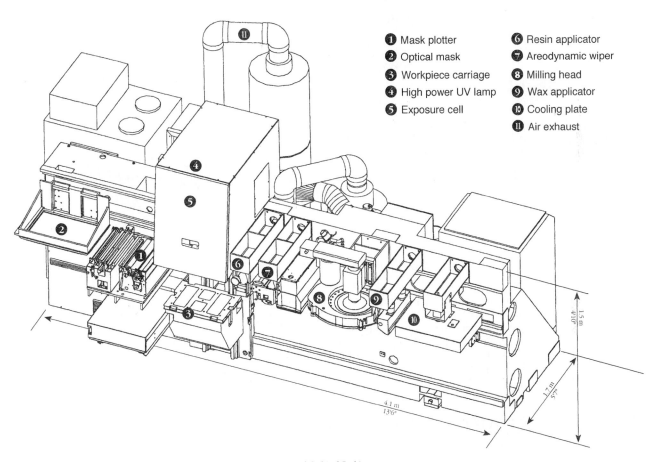

❶ Mask plotter   ❻ Resin applicator
❷ Optical mask   ❼ Areodynamic wiper
❸ Workpiece carriage   ❽ Milling head
❹ High power UV lamp   ❾ Wax applicator
❺ Exposure cell   ❿ Cooling plate
                   ⓫ Air exhaust

FIGURE 19.12 The Solid Ground Curing SGC system. *(Courtesy of Cubital Ltd.)*

The SGC system charges a glass mask plate as it passes over an ion gun and shoots ions on the glass at a resolution of 300 dots per inch (118 dots per cm). This forms a pattern that is a negative image of the cross section. The system applies black electrostatic toner that adheres to the ion-charged portions of the plate. The transparent areas are precise representations of the part(s') cross sections. The system positions the plate closely over the top of a thin layer of liquid polymer. An intense flood of ultraviolet radiation then shines through the plate, exposing the entire layer.

After being exposed to the ultraviolet radiation for a few seconds, the polymer solidifies and the system moves the partially finished part away from the exposing chamber. The solidified layer then undergoes several processes before the system produces a new layer. While these processes are under way, the system wipes the toner from the glass plate and processes the next cross section.

The system removes, by suction, the unhardened liquid surrounding the hardened layer. The system then spreads a thin layer of wax over the entire layer, filling the areas that previously held liquid poly-

After the final layer has been milled
a solid block of wax remains
encasing the finished models.
The models are then retrieved
by melting or rinsing away the wax.

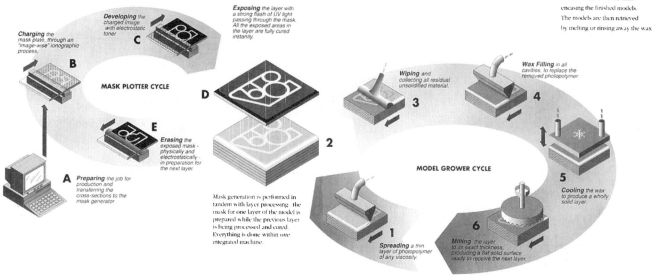

FIGURE 19.13 The SGC process. *(Courtesy of Cubital America Inc.)*

mer. The wax, which goes through a cooling process, surrounds and supports the part. Finally, the partially finished part moves to a milling station. The layer is then milled, producing a flat surface ready for the next layer. This sequence repeats, automatically, until the part is complete. The surrounding wax must be melted away using hot water, hot-air, heat lamps, conventional dish washer, or Cubital's special dewaxing unit. Figure 19.14 (see color insert) shows a prototype product from the SGC system.

19.8   Laminated Object Manufacturing (LOM)

The LOM systems from Helisys, Inc. (see Fig. 19.15) are similar in concept to other RP systems that build parts using thin layers. However, the LOM machine builds parts using sheet material. The machine automatically positions a thin sheet of paper material from a roll onto an elevator platform. It then uses a CO_2 laser to cut the sheet, using a computer-controlled x-y plotter system and mirrors to direct the laser beam. The cuts are representations of the cross sections obtained from the STL file (see Fig. 19.16).

The machine bonds fresh sheet material to the previous sheet using a heated roller that presses the two sheets together. The heat from the roller causes the polyethylene-coated paper to fuse. The laser then cuts additional sheets and the process repeats until the part is complete. When the operator of the LOM machine removes the part, unwanted pieces must be separated and removed from the part. This material supports the part during the building process; no additional support is necessary. LOM parts do not require postcuring, although they should be sealed with a spray coating such as polyurethane.

LOM parts have the look and feel of wood (see color insert, Fig. 19.17). For large bulky parts, this process may be faster than other layering processes because the laser outlines only the periphery of the part instead of making contact with the entire surface of the part. The machine produces thick walls as

FIGURE 19.15 The Laminated Object Manufacturing LOM system. *(Courtesy of Helisys, Inc.)*

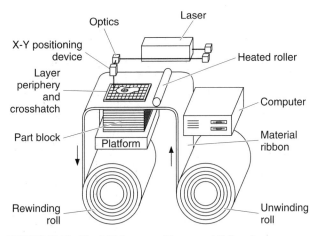

FIGURE 19.16 The LOM process. *(Courtesy of Helisys, Inc.)*

fast as thin ones. What's more, cutting the material, instead of solidifying it, preserves the original properties of the material.

19.9   Fused Deposition Modeling (FDM)

The 3D Modeler and FDM systems from Stratasys, Inc. (see Fig. 19.18) use a spool of 0.050-in (1.27-mm) diameter modeling filament resembling wire. The system feeds the filament through a heated extrusion head and nozzle (see Fig. 19.19). Just before deposition, the head heats the thermoplastic filament to a temperature slightly above its solidification state. The material solidifies as it is deposited.

The 3D Modeler's FDM head operates at up to 15 in (38.1 cm) per second. Successive laminations adhere to one another to form models up to $12 \times 12 \times 12$ in ($30.5 \times 30.5 \times 30.5$ cm) in size. The system does not waste material during or after producing the model, so the process requires little cleanup.

The system uses thermoplastic materials (see color insert, Fig. 19.20), including a machinable wax, an investment casting wax, polyolefin, polyamide, and ABS. The investment wax material is appropriate for lost wax investment castings, leaving little residue in the cavity. It is possible to achieve a glassy finish on the surface of the wax part by applying a special solvent.

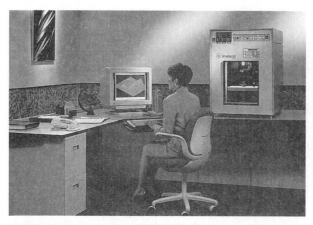

FIGURE 19.18 The Fused Deposition Modeling FDM system. *(Courtesy of Stratasys, Inc.)*

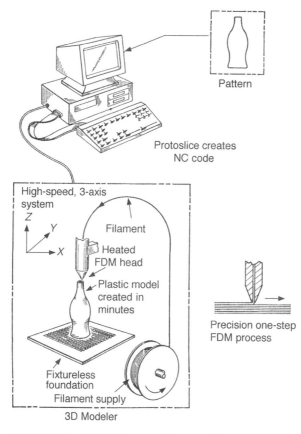

FIGURE 19.19 The FDM process. *(Courtesy of Stratasys, Inc.)*

19.10 Conclusions

Organizations around the world are benefiting from RP technology. If you either are or will be involved with SM, you stand to benefit as well. Over time, RP developers will enhance their systems, making them faster and more accurate. Researchers will produce materials that offer improved mechanical properties, making it possible to use RP parts for rigorous fit-and-function testing. As these advances take place and as prices drop, expect RP technology to penetrate new markets.

19.11   Additional Resources

19.11.1   Articles and Technical Papers

Note: The following articles and technical papers are authored by Terry T. Wohlers.

"Cashing in on Rapid Prototyping," *Computer-Aided Engineering,* vol. 12, no. 9, September 1993.

"Make It Real: Soft vs. Hard Modeling," *CADENCE,* vol. 8, no. 5, May 1993.

"STL Is the Key to Rapid Prototyping," *CADENCE,* vol. 7, no. 11, November 1992.

"Chrysler Compares Rapid Prototyping Systems," *Computer-Aided Engineering,* vol. 11, no. 10, October 1992.

"The World of Rapid Prototyping," *Fourth International Conference on Desktop Manufacturing,* September 1992, San Jose, California.

"Rapid Prototyping Systems: Buy Now, Next Year or Never?" *Third International Conference on Rapid Prototyping,* June 1992, Dayton, Ohio.

"Rapid Prototyping Systems," *First European Rapid Prototyping Convention,* June 1992, Paris, France.

"CAD Meets Rapid Prototyping," *Computer-Aided Engineering,* vol. 11, no. 4, April 1992.

"Rapid Prototyping: The Natural Extension of Solid Modeling," *CADENCE,* vol. 7, no. 2, February 1992.

"Advances in Rapid Prototyping," *Computer Graphics World,* vol. 14, no. 12, December 1991.

"Guidelines for Rapid Prototyping Success," *Rapid Prototyping Report,* vol. 1, no. 6, November 1991.

"The Real Cost of Rapid Prototyping," *Manufacturing Engineering,* vol. 107, no. 5, November 1991.

"Running a Rapid Prototyping Facility: The Economic and Organizational Issues," *Second International Conference on Rapid Prototyping,* June 1991, Dayton, Ohio.

"Make Fiction Fact Fast, Roundup of Rapid Prototyping Systems Ranging from StereoLithography to 3D Printing," *Manufacturing Engineering,* vol. 106, no. 3, March 1991.

"3D Prototyping Systems Streamline," Improve Design, *Computer Graphics Times,* March 1991.

"Plastic Models in Minutes," *CADENCE,* vol. 5, no. 7, July 1990.

"Practical Prototypes," *Computer Graphics World,* vol. 13, no. 3, March 1990.

"Creating Parts by Layers: 3D Presentation Output with SLA, SLS, LOM and BPM," *CADENCE,* vol. 4, no. 4, April 1989.

"3D Hard Copy: Sintering, StereoLithography and Other Scintillating Subjects," *CADENCE,* vol. 4, no. 3, March 1989.

"3D Printing: From CAD Model to Prototype," *Computer Graphics World,* vol. 11, no. 5, May 1988.

19.11.2   Newsletters

Rapid Prototyping Report, newsletter by CAD/CAM Publishing, San Diego, Calif., (619) 488-0522.

19.11.3   Books

Paul F. Jacobs, *Rapid Prototyping and Manufacturing: Fundamentals of StereoLithography,* 1st ed. Society of Manufacturing Engineers, Dearborn, Mich., 1992; (313) 271-1500.

Rapid Automated Prototyping: An Introduction, Industrial Press, Inc., New York, N.Y., (210) 490-8081.

Marshall Burns, *Automated Fabrication: Improving Productivity in Manufacturing,* PTR Prentice-Hall, Englewood Cliffs, N.Y., 1993.

19.11.4   Associations

Rapid Prototyping Association (RPA) of the Society of Manufacturing Engineers (SME), a nonprofit organization aimed at offering educational programs, and encouraging the use of rapid prototyping and related processes. RPA/SME, One SME Drive, P.O. Box 930, Dearborn, MI 48121-0930, (313) 271-1500.

19.11.5   Conferences

1. *Rapid Prototyping & Manufacturing*
   Sponsor: Rapid Prototyping Association (RPA) of SME, (313) 271-1500.

2. *International Conference on Rapid Prototyping*
   Sponsor: University of Dayton, (513) 229-3042

3. *Autofact*
   Sponsor: CASA/SME, (313) 271-1500.

4. *Solid Freeform Fabrication Symposium*
   The University of Texas at Austin, (512) 471-1131.

19.12   RP System Manufacturers Outside the United States

1. Teijin Seiki, Office of Corporate Technology, Kanagawa Science Park, 4DF, 2-1 3-chome, Sakado, Takatsu-ku, Kawasaki-city 213, Japan, 011-03-3348-2185, fax 011-03-3348-1050.

2. EOS GmbH, Electro Optical Systems, D-82152 Planegg/Munchen, Pasinger Str. 2 Germany, 49 (89) 89 91 31-0, fax 49 (89) 8 59 84 02.

3. D-MEC Ltd., JSR Building, 2-11-24, Tsukiji, Chuo-Ku, Tokyo, Japan, (81) (3) 5565-6661, fax (81) (3) 5565-6631.

4. CMET, Kamata Tsukimura Bldg., 15-8 Kamata, 5-Chome, Tokyo 144, Japan, (81) (03) 3739-6605, fax (81) (03) 3739-6680.

5. Fockele und Schwarze, Alter Kirchweg 34, W-4799 Borchen-Alfen, Germany, Phone/Fax (05251) 391925.

STL Interface

SMA.19.1   Surface Gaps

For SLA customers, 3D Systems offers a fix to the problem of STL surface gaps by providing software that detects small holes and cracks in STL models and corrects them. The software is particularly useful to those using surface-modeling systems. The surface gap problem can occur when the SM system tessellates (triangulates) the surfaces of the model. The planar polygons in the mesh do not always accurately meet.

SMA.19.2   Facet Adjustment

Many STL translators make it possible to adjust the size of the facets. Reducing their size produces a smoother and more accurate surface, but at the expense of a larger file size. Large files consume storage space and require more time to process. The CAD model can be split into separate files to alter the facet density in specific areas.

Don LaCourse, President
The Solid Modeling ExChange, Algood, Tenn.

Note: The following SLA advice covers a wide range of topics, including SM and SLA production. If you are not directly involved in SLA production, some advice may not apply. However, additional understanding of the entire SLA process can be beneficial.

SLA Part Modeling

SMA.19.3   Additional Modeling Effort

In some cases, preparing a surface or solid model for SLA may require additional modeling effort. If so, create a duplicate CAD model that includes all SLA-specific modifications. Always keep a copy of your original part model.

(Continued)

SLA Part Modeling
(Continued)

SMA.19.4   Part Orientation

Prior to SLA production, your part model and support structure (if you modeled it manually) should be oriented with reference to the SLA vat. It is a good idea to model the SLA vat as a cube and position your part within this volume. This will simplify the correct positioning of single or multiple parts during production. Part orientation can be handled by the SLA operator. However, foreknowledge of the part's relationship to the SLA vat may reveal modeling concerns and reduce wasted time and effort.

SMA.19.5   Multiple Parts

If your part is small compared to the SLA vat, consider producing enough parts to fill the platform. This may reduce the production cost per part and give you additional parts to fill your needs.

SMA.19.6   Additional Features

Your SLA CAD model may require additional features that are not normally required. The inside of a milk bottle, for example, would have to be modeled where other CAD applications such as NC or assembly modeling would require modeling only the exterior surfaces. Other features may include special consideration for the SLA process such as thicker walls or added material to enhance the final parts integrity. These considerations are specific to the properties of the chosen SLA material.

SMA.19.7   Part Size

Your part may not fit within the SLA vat. Dividing your part into two or more models and producing them separately may be required. Consideration should be given as to how the parts will be reassembled after production. This may require the modeling of additional features such as flanges or tongue and grooves.

Don LaCourse, President
The Solid Modeling ExChange, Algood, Tenn.

SMA.19.8   Model Closure

STL files can be produced from both surface and solid models. In either case, ensure a geometrically closed model. This means that if you were to fill the volume of the model with water, it should not contain holes that would allow it to leak. It is not common practice in surface modeling to create fully closed models, so additional modeling time may be required. A governing rule of an SM database is that the model maintains geometric closure. This is why most CAD operators who create STL files regularly prefer SM.

Also, closed models produce closed 2D contours. The contours are the horizontal cross sections that drive the layering mechanism of the RP machine. If a 3D model contains a hole or large gap in its surface, one or more contours will reflect this gap. These gaps cause the SLA process to halt because critical geometric information is missing.

Note: The creation of SLA support structures can be a manual or automatic process and can be carried out by the SM part designer or the SLA operator.

SLA Supports

SMA.19.9   Internal Supports

Some parts may include internal chambers that occur naturally during production. These may include any variety of formed or blow-molded tubes or bottles. These parts may need to be supported internally. If the SLA part must be produced in one piece, any added internal support structures may not be removable. Design considerations should be made to allow the normal function of these parts if a working model is to be produced.

SMA.19.10   Self-Supporting Features

If you are modeling support structures manually, review your part model to determine which features can be self-supporting. You may discover that very little or no support structure will be needed

(Continued)

SLA Supports
(*Continued*)

in certain orientations. For example, a self-standing cube or pyramid would require no support. If you were to build a tree, the trunk would require no support, while the upper branches and tributaries may collapse or float away without support, depending on their location.

SMA.19.11 Avoid Delays and Rework

Again, if you are modeling support structures manually, always review your part model carefully to ensure that all necessary features will be supported. As experience is gained in designing support structures, you will discover more areas where support can be eliminated. At the expense of production and processing time however, more support is far better than not enough.

SMA.19.12 Review Support Structure Designs

Ask your service bureau to return any support structure models that they design for you if you have the capability to display it or a hardcopy plot if you do not. Study the support structure design so you can learn and become more self-sufficient in the future.

SMA.19.13 Support Generation

Many features can gain enough support from surrounding structures. Learn these relationships well so that the amount of support required will be minimized. Remember that support structures can scar the surface of your part when removed.

SMA.19.14 Separate STL Files

If you are modeling support structures manually, always provide them in a separate STL file. SLA processing parameters are set differently for support structure files. Also, remember to orient your support structure model in the proper position in relation to your part model. If two models are to be merged, they should position themselves as if they were one model.

Don LaCourse, President
The Solid Modeling ExChange, Algood, Tenn.

SMA.19.15 Support Structure Software

The popularity of SLA has motivated third-party software developers to market support structure software. For example, Solid Concepts (Los Angeles, California)[8] has developed a widely used product called Bridgeworks™ that examines an STL file and automatically creates a support-structure file as needed. Bridgework operators claim that the software creates supports faster and better than alternative methods. Support structure software called MAGICS is also available from Materialise (Belgium) and distributed by Laserform[10] (Auburn Hills, Michigan) in the United States.

Note: The following can assist in understanding the SLA build process and highlight areas of concern that can directly influence modeling and SLA part production.

SLA Production

SMA.19.16 Surface Finish

Surface finish can be directly related to part geometry and layer thickness. When the part geometry involves an angled vertical "ramp," a stair-step effect occurs. The height of each step will be determined by the specified layer thickness, and the width will be determined by the local slope. The outside corners of the step will represent the extreme exterior of the part. This condition will not occur on true horizontal or vertical surfaces.

If surface finish is critical in these areas, a thinner layer thickness will produce smaller steps, but may sacrifice processing and build time depending on the resin used. Consider allowing manual rework of these areas with filler or sanding away the steps during the finishing process.

(Continued)

SLA Production
(Continued)

FYI

SMA.19.17 Layer Thickness

Layer thickness influences production. Thin layers (e.g., 0.003 to 0.006 inch) result in a smoother surface, but since more cross sections will be created, processing time increases even though the actual time required for the laser to print and cure each thinner layer will be reduced. Thicker layers (e.g., 0.007 to 0.012 inch) have a corresponding opposite effect. The optimization of these factors can only occur through trial and error of producing a family of similar parts.

SMA.19.18 Resin Viscosity

Resin viscosity can influence processing time. Since the process involves the recoating of hundreds of individual layers, the speed at which these layers will be coated is critical. Thicker, more viscous resins require more time. (Imagine trying to quickly spread a thin coat of honey versus a thin coat of water.)

SMA.19.19 Photo Sensitivity

Some resins are more sensitive to laser radiation. Resins that are less sensitive require more exposure to polymerize (solidify). The amount of exposure required for the onset of polymerization is referred to as the resin's *critical exposure* (*Ec*). Resins having an *Ec* of 10 millijoules/cm^2 require twice as much exposure time or energy as resins with an *Ec* of 5 mJ/cm^2. Therefore, consider the resin's *Ec* when estimating production time.

SMA.19.20 The SLA Unit

There are different SLA units, some of which are faster than others. The speed of the attached control computer and laser output are major factors. Remember that the lasers have a fixed life expectancy. As the laser reaches the end of its life cycle, output and efficiency decrease and it will take longer to print and cure each layer.

SMA.19.21 Production Time

There are many factors, such as layer thickness and resin viscosity, that can directly influence the amount of production time a particular part requires. Seemingly minor issues can have a great effect on processing and actual part production.

SMA.19.22 Unnecessary Geometric Features

As an SM operator or manager, try to learn as much about the SLA production process as possible. As in conventional manufacturing methods, sometimes a slight part design modification can dramatically reduce SLA production times. Look for and remove features unnecessary for the intended purpose of the SLA part. For example, a part produced for its external visual appearance may not require hidden or internal features.

Don LaCourse, President
The Solid Modeling ExChange, Algood, Tenn.

SLA Recommendations

SMA.19.23 Look for Stress

Be aware that as the liquid polymer of the part cures, it undergoes some shrinkage and stress occurs. Parts of large cross-sectional areas are at greater risk. This condition can cause layers to peel away or the entire part to pull from its support. Support structure design and processing parameters can alleviate much of this condition. With the latest epoxy resins, these stresses are greatly reduced and large, flat sections can now be built with much greater accuracy.

SMA.19.24 Let the Polymer Drain

When the SLA part is complete, the elevator platform will be raised above the vat of liquid polymer. This allows excess liquid to drain from the part back into the vat. If your part features large cav-

(Continued)

**SLA
Recommendations**
(*Continued*)

ities, you may have to model a hole in the part to allow the polymer to drain properly. Such openings can be corrected during the finishing process.

*Don LaCourse, President
The Solid Modeling ExChange, Algood, Tenn.*

SMA.19.25   Polymer Materials

There are now a variety of SLA polymer materials from which to choose, each with varying degrees of toughness and strength. Consult your 3D Systems representative to determine the type of materials available. Request a specific material when arranging for production to be performed by a service bureau.

SLS

SMA.19.26   Thermal Stress

Users of the Sinterstation Selective Laser Sintering (SLS) system claim that certain geometries may require supports to anchor cantilevers. The anchors minimize the possibility of curl, a distortion that can occur as a result of thermal stresses imposed by the heating of the material by the laser.

LOM

SMA.19.27   Drafts and Radii

If the Laminated Object Manufacturing (LOM) part is to be used as the actual pattern for castings, then the proper draft must be added to the solid model. To save time in the modeling process, leave off the rounds and fillets, as they can be added to the LOM by the pattern maker (only small—1.5-, 3-mm, etc.—rounds, not major features that have large radii). If the LOM part is to be used only as a packaging model, leave the external feature out. This will speed up both the modeling process and LOM manufacture time, decreasing the cost of the LOM model.

*Donald N. Wentworth, Project Engineer
Eaton Corp., Super Charger Div., Marshall, Mich.*

Note: Whenever there's a challenge, there's an opportunity. So we (designers, researchers, and system manufacturers) need to work together to translate these challenges into new areas of business.

**Needed
Improvements**

SMA.19.28   The Right Tool for the Job

Don't use a screwdriver when a chisel works better. Determining how and when to use RP technology is not always easy. Don't consider it a solution for every job. Continue to apply traditional model-making techniques. At the same time, take advantage of RP. You'll benefit the most when the part geometry is very complex. Also, if you already have a solid model of it, you're halfway there.

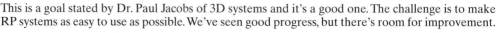

SMA.19.29   A Push-Button System

This is a goal stated by Dr. Paul Jacobs of 3D systems and it's a good one. The challenge is to make RP systems as easy to use as possible. We've seen good progress, but there's room for improvement.

(*Continued*)

Needed Improvements
(*Continued*)

SMA.19.30   Build Directly

Many companies have expressed a strong interest in building metal parts and tooling using RP processes, and DTM Corporation is making some headway in this area. Meanwhile, it's now possible to produce metal parts using the RP as a pattern for plaster, sand and investment castings.

SMA.19.31   Accept Smooth Surface Data

STL works because nearly all 3D CAD systems can tesselate models and produce a polygonal mesh. The STL format, however, is inefficient. Files grow large, requiring large amounts of disk space and transmission time. Also, the triangle facets often appear on the surface of the RP part. In addition to STL, we need a standard way of moving smooth surface data, such as NURBS, to RP systems. STEP (see Chap. 22) may be a vehicle to accomplish this.

SMA.19.32   Become Fiscally Sound

We need to look at ways of pooling our resources. The purpose would be to make the whole RP industry stronger than the sum of its parts.

SMA.19.33   Improve Price/Performance Ratio

Many will agree that it has improved dramatically. Also, many agree that present RP systems can pay for themselves after a few major projects. However, this doesn't mean that small companies have access to them and can afford their benefits. For every small company that understands the benefits of RP, there's another dozen that don't. Price/performance must continue to improve.

SMA.19.34   Education

Educate the thousands of small companies across America. Getting accurate information to these companies is very important. They want and need this information as much as large corporations.

SMA.19.35   Dispel the RP Myths

1. *RP parts crack easily.*   No longer true.

2. *RP parts warp easily, making them inaccurate.*   Not as true as it once was.

3. *The resins are toxic.*   They're becoming much safer.

4. *RP systems are difficult to use.*   They're becoming easier to operate.

We need to constantly provide updates on our progress in the industry. When you have a success to share, please do. This excitement is contagious.

SMA.19.36   Expand the Use of SM

This is the single biggest challenge and barrier to rapid growth of RP. If you must first convert your drawings to a solid model in order to take advantage of RP—it may not pay. It suddenly becomes a bottleneck. The good news is that SM is growing like never before. Here are two reasons why:

1. Hardware prices continue to drop, making SM more practical and affordable.

2. With SM, it's possible to subtract the model from a block, creating a mold cavity, for example. You can then produce a mold directly using RP.

References

1. Laminated Object Manufacturing (LOM), Helisys Inc., 2750 Oregon Court Bldg. M-10, Torrance, CA 90503, (310) 782-1949, fax (310) 782-8280.

2. StereoLithography Apparatus (SLA), 3D Systems, Inc., 26081 Avenue Hall, Valencia, CA 91355, (805) 295-5600, fax (805) 295-0249.

3. Fused Deposition Modeling (FDM), Stratasys, Inc., 14950 Martin Drive, Eden Prairie, MN 55344-2019, (612) 937-3000, fax (612) 937-0070.

4. Solid Ground Curing (SGC), Cubital Ltd., 1307F Allen Road, Troy, MI 48083, (313) 585-7880, fax (313) 585-7884.

5. Selective Laser Sintering (SLS), DTM Corporation, 1611 Headway Circle, Building 2, Austin, TX 78754, (512) 339-2922, fax (512) 339-0634.

6. Brock Rooney & Associates, 268 George Street, Birmingham, MI 48009, (313) 645-0236.

7. C-TAD Systems Inc., Atrium Office Center, 900 Victors Way, Ann Arbor, MI 48108, (313) 665-3287, fax (313) 665-9736.

8. Solid Concepts, 3650 Midvale Avenue, #205, Los Angeles, CA 90034, (213) 202-7285, fax (213) 202-7285.

9. MasterGraphics, Waukesha, Wis., (414) 785-9495.

10. Laserform, Inc., 1124 Centre Road, Auburn Hill, MI 48326, (810) 373-4400, fax (810) 373-4403.

Chapter 20
Preparing for Data Exchange

Harlan Stokes
VP Sales and Marketing
IGES Data Analysis, Inc.

As organizations progress down the path of CAD/CAM implementation, they often seek tighter integration by electronically exchanging CAD/CAM data, and are faced with a new set of challenges. There are technical concerns that may not become visible until electronic data exchange is attempted. Furthermore, most organizations have design procedures and management practices that are appropriate only for paper-based transactions. In this chapter, we will discuss issues that will affect the ability of an organization to reap the benefits of CAD/CAM data exchange. These issues include data exchange options, trends, preparation, measuring success, needed improvements, as well as specific tips and suggestions.

20.1 Data Exchange Options

Since CAD/CAM systems generally have their own proprietary file formats, the only way to exchange CAD/CAM data in the early days was between identical systems. Yet, as the use of CAD/CAM grew, so did the requirements for exchanging CAD/CAM data between dissimilar systems. Two methods of data exchange emerged as the most common. These are *direct translation* and *neutral file exchange*. A third, *data sharing,* will become prevalent in the future. Figure 20.1 illustrates these three options. A discussion of each follows.

20.1.1 Direct Database Translation

Direct database translation involves the use of software that directly reads the proprietary data files of the sending CAD/CAM system and converts them to the proprietary file format of the receiving system. While direct translators often yield excellent exchange results, they have certain disadvantages: they need to be replaced for each new version of either CAD/CAM system, and the required number of direct translators grows exponentially with the number of CAD/CAM systems (see Fig. 20.2). Direct database translators have been written by CAD/CAM system vendors for use with their own products and also by third-party software vendors.

20.1.2 Neutral File Exchange

Neutral file exchange involves using one translator, called a *preprocessor,* to convert the sending CAD/CAM system's proprietary file format into a common neutral file format for transport to the receiving system. Once received, the neutral file is translated by another translator, called a postprocessor, where it is converted into the proprietary format of the receiving system.

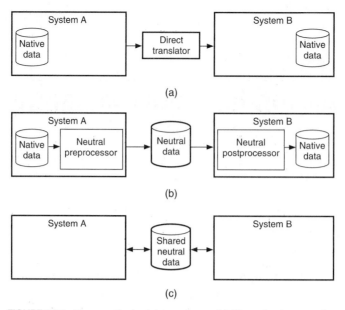

FIGURE 20.1 Three methods of data exchange. (*a*) Direct database translation; (*b*) neutral file exchange; (*c*) data sharing. (*Courtesy of IGES Data Analysis, Inc.*)

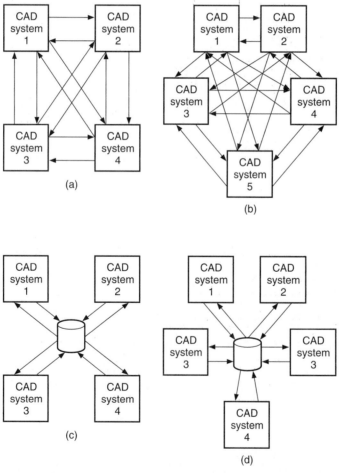

FIGURE 20.2 The exponential versus linear growth of direct and neutral CAD/CAM translators. (*a*) 4 CAD/CAM systems require 12 direct translators; (*b*) 5 CAD/CAM systems require 20 direct translators; (*c*) the same 4 CAD/CAM systems require only 8 neutral translators; (*d*) the same 5 CAD/CAM systems require only 10 neutral translators. (*Courtesy of IGES Data Analysis, Inc.*)

Among the advantages of the neutral format approach is that the CAD/CAM vendor needs to write and maintain only two translators, the pre- and the postprocessor, for each neutral file format (see Fig. 20.2). Among the disadvantages of neutral file exchange is the fact that some CAD/CAM systems have entities or constructs that cannot be readily translated into these neutral formats without some loss of information. Neutral format translators are most often written by CAD/CAM vendors who best know their own proprietary file formats.

20.1.3 Data Sharing

A new standard of product data exchange is emerging in the Standard for the Exchange of Product Data (STEP) from the International Organization of Standards (ISO 10303). The vision for STEP is that it will lead to data sharing. This is where the neutral database format serves as the native database, and applications would be written to access the database through application interfaces. The advantages include the elimination of translations between native formats and consistent representations for data. The disadvantages include a possible increase in computer system infrastructure and organizational impacts caused by the shared data paradigm. (See Chap. 22 for more on SM and STEP.)

20.2 Data Exchange Surveys, Studies, and Trends

Since the late 1980s, there have been several surveys and studies that indicate trends for CAD/CAM data exchange in government and industry.

20.2.1 Automotive Industry Action Group (AIAG)

One survey comes from the Automotive Industry Action Group (AIAG) located in the Detroit area. The CAD/CAM Data Exchange Working Group of AIAG conducted a product data exchange survey in late 1989.[1] There were 96 respondents to the section dealing with data exchange formats. The respondents were asked which data formats were "required to do business," and which were required for "in-house capability."

Of the industry neutral formats identified, IGES was required to do business by 61 percent of the respondents, and used for in-house capability by 71 percent. DXF was next, having been required to do business by 15 percent of respondents and used for in-house capabilities by 24 percent. VDA (data exchange formats from Verband der Automobilindustrie, the German automotive manufacturing association) and the CGM (Computer Graphics Metafile) formats together had less than 3 percent usage. The number of respondents using customer neutral and native formats for systems from Chrysler, Ford, and GM were all less than 25 percent.

20.2.2 North American Manufacturing Technology Survey

Another assessment of the use of data exchange technologies can be found in the annual surveys of North American Manufacturing Technology conducted by Deloitte & Touche.[2,3] In 1989 and 1991, 759 and 872 (respectively) manufacturing executives were surveyed to determine those characteristics that are critical for manufacturing excellence. One such characteristic they identified is the use of IGES. The results are compiled and represent a composite of the perceived status of manufacturing in North America for that year.

The 1989 report indicated that 16 percent of the respondents had moderate experience with IGES, and another 0.5 percent considered their use of IGES as being state of the art. In the 1991 report, the number of IGES users with moderate experience had grown to 17 percent, and state-of-the-art users grew to 3 percent. To give these figures more perspective, the same reports placed overall CAD usage at these manufacturing firms at 68 percent in 1989 and 72 percent in 1991. This indicates that the proportion of all CAD users surveyed who also used IGES grew from 24 to 28 percent between 1989 and 1991.

20.2.3 Report to the President of the United States

The importance of developing effective interoperability among CAD systems is made clear in the March 1991 report to the President of the United States from the National Critical Technologies Panel. This report identifies IGES and PDES/STEP as "essential if the benefits of flexible computer integrated manufacturing (CIM) are to be realized fully."[4] This report also says that "Future systems, or variants of existing systems, will become on-line databases to allow more than simple exchange of information." The report is used to focus attention on technologies that should be developed and deployed to maintain U.S. competitiveness.

20.2.4 Continuous Acquisition and Life-Cycle Support (CALS)

One of the most visible examples of a large-scale implementation of CAD/CAM data exchange is the Continuous Acquisition and Life-Cycle Support (CALS) initiative. CALS is a U.S. Department of Defense and industry strategy to transition from paper-intensive processes to automated and integrated methods related to the design, manufacturing, and support of weapon systems.

CALS focuses on the generation, access, management, maintenance, distribution, and use of technical data such as engineering drawings, technical manuals, product definition, and logistic support analysis record data. CALS will facilitate data integration, exchange, and access in government and industry, with emphasis placed on creating data once and using it many times. Figure 20.3 illustrates the evolutionary path of CALS.

In 1988, the Deputy Secretary of Defense required that CALS be an active part of weapon system contracting and DoD planning. There is a long list of estimated benefits of CALS, including 50 to 60 percent time savings in engineering design activities, a reduction of the time required for engineering changes by 30 to 50 percent, and a reduction of cycle time for technical documentation by 30 to 50 percent.

The umbrella standard for CALS is MIL-STD-1840A,[5] which identifies other standards which describe the requirements for the exchange of technical information. One of these standards is MIL-D-28000A,[5] which describes several subsets of IGES and which subset should be used, depending on the type of data contained in the CAD/CAM file.

There are several characteristics of CALS that make it interesting to CAD/CAM users. From a technical perspective, CALS identifies IGES as the accepted data exchange format for CAD/CAM graphics, and identifies STEP as the standard of choice for the future. There are data exchange testing methodologies and organizations to help users. Furthermore, there are specifications for expected media types, media packaging requirements, telecommunications, and database access methods.

Another characteristic of CALS is the attention it pays to the management process changes and infrastructure modernization issues that must occur before the technologies can be successfully applied (see SMA.20.15). This emphasis on management process highlights the fact that most of these issues apply to both CALS implementations for government work and so-called commercial CALS implementations in industry.

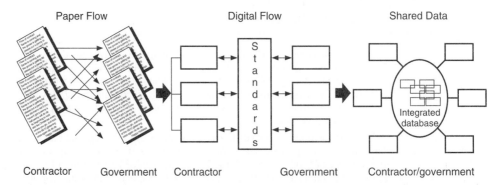

FIGURE 20.3 The evolutionary path of CALS. *(Reprinted from the CALS "blue book" brochure with permission from the CALS Office in the Office of the Secretary of Defense, United States Department of Defense.)*

20.3 Data Preparation

As you proceed with implementing data exchange, there are several technical issues that will affect your success. This section will identify important characteristics for CAD/CAM systems and translators, will discuss common data delivery mechanisms, and the importance of designing for data integrity.

20.3.1 Characteristics of SM and Translators

Every CAD/CAM system uses its own mix of internal constructs (construction techniques) and entity types, which is what distinguishes its functionality from other systems. However, since there are often several ways for internal entities to be converted to neutral formats, you can not assume that the functionality of translators can be easily predicted. The way any given translator will read and write exchanged data depends on these issues:

1. How well the internal CAD/CAM constructs match with those available in a standard format
2. How internal entities are translated into standard entities (referred to as "entity mapping")
3. The options that are provided to the operator during translation

It is therefore not enough simply to ask if the system supports a standard.[6] Also refer to The SM Adviser at the end of this chapter for advice on evaluating translator capability.

20.3.2 Design for Data Integrity (DFDI)

The effective downstream use of CAD/CAM data depends largely on the quality or integrity of CAD geometry. Data integrity, then, can be defined as the extent to which CAD/CAM data meets the needs of downstream users. Designers who generate CAD/CAM models with data exchange in mind are said to be following the tenets of a data-oriented discipline called Design for Data Integrity (DFDI). These designers know that it is their own CAD/CAM models and drawings, not paper prints, that will be used by others for many purposes downstream. DFDI means creating good data, not pretty pictures.[7] See The SM Adviser at the end of this chapter for more advice on DFDI.

CAD/CAM Data

Once it is determined that your CAD/CAM data will be translated to other systems, review the data itself. It is important to determine if your CAD/CAM data is what the receiver wants or needs. Many designers and drafters concentrate only on how things look on the CAD display and on paper. It is a deeply rooted habit carried over from traditional board drafting that "drawings" were created as paper representations of what a designer has in mind for a part. These drawings were made for human interpretation. Now that the technological tools of CAD/CAM have entered the design/drafting world, there is a growing concern that CAD/CAM operators do not create designs with data exchange in mind.

Areas of Concern

Traditional board drafting relies on dimensions for most quantitative information about feature sizes and locations. With CAD/CAM, especially SM systems, the geometry is the driver of most functions since it contains all the necessary information. However, while the geometry may seem to be highly accurate, it is only as accurate as the construction technique employed.

Geometry may be created incorrectly or corrupted by hastily moving it around so that it looks right. For example, the common board-drafting practice of changing dimensional values without changing the geometry clearly thwarts the purpose of using CAD/CAM. If extraneous geometry is left floating out in space, either visible or blanked, it can cause problems for the downstream user. If gaps are left between geometries, some NC programming packages will halt (see Chap. 15 for more on entity gaps and NC). Downstream users should not have to guess at the true intention of your design.

CAD/CAM Survey

A survey of 105 tooling manufacturers in southern Michigan seems to be the first to quantify CAD/CAM data problems for interorganizational data exchange.[8] Respondents were asked to estimate the proportion of all their CAM jobs in the past years in which certain problems were present in the CAD files received from customers in IGES or other data exchange formats (see Table 20.1 for the survey results).

TABLE 20.1 Results of Michigan Survey Tabulating Problems with Tooling Jobs

(Reprinted with permission from Fleischer, Mitchell, Thomas Phelps, and Michael Ensing, "CAD/CAM Data Problems and Costs in the Tool and Die Industry," final report on a study conducted for the Michigan Modernization Service by The Industrial Technology Institute and the Detroit Chapter of the National Tooling and Machining Association, March 12, 1991.)

Problem	Average % of jobs with each problem
Lines do not meet at corners	49%
Lines cross at corners	47%
Curves or lines drawn as short segments	44%
Same features drawn more than once	41%
Lines or surfaces coincident	38%
Surfaces that do not meet at lines	37%
Geometry, dimensions, notes on incorrect layer	33%
Some or all of geometry not translated	33%
Planar features drawn out of plane	12%
Geometry of features not drawn to scale	11%

Some examples of these problems were: (1) lines not meeting at corners, (2) the same features being drawn more than once, (3) incorrect layering, and (4) geometry of features not drawn to scale. Because of the problems present in the CAD files, the tool and die shops had to fix the data in about half of their jobs, while in another quarter of the jobs they had to re-create the files altogether. The average added tooling cost was estimated to be between $4000 and $20,000.

Perhaps more significantly, about one-fourth of the calendar time spent producing tooling was wasted re-creating or repairing CAD data. The primary problem sources were in translation, designer errors, and the limitations of the tool and die shops' own CAD or CAM systems.

20.3.3 Data Delivery Mechanisms

In general, the exchange of information can be achieved through the use of any of the delivery mechanisms discussed below. While it is outside the scope of this chapter to provide a rigorous explanation of encoded or network media, several of these media types are listed for your review.

Encoded Media

Encoded media includes data delivery mechanisms where data is written to a physical media and the media is then moved to the destination system. The following are popular examples of encoded media.

Half-Inch Tape.　The oldest and perhaps the best understood media is nine-track half-inch magnetic tape. This is the reel-to-reel computer tape most commonly recognized for its use by mainframes. For example, ASCII IGES files are typically written to ANSI-formatted tapes, unlabeled, with 80 characters per record and 10 records per block (or 800 characters per block). Each line of text in an ASCII file is a single record. Ten lines or records equals one block. It is common to find 1600- and 6250-bpi densities. If you are unsure what the receiving system supports, ask your exchange partner's CAD/CAM data coordinator. It is usually safe to go with 1600 bpi.

Floppy Disks. Floppy disks are most often associated with personal computers. The two most common sizes for floppy disks are 5.25 and 3.5 inch. These are used by the two most popular PC computer types, MS-DOS-based IBM PC compatibles and Apple Macintoshes. Each platform has its own logical method for placing data on the diskette. The amount of data that can fit on the disk is dependent upon the floppy drive and the density of the disk. Typical IBM PC disk configurations include 5.25-inch double and high-density disks holding 360 Kb and 1.2 Mb, and 3.5-inch double and high-density disks holding 720 Kb and 1.44 Mb. Typical Macintosh configurations include 800-Kb double density and 2-Mb high-density disks. Higher-capacity removable disks are becoming available.

Since the capacity of floppy disks is limited and CAD/CAM data files are often quite large, floppies may not be practical. One way to get around these limitations is by applying data compression to the files, or breaking them up to fit on multiple disks. There are many utilities available both commercially and in the public domain to compress or split up files.

Quarter-Inch Cartridge (QIC) Tape. With the advent of UNIX operating system workstations, the quarter-inch cartridge or QIC tape has become common. A QIC tape contains quarter-inch-wide tape packaged in a cartridge of two sizes. The larger 5.25-inch size is most often used by midsized workstation computers and can be identified by the 6XX or 6XXX series number on the cartridge. The smaller 3.5-inch size is most often used by desktop or personal computers and can be identified by the 2XXX series number on the cartridge.

While cartridges may be of common sizes, there are many format densities available for each size. The larger cartridges range in format densities that can contain between 60 Mb and 5 gigabytes of data. The smaller cartridges range from the QIC-40 format (40 megabytes) to the QIC-120 format (120 megabytes).

Network Media

Network media includes data delivery mechanisms where data is transmitted over a stationary media such as a wire, or broadcast through space via radio. The following are popular examples of network media.

POTS (Plain Old Telephone Service). If communication between computers involves dialing through normal telephone lines, this is called a *switched line*. These networks are administered by your local phone company, and sometimes organizations add their own internal phone networks called *private branch exchanges* or PBXs. Because the use of these networks involves constant switching and amplification, there is often considerable electronic noise on these lines.

Computer communication over these types of networks generally requires the use of a telephone modem and communication software. The amount of line noise limits the speed with which data can be passed, and has given rise to a number of error-correction and data-compression schemes. Some modems offer hardware-based error correction and data compression. Software applications can also take advantage of these features, and can offer their own file exchange protocols to further speed data exchange and improve reliability. There are many file exchange protocols, such as Kermit, Xmodem, etc. Unix users may be able to use Unix-to-Unix (UUCP) or Transmission Control Protocol/Internet Protocol (TCP/IP) services, and may use standard TCP/IP transfer protocols like File Transfer Protocol (FTP) or Remote Copy (rcp).

Leased Lines. A leased line is a permanent connection between locations that is provided by the local phone company. An advantage to a leased line is less noise, so data can be moved at much faster transfer rates. A variation of the leased line is the "multidrop" or "multipoint line," which allows more than one computer to use the same line.

Local Area Networks. A local area network (LAN) provides even better performance than switched or leased lines, but is limited to local sites. However, LANs in remote locations can be connected via leased lines. The most common physical topologies for LANs are ethernet and token ring. There are a number of possibilities for communications protocols and software that can run on the physical hardware including TCP/IP, Network File System (NFS) and Novell Netware®. Each LAN requires site-specific configuration.

20.4 Measuring Success

One of the challenges in data exchange is judging how good your results are and how good they must be to be considered useful, adequate, or successful. There are two concepts that may be used as judgmental criteria. These are *functional* and *visual equivalence.*[9]

20.4.1 Functional Equivalence

Transferred CAD/CAM data is considered to be functionally equivalent to the original data if the receiver is able to make sense out of the exchanged CAD/CAM drawing or model and, if required, can modify and reissue it from within the receiving CAD/CAM system. It may not be picture perfect, but it is useful data and does the job.

20.4.2 Visual Equivalence

Transferred data is considered to be visually equivalent if the image created on the receiver's system "looks the same" as it did on the sending system (see Fig. 20.4). It was never the intention for standards like IGES to maintain the visual fidelity of CAD/CAM drawings, and therefore it is usually difficult to maintain perfect visual equivalence. However, IGES is well suited when functional equivalence is the goal.

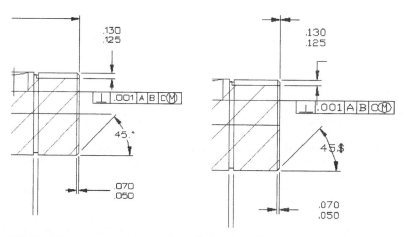

FIGURE 20.4 Loss of visual equivalence. Notice that while text fonts are changed and minor errors occurred with dimensions, the geometry remained unchanged and is considered functionally equivalent.

20.4.3 Criteria Judgments

Functional and visual equivalence are criteria judgments that can be made only by you and your exchange partner. Determine the worst possible level of transfer result that can still be considered functionally equivalent, and your exchanges should maintain information at least at this level. These requirements can be determined by surveying the receivers of your translated data. Similarly, if you are receiving translated data, you can specify your data requirements to your exchange partners based on your intended usage of their data.

20.5 Needed Improvements for Data Exchange

The same SM characteristics that are discussed in this chapter provide the areas where SM technology can stand improvement. While there is a potential for an SM system to have unique features and constructs that cannot be mapped to other systems, all systems should strive to maintain the highest possible amount of entity information in their data exchange mechanisms.

Solid Modeling vendors will arrive at a business case wherein it is most profitable for their SM product to excel at interoperability with other systems through data exchange. They should offer robust translators with options for reducing the loss of entity content or context.

**Protection
and Integrity**

SMA.20.1   Security Plan

Any time there is a conversion from paper to electronic methods, it is common for the risks to data security and integrity to increase. There are many forms that these risks take, so it is important to devise and implement a security plan. Such a plan would address issues like communications security, computer system security, physical security of systems and materials, personnel security, and information security.

SMA.20.2   Access Limitations

As part of your security plan, you may decide to limit exchange-partner access to data that has not been validated, including proprietary information, or to data outside the scope of that exchange partner's project or contract. Ideally, the plan would address system availability, data rights, privacy, legal liability, and limitations on the transfer of technology due to international export bans.

To meet these goals, develop and follow procedures that control and safeguard data to at least the level of the paper-based environment. These procedures should authenticate users and data, verify the validity of transactions, and protect data and systems from unauthorized access, use, or change.[10]

SMA.20.3   Security Measures

There are several simple starting points for achieving the goals of a security plan. Run virus-protection software. Assign passwords and change them periodically. Delete old system user IDs. Limit modem access through "callback" options. Use audit trails[11] and use signed agreements to limit legal exposure.[12]

SMA.20.4   Design for Data Integrity (DFDI)

If your organization produces CAD/CAM data for others, focus on providing the infrastructure within which good design and DFDI will take place. If you use CAD/CAM data produced by others, improve your own internal infrastructure so that you will be able to accept data at a level commensurate with your product data needs. Individual designers can have a major impact on the ability of others downstream to use their data.[13] (See Sec. 20.3.2 for more on DFDI.)

Legal Issues

SMA.20.5   New Questions

Product data exchange will naturally spawn legal questions. Many customary business agreements still use antique phrases such as "you must build according to the blueprint." But what if there is no print in the traditional sense, but a CAD/CAM file instead? Who is responsible? Who has authority? What procedures can be instituted so that the interests of both sender and receiver are protected? How can we avoid the disagreements that can lead to legal actions?

SMA.20.6   Anxieties and Perception

The anxieties surrounding the electronic exchange of CAD/CAM files are due mostly to the perception that they may become unintentionally garbled, erased, or even intentionally changed or accessed by unauthorized users. Although these are valid concerns, there are no guarantees that paper documents are immune to these problems. Legal author Benjamin Wright points out that "Paper documents can rather easily be forged, misassembled, changed, and lost. No signed commercial document is guaranteed to be accepted as authentic by a court."[14] By applying existing technologies, some of the problems with electronic data exchange can be reduced to a level comparable with paper.

SMA.20.7   The Uniform Commercial Code

The law is not intrinsically opposed to the advancement of electronic data exchange. The Uniform Commercial Code, one of the cornerstones of commercial law, clearly states that one of its underlying purposes is "to permit the continued expansion of commercial practices through custom, usage, and agreement of the parties."[15] Yet, where there are barriers to change because of established business customs or an unwillingness to discuss data exchange issues, there is a high potential for legal exposure. A business decision has been made, not a legal one.

(Continued)

SMA.20.8 New Agreements

One way of avoiding legal complications is to reach an agreement with your data exchange partner before exchanging any data. In this context, an agreement is a meeting of minds between people, often with an exchange of promises or value. It can be put in place in a blanket fashion, included as boilerplate additions to other legally binding business forms, or explicitly established in a contract. Written agreements are a great way of communicating the responsibilities and authorities for interactions across organizational boundaries. Figure 20.5 provides a sample CAD/CAM data exchange agreement.

Caution: The agreement shown here is only an example. Proper legal counsel should be obtained prior to adopting any legal document.

SMA.20.9 Record Keeping

Wright[16] also says (see SMA.20.6):

> Electronic transaction users should make their record-keeping and control policies rational and explicit. As explained, the presence of thoughtful, written policies on record creation, retention, and destruction, and on internal control can rebut charges of unlawfulness. Further, the very act of writing can force users to consider the issues deliberately and thus be more likely to address them soundly. Policies are especially persuasive if based on industry standards, provided any exist.[14]

SMA.20.10 Existing Agreements

To give you an idea what you're up against, try acquainting yourself with some of the contracts and agreements that your company already uses for interorganizational matters. Look at the terms and conditions on purchase order forms. Look at sales contracts. Pay special attention to those sections discussing information and documentation. Attempts to address CAD/CAM data exchange issues should start with a recognition of existing agreements and the importance of these agreements to your business.

SMA.20.11 Ten Commandments of Data Exchange

The field of electronic data interchange (EDI) addresses business documents such as purchase orders, invoices, and funds transfers, offering many guidelines and principles that can be applied to CAD/CAM data exchange agreements. A good starting point for the development of data exchange rules is the "ten commandments" for EDI, summarized by Wright.[16] The first nine can be applied quite easily to CAD/CAM data exchange, and the tenth is replaced with a new one addressing CAD/CAM usage conventions. Generally speaking, the ten commandments of product data exchange require that participants:

1. Abide by their chosen product data exchange standard.

2. Communicate with care.

3. Instruct networks not to change files without authority.

4. Properly identify themselves in files.

5. Acknowledge or confirm good receipt when requested to do so.

6. Take remedial action if a received file is not in good order or wrongly delivered.

7. Maintain the security of protected data.

8. Keep an unchanged log of exchanged data.

9. Designate a person to certify the log.

10. Clearly identify product data (CAD/CAM) usage conventions, including the relationship of product data to data in other forms such as paper.

These principles should be addressed in any product data exchange agreement. They can be incorporated into paragraphs covering CAD/CAM usage conventions, receipt and usage acknowledgment, media, data exchange standard revision level, authenticity, security, transfer procedures, responsibilities, verification, hardcopies, costs, records retention, and conflicts between geometric data and dimensional data.[12]

PRODUCT DATA EXCHANGE AGREEMENT

Date: _____

This is a data exchange agreement anticipating future exchange of CAD/CAM data in electronic form ("CAD/CAM drawing(s)") and other information between [my organization] and [other organization], hereinafter called "data exchange partners." The parties each wish to maintain their respective rights without making CAD/CAM drawings or their contents generally accessible or public or common knowledge.

This agreement shall become effective as of the date of its acceptance by the [other organization] and shall continue in effect until terminated by either party upon _____ days prior written notice. The termination of this agreement shall not affect the obligations of either party to the other for any usages of CAD/CAM drawings issued pursuant to this agreement, but such obligations shall continue in effect as though this agreement had not been terminated and were still in effect with respect to said usages.

1. *Usage Conventions.* The sender of the CAD/CAM drawing(s) will provide documentation explaining the characteristics of the CAD/CAM drawing(s) and conventions used by the sender. These characteristics and conventions may include file naming, leveling or color conventions, entity types used, b-spline orders, or other characteristics or conventions, including any known peculiarities in IGES translations.

2. *Usage Acknowledgment.* The party receiving CAD/CAM drawings will acknowledge receipt and usage of each CAD/CAM drawing. Receipt and usage will be acknowledged by written letter, referencing the drawing file names and the part names of the CAD/CAM drawing(s) transmitted. Acknowledgments must be returned to the sender within _____ days of receipt of the CAD/CAM drawing(s).

3. *Format.* Either party may transmit data to the other by utilizing an electronic media agreed upon by both data exchange partners. Unless otherwise specified, all CAD/CAM drawings contemplated by this agreement shall be transmitted and formatted in accordance with the [*Initial Graphics Exchange Specification ("IGES") version 5.0*].

4. *Authenticity.* All CAD/CAM drawings must identify the organization from which they came. Drawings from either data excahnge partner must have text identifying their source in the Start Section of the IGES file. If agreed upon by both parties, text in the title block of the drawing itself may suffice as identification. Unchanged CAD/CAM drawings with either of these identifications shall be deemed to be genuine for all purposes.

If it is necessary for the receiving party to change geometry, dimensions, or any other part of a CAD/CAM drawing to make it useful in their intermediate CAD/CAM processes, the changed CAD/CAM drawing no longer is considered an authentic drawing. If a change is to be made, the receiving party must keep an unchanged copy of the CAD/CAM drawing. If the IGES format was used for the transfer of the original CAD/CAM drawing, the unchanged IGES file may serve as an authentic original. A note on the changed CAD/CAM drawing, on a physical label on the storage media or some other note system must identify the changed CAD/CAM drawing to indicate that it was changed and explain the nature of the changes. [*Other organization*] is responsible for making an end product that matches the original CAD/CAM (and hard copy) drawing.

5. *Identification Codes.* For security reasons, either party shall have the right to routinely change usernames, passwords, or other identification codes immediately with oral notification to the other party, which shall be confirmed by written notice within _____ days of the change. Each party will take appropriate steps to ensure that usernames, passwords, or other identification codes remain secure to the parties covered by this agreement.

6. *Responsibility.* Both parties agree as follows:

   a. Not to disclose CAD/CAM drawings to anyone except their employees who have a "need to know."

   b. To have written agreements with their employees who are allowed access to CAD/CAM drawings sufficient to enable the party to comply with all the terms of this agreement.

   c. That no license under copyright or any patent now or hereafter obtained is granted or implied either by signing this agreement, or by either party's disclosure of CAD/CAM drawings.

   d. Either party may request at any time in writing that CAD/CAM drawings previously transferred be returned or deleted. Compliance must be within _____ days of the request. Confirmation must be provided, in writing upon return or deletion of CAD/CAM drawings, that all have been returned and/or deleted and that no partial or complete copies have been retained in any form whatsoever.

7. *Authorized Access and Use.* Both data exchange partners understand and agree that they are authorized to use the CAD/CAM drawings and other documentation received under this agreement solely for the purpose of performing work as required by business arrangements between the two parties. No other use is authorized. [*Other organization*] is authorized to have access only to files located within the _____ [system] in the _____ [catalog(s)]. Access to other files is not authorized. All authorized access must be made using the user name and password assigned by [my organization]. [My organization] reserves the right to change such user names and passwords and assign them at its discretion. Use of any other password or user name except those assigned to [*other organization*] by [my organization] is not authorized. [*Other organization*] is responsible for all access and use of the CAD/CAM drawings and other documentation and access to the network made using its password and user name. Any unauthorized use or attempted use of the network, or any unauthorized access or attempted access to unauthorized files will be a breach under this agreement. In the event of such a breach, [my organization] will have the right to immediately terminate [*other organization*]'s access privileges and terminate this agreement and any other agreement between [*other organization*] and [my organization] without further obligation or liability on [my organization]'s part. Further, in the event of such a breach, [my organization] shall have the right to recover such damages as [my organization] may suffer as a result of such breach, including without limitation the damages arising from nonperformance of any unperformed work under any terminated agreement.

8. *Verification.* Within _____ days of transmission of CAD/CAM drawings, each party will take steps to verify CAD/CAM drawings if necessary to ensure the other party receives a nongarbled, properly formatted version of such transmission. The party receiving the garbled or improperly formatted transmission shall notify the other party within _____ days if the identity of the party originating such transmission can be determined.

9. *Hard Copies.* Unless otherwise specified, the sender will provide hard copies (usually on paper) of transferred CAD/CAM drawing(s) which may include information not contained in the CAD/CAM data and may aid in verification of successful exchange. Both parties may agree to discontinue sending hard copies if electronically transmitted CAD/CAM drawings are proven to be complete to satisfy the need of the receiver.

10. *Conflicts Between Geometric Data and Dimensional Data.* All geometry must be constructed following the rules of Design for Data Intergrity (DFDI). The actual size or location of geometry should match that displayed as textual dimensions on detailed drawings. If textual dimensions do not match geometric data due to rounding or other reasons, the geometric values must be used for all fabrication. Other directions may be provided in notes on the drawing. If a conflict other than rounding is discovered, the receiver must notify the sender before continuing the use of the CAD/CAM data.

11. *Costs.* The sender of CAD/CAM drawings will pay for the usage of its computer to process CAD/CAM drawings and for magnetic media if required. The receiver will pay for the usage of its computer and telephone or network charges related to the transmission of the CAD/CAM drawings.

12. *Record Retention.* Both data exchange partners will store and maintain their respective CAD/CAM drawings and hard copies until both parties agree they may be returned, deleted, or removed. Authentic copies of the transferred CAD/CAM drawings and hard copies, stored by [my organization] and [*other organization*], shall constitute evidence of the intended contents of the CAD/CAM drawings covered by this agreement, and shall be machine-readable and capable of reproduction into a printed form on paper.

This agreement may be modified in writing only and signed by an authorized representative of each party. It may be used to complement other agreements between the parties.

Agreed to by [*other organization*]:

_____
By (Authorized Signature)

_____
Name (Type or Print)

_____
Title (Type or Print)

_____
Date

Accepted by [my organization]:

_____
By (Authorized Signature)

_____
Name (Type or Print)

_____
Title (Type or Print)

_____
Date

Note: This is a sample document. Do not use this document without seeking proper legal advice.

FIGURE 20.5 Sample product data exchange agreement. (*Reprinted with permission from Stokes, Harlan, "IGES and the Law,"* Computer-Aided Engineering (CAE), *October 1992, pp. 60, 62.*) *Caution:* The agreement shown here is only an example. Proper legal counsel should be obtained prior to adopting any legal document.

Utilizing Existing Guidelines

SMA.20.12   Why Reinvent the Wheel?

There are many conventions and guidelines from industry and government that can be helpful in preparing an organization for CAD/CAM data exchange. While these guidelines were developed to meet their own specific needs, many of the concepts can be adapted to other contexts. There is no sense reinventing the wheel when it comes to organizational issues.

SMA.20.13   AIAG Label Conventions

The Automotive Industry Action Group (AIAG), a not-for-profit organization of North American vehicle manufacturers and suppliers that focuses on improving productivity, has defined a guideline for labeling media for CAD/CAM data exchange. The intention of the guideline is to provide a format and establish required information for media identification to be used for CAD/CAM data exchange. Sample labels are shown in Fig. 20.6.

CAD/CAM DATA TAPE

Data:_/_/_ Char Format_____ Block/Record: ___ /_____
File Format:____Ver:_____ Generating CAD System:_____Ver:____
Files:_____ Media Density: ____ bpi _____   Other:_____
Tape Label:_____Vol. ID:_____ Run #:_____
Return: ___ Contact Name_____ Phone:(__)___–____
Contents:

(a)

CAD/CAM DATA TAPE

Data:_/_/_ Char Format_____ Block/Record: ___ /_____
File Format:____Ver:_____ Generating CAD System:_____Ver:____
Files:_____ Media Density:____ bpi_____   Other:_____
Tape Label:_____Vol. ID:_____ Run #:_____
Return: ___ Contact Name_____ Phone:(__)___–____
Contents:

(b)

FIGURE 20.6   CAD/CAM media label examples. (*a*) Media identification form; (*b*) label for use on cartridge tape or disk media. (*Reprinted with permission from "CAD/CAM Media Label Guideline" Automotive Industry Action Group, Southfield, Michigan, 1989, p. 5.*)

SMA.20.14   Auto Company Guidelines

Each of the major U.S. automotive companies has published data exchange documents in the late 1980s and early 1990s. These documents define technical requirements and business policies, establish usage guidelines, offer technical explanations, and list points of contact for further questions.

The U.S. automotive industry relies heavily upon CAD/CAM data exchange, and these documents reflect the decisions U.S. automotive companies have made based on their years of experience. While you may not agree with some of the policy positions they take, the documents offer an excellent template of the organizational issues that must be addressed.

To obtain copies of these guidelines contact the following.

1. Chrysler Corporation CAD/CAM Data Exchange Policy:

Chrysler Corporation
Chrysler Technology Center, Eng. Standards Dept.
800 Chrysler Drive East
C.I.M.S 483-01-07
Auburn Hills, MI 48326-2757

(*Continued*)

Utilizing Existing Guidelines
(*Continued*)

2. Ford—Supplier CADCAM Data Exchange Policy:

Ford Motor Company
CADCAM Data Exchange Help Facility
23400 Michigan Avenue
Suite 100
Dearborn, MI 48124
(313) 322-3943 CADCAM Data Exchange Help Line

3. General Motors Corporation / Electronic Data Systems CAD/CAM

Data Exchange:
GM/EDS—C4 Technology Program
Data Definition and Exchange Group
750 Tower Drive
Troy, MI 48098
(810) 265-7475 Math (CAD/CAM) Data Exchange Help Desk

SMA.20.15 CALS Implementation

As discussed in Sec. 20.2.4, the government's CALS program has defined many of the management process changes and infrastructure modernization issues needed to institutionalize the electronic exchange of technical information. The program implementation guide for CALS, MIL-HDBK-59A,[10] covers the policies and procedures for implementing data exchange requirements in contracts. There are many committees and organizations such as the CALS/CE Industry Steering Group that continue to work through issues like verification testing, data protection and security, cost/benefit analysis, standards development, and training for small businesses. Many commercial companies find that the work from the CALS initiative provides an excellent agenda for their own efforts, even if the specific methods may be slightly different.

For more information on the CALS/CE Industry Steering Group, contact the National Security Industrial Association, 1025 Connecticut Avenue NW, Suite 300, Washington, DC 20036.

Managing Expectations

SMA.20.16 Time and Effort

It will take time and effort to achieve acceptable data exchange results. Business practices will not automatically change to include data exchange. The typical manufacturer's criteria of selecting suppliers, for example, includes such things as quality, price, and delivery history, but probably not CAD/CAM capabilities.

Furthermore, standards are not perfect, and all have their limitations. The use of any neutral data standard depends not only on the quality or robustness of the standard itself, but also on how well vendors write translators and applications to use the neutral data and how well operators can implement them in their design and business infrastructure.

SMA.20.17 Strive for Value, Not Perfection

Any standard can be made to work with some level of success. Strive for value and benefits in data exchange, not perfection. Limit your scope to achievable goals. Limit early phases to an approach which either works with the lowest common denominator of end-user functionality or makes the best use of low-quality CAD/CAM data. Use exchange testing to determine probable transfer results. Leave the questions of file transfer speed for later. High transfer rates mean little if the CAD/CAM drawing data is not useful to the receiver.[7]

Evaluating Translator Capability

SMA.20.18 Translator Flexibility

Since the purpose of a translator is to maintain as much information as possible, one characteristic to look for is flexibility. Sometimes, those receiving exchanged data from an SM system will require nonsolid data such as surfaces or wire frames. Since the solid contains a more complete mathematical description of the model, many SM systems offer translator options that allow data to be exported to these less intelligent data types.

(Continued)

Evaluating Translator Capability
(*Continued*)

While this degeneration of a solid is possible for exporting data, it is usually not possible to import less intelligent data types and have the SM system automatically generate solid entities. Along these same lines, look for translators that allow unsupported entity types to be mapped to supported entities.

SMA.20.19   Translator Accuracy or Granularity

Another characteristic important to data exchange is system accuracy or granularity. This is the way a CAD/CAM system assigns a resolution to its data. It will use the granularity to round off values, reducing file sizes and computer resource requirements.

It is important that a resolution is chosen that is not too large for the geometries you are exchanging. This would remove too much entity information, leading to round-off errors or granularity mismatch between the sending and receiving systems. Some translators assign default granularity values and others ignore it altogether. Some assign the value dynamically based on a ratio of the largest features (or overall size of the geometries) to the smallest features.

The historical reason for problems with granularity is that each vendor interprets the requirements for setting resolution differently. In IGES, for example, there is a "minimum user-intended resolution" value and four "precision" values defined in the global section of the file. While they loosely define the granularity of the file, it is not clear whether this granularity applies only to geometric coordinate data or to all floating-point data. Rounding errors can compound even if the coordinates for an entity follow the granularity guideline, but are multiplied through transformations matrices that are themselves impacted by the granularity values.

Furthermore, since different vendors interpret the standard differently, some may apply the granularity parameters to noncoordinate data such as spline or conic coefficients.

SMA.20.20   What to Look For

The best time to investigate the functionality of an SM system is before you buy it. Check the documentation for entity maps to be sure that it supports the entities required by other systems targeted for data exchange. Look for options that allow solid data to be degenerated to simpler entities. Ask how granularity values are assigned internally and how these values are transferred. Then run tests with your own data (see Chap. 21, Sec. 21.7, for more on IGES testing). Observe how well the translator maintains the information through the transfer without loss of content or context.

SMA.20.21   What to Ask

When evaluating the functionality of translators, here are some questions to ask system vendors.[6,17]

1. Can you specify level (or layer), line weight, and color mapping?

2. Do the pre- and postprocessors support nested subfigures.

3. If it is an IGES translator, is the preprocessor CALS-compliant?

4. How many software developers within the vendor firm are working on translators?

5. How many translators have been installed?

6. With which other systems have you exchanged data?

7. What specific experiences can you present that show the effectiveness of your translators?

8. Do you have someone in your organization that participates in industry standards committees such as the IGES/PDES Organization or the International Standards Organization? This will help indicate the level of commitment to standards-based data exchange.

Delivery Mechanisms

SMA.20.22   Check Compatibility

Check with the coordinator of the receiving CAD system to ensure that a compatible delivery mechanism is used.

(*Continued*)

Delivery Mechanisms
(*Continued*)

SMA.20.23   Floppy Disks

If PC DOS-based backup utilities are used to transfer data files to floppy disk, be sure your data transfer partner operates on the same version of DOS or the backup utility. These utilities may be version-dependent.

Don LaCourse, President
The Solid Modeling ExChange, Algood, Tenn.

SMA.20.24   Tape-Drive Densities

As with floppy disks, higher-density tape drives can read and write lower-density tapes; lower-density tape drives cannot read or write higher-density tapes. It is therefore important to make sure your drive is capable of handling the density required by your exchange partner.

SMA.20.25   UNIX Tape Archive (TAR) Utility

Each operating system has different logical methods of placing data on tape. Tape exchanges with like operating systems (*intrachange*) are usually possible, while exchanges between dissimilar operating systems (*interchange*) are often not possible. For Unix workstations, it is very common to use the Unix tape archive or TAR utility to read and write QIC tapes. As long as the receiver has a drive capable of reading the right density and a TAR utility, the exchange should be successful.

Data Compression

SMA.20.26   ASCII IGES Format

Since there are many good compression methods available, the binary IGES and compressed ASCII IGES formats discussed in the IGES specification have been all but abandoned. The IGES community generally uses the full ASCII IGES format in conjunction with separate compression methods.

SMA.20.27   UNIX Platforms

On Unix platforms, use the Unix compress utility to create a compressed binary version of the file. Then use the uuencode utility to convert the file to an ASCII version of the compressed binary file. Transfer on tape or by E-mail, use uudecode to convert back to compressed binary and uncompress to convert back to ASCII. Compressed files typically have ".z" as a filename extension.

SMA.20.28   Personal Computer (PC) Platforms

On MS-DOS PCs, there are many common public domain and shareware compression/decompression utilities.[18] Each uses a slightly different compression algorithm, so it is typical to accompany the compressed files with the decompression utility, or compress the files as "self-extracting" executables. The following table lists a few compression utilities and their corresponding file extension designations.

Utility	Filename Extension
LHARC	.LZH
PKZIP	.ZIP
ARCE	.ARC
ARJ	.ARJ
NARC	.ZIP, .ARC

Checklists

SMA.20.29   Rules for Data Integrity[8,13,19,20,21]

1. Establish and enforce CAD design standards for designers.

2. Change reward systems to quality, not quantity, of designs.

3. The organization creating CAD data is responsible for its accuracy.

(Continued)

4. Obtain and use tools that improve data translations and data integrity.

5. Drafting checkers should implement data integrity checking criteria.

6. Allow revisions to CAD-generated documents on CAD only, rather than manually on paper.

SMA.20.30   Data Integrity Checklist[13,19,20,21,22]

1. Data integrity rules are independent of viewing angle or display resolution.

2. Don't just eyeball it. Understand the CAD/CAM data, not just the display.

3. Understand the difference between the dimension text and the geometry data, and when each is used downstream.

4. Use appropriate system tolerances for CAD models.

5. All geometry should be drawn to full scale.

6. Use layers or levels to separate geometry for parts in assemblies and for nongeometric data.

7. Keep models clean and model size small.

8. Let the computer do the math for geometric construction.

9. Use the simplest possible geometry.

10. Operate on intersecting rather than tangent solids.

11. Avoid coincident vertices, edge faces.

12. Create geometry only once. Avoid duplicate entities.

13. Use object snaps during construction to ensure that geometry endpoints meet, leaving no gaps.

14. Wherever possible, represent continuous object lines with a single line entity.

15. Use clearance- and interference-checking tools.

16. Dimensions should match exactly the size of the geometry they are dimensioning. Thus, all dimensions should be computer-generated.

17. Delete unnecessary entities before transfers, including lines and notes used for construction.

18. The manufacturing tolerances of the final part should be noted in the CAD file on the layer(s) or level(s) containing dimensions. This includes any block tolerances.

19. The sender of CAD/CAM data should accompany each file with at least one 3D isometric picture of the entire part, complete with scale or dimensions.

SMA.20.31   Contingency Plans[20,22]

In general, the more complex the entity, the more likely that there will be a problem with data exchanges. Sending simpler entities may still allow the receiver to attain an adequate level of functional equivalence from the exchange.

1. Add points to form grids on surfaces.

2. Add surface edge and intersection curves.

3. Reduce complicated groups of geometries down to the surfaces that define faces. For example, resulting trimmed surfaces can be reduced to bounded surface patches.

4. Expand (or explode) details and symbols.

5. Leave points along curves, at tangents, at start/end of arcs.

SMA.20.32   2D Drawing File Sizes

Our experience with attempting to exchange CAD data in general with the outside world has proven difficult in most cases. Due to the ability to generate full-scale, accurate 3D representations of parts and call them together into subassemblies and higher-level assemblies, the resultant 2D drawing can contain an enormous amount of entities, causing file sizes to be unmanageable when transferred to systems with lesser ability.

Kevin P. Alexander, CAD/CAM/CAE System Administrator
Littleford Day, Inc., Florence, Ky.

Good to Know
(Continued)

SMA.20.33 Organizational Preparation

Planning for CAD/CAM data exchange includes looking at organizational issues as well as technical ones. This is because the electronic exchange of information represents a departure from traditional paper-based business methods. Depending on how heavily you rely on data exchange, new management and engineering policies may be required. Since CAD/CAM data represents official engineering documentation, document-control practices may need to be revised. New policies on data management may be required.

In order to reduce exposure to legal issues that can arise when converting to electronic data exchange, business and legal agreements may need to be modified. If you are going to use data exchange in common practice, these organizational issues are every bit as important as technical issues.

SMA.20.34 Macintosh Drives

The standard floppy drive for newer Macintosh computers, called a *superdrive,* is capable of reading and writing files from both PC and Macintosh disks. Cross-platform exchange of disks may require software utilities, such as "Apple File Exchange," to convert these files.

SMA.20.35 System ASCII Support

For the time being, the most foolproof way to exchange CAD/CAM data is through the use of ASCII text files, where each character takes up 8 bits (1 byte). This is because different computer systems usually have incompatible binary file structures. By converting all files to ASCII for file exchanges, you avoid questions of how to handle the extended binary-coded decimal interchange code (EBCDIC) character set used by some computers. While ASCII files are common across platforms, they are also generally larger than binary files. Since the IGES, DXF, and STEP physical file formats each can support ASCII, binary file exchange is generally not to be considered an issue.

SMA.20.36 Emerging Delivery Mechanisms

Look for emerging mechanisms that will provide options for delivering data. For encoded media, CD-ROMs, WORMs and rewritable optical disks are available. There are several tape technologies such as 4- and 8-mm DAT. Magneto-optical or "floptical" disks are also on the market. For network media, look for wide area network (WAN) technologies such as Integrated Services Digital Network (ISDN), Frame Relay, and Switched Multimegabit Data Service (SMDS), and local area network (LAN) technologies like Fiber Distributed Data Interface (FDDI). Also look to the International Standards Organization (ISO) for new Open Systems Interconnection (OSI) network protocols.

References

1. "Product Data Exchange Survey Results—Winter 1989," the Automotive Industry Action Group, CAD/CAM Data Exchange Working Group, Southfield, Mich., July 25, 1990.

2. "Third Annual Survey of North American Manufacturing Technology—Making the Grade in the 1990's," Deloitte & Touche Manufacturing Consulting Services, Cleveland, Ohio, 1989, pp. 10–11.

3. "Annual Survey of North American Manufacturing Technology—Taking Aim at World Class Manufacturing," Deloitte & Touche Manufacturing Consulting Services, Cleveland, Ohio, 1991, pp. 14–15.

4. Report of the National Critical Technologies Panel, William Phillips, Chairman, March 22, 1991, p. 47.

5. MIL-STD-1840A with change notice 1, "MILITARY STANDARD—AUTOMATED INTERCHANGE OF TECHNICAL INFORMATION," December 20, 1988.

   MIL-D-28000A, "MILITARY SPECIFICATION—DIGITAL REPRESENTATION FOR COMMUNICATION OF PRODUCT DATA: IGES APPLICATION SUBSETS AND IGES APPLICATION PROTOCOLS," February 10, 1992.

   (Copies of the referenced federal and military specifications, standards, and handbooks are available from the Department of Defense Single Stock Point, Commanding Officer, Naval Publications and Forms Center (NPFC), 5801 Tabor Avenue, Philadelphia, PA 19120. For specific acquisition functions, these documents should be obtained from the contracting activity or as directed by the contracting activity. FIPS PUB documents are available to government agencies only from NPFC; nongovernment availability is from the National Technical Information Service.)

6. Mayer, Ralph, "Using IGES, DXF and CALS for CAD/CAM Data Transfer," Management Roundtable, Inc., 1992.

7. Stokes, Harlan, "IGES Success on a Shoestring: A Case Study of CAD/CAM Data Exchange," *Proceedings, Design Productivity International Conference,* vol. 2, February 3–9, 1991, Honolulu, Hawaii, pp. 627–633.

8. Fleischer, Mitchell, Thomas Phelps, and Michael Ensing, "CAD/CAM Data Problems and Costs in the Tool and Die Industry," final report on a study conducted for the Michigan Modernization Service by the Industrial Technology Institute and the Detroit Chapter of the National Tooling and Machining Association, March 12, 1991.

9. Morea, Greg, "Seawolf DDE Program," *Proceedings of the Product Data Exchange for the 1990s Seminar,* sponsored by the IGES/PDES Organization, the National IGES User Group and NCGA, New Orleans, La., February 20–22, 1991.

10. MIL-HDBK-59A, "MILITARY HANDBOOK—DEPARTMENT OF DEFENSE COMPUTER-AIDED ACQUISITION AND LOGISTIC SUPPORT (CALS) PROGRAM IMPLEMENTATION GUIDE," September 28, 1990.

    (Copies of the referenced federal and military specifications, standards and handbooks are available from the Department of Defense Single Stock Point, Commanding Officer, Naval Publications and Forms Center (NPFC), 5801 Tabor Avenue, Philadelphia, PA 19120. For specific acquisition functions, these documents should be obtained from the contracting activity or as directed by the contracting activity. FIPS PUB documents are available to government agencies only from NPFC; nongovernment availability is from the National Technical Information Service.)

11. Tanenbaum, Mitch, "Locking the Front Door," *Proceedings, CALS Phase II: Data Security Issues & Concurrent Engineering Applications,* Society for Computer Aided Engineering, Arlington, Va., September 12–14, 1990.

12. Stokes, Harlan, "IGES and the Law," *Computer-Aided Engineering (CAE),* October 1992, pp. 60, 62.

13. Stokes, Harlan, Mitchell Fleischer, and Thomas Phelps, "Design for Data Integrity," *MCN (MicroCAD News),* December 1991, pp. 52–55.

14. Wright, Benjamin, *The Law of Electronic Commerce—EDI, Fax, and E-mail: Technology, Proof and Liability,* Little, Brown and Company (Canada) Limited, Toronto, 1991.

15. Uniform Commercial Code (1978 text with 1987 amendments), American Law Institute and the National Conference of Commissioners on Uniform State Laws, Philadelphia, Pa.

16. "The Uniform Rules of Conduct for Interchange for Trade Data by Teletransmission," International Chamber of Commerce, ICC pub. no. 452, New York, N.Y., 1991.

17. Stokes, Harlan, "Testing IGES Exchange Methods," *MCN (MicroCAD News),* July 1991, pp. 46–51, 80.

18. Merrick, Lew, "A Better Way to Send Engineering Drawings," *Machine Design,* June 25, 1992, pp. 44, 46.

19. Arnsdorf, David R., "Draft CAD File Specifications, version 0.1," Industrial Technology Institute, Ann Arbor, Mich., September 24, 1992.

20. Stokes, Harlan, "Design for Data Integrity: Part II," *DesignNet,* January 1992, pp. 34–37.

21. Guay, Pierre T., "Common Sense Rules for CAD Systems," *Machine Design,* April 12, 1990, pp. 112–113.

22. Lichten, Olga, "Catia Data Transfer," *COE,* Phoenix, Ariz. October 1992.

Suggestions for Further Reading

Initial Graphics Exchange Specification (IGES)—Version 5.1, NISTIR 4412, U.S. National Bureau of Standards (NIST), 1991.

IGES 5.1 Recommended Practices Guide, IGES/PDES Organization, January 1992.

"CALS: An Industry/User Report," CAD/CIM Management Roundtable, Inc., 1990.

Chapter 21

Solid Modeling and the Initial Graphics Exchange Specification (IGES)

Harlan Stokes
Vice President, Sales and Marketing
IGES Data Analysis, Inc.

The Initial Graphics Exchange Specification (IGES) is a neutral data format for describing product design and manufacturing information created and stored in CAD/CAM systems. It is intended for exchanging the geometry, annotation, and structure information from CAD/CAM data between dissimilar systems.

Version 1.0 of IGES was published in 1980, and included only basic capabilities for drawings created with wireframe geometry. It has been updated consistently with version 2.0 in 1982 through to version 5.2 in 1993. More capabilities were added to the standard with each version, including complex curves and surfaces, non-English character sets and application-specific entities for electrical, finite element modeling (FEM), drafting, and AEC systems. While IGES is not expected to grow appreciably past version 6.0, it will be maintained as long as there is a market demand for it.

IGES first became capable of describing Solid Modeling (SM) data in version 4.0 with support for CSG solids. Then, in version 5.1, B-Rep solids became supported with entities included in the untested entity section of the specification. B-Reps are expected to be moved into the main body of the IGES standard with version 6.0 in the mid-1990s (see Chap. 4 for more on CSG and B-Rep SM database structures). With the support of both CSG and B-Rep solids in IGES, vendors are now beginning to support SM data in their IGES translators. While the industry is building experience with SM data transfers through IGES, the topics in this chapter should still apply regardless of the type of data being exchanged.

As you can see from its history, IGES has expanded to follow CAD/CAM technology. This is partly because the IGES standard is developed and maintained by volunteer CAD/CAM users and vendors as a group called the IGES/PDES Organization and is motivated by the data exchange requirements of its members (see SMA.21.32). While many charge that IGES lags the state of the art in CAD/CAM capabilities, most designers find that it can be made to work quite well for the established technologies that form the mainstream of CAD/CAM use.

21.1 IGES in Production

The classical IGES translator configuration involves two CAD/CAM applications and two translators[1] (see Fig. 21.1). A drawing or model is created in a CAD/CAM system and is written into the IGES format using translator software called an IGES preprocessor. The IGES file is then transferred to the target system on tape, disk, over a modem, or network where translator software called an IGES postprocessor converts the file to the target CAD/CAM system's native data file format. Most translators come from the vendors of particular CAD/CAM systems, although there are third-party translators available.

This is the normal process for "production" or day-to-day IGES exchanges. Many companies and government agencies use IGES in this way to great benefit. However, most experienced users know

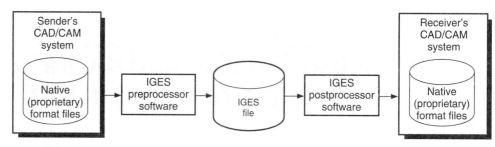

FIGURE 21.1 The classical IGES translator configuration. Data from a sending system is translated by a pre-processor into IGES, transferred, and then translated by a postprocessor into data for the receiving system. *(Courtesy of IGES Data Analysis, Inc.)*

that it is not practical to expect IGES to provide immediate and glowing successes. IGES has several intrinsic characteristics that require the designer to take some preliminary steps before entering the production data exchange phase. The bulk of this chapter will explain how an "IGES evaluation process" can help to characterize, test, debug, and improve data exchange so that IGES can provide the results needed in production.

21.2 The IGES Evaluation Process

If there are going to be problems with IGES exchanges, you want them to show up during the evaluation process and not in production. There are several components of the IGES evaluation process that can be applied separately or together. First, it is important to have a basic understanding of how IGES files store information. Then with the assistance of entity maps, IGES modification techniques, IGES utilities, interoperability testing, and debugging, a determination can be made on how production exchanges should be performed. Figure 21.2 illustrates the IGES translator configuration and data flow during the evaluation process.

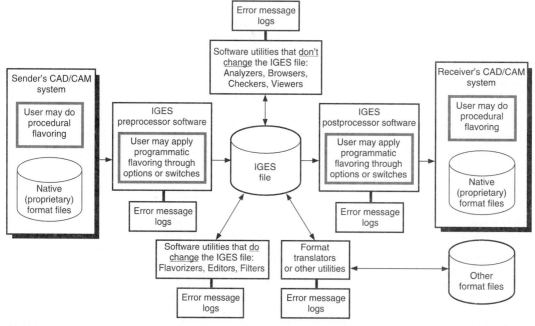

FIGURE 21.2 IGES translator configuration for the evaluation process. Error message logs can be vital to the evaluation process. Flavoring can take place within either translator, within either CAD system, or external to either system through the use of utilities. Most utilities work directly with the IGES file, minimizing errors caused by pre- and postprocessing. *(Courtesy of IGES Data Analysis, Inc.)*

When exchanging IGES data between two systems for the first time, it is important to go through an IGES evaluation process to characterize the exchange and identify problems that might occur during production exchanges. It will also be necessary to enter into an evaluation process when problems arise with exchanges already in production. Problems are detected using entity maps (see Sec. 21.4) and interoperability testing (see Sec. 21.7). Once identified, problems can be corrected using system-level commands, translator options, and IGES utilities to apply flavoring techniques. Some of the utilities and flavoring techniques used in the evaluation process may need to be left in place for production IGES exchanges as well.

21.3   Anatomy of an IGES File

An IGES file contains fundamental CAD/CAM units called *entities*. Entities make up the geometric model, annotations, viewing parameters, and structural characteristics of the 2D drawing or 3D model. IGES files are ASCII text files (see Fig. 21.3) consisting of 80 column records (80 characters per line). A binary and a compressed ASCII form were defined in earlier releases of IGES but are seldom used, so this discussion will focus on the full ASCII IGES format. The typical IGES file consists of five mandatory sections:

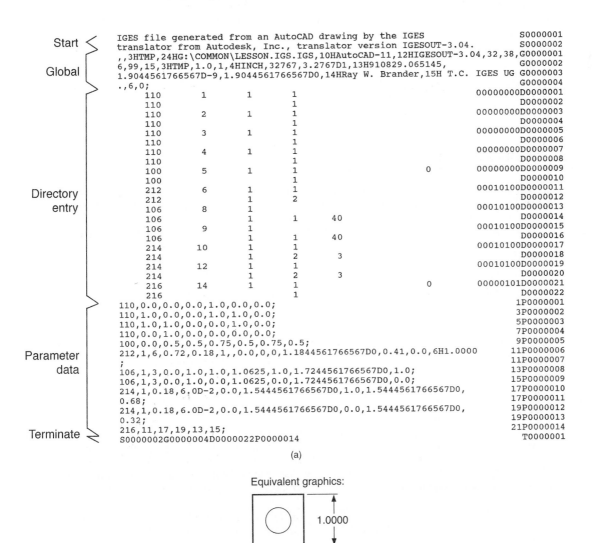

FIGURE 21.3   Anatomy of a sample IGES File. (*a*) IGES file with sections labeled; (*b*) equivalent graphics. (*Courtesy of the Twin Cities IGES User Group.*)

1. Start section
2. Global section
3. Directory entry section
4. Parameter data section
5. Terminate section

Each of the five sections can be identified by the letters S, G, D, P, and T (respectively) appearing in the 73rd column of each record or line in the IGES file. A sixth section, the flag section, is identified by the letter F and is used only in the compressed ASCII form. Each section has a role in describing the CAD/CAM model.

21.3.1 Start Section

The start section is for free-form text generated by the designer or the CAD/CAM system to tell the receiver something about the IGES file. Some CAD/CAM software programs allow you to specify your own text file, called a *start section file*, to be merged into the start section of the IGES file being created. Your start section file should be in ASCII format with no more than 72 character record lengths. This is an appropriate location to record your exclusive engineering information such as part number, description, revision level, product specifications, and data transfer notes. You can then update your start section file for each consecutive transfer of the model. The following is the start section example from Fig. 21.3:

```
IGES file generated from an AutoCAD drawing by the IGES        S0000001
translator from Autodesk, Inc., translator version IGESOUT-3.04.    S0000002
```

21.3.2 Global Section

The global section provides information that pertains to the entire file. It is a fairly short section, consisting of 25 pieces of information, typically in three or four lines. This information includes the name of the file translated into IGES, the CAD system ID, units of measure used (see SMA.21.2), author or originator, the version of the IGES standard to which the file should conform, the version of the translator software that wrote the IGES file, the drafting standard used, and more. It also contains a granularity value used to describe the resolution of the data (see Chap. 20, SMA.20.19). The following is the global section example from Fig. 21.3:

```
,,3HTMP,24HG:\COMMON\LESSON.IGS.IGS,10HAutoCAD-11,12HIGESOUT-3.04,32,38,G0000001
6,99,15,3HTMP,1.0,1,4HINCH,32767,3.2767D1,13H910829.065145,        G0000002
1.9044561766567D-9,1.9044561766567D0,14HRay W. Brander,15H T.C. IGES UG G0000003
.,6,0;                                                            G0000004
```

21.3.3 Directory Entry

The directory entry (DE) section is an index listing each entity in the file. Each entity is represented by two 80-column records (two lines of text) that together contain 20 fields for attribute information concerning that entity. These attributes include the entity type and form, the line font used, the entity color, pointers to the correct record where parameter data can be found, and more. You can think of the DE section as the card catalog at a library, where each card (DE record) contains information about a book (entity).

The following is an example of the DE records for one of the leader arrows in the dimension from Fig. 21.3. Notice that some fields are left blank and are considered to have default values, as defined in the IGES standard.

```
214      10       1       1                         00010100D0000017
214               1       2       3                         D0000018
```

21.3.4 Parameter Data

The coordinate data and the other values used to define each entity are then stored in the parameter data section. Using the library analogy, the PD data is like a book (entity) in the library (model), giving most of the mathematical definitions of the entity. The number of fields and the purpose of each field for each entity depends upon the entity type. The PD data also contains a pointer that identifies where its DE record can be found. The following is an example of the PD records for the same leader arrow in the dimension from Fig. 21.3.

```
214,1,0.18,6.0D-2,0.0,1.5444561766567D0,1.0,1.5444561766567D0,      17P0000010
0.68;                                                               17P0000011
```

21.3.5 Terminate Section

The last section in the IGES file is the single-record (one-line) terminate section which provides a count of how many records (lines) are in each section and signals the end of the IGES file. The following is the terminate section example from Fig. 21.3:

```
S0000002G0000004D0000022P0000014                                    T0000001
```

21.3.6 IGES Entities

Each entity in the model or drawing file will be assigned an entity type number in the IGES file to define what kind of entity it is. Some entities have subcategories defined through form numbers that further define or classify their use.

For example, a rational B-spline surface is a type 128 geometry entity with 10 different forms, where form 0 is a free-form surface defined by the parameters given in the IGES file, form 1 is a planer surface, and form 3 is a cone surface. With only a few exceptions, geometry entities have type numbers between 100 and 199, annotations between 200 and 299, entities that define structures between 300 and 399, and instances of structures between 400 and 499. Table 21.1 provides an entity list for IGES version 5.1.

TABLE 21.1   IGES Version 5.1 Entity Table

Notice that some entities have many forms. (Courtesy of the U.S. Product Data Association.)

IGES entity no.	Form nos.	IGES entity name
0		NULL ENTITY
100		CIRCULAR ARC
102		COMPOSITE CURVE
104	0–3	CONIC ARC
106	1–63	COPIOUS DATA
108	(–1)–1	PLANE
110		LINE
112		PARAMETRIC SPLINE CURVE
114		PARAMETRIC SPLINE SURFACE
116		POINT
118	0–1	RULED SURFACE
120		SURFACE OF REVOLUTION
122		TABULATED CYLINDER
123		DIRECTION (G)
124	0–12	TRANSFORMATION MATRIX
125	0–4	FLASH
126	0–5	RATIONAL B-SPLINE CURVE
128	0–9	RATIONAL B-SPLINE SURFACE
130		OFFSET CURVE
132		CONNECT POINT
134		NODE

TABLE 21.1   IGES Version 5.1 Entity Table (*Continued*)

IGES entity no.	Form nos.	IGES entity name
136		FINITE ELEMENT (G)
138		NODAL DISPLACEMENT AND ROTATION
140		OFFSET SURFACE
141		BOUNDARY (G)
142		CURVE ON A PARAMETRIC SURFACE
143		BOUNDED SURFACE (G)
144		TRIMMED SURFACE
146		NODAL RESULTS (G)
148		ELEMENTS RESULTS (G)
150		BLOCK
152		RIGHT ANGULAR WEDGE
154		RIGHT CIRCULAR CYLINDER
156		RIGHT CIRCULAR CONE FRUSTUM
158		SPHERE
160		TORUS
162	0–1	SOLID OF REVOLUTION
164		SOLID OF LINEAR EXTRUSION
168		ELLIPSOID
180		BOOLEAN TREE
182		SELECTED COMPONENT (G)
184		SOLID ASSEMBLY
186		MANIFOLD SOLID B-REP OBJECT (G)
190		PLANE SURFACE (G)
192		RIGHT CIRCULAR CYLINDRICAL SURFACE (G)
194		RIGHT CIRCULAR CONICAL SURFACE (G)
196		SPHERICAL SURFACE (G)
198		TOROIDAL SURFACE (G)
202		ANGULAR DIMENSION
204		CURVE DIMENSION (G)
206		DIAMETER DIMENSION
208		FLAG NOTE
210		GENERAL LABEL
212	0–105	GENERAL NOTE (F,G)
213		NEW GENERAL NOTE (G)
214	1–12	LEADER (ARROW)
216	0–2	LINEAR DIMENSION (G)
218	0–1	ORDINATE DIMENSION (G)
220		POINT DIMENSION
222	0–1	RADIUS DIMENSION (G)
228	0–3	GENERAL SYMBOL (G)
230	0–1	SECTIONED AREA (G)
302		ASSOCIATIVITY DEFINITION
304	1–2	LINE FONT DEFINITION
306		MACRO (G)
308		SUBFIGURE DEFINITION
310		TEXT FONT DEFINITION
312	0–1	TEXT DISPLAY TEMPLATE
314		COLOR DEFINITION
316		UNITS DATA (G)
320		NETWORK SUBFIGURE DEFINITION
322	0–2	ATTRIBUTE TABLE DEFINITION
402	1–21	ASSOCIATIVITY INSTANCE (F,G)
404	0–1	DRAWING (G)
406	1–31	PROPERTY (F,G)
408		SINGULAR SUBFIGURE INSTANCE
410	0–1	VIEW (G)
412		RECTANGULAR ARRAY SUBFIGURE INSTANCE
414		CIRCULAR ARRAY SUBFIGURE INSTANCE
416	0–4	EXTERNAL REFERENCE (G)
418		NODAL LOAD/CONSTRAINT
420		NETWORK SUBFIGURE INSTANCE
422	0–1	ATTRIBUTE TABLE INSTANCE
430		SOLID INSTANCE
502		VERTEX (G)

TABLE 21.1   IGES Version 5.1 Entity Table (*Continued*)

IGES entity no.	Form nos.	IGES entity name
504		EDGE (G)
508		LOOP (G)
510		FACE (G)
514		SHELL (G)

Notes: 1. All information is based upon IGES version 5.1, September 1991.
   2. F = Some or all forms of this entity have been obsoleted by newer entities.
   3. G = Some or all forms of this entity have not been fully tested.

Entities that define structures include associativities which are incorporated to establish relationships between entities and properties. This allows specific characteristics to be assigned to an entity. The view and drawing entities allow for the definitions of how the model will be presented from different angles and how those views are arranged on the screen.

Transformation matrices can be defined to apply translation and rotation to entities, including view and draw entities, for the construction of a model. The IGES specification also allows for implementor-defined entities that are not defined within the specification. Implementor-defined entities are sometimes used when IGES is intended as a neutral archive format but must contain data that is unique to a particular system.

Anatomy

SMA.21.1   Custom Start Sections

A desirable characteristic of an SM system is to have the ability to incorporate one's own information into the start section of an IGES file. Most of the better SM systems offer this capability, but many do not.

For those systems that do not facilitate custom start sections, many users resort to manually editing IGES files to insert their data. They use a text editor to construct a customized start section at the beginning of the file, always following the strict formatting guidelines of IGES. Yet, because of the complexities of the IGES syntax, this can be a risky endeavor for all but the most knowledgeable users. For this reason, it is advisable to avoid hand-editing IGES files. Look instead for an SM system with an IGES preprocessor capable of adding custom start section data.

SMA.21.2   If Resulting Scale Is Too Large

If you look at the global section of an IGES file you will see the characters "4HINCH" or "2HMM" in the fifteenth field (see Sec. 21.3.2 and Fig. 21.3). Since this is the global section, these characters tell the receiving CAD system whether all entities in the file have coordinates in units of inches or millimeters. Some CAD systems default to inch units when millimeters were used.

If your resulting model after translation is too large (exactly 25.4 times) in the receiving CAD system and you know that the original model's units are millimeters, check to see if the characters "2HMM" appear in the global section of the IGES file. If the characters "4HINCH" appear, then your model is being translated incorrectly.

Look for an option switch on the sending system's IGES preprocessor to force the correct units to be used, and translate the file again. Otherwise, if an IGES utility is available, you may be able to edit the IGES file to correct the units.

21.4   IGES Entity Mapping

Through the IGES translation process, the preprocessor of the sending CAD/CAM system converts geometry into IGES entities that most nearly correspond to the native entity in mathematical form or intended content. Similarly, the postprocessor of the receiving CAD/CAM system must convert IGES entities into its own appropriate native geometry.

How these IGES processors translate native geometry to and from IGES entities is determined by whoever writes the translator, usually the CAD/CAM system developer. The list describing how native and neutral entities are translated is called an *entity map*. Table 21.2 provides part of an actual IGES entity map from an SM system vendor. Since there is more than one way to map entities, mapping often becomes a major contributor to the way designers perceive the value or quality of IGES processors. Figure 21.4 illustrates the support for solid entities in IGES version 5.1. See Tables 21.3 and 21.4 for the CSG and B-Rep entity types supported by IGES version 5.1.

TABLE 21.2 Example of IGES Support in the I-DEAS® Commercial CAD System from SDRC

(a) IGES entities written by the I-DEAS® Drafting IGES preprocessor; (b) IGES entitites read by the I-DEAS® Drafting IGES postprocessor; (c) three possible mapping options for converting an I-DEAS® solid model into IGES entities. Notice that options 1 and 2 create solid entities, while option 3 coverts to nonsolid entities. Note that this listing may not reflect the latest version of the I-DEAS® software. (Courtesy of Structural Dynamics Research Corporation, SDRC.)

(a) I-DEAS® Drafting-to-IGES Support	
IGES entity no.	IGES entity name
100	CIRCULAR ARC
104	CONIC ARC
106	COPIOUS DATA
108	PLANE
110	LINE
112	PARAMETRIC SPLINE CURVE
116	POINT
124	TRANSFORMAT ION MATRIX
202	ANGULAR DIMENSION
206	DIAMETER DIMENSION
210	GENERAL LABEL
212	GENERAL NOTE
214	LEADER (ARROW)
216	LINEAR DIMENSION
218	ORDINATE DIMENSION
220	POINT DIMENSION
222	RADIUS DIMENSION
304	LINE FONT DEFINITION
308	SUBFIGURE DEFINITION
402	ASSOCIATIVITY INSTANCE
404	DRAWING
406	PROPERTY
408	SINGULAR SUBFIGURE INSTANCE
410	VIEW

(b) IGES-to-I-DEAS® Drafting Support	
IGES entity no.	IGES entity name
100	CIRCULAR ARC
102	COMPOSITE CURVE
104	CONIC ARC
106	COPIOUS DATA
108	PLANE
110	LINE
112	PARAMETRIC SPLINE CURVE
116	POINT
124	TRANSFORMATION MATRIX
126	RATIONAL B-SPLINE CURVE
202	ANGULAR DIMENSION
206	DIAMETER DIMENSION
208	FLAG NOTE
210	GENERAL LABEL
212	GENERAL NOTE
214	LEADER (ARROW)
216	LINEAR DIMENSION
218	ORDINATE DIMENSION

(Continued)

TABLE 21.2   Example of IGES Support in the I-DEAS® Commercial CAD System from SDRC (*Continued*)

(b) IGES-to-I-DEAS® Drafting Support (Continued)

IGES entity no.	IGES entity name
220	POINT DIMENSION
222	RADIUS DIMENSION
228	GENERAL SYMBOL
304	LINE FONT DEFINITION
308	SUBFIGURE DEFINITION
402	ASSOCIATIVITY INSTANCE
404	DRAWING
406	PROPERTY
408	SINGULAR SUBFIGURE INSTANCE
410	VIEW

(c) I-DEAS® Solid-to-IGES Mapping

I-DEAS®	Possible IGES mappings
I-DEAS® part entity	1) MANIFOLD SOLID BOUNDARY OBJECT: MODEL SPACE REPRESENTATION ONLY*
	2) MANIFOLD SOLID BOUNDARY OBJECT: MODEL SPACE AND PARAMETER SPACE*
	3) OUTPUT UNDERLYING SURFACE, CURVE AND POINT GEOMETRY[†]

*All underlying surfaces and curves will be output as NURBS.
[†] Underlying surfaces and curves will be output according to their preferred mapping.

TABLE 21.3   CSG Entity Types Supported in IGES Version 5.1

IGES entity type number	Entity name
150	Block
152	Right-angular wedge
154	Right-circular cylinder
156	Right-circular cone frustum
158	Sphere
160	Torus
162	Solid of revolution
164	Solid of linear extrusion
168	Ellipsoid
180	Boolean tree
182	Selected component
184	Solid assembly
430	Solid instance

TABLE 21.4   B-Rep Entity Types Supported in IGES Version 5.1

IGES entity type number	Entity name
186	Manifold solid B-Rep object
502	Vertex
504	Edge
508	Loop
510	Face
514	Shell

Notes: 1. The entities listed above use other IGES surface and curve entities in the definition of B-Rep solid models.
2. In IGES version 5.1, B-Rep entities are included in the Untested Entities section of the specification.

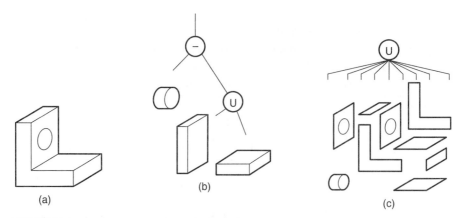

FIGURE 21.4 Sample solid representation in IGES version 5.1. (*a*) Sample solid; (*b*) CSG representation in IGES; (*c*) boundary representation (B-Rep) in IGES.

21.4.1   Entity Subsets

Quite often, it is obvious to the translator developer which IGES entities are appropriate to map with their native CAD/CAM geometry. This is because these entities have mathematical formulations that are commonly accepted, such as lines or points. IGES has grown to contain many types of entities. This is partly as a result of vendors adding their own entity definitions to the standard, so there is a rich selection of entities to map to.

For example, IGES version 5.1 contains 13 forms of the general note entity, including variations for different methods of super- and subscripting, justifications, and more. There are 12 forms of the arrow entity, including arrowheads that are wedge-shaped, triangular, filled, and more. While this rich selection of entities offers more choices to the translator developer, it also means that no CAD/CAM system supports all of the IGES entities.

Table 21.5 illustrates incompatible entities between dissimilar SM systems. Although each system represented in the table claims to supports lines, conics, and splines, it is still possible for data to be lost because of incompatibilities in their entity maps. Notice that the receiving system doesn't support the hyperbola form of the conic, so hyperbolas cannot transfer. Also notice that the sending system has a mapping option for spline curves, exporting them as either the IGES 112 or 126 entities, depending on user input. Since the receiving system can accept only 126 entities, any 112 entities will not transfer. If the IGES 126 mapping option is used upon export, the splines will transfer.

TABLE 21.5   Example of Incompatibilities in IGES Entity Maps

Sending system entity map					Receiving system entity map		
Native entity type	IGES name	IGES type: form		Transfer possible?		IGES type: form	IGES name	Native entity type
Line	Line	110	→	Yes	→	110	Line	Line
Ellipse	Conic arc (ellipse)	104:1	→	Yes	→	104:1	Conic arc (ellipse)	Conic
Hyperbola	Conic arc (hyperbola)	104:2		No		NA		
Spline curve	Option 1: parametric spline curve	112		No		NA		
Spline curve	Option 2: rational B-spline curve	126	→	Yes	→	126	Rational B-spline curve	Spline curve

While it is true that a developer may be faulted for using a sparse subset of entities, it is also true that IGES contains entity types that can be used by vastly different types of CAD/CAM systems which, by their nature, must concentrate on entity subsets. One would not expect a purely mechanical SM system to read the IGES flash entity that is used in electrical CAD/CAM systems. Nor should an industrial design imaging system be expected to read the IGES finite element node entity. See SMA.21.3 for more on IGES entity subsets.

21.4.2   Approximations

Sometimes, a CAD/CAM system will use entities for which there are no obvious IGES entities to map to. In these cases the developer must pick IGES entities closest to the native entities. The translator may have to make slight changes to some geometry definitions through mathematical approximations in order to map to differing IGES entity definitions. This is where the quality of the translator may become apparent.

21.4.3   Mapping Solids to Other Data Types

As mentioned previously, the support for SM data by IGES translators is a rather recent development, and a steep increase in SM data exchanges is expected. Even so, SM systems have still made good use of IGES. Solid models contain substantial mathematical information about geometry and can therefore map SM data to different entity types like surfaces or wireframes without the requirement of human interpretation. This is often an entity-mapping option on the IGES preprocessor for an SM system.

Likewise, do not disregard the option of importing nonsolid data into your SM system. Many SM systems can make use of wireframe and surface geometry for the construction of solids. When the alternative is creating solids from scratch, you may find this data to be quite a time-saver. However, the IGES postprocessor for an SM system should not be expected to automatically map these data types to a solid model. This type of entity mapping usually requires human interpretation of the model.

Entity Mapping

> **SMA.21.3   IGES Subsets**
>
> As a matter of practicality, most translators can read and write only a subset of IGES entities. This is a common cause of data loss during translation. If a preprocessor is writing entities that are not supported by a postprocessor, there will be a loss of data.
>
> **SMA.21.4   Mathematical Approximations**
>
> A poor translator may introduce rounding errors or use erroneous assumptions while conducting mathematical approximations. A good translator will offer options regarding entity mapping or the type of mathematical approximations to employ.
>
>
>
> **SMA.21.5   Entity Mismatch in Loop Testing**
>
> Sometimes there is a mismatch of which IGES entities are supported by a particular CAD/CAM system's pre- and postprocessor. This may cause the CAD/CAM system to be unable to read all of the data from an IGES file it created. While this does not necessarily indicate a poor translator, it does indicate that the two translators were not meant to work together. Such a system would not be able to use IGES for archival or for same-system transfers.

21.5   Flavoring an IGES File

In this chapter we have seen so far that different CAD/CAM systems may use IGES entities in different ways. An IGES preprocessor may be capable only of writing data according to an older version of IGES. The translator developer may have made some bad mapping choices or the translator might simply contain errors. Whatever the cause, a portion of the data may not be in a form that can be completely understood by a particular postprocessor.

Because of the importance of good data exchange, it is becoming common for designers to correct many of these problems by modifying their creation methods for CAD/CAM data or editing data within the IGES file. This is called *flavoring*. Flavoring is the process of modifying entities in an IGES file to make them more compatible with the receiving system,[2] to correct errors,[3] or to maximize the amount of data that is exchanged.[4] Flavoring can be classified into two groups. These are described as *procedural* and *programmatic* flavoring. A discussion of each follows.

21.5.1   Procedural Flavoring

Procedural flavoring is usually done at either the CAD/CAM system level using normal CAD/CAM commands or at the IGES file level using an external flavoring or editing utility.[4] Types of procedural flavoring include:

1. Following design rule guidelines for model building that may include what entity types, attributes, and file structures are preferred to optimize the effectiveness of subsequent data exchanges.[2,3]

2. Conducting a manual, step-by-step process of modifying a model based upon a script or set of commands.

21.5.2   Programmatic Flavoring

Programmatic flavoring involves using software that modifies the IGES data for a specific target system.[2,3] This may involve applying option switches on the IGES pre- or postprocessor, or automating procedural flavoring techniques to reduce or remove human interaction.

21.5.3   Flavoring Approaches

Following are several approaches to flavoring.[5]

Validation.   Making syntactic and semantic additions or changes so the IGES file or native model will conform to a specific version of the IGES specification, recommended practice, or other generally accepted method.

Projection.   A simplification where 3D data is projected onto a work plane to produce a 2D equivalent.

Decomposition.   A simplification where the complexity of an entity is reduced.

Explosion.   A simplification where entities are created for every defined instance of that entity.

Conversion.   Replacing entities that cause problems with entities that are near equivalents. This type of flavoring often requires the employment of mathematical approximations.

Sometimes called "IGES-to-IGES" conversion, flavoring is a viable course of action when data exchanges are troublesome. Designers can find utilities and IGES translator products that offer many useful flavoring options. However, poorly executed attempts at flavoring may cause even worse problems than if no flavoring was done at all. Since flavoring means changing data, success depends on the experience or know-how of the designers and the quality of flavoring products.

21.6   IGES Utilities

There are other software products besides the IGES pre- and postprocessors that can be used in IGES production and evaluation processes.[6] These IGES utilities can be separated into three categories: (1) those that *do not change* the IGES file, (2) those that *do change* the IGES file, and (3) *other* translators or utilities. A discussion of each category follows.

21.6.1   Utilities That *Do Not Change* the IGES File

Utilities that *do not change* the IGES file can be classified as analyzers, browsers, checkers, and viewers. The following actions are taken by these utilities (see Fig. 21.2):

Analyzer.   Summarizes general characteristics of the IGES file and the relationships it contains, such as those between sections or entities.

Browser. Skims through the contents of the file, often displaying entity information.

Checker. Detects syntactic or semantic errors within the file. May check that file structure or entity representations are in accordance with the IGES standard.

Viewer. Displays a graphical representation of the IGES file.

These utilities generally help the designer understand the contents of an IGES file without having them deal with the raw data itself. They also offer the security of ensuring that the original IGES file is left unchanged. They may be either graphical or nongraphical (textual) in their primary mode of user interface.

21.6.2 Utilities That *Do Change* the IGES File

Utilities that *do change* the IGES file do so by modifying either the original file or a duplicate one. These utilities can be classified as flavorizers, editors, and filters. The following actions are taken by these utilities (see Fig. 21.2):

Flavorizers. Modifies the IGES file to improve exchange results. Flavorizers may utilize a combination of validation, projection, decomposition, explosion, and conversion techniques.

Editors. Allows the manual editing of entities or structures in the IGES file, often while controlling syntax and file structure.

Filters. Automatic utilities that remove certain entity types or structures.

These utilities may be either graphical or nongraphical (textual) in their primary mode of user interface. In addition, they may automate command execution through macro capabilities (see Chap. 16). Flavorizers may have system-to-system flavors predefined and available from the vendor, relieving the designer of the task of defining certain flavoring actions that are required. These utilities offer a more direct method of changing the IGES file than the IGES pre- or postprocessor. Once again, these utilities are best applied by a designer with at least some knowledge of CAD/CAM, IGES, or data exchange concepts. No utility can provide the flexibility or power of a knowledgeable designer.

21.6.3 Other Translators and Utilities

There are other translators and utilities available. Tailored IGES translators are designed to exchange data between specific systems. Additional utilities are available as well and are vendor-defined.

Utilities

SMA.21.6   What IGES Utilities Can Do

If IGES utilities are available, they can help identify and repair the causes of many problems. An analysis or checker utility applied at steps 6*a,* 8*a,* or 13*a* in the interoperability test (see Sec. 21.7.4) can help find problems with syntax and file structure such as:

1. Data extending past field boundaries, such as parameter data written past column 64 in the parameter data section.

2. Misdefined entity form numbers, such as a 3D entity being written as a 2D form.

3. Problems with associativities and properties, such as incorrectly applied pointers.

4. Data values that are out of range, such as zero-length lines or negative text heights.

SMA.21.7   Pinpointing Pre- or Postprocessor Errors

When an analysis or checking utility is available, it may be possible to determine which of the IGES processors is responsible for causing certain errors. For example, if a postprocessor reports problems with an entity that were also reported by an analysis utility, then the preprocessor may be suspect. If, however, there are problems with a transferred file that passed the analysis without incident, the postprocessor may be suspect.

(Continued)

Utilities
(*Continued*)

SMA.21.8   IGES Viewing Utilities

If an IGES viewing utility is available, it too can be used to help pinpoint translation problems. It can highlight the same problems that were visible on plots, as well as some that were not visible. Deductive reasoning can help pinpoint the causes. IGES viewers can find:

1. Improperly placed clipping planes, drawing entities, or view entities. A viewer will explicitly identify these problems rather than require you to guess at problems that are implied by how plots look.

2. Entities that have been changed or converted to other entity types in such a way as their function has been changed, such as B-splines being converted to polylines.

3. Data that has been lost through degeneration of entities, such as circles broken into straight line segments or dimensions exploded to text and geometry.

SMA.21.9   Product Capability

Any IGES utility will utilize the vendor's own methods for interpreting IGES files. This is what sets the vendors apart: their abilities to perform mathematical approximations (as when mapping higher-order B-splines to lower orders), their ability to read and write the newest (or oldest) versions of IGES, and the robustness of their ability to handle and report problems with IGES files.

SMA.21.10   Product Reliability

Perhaps the most important characteristic of IGES utilities and services is the extent to which you trust the product or vendor. If you want to use a product as a debugging tool, you will be relying on the product to properly identify the problems and to find all errors present in an IGES file. To put it another way, you should believe that the product is doing what you intend it to do.

SMA.21.11   Human Understanding

Do not expect any IGES utility to remove the requirement of human understanding of the IGES standard or the physical file layout requirements. Many IGES utilities assume that you are somewhat familiar with IGES already. However, many offer mechanisms to make it easier to understand the data in an IGES file by identifying fields and explaining the true meanings of cryptic values.

21.7   IGES Testing

IGES testing plays an important part in successful data exchange. There are three distinct categories of IGES tests: (1) verification, (2) conformance, and (3) interoperability. Verification testing is when you verify the vendors' claims for the behavior of their IGES processors. Conformance testing checks a processor for specific characteristics required by the IGES specification.[7] In other words, these first two test categories verify that IGES translation software does what the vendor says it does and creates IGES files that conform to the IGES standard. While these tests are important for successful data exchange, they are of most interest to the developers of IGES translators.

IGES Testing

SMA.21.12   Vendor Verification and Conformance Tests

Ask to see the results of a vendors' IGES translator verification and conformance tests. You should not have to run such tests yourself. Since your primary objective is to transfer IGES data from system to system, concentrate on interoperability testing.

21.7.1   Interoperability Testing[8]

Interoperability testing is aimed at evaluating the effectiveness and usability of data exchange mechanisms within a production environment given certain requirements. The goal is to test how well CAD/CAM data can be transferred within your environment, and then improve upon it in such a way as to allow the prediction of potential for future transfers. Three types of interoperability tests are described (see Fig. 21.5):

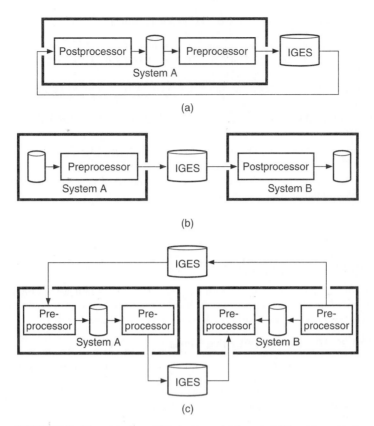

FIGURE 21.5   Three interoperability test types. (*a*) Loop test; (*b*) end-to-end test; (*c*) round-trip test. Notice that the loop test involves one system only, while the end-to-end and the round-trip tests involve two systems. *(Adapted from "Interoperability Acceptance Testing Methodology—IGES Guidelines," Working Document v0.96, Interoperability Acceptance Test Methodology Committee, IGES/PDES Organization, January 22, 1993.)*

Loop Test.   In a loop test an IGES file is written by source CAD/CAM system A, then read back into system A. This exercises the pre- and postprocessor of system A. Loop testing is the easiest type of testing since it uses only one system. However, since only one system is involved, it will prove little about transfers between dissimilar systems.

End-To-End Test.   In an end-to-end test an IGES file is written by source system A, the sending system, and read by target system B, the receiving system. Thus, both the preprocessor of system A and the postprocessor of system B are exercised. While this provides better real-world results than loop testing, it is only an indicator of transfer results in one direction, from A to B.

Round-Trip Test.   In a round-trip test an IGES file is written by system A and read by system B, then written into IGES by B and read back into system A. This test exercises pre- and postprocessors on both system A and system B, and therefore is a better simulation of an environment where product data is being frequently exchanged by these systems. Still, it indicates data exchange results from the standpoint of the originating system A only, since system B will never preprocess data lost in the A-to-B transfer.

21.7.2   Test Preparations

The first phase of interoperability testing involves establishing exchange requirements and assembling the resources that are needed for the test. This phase is critical, for here you define which types of data will be exchanged, how data will be exchanged, and what kind of exchange results are required for the data to be useful.

Plan on assembling the following resources for your test:

1. Check with testing resources such as the National IGES User Group for any preexisting interoperability test reports and case studies so you can learn from the experiences of others (see SMA.21.32).

2. Obtain access to at least the sending CAD/CAM system, its IGES preprocessor, and documentation.

3. If possible, obtain access to the receiving CAD/CAM system, its IGES postprocessor, and documentation.

4. If you cannot gain direct access to the receiving CAD/CAM system, determine who operates the system's postprocessor and discuss all aspects of the exchange with that person directly.

5. Become familiar with the operation of the CAD/CAM systems, printers or plotters, the IGES translators, and data transfer commands.

IGES Testing

SMA.21.13   Scope the Test

Since IGES has so many entity types and covers several application domains, it would be extremely costly and time-consuming to test all IGES data. It is important to narrow the scope of the tests to data types representative of those used in your own environment.

SMA.21.14   Compare Entity Maps

Since it is usually important to know which types of entities are used by both the sending and receiving CAD/CAM systems, a comparison of entity maps from both systems is advisable. These entity maps may reveal incompatibility between systems before actual testing begins.[8] Then decide which of the test types described in Sec. 21.7.1 will provide the level of characterization needed for your application.

The knowledge gained from comparing entity maps will help define exchange requirements. This is where the concepts of functional and visual equivalence discussed in Chap. 20 come into play.

SMA.21.15   Visual Equivalence for Good Pictures

If your goal is to transfer a good picture, as for use in technical publications, it may be adequate for entities to be changed or remapped to simpler entity types if it will cause the resulting picture to be visually equivalent to the original. (Also see Chap. 20.)

SMA.21.16   Functional Equivalence for Good Data

Your test requirements will be quite different, for example, if you need highly accurate data for an NC application where entities are to remain unchanged. If the receiver is able to make sense out of the drawing or model—can use it, modify it, and reissue it from within their CAD/CAM system— the transferred data can be considered functionally equivalent.[9] (Also see Chap. 20.)

SMA.21.17   Measuring Results

After establishing the test requirements, decide how the results will be measured. You might count errors in the pre- and postprocessor error message logs that pertain to critical entity types. You might conduct a visual check of the resulting drawing and use the receiving system's "check entity" type commands to verify a sample of entities. Or you might use a third-party IGES verification or analysis utility to obtain a detailed report.

21.7.3   Test Cases

The operative component of an interoperability test is the test case. A test case includes IGES files, a methodology consisting of purposes and procedures for the test, a way to document the test, and (optionally) a script for specific commands or measurement procedures. You can develop your own test cases or use existing ones.

IGES Testing

SMA.21.18 Test Case Characteristics

There are important characteristics and issues to be considered when selecting or developing a test case.[8] These are:

1. They should be relevant to your normal way of doing business.

2. They should be developed and used on systems consistent with those you normally use.

3. They should be developed with design methods similar to those normally used in your business.

4. They should cover many, and ideally *all*, of the entities and constructs normally used or anticipated for use.

5. They should take advantage of the capabilities of your systems to influence and record the systems' configuration and switch settings.

6. Always record your test results and submit the documentation to the National IGES User Group to help others with their testing efforts.

SMA.21.19 Test Case Sources

Some test cases should be derived from your own representative CAD/CAM models. Yet creating robust test cases can be a difficult and time-consuming task, so the use of additional existing test cases can help make testing practical. There are several organizations that compile and distribute test cases, including the National IGES User Group, the IGES/PDES Organization, the CALS Test Network, and vendors (see SMA.21.31, 32).

21.7.4 Running Interoperability Tests

Once you have prepared your requirements and test cases, you are ready to conduct some tests. The general steps for an end-to-end interoperability test (see Sec. 21.7.1 and Fig. 21.5) are as follows.[8] While these steps are listed sequentially, you may need to loop through this interaction process several times to achieve exchange goals (also see Fig. 21.7).

Steps for End-To-End Test

Step 1. Establish native CAD/CAM model A.
Techniques should reflect real-world usage. Record CAD/CAM system model composition and techniques used so conditions can be re-created.

    a. Apply flavoring if required (see Sec. 21.5).

Step 2. Record environment variables for system A.
Include any information that may affect the native model, such as hardware platform, operating system level, software version, or default tolerances.

Step 3. Plot and label the native CAD/CAM model.
Make additional plots to show close-up details as needed. Labeling should include model information, system identification, view identifications, etc.

Step 4. Run preprocessor (A → IGES).
Set options or switches as needed and record switch settings used.

    a. Apply flavoring through switches if required (see Sec. 21.5).

Step 5. Inspect and record preprocessor error log.

Step 6. Verify resulting IGES file (see SMA.21.22).

    a. Apply utilities if required (see Sec. 21.6).

    b. Apply flavoring if required (see Sec. 21.5).

Step 7. Transfer file from system A to system B. (Also see Chap. 20, Secs. 20.3.3 and SMA.20.36.)

Step 8. Verify transferred IGES file (see SMA.21.22).

    a. Apply utilities if required (see Sec. 21.6).

    b. Apply flavoring if required (see Sec. 21.5).

Step 9. Record environment variables for system B.
Include any information that may affect the native model, such as hardware platform, operating system level, software version, or default tolerances.

Step 10. Run IGES postprocessor (IGES → B).
If it is necessary to first establish a base CAD/CAM file to receive the translated IGES data, do so now. Record CAD/CAM system model composition. Set options or switches as needed, recording switch settings used.

   a. Apply flavoring through switches if required (see Sec. 21.5).

Step 11. Inspect and record postprocessor error log.

Step 12. View and/or plot resulting CAD/CAM model on system B.
Make additional plots to show close-up details as needed. Labeling should include model information, system identification, view identifications, etc.

Step 13. Perform analysis of resulting CAD/CAM model.
Loop back through previous steps as needed.

   a. Apply flavoring to IGES file or to the system B model if required (see Sec. 21.5).

Note: All steps mentioned here refer to the end-to-end interoperability test outlined in Sec. 21.7.4.

Analysis and Debugging

SMA.21.20 Analysis and Verification

Steps 5, 6, 8, 11, and 13 require analysis and verification. The depth of the analysis depends on the utilities that are available and the results that are being experienced.

SMA.21.21 Debugging Hints

1. Compare entity maps for the sending and receiving systems. While this will identify entities that are and are not supported by the translators, the maps usually will not document bugs or poor translation characteristics of the translator software.

2. The pre- and postprocessor error message logs in steps 5 and 11 should show any fatal errors in execution or excessive nonsupport of entities.

3. Check for discrepancies between the vendors' claims for the translators and the error messages in the log.

SMA.21.22 IGES File Verification

The verifications in steps 6 and 8 involve checking that the resulting IGES file was created, that it is indeed a neutral (ASCII) file and that it has a size greater than zero. These verifications will indicate gross failures of the pre- or postprocessor. In step 7, locate the neutral file in the directory system of the receiving computer and check that its size is nearly equivalent to its size on the sending system. If the file cannot be found or is a different size, the physical transfer may have failed.

SMA.21.23 If the IGES File Will Not Load

If the IGES file will not load into the receiving CAD/CAM system's postprocessor in step 10, there are several possible causes. These are as follows:

1. There may be a header on the file such as those required for CALS files or those used by E-mail systems. Headers can be identified as data occurring before the IGES flag or start section. Remove the header with a text editor.

2. The file may have improper end-of-line characters as record delimiters. This is common when exchanging files between DOS and Unix systems. ASCII files on DOS use a carriage return/line feed at the end of each line, while on Unix they use a single new line character. Use commands such as "fold" on Unix or similar utilities to fix the delimiters. This conversion may also be accomplished through the ASCII file transfer mechanisms between DOS and UNIX.

3. Some operating systems require that the IGES file's file name (such as FILENAME.IGS) or file type (such as TEXT versus BINARY) be set correctly before translators can access them. Use operating system commands to change the file types as documented in the translator manual.

(Continued)

4. Since the binary and compressed ASCII forms of IGES files are considered obsolete, most post-processors cannot read these forms. The compressed ASCII form will have human-readable ASCII characters, but will not follow the 80-column format of the full ASCII form. The binary form will use non-ASCII characters and will probably make no sense to the human eye. Be careful not to draw a premature conclusion that a file is binary when it may simply have been compressed with a file compression utility. If it will not uncompress with a utility corresponding to its file name extension, it may indeed be the binary form of IGES.

5. Look for the terminate section to be the last line in the IGES file. If it is missing, it is likely that some of the file was lost in the physical file transfer process.

6. Additional data following the terminate section in the IGES file may cause some postprocessors to fail. Remove the extra data with a text editor.

SMA.21.24   Plot-to-Plot Comparisons

For the analysis in step 13, look at the resulting drawing as displayed on the receiving CAD/CAM system or the plot created in step 12. Compare them to the plot of the original drawing created in step 3. Look for visible differences between the original and the resultant drawing such as:

1. Parts of drawing or models are missing.

2. Deformed entities. These entities will seem to have stretched or warped, often streaking over the entire drawing in an obvious way.

3. Overlapping entities. This is especially visible when text entities overlap geometry or other text.

4. Leader lines or arrow heads pointing in the wrong direction.

5. Problems with line widths.

6. 3D models that cannot be rotated.

7. Entities that cannot be selected and/or modified.

8. Original entity colors that are not retained.

Problems discovered in this manner cannot be attributed to either the pre- or postprocessor since it is not clear which is to blame or whether there is an incompatibility between the two translators. Use the error message logs in comparison to the visible results to offer further insight in pre- and postprocessor problems. Deductive reasoning can help pinpoint some errors.

SMA.21.25   The Final Judge

The final part of an interoperability test involves deciding if the requirements you established in the beginning have been met during the exchanges you have conducted. A pass or fail decision can be based upon the completeness of the exchanges, or whether the information content or functionality of entities was changed by the exchanges.[8] Someone else may reach a different decision, but you are the only judge of which results are important to you and how good is good enough. If your requirements and measurements were defined up front, it should be possible to be objective.

SMA.21.26   Case Study Repositories

Remember that interoperability testing and the IGES evaluation process as a whole are basically learning experiences. You will want to refer back to recall problems that existed, why they existed, and how they were overcome. This means that documents are critical to the IGES evaluation process, representing reference material and your recording medium. If someone else has solved an exchange problem and documented how it was solved, and if that documentation is available, much of the interactive nature of the evaluation process can be avoided. Therefore, always check in the public and private case study repositories for any information that will get you to production faster (see SMA.21.31, 32).

SMA.21.27   Documentation

Whenever possible, document your own evaluations and make them useful to improve later transfers. Whenever the rules of your organization allow it, share your results with:

1. Your own organization, so they can benefit from your efforts later on.

(*Continued*)

2. Your CAD/CAM vendor, so they can correct any problems you discover.

3. Designers everywhere, so they too can benefit from your learning experiences.

There are public organizations that would appreciate copies of your reports so they might make this information available to others (see SMA.21.31, 32). The CALS Test Network can help by performing or assisting, you with actual evaluations and then publishing the results. The National IGES User Group and the IGES/PDES Organization have developed a short case study form (see Fig. 21.6) that you can fill out and return to be included in their repository of case studies.

SMA.21.28 Record Keeping

When recording evaluation efforts, it is a good idea to include the following items[8]:

1. The domain of your application (mechanical design/drafting, electrical, finite element, piping, etc.).

2. Test type (loop, end-to-end, round-trip).

3. Exchange requirements.

4. Measurement criteria.

5. Test case description.

6. Environment settings, including hardware types, operating system, CAD/CAM software and translator versions for both sending and receiving systems. Also include translator switch settings.

7. Plots from both sending and receiving systems.

8. All error message logs from both pre- and postprocessors, including error messages, warning messages, informational messages and messages about limitations due to nonsupport of entities.

9. Results—analysis and measurements against criteria. If there is a failure, document the nature of the failure as either: (1) a physical file transfer failure, (2) a gross processor failure, (3) entity map incompatibility, or (4) poor translator implementation. Include the effects of design techniques or hardware effects.

10. Summary and recommendations.

Note: We have seen how entity mapping, flavoring, utilities, and interoperability testing all have a role to play in the IGES evaluation process. These components, however, do not represent an end in themselves. The reason for entering the IGES evaluation phase was to find out how to get the best possible data exchange results during production IGES exchanges. With this in mind, here is some advice on how these components can be used together to get you into production with better IGES exchange results. (Also refer to Fig. 21.7.)

SMA.21.29 An Iterative Approach

An iterative approach may be able to remedy problems that are discovered. This process includes locating where the error originated, going back to either the original CAD/CAM system or the IGES file, making changes, running the translator(s), and analyzing the results again. Problems can be fixed by applying option switches on the pre- and postprocessor, running a flavorizer, or making changes to the IGES file with a text editor or IGES editing utility.

SMA.21.30 Know the Model's History

It is important to know the history of a drawing or model when analyzing the results of an interoperability test. This is because the IGES file is the product not only of the sending CAD/CAM system and preprocessor, but of all CAD/CAM systems that have previously translated it. Any time an IGES file has been translated by more than one system, it makes it harder to pinpoint the cause of problems.

Case Study Form and Questionnaire

Subject/Keywords: _____

Submitter's Name: _____   Date Submitted: _____

Company: _____   Telephone: _____

Address: _____   Fax/Email: _____

City/State: _____

Sending System, Vendor Name and Type

Hardware: _____
Operating system/version: _____
Software product/version: _____
Translator software/version: _____
Medium: _____

Auxiliary Software Used (if any): Vendor Name and Type

Operating system/version: _____
Software product/version: _____

Receiving System, Vendor Name and Type

Hardware: _____
Operating system/version: _____
Software product/version: _____
Translator software/version: _____

Application Use of Data

❑ Drafting
❑ Electrical
❑ AEC
❑ Piping
❑ N/C
❑ FEM/FESA
❑ Other: _____
_____
_____

Type of Data

❑ Point
❑ Curve
❑ Wireframe
❑ Surface
❑ Solids
❑ Annotation
❑ Embedded data
❑ Data structure
❑ Other: _____

Type of Transfer

❑ To file (system A → file)
❑ From file (file → system A)
❑ One-way (system A → system B)
❑ Bidirectional (system A → system B → system A)
❑ Other: _____

Success of Transfer

❑ Worked well
❑ Worked with modification
❑ Did not work, used alternate method
❑ Did not work, no resolution to date

Impact of Operations

❑ Major success, worked well, saved time/cost
❑ Minor difficulty, work around, inconvenience, tolerable
❑ Major difficulty, work stoppage, incorrect result
❑ Other, define: _____

Vendor was notified, vendor name, phone, tracking number: _____

FIGURE 21.6 IGES case study form. Use this form to document the results of IGES transfers. *(Courtesy of the National IGES User Group.)*

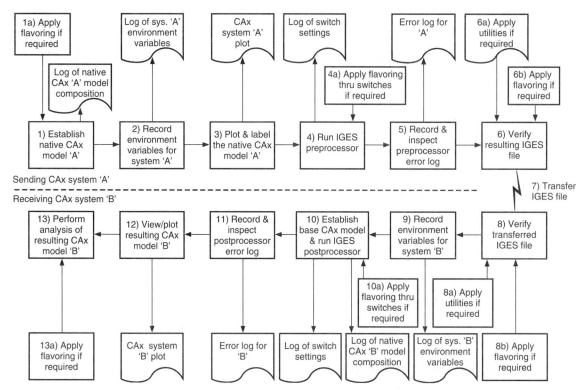

FIGURE 21.7 The overall IGES evaluation process. Notice that there are many opportunities to document the process by capturing data logs and plots. *(Adapted from "Interoperability Acceptance Testing Methodology—IGES Guidelines," Working Document v0.96, Interoperability Acceptance Test Methodology Committee, IGES/PDES Organization, January 22, 1993.)*

21.8 Emerging Functionality Enhancements to IGES

Since IGES is a stable data exchange standard, much of the work to enhance its functionality is in the areas of application protocols (APs) and IGES subsets. Unlike the IGES specification itself that defines raw entities, an application protocol defines the context in which the entities will be used.[10] An AP provides a documented link between an IGES entity and what that entity represents in a particular kind of application.

21.8.1 Application Protocols (APs)

To illustrate an application protocol, imagine that an IGES file is created by a printed circuit board design system. Here a line entity is used to describe a copper circuit trace on the circuit card, including attribute information that would be useful in the electronic design and testing context. If you send that IGES file to a mechanical design/drafting system, the context has changed, for here a line means the edge of a physical part. You are left with a bunch of lines that only visually look as they did in the electrical design system, but the attribute information is no longer of use. Similarly, a line in a 3D piping application used by architects may mean a length of straight pipe, again having its own set of important attributes that may be lost when taken out of context.

There are three official IGES application protocols that are maintained by the IGES/PDES Organization. They address: (1) engineering drawings (in the mechanical domain), (2) electronic microcircuit assemblies (in the electronic domain), and (3) 3D piping (in the AEC domain). There are other IGES applications protocols proposed by other industry associations.

21.8.2 IGES Subsets

IGES subsets involve restricting the allowable entity types that should be supported by translators for a specific application area. In this way, some of the ambiguity involved in the entity mapping is removed so the translator developer can pick entities that are more likely to be broadly supported. There are several IGES subsets in common use, including the CALS IGES classes 1 through 4[11] and the German VDA-IS standard. Some large companies embrace their own subsets, and there are also subsets for use in various government organizations such as the Department of Energy's DOEDEF and NASA's subset for computational fluid dynamics applications.

21.9   Improving Solid Modeling for IGES

As mentioned in the opening of this chapter, support for solids in IGES has been almost a nonissue. While CSG solids have been part of the IGES specification since 1988, very few CAD/CAM vendors implemented CSG support in their IGES translators. B-Rep solids were added to IGES in 1991, but vendors have been slow to implement these as well.

Vendors have several reasons for their translator policies. Many have seen little reason to add SM support because they perceived a weak overall usage of SM, and thus only a meager demand for SM in IGES. Some were waiting for B-Rep to be included in IGES before making major changes to their translators, while others wait for the next generation of data exchange standards. Still more would say that IGES constructs are inadequate to completely transfer the rich content of their proprietary data structures. These factors have meant that the use of IGES solids has not reached a critical mass in the user community.

When IGES-based SM capabilities are unavailable, it forces the SM designer either to use only one CAD/CAM system within their enterprise or to implement data exchange methods that allow them to coexist with nonsolids-based systems. IGES has proven useful for this latter case, and many designers demand even further capabilities of their SM vendors to support this coexistence. An example of a needed SM feature is the ability to easily create solid models using construction geometry imported through IGES as wireframe or surface data.

As the demand for SM-based CAD/CAM grows, more designers will expect enhanced data exchange capabilities, including B-Rep and/or CSG support. Many vendors will find it very difficult to develop new data exchange architectures for the next-generation standards and will implement solids in their existing IGES translators. Those SM vendors looking for a competitive advantage may add implementor-defined entities to their translators to capture more information not predefined in IGES from their SM system. These added capabilities would give the designers more options as they develop their archive and integration strategies.

Contacts

SMA.21.31   CALS Test Network (CTN)

The CALS Test Network is a confederation of organizations in government and industry that demonstrates the CALS standards and tests their effectiveness.[12] One of the CALS standards, MIL-D-28000,[11] defines subsets of IGES for use in exchanging product data (see Chap. 20). You may join the CALS Test Network without charge as long as you agree in writing to adhere to their testing procedures.

Test cases and results available to CTN members are:

1. MIL-D-28000 Class I Reference Illustration Packet, Revision A. The class I subset is for use with technical illustrations. The test case includes a procedure manual and IGES files.

2. MIL-D-28000 Class II Reference Illustration Packet, Revision C. The class II subset is for use with engineering drawings. The test case includes a procedure manual and IGES files.

3. Many exchange test reports are available through the CTN regarding the performance of specific systems in IGES exchanges.

For more information contact:

CALS Test Network
HQ AFMC/ENCT
4027 Colonel Glenn Hwy., Suite 200
Dayton, OH 45431-1601

(Continued)

Contacts
(*Continued*)

SMA.21.32   The National IGES User Group and the IGES/PDES Organization (IPO)

The National IGES User Group (NIUG) is a membership organization of individuals from industry, government, and academia who share a common goal to increase and improve the use of IGES. It provides a neutral forum for the sharing and exchange of information about IGES technology through its national organization and several regional affiliates. NIUG acts as the user group for the IGES/PDES Organization (IPO), which is responsible for the development and maintenance of product data exchange standards in the United States.

NIUG leverages its relationship with the IPO by offering to its members test cases and other resources that are developed and recommended by the IPO's Testing Project. NIUG also maintains its own collection of widely available IGES files that can be used for interoperability testing.

Information available to NIUG and IPO members includes:

1. IGES specification documents

2. IGES recommended practices documents

3. IGES Application Protocol documents

4. A database of case studies from the IPO and the NIST Manufacturing Technology Centers

5. Over 100 IGES files from the IPO's Testing Project, including Autofact6 (MBB Gehaeuse), Multinty, and the SAE single-entity test suite

6. Interoperability Acceptance Testing Methodology—IGES Guidelines document from the Interoperability Acceptance Test Methodology Committee of the IPO

7. IGES case study forms

For more information contact:

National IGES User Group *or* IGES/PDES Organization
c/o National Computer Graphics Association
2722 Merrilee Drive, Suite 200
Fairfax, VA 22031
(703)698-9606

SMA.21.33   Translator and Utility Vendors

As mentioned before, the most important software used in the data exchange process are the IGES pre- and postprocessor translators. There are also separate translators and utilities intended to improve data exchange.

Good to Know

SMA.21.34   Don't Jump to Conclusions

When viewing an incoming IGES model, don't be too quick to discount your results. Try applying display techniques, such as smoothing, and adding isolines to surfaces. Sometimes surfaces come across in such low display resolution that you may be mislead by the display.

Don LaCourse, President
The Solid Modeling ExChange, Algood, Tenn.

SMA.21.35   Check Modeling Tolerances After Transfers

When loading data files such as IGES or DXF, some SM systems adjust the modeling tolerance to match the tolerance in the header section of the data file. Make sure that the modeling tolerance is reset after loading. A tolerance left too small (1E-12) will result in a data explosion making the resulting model file to large and slow to work with. A modeling tolerance left too large (0.1) will allow data to be overlooked, causing an incorrect model.

Wally Frederick, Director Customer Support
Varimetrix Corp., Palm Bay, Fla.

Good to Know
(Continued)

SMA.21.36   Not Just SM Data

When SM data is to be conveyed via IGES even though the SM definition is not used, it is wise to convey as many corresponding CAD-specific model elements as possible in order to allow the receiver to rebuild the model in SM if necessary. For example, topological elements such as vertices and edges should be conveyed in parallel to the pure geometry elements.

Hermann Ruess
Hewlett-Packard Co., Mechanical Design Div.,
Boeblingen, Germany

SMA.21.37   View-Dependent IGES Transfers

Some SM systems have an IGES file transfer option that can be a real time-saver if you are using another wireframe CAD system for producing detail drawings and/or technical illustrations. This option is called a *view-dependent IGES transfer*. Basically, this function will take any view of your solid and remove all hidden lines prior to the IGES conversion process. The IGES file can then be read into your detailing CAD system. When you display the converted file you must duplicate the same angular orientation of the view in order to properly position the geometry. Very complex exploded views can be assembled very quickly with this IGES option and annotated with your powerful CAD tools.

George E. Mock, Member Technical Staff
AT&T Network Cable Systems, Norcross, Ga.

SMA.21.38   Typical Record-Length Problem

One common problem when exchanging ASCII data between different computer platforms is record length. Some computers use fixed length records, where the operating system uses a fixed number of characters for each line or record in a file. The first 80 characters define the first record, the second 80 define the second record, and so on, with no delimiting characters between records.

Other computer platforms, such as DOS and Unix computers, use variable-length records. These systems have records that end with a new line (Unix operating systems) or a combination of carriage return, line feed, or both (DOS operating systems).

For CAD/CAM data exchange, most translators are written to recognize missing or extra record delimiting characters, so you may never see a problem. If the translator fails, it is only necessary to know which type of system is the source and which is the destination. You can then get around mismatches by using operating-system- or network-level utilities provided by most computer platforms to convert files between fixed- and variable-length records.

SMA.21.39   Limited IGES File Size Acceptance

Some SM and CAD/CAM systems have limitations on the size of the file that can be imported. This is usually due to system resource limitations set by the system administrator. If an IGES file is too large, these limitations may cause the postprocessor to stop midway through a job, leaving an incomplete drawing or no drawing at all.

Some of these systems offer option switches on the postprocessor that allow you to distribute data to multiple drawing files. Utilities that do the same thing can be purchased. While this fracturing of the data into multiple files can be a headache for tracking the data, at least it allows the data to be imported into the receiving CAD/CAM format where it can be manipulated using the capabilities of the CAD/CAM system.

SMA.21.40   Useful Facts About IGES Files

Here are some useful facts about IGES files that can make them easier to deal with.[13]

1. The number of entities in an IGES file equals the number of directory entry (DE) records divided by 2.

(Continued)

Good to Know
(*Continued*)

2. An entity can be uniquely identified by its DE number.

3. An entity's DE number will always be an odd number.

4. The DE data for an entity contains a pointer to its corresponding parameter data (PD).

5. The PD data for an entity contains a pointer to its corresponding DE data.

6. In general, an entity can be deleted by replacing its entity type number with type zero in both DE and PD sections.

SMA.21.41 Editing and Browsing

If you must edit an IGES file manually, edit with care, and follow the syntax defined by the IGES standard document. Always make a backup copy first. If you must use a text editor, be sure it is not the kind that substitutes TAB characters for spaces.

SMA.21.42 Standardization

The Initial Graphics Exchange Specification (IGES) evolved from the Boeing Company's need to off-load some of their plotting work to the General Electric Company. The need to transmit data generated the need for a common tape format for use between the two companies. The rest is history.

IGES evolved with the CAD/CAM software industry and therefore includes many ways to represent curves, surfaces, and annotations that make up a drawing. An underlying problem is that the drawings themselves are not standardized, let alone the means of representing them in a computer. Drawings are an art form, with each industry and each company interjecting their own idiosyncrasies. CAD/CAM software has evolved to address these idiosyncrasies in different ways. It should not be surprising that very little information is transportable through IGES that is not basic geometric definitions.

Geometric definitions are well documented and represent a common language to implementors. Annotation is relatively ad hoc. Even though there are standards for annotation content, their form is not incorporated into computer models in a way that makes automated translation practical.

SMA.21.43 The Concept of an Object

Unfortunately, IGES can be considered a collection of data types rather than a standard. One reason for this is that there is no underlying concept of an object that is to be represented in IGES. From its inception, IGES has been a documentation process of implemented data formats. Most of the formats are devised to support various schemes for representing drawings. IGES does not represent a geometric representation of an object, but, rather, it represents a collection of geometry (curves, surfaces, etc.) which may or may not geometrically define an object.

Michael A. Dincau, President
Graphic Systems Inc., Burbank, Calif.

References

1. Stokes, Harlan, "Tooling the IGES Exchange Process," *MCN (MicroCAD News)*, September 1991, pp. 53–55, 64.

2. Stokes, Harlan, "Tools for the Data Exchange Process," *Proceedings of the National IGES User Group seminar at Autofact '92*, November 9, 1992, Detroit, Mich.

3. Ard, Joseph H., Jr, Don M. Hemmelgarn, Edward J. Carl, "Emerging Standards Save Bucks with Efficient Product and Process Development," *MicroCAD News*, May 1991, pp. 62–67.

4. Jaramillo, Jorge, "Flavoring," *Newsletter of the Twin Cities IGES User Group*, Minneapolis/St. Paul, winter 1991.

5. Tensmeyer, John, "Making IGES Work with Tools," handout from the National IGES User Group seminar at Autofact '92, November 9, 1992, Detroit, MI.

6. Stokes, Harlan, "IGES Product and Services Vendors Stand Alone," *DesignNet*, April 1992, pp. 59–61.

7. "National IGES Processor Testing Program—Organization, Methodology, and Procedures," Version 1.1, Conformance and Verification Testing Methodologies Committee, IGES/PDES Organization, October 16, 1992.

8. "Interoperability Acceptance Testing Methodology—IGES Guidelines," Working Document v0.96, Interoperability Acceptance Test Methodology Committee, IGES/PDES Organization, January 22, 1993.

9. Morea, Greg, "Seawolf DDE Program," *Proceedings of the Product Data Exchange for the 1990s Seminar,* sponsored by the IGES/PDES Organization, the National IGES User Group and NCGA, New Orleans, La., February 20–22, 1991.

10. Deeds, Lisa V. and Ben Kassel, "MIL-D-28000A Upgrade Plan," Naval Surface Warfare Center Technical memorandum, CDNSWC/TM12-92/79, June 30, 1992.

11. MIL-D-28000A, "MILITARY SPECIFICATION—DIGITAL REPRESENTATION FOR COMMUNICATION OF PRODUCT DATA: IGES APPLICATION SUBSETS AND IGES APPLICATION PROTOCOLS," February 10, 1992.

12. *CALS Test Network Handbook,* Air Force CALS Technical Center of the U.S. Air Force Logistics Command, CTN 91-042, July 1991.

13. Mattei, David, "IGES Fundamentals and Improving Data Exchange," *Proceedings of the National IGES User Group seminar Autofact '92,* November 9, 1992, Detroit, Mich.

Suggestions for Further Reading

Mayer, Ralph, *Using IGES, DXF and CALS for CAD/CAM Data Transfer,* Management Roundtable, Inc., 1992.

Initial Graphics Exchange Specification (IGES)—Version 5.1, NISTIR 4412, U.S. National Bureau of Standards (NIST), 1991.

IGES 5.1 *Recommended Practices Guide,* IGES/PDES Organization, January 1992.

Brander, Ray, "An IGES Tutorial," *Newsletter of the Twin Cities IGES User Group,* Minneapolis/St. Paul, spring 1991.

Stokes, Harlan, "Testing IGES Exchange Methods," *MCN (MicroCAD News),* July 1991, pp. 46–51, 80.

Chapter 22

Solid Modeling and Product Data Exchange Using STEP (PDES/STEP)

Michael A. Dincau
President
Graphic Systems, Inc.

Computers have become an important means of capturing, storing, and communicating information. Today, the ability to share computerized product information is virtually nonexistent for a variety of technical and business reasons. Some companies have exchanged some data via translators; however, translators can be described as tenuous at best, even when only translating geometry. Computerized information (other than geometry) is, essentially, not transferable.

Many users of CAD/CAM systems have recognized the need to improve the communication of product information between organizations. Standards provide the foundation for communication. This chapter provides an overview of an international standardization effort known as PDES/STEP.

Note: PDES (Product Data Exchange using STEP) is the name given to the United States development activity in support of the international standard known as STEP (Standard for the Exchange of Product Model Data). The definition of PDES was made more explicit in 1990 by altering the meaning of the acronym from its earlier one, Product Data Exchange Specification.

The goal of the PDES/STEP standards project is to make all of the data necessary to design, develop, produce, and support a product transportable between organizations and computer systems.

An important point to keep in mind is that the PDES/STEP standard is very much in evolution. Further, because the standard will be very broad in application, and due to the limited scope of this chapter, no attempt is made to cover this subject in its entirety. Future editions of this publication will continue to provide assistance to SM operators and managers as the PDES/STEP standard evolves.

22.1   PDES/STEP History

First, a little background on what it was that led to this standardization effort. Customers, primarily the United States Department of Defense (DoD), recognized that the products that they purchase are expensive to procure and maintain. The Product Data Exchange Specification (PDES) originated as a project sponsored by the United States Air Force (USAF) in 1979 to alleviate this problem. A major impetus for PDES came from government procurement agencies that perceived value in the ability to easily transfer development programs to other contractors. This would allow them to bid competitively on production or maintenance after development had matured. There may be many advantages and disadvantages in this concept, but it did start people thinking.

22.1.1   PDDI and GMAP

Two important projects sponsored by the USAF documented the need for improved data representation and tested some concepts. The Product Data Definition Interface (PDDI) project was a pilot program to attempt to document and improve product data definition. The Geometric Modeling Applications Interface Program (GMAP) was a follow-up program to demonstrate and extend PDDI. These were important programs because they demonstrated failings of the existing technology and documented the need for improvement.

The goal of the PDES project was to provide a standard by which all product data could be exchanged. The product models were envisioned to include all of the information that documents a product from inception through production and support. In addition to geometry, PDES was expected to support a wide range of nongeometric data. The goal was to provide a foundation for next-generation CAD/CAD systems. The PDES project came about due to recognized limitations of the Initial Graphics Exchange Specification (IGES) standard (see Chap. 21).

22.1.2 ANSI and ISO

As the need for improved product data representation methods has become more widely recognized, government standards organizations have become involved—notably, the American National Standards Institute (ANSI) and the International Standards Organization (ISO). In 1983 the ISO agreed on the need to create a single international standard for product data exchange. ISO established Technical Committee 184 on Industrial Automation Systems (TC184), which in turn formed Subcommittee 4 (SC4) to work in the area of representation and exchange of digital product data. Thus, we have ISO TC184/SC4. The subcommittee's efforts were unofficially named STandard for the Exchange of Product Model Data (STEP).

22.1.3 NIST and USTAG

The United States Department of Commerce has an organization called the National Institute of Standards and Technology (NIST). NIST was delegated by ANSI to act as Secretariat of SC4. Twenty-five countries are involved in the work of SC4. The voting of the position for the United States was done by a consensus group in the United States called the United States Technical Advisory Group (USTAG). The USTAG was accredited by ANSI and operates under ANSI rules and procedures. NIST acts as the administrator of the USTAG.

The U.S. Department of Commerce redirected the ANSI/PDES effort to coordinate with the international effort. This brought about a change. The Product Data Exchange Specification (PDES) acronym was changed to Product Data Exchange using STEP (PDES). The acronym is also seen written PDES/STEP. The U.S. Department of Commerce would like the STEP acronym to replace the PDES acronym completely. We will comply for the remainder of this chapter, except where reflections require the use of the PDES acronym. The goals remain the same but have taken on an international flavor. Of course, there are many pros and cons to broadening the scope, which the reader may judge.

22.1.4 IGES/PDES Organization (IPO)

There was another interesting turn of events in the history of PDES. Solid geometry modeling is the cornerstone of PDES, and is one of the more mature aspect of the effort. The IGES organization recognized that if they adopted the geometry forms proposed in PDES, they could better provide a migration path between IGES and PDES. Hence, the IGES-promoting organization that was formed in 1979 adopted the new name IGES/PDES Organization (IPO). The IPO is an open, voluntary organization developing specifications for the exchange of product data. The IPO has over 500 volunteers from industry, government, and academia who meet quarterly to work on IGES, STEP, and testing methodologies related to these standards.

22.2 STEP Structure

22.2.1 Geometric and Nongeometric Data

The information used to design, fabricate, assemble, and support a product, and hence the STEP standard, can be divided into two general classes of information: geometric and nongeometric. Here, *geo-*

metric refers to the information normally found on drawings to specify dimensions and tolerances. In practice, the actual geometric definition may reside in reference drawings, standards, tables, and/or in a CAD system. *Nongeometric* here refers to virtually all of the additional information that is used to design, fabricate, assemble, and support a product. This could include test data supporting a design; configuration data; process planning for tooling, part fabrication, assembly, quality assurance; and so on.

The need to standardize nongeometric data, such as configuration and process information, has been recognized but is in its infancy. There are organizations actively working on the needs for specific disciplines. One example is the Process Data eXchange Institute (PDIX). PDIX is an initiative of the American Institute of Chemical Engineers to promote electronic exchange of manufacturing process information. This is a cooperative effort, with participation of over 30 industrial companies. Their goal is to develop standards for the exchange of process information between computer programs, databases, and organizations.

22.2.2 The Parts of STEP[1]

Currently, STEP consists of several dozen documents called *parts* (see Fig. 22.1 and Table 22.1). These parts are assigned a name and number and grouped together with common functions within a specific numeric range. As STEP is implemented, new STEP parts will be developed, increasing its scope and breadth. There are currently six (6) series of STEP parts.

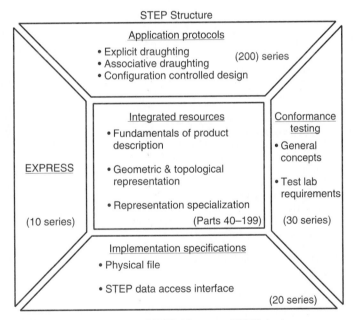

FIGURE 22.1 The structure of STEP. *(Courtesy of PDES, Inc.)*

The 10-Series. The 10-series parts comprise the computer-interpretable area of STEP. This area allows all users to operate by the same guidelines and rules necessary to maintain consistent, accurate data exchange. EXPRESS is the data modeling language used to make STEP computer-interpretable. This language can be compiled to produce "C" structures, SQL statements, or other similar types of information. This language is an important advantage of STEP over IGES, which offers nothing comparable.

The 20-Series. The 20-series parts define the physical file and database-sharing exchange area and are the enabling tools for STEP data transfer.

The 30-Series. The 30-series parts define conformance testing requirements and are used for data and application verification.

TABLE 22.1   The STEP Standard

STEP is made up of a group of parts (application protocols) which are a collection of working documents that address varying disciplines. There are currently six series of parts within the STEP standard. Parts are added as required. The status of each part as an International Standard is indicated as of June 20, 1994. STEP is governed by the International Standards Organization (ISO), Technical Committee 184 on Industrial Automation Systems (TC184), Subcommittee 4 (SC4), which addresses the area of representation and exchange of digital product data (ISO TC184/SC4). (Courtesy of PDES, Inc.)

Part	Document name	Status*
1	Overview	IS
11	EXPRESS Language	IS
12	EXPRESS-I Language	WD
21	Physical File Structure	IS
22	Data Access Interface	CD
31	Testing Concepts	IS
32	Test Lab Requirements	CD
33	Abstract Test Suites	WD
34	Abstract Test Methods	WD
41	Product Description	IS
42	Geometric and Topological Representation	IS
43	Representation Structures	IS
44	Product Structure Configuration	IS
45	Materials	CD
46	Visual Presentation	IS
47	Shape Tolerance	CD
48	Form Features	WD
49	Process Structure	CD
101	Draughting Resources	IS
102	Ship Structures	In development
103	E/E Connectivity Editor	WD
104	Finite Element Analysis	CD
105	Kinematics	CD
201	Explicit Draughting	IS
202	Associative Draughting	CD
203	Configuration Controlled Design	IS
204	Mechanical Design Using B-Rep.	WD
205	Mechanical Design Using Surface	WD
206	Mechanical Design Using Wireframe	Not funded
207	Sheet Metal Die Planning	CD
208	Life Cycle Change Process	WD
209	Composite Structures	CDC
210	PCA: Design and Manufacture	CDC
211	Electronic Test, Diagnostics, and Remfg.	In development
212	Electrotechnical Plants	CDC
213	Numerical Control Process Plans	CDC
214	Automotive Design Processes	CDC
215	Ship Arrangement	In development
216	Ship Molded Forms	In development
217	Ship Piping	In development
218	Ship Structures	In development
219	Inspection Process Plans	In development
220	PCA: Manufacturing Planning	In development
221	Functional Data and Schematic Rep. for Process Plants	In development
222	Exchange of Product Definition Data from Design Eng. to Mfg. Eng. for Composite Structures	In development
223	Exchange of Design and Manufacturing Product Information for Cast Parts	In development
224	Mechanical Products Definition for Process Planning Using Form Features	In development
225	Structural Building Elements Using Explicit Shape Rep.	In development

*Abbreviations used:
IS = International Standard
DIS = Draft International Standard
CD = Committee Draft
CDC = Committee Draft for Comments only

The 40-Series. The 40-series parts are considered to be the bread and butter of STEP. These parts contain such generic resource information as raw geometry and display attributes, among other things. These and the 100-series parts are the tools used to create application protocols (APs).

The 100-Series. The 100-series parts are similar in concept to the 40-series parts in their use to create application protocols. The difference between the two is that the 100-series is specific to an application area.

For example, multiple electronic APs may use the concept of a drilled hole in a circuit board. The 40-series parts do not contain anything as specific as this, but a 100-series part could be created that defines a drilled hole. Then, the multiple electronic APs would reference this 100-series part. This avoids multiple definitions of the same physical component in similar APs.

The 200-Series. The APs in the 200-series parts are where STEP meets the real world. They are specific applications of this technology in various industries. Today, the automotive, sheet-metal, and electronic industries are just a few examples of companies defining how STEP will be used in their specific applications. As this technology is more widely implemented, this area of STEP will be in a constant state of change and growth as more and different applications are developed.

22.2.3 A Solid Basis

Although traditional 2D and 3D data is supported, with the STEP concept, "topologically closed" solid models are the basis on which all other information is built. Being topologically closed is important because it provides a pass-fail test to ensure that a part is completely geometrically defined (see Chap. 4). Design analysis, tolerance, and process information are related to the solid model. Drawings are produced from and are subservient to the solid models. Assembly models contain configuration variations. Parts lists result from the assembly configuration models. Assembly drawings reflect the configuration of the assembly models. With this approach, the solid models can be used with confidence that they do not conflict with requirements on drawings.

22.2.4 Functional Goals

The functional goal of the STEP effort is to overcome the incompatibilities that exist between companies today. The differences have arisen from the need for companies to integrate the use of computerized information within the company. Integration within a company has long been recognized as a means of maximizing the usefulness of information. To this end, large companies tend to develop their own software integration tools. This is required because integration software that addresses the cultural differences of individual companies is not commercially available. Having integrated internal systems presents problems for companies and for those with whom they wish to share information. Their information is generally full of reflections of their corporate culture. Further, companies must deal with legacy systems, information, and formats.

As a means of interfacing, some companies have chosen to use common systems as a method for minimizing information exchange problems. This approach may seem to be a good solution at the time, but it actually promotes the problem. Rather than supplying the incentive to promote better interface or exchange methods, it hinders exchange development by attempting to avoid the problem. As is often discovered, such "common systems" are not integrated into the business of the team members. The result is a high cost for integration of yet another system and one more lost opportunity to supply the incentive to solve the interface problem.

The goal of STEP is to interrelate all geometric and nongeometric data in a useful and meaningful way so that common systems can be developed to manage the data—instead of having every business develop their own methods and computer programs.

22.2.5 Why Not IGES?[1]

The STEP standard provides access to product data far beyond what IGES or any other data transfer standard can do. According to Dr. Anthony Cuilwik, chief operating officer of International Techne-Group, Incorporated:

Today's product and process development technologies center around designing the wants and needs of the customer into the final product at its outset, thus empowering design teams to greater impact early stages of product development. This is nothing new; we've been preaching it for years.

STEP complements existing technology by enabling the user to maximize the full power and effectiveness of these tools. Especially significant is the way STEP manages information relative to the project. Once created, data pertaining to the product's entire life cycle may be accessed by all parties—from design and engineering through manufacturing and marketing, eliminating any need to re-create this data. As a result, STEP should help drive the emergence of new and improved products, tools, and techniques.

Today's advanced data collection tools and methods give designers greater access to a broad range of more detailed product and customer information than ever before. Now that engineering organizations have all of this data, they need ways to organize, manipulate, and access it. What's more, they use that data over the entire life of a product—from concept, analysis, design, and manufacturing to testing—not just its geometry.

There are functions that IGES was not designed to handle. Indeed, the graphics-based format of IGES often means that key nongeometric data cannot be electronically communicated. As a result, this data must be re-created.

22.3 Solid Modeling and STEP

The PDES specification for solid geometry models, as it was proposed in the mid-1980s, was complete and concise. It had a solid (excuse the pun) mathematical basis that was developed and well proven in universities. The proposed solid geometry modeling standard was based on a proven foundation from earlier work.

Looking further back, an exciting thing occurred about 300 years ago. A mathematician named Euler showed that any object can be proven to be solid by its topology (see Chap. 4). Though the field has grown substantially since Euler introduced his proofs, his topology of solids is as valid today as it was then. Euler showed that there is a mathematical relationship between the vertices, edges, and faces of an object, and that the relationship can be used to prove that an object is a closed solid. An SM system that incorporates Euler's test for object closure, and thus complete definition, is termed a Topological Solid Modeler. This is a crucial concept for SM systems. The test for closure provides a simple pass-fail test for whether an object is completely geometrically defined.

Complete definition is a critical requirement for solid models that are envisioned as improving the design and manufacturing interface. Manufacturing must be able to easily test for complete definition before designs enter the manufacturing processes. If this test is not available, manufacturing is doomed to the process of finding that definition is lacking while they are involved in the manufacturing process. The cost of definition clarification during the manufacturing process is a major cost driver in the design development process.

A more recent maturation in mathematics has been in the field of parametric curve and surface representations. The Non-Uniform Rational B-Spline (NURBS) is important because it is a superset of many other curve and surface forms that have become widely used in CAD/CAM applications.

These two fields in mathematics came together during the 1970s to provide an elegant and important object modeling technology. This is the basis of the proposed geometry modeling standard included in PDES. NURBS can be used to represent any manufacturable surface. Topology can be used to prove closure of any manufacturable object. Any system embracing these technologies for SM will be compatible because the underlying mathematics is well documented and understood. The geometric basis of PDES is extremely important to the future of interchange of geometric data.

22.3.1 Who Should Use STEP and Why?

Generally, on government procurement programs, STEP support is a request, not a requirement. An incentive for change is necessary. Corporations must view standards as economically rewarding before they will be fully implemented. Unfortunately, there are some in industry who do not see the economic benefit of standards. In fact, deviation from standards is a long-standing pricing issue. The logic here is that, since the company does not normally comply with the standard and since they have priced their product based on their normal "fully optimized methods," the customer will have to pay more to have the new method (standard) incorporated. Well, you get the idea, it will always cost more to incorporate a standard because requested change always carries a higher price, regardless of costs.

Companies will embrace STEP when there is economic justification to do so. Current world competitive pressures may provide the incentive necessary for adopting STEP.

Of course each company and industry must make its own judgment as to the need to embrace STEP. For many manufacturing companies there may be ample justification to adopt the geometry and drawing-documentation portions of STEP as a means of improving their productivity on internal programs. Companies that are suppliers and contractors must jointly decide on the timing and cost effectiveness of mutually relying on STEP as a means of communicating information. There is no magic wand here. Each company must make its own justification.

22.3.2   Preparing for STEP

Every company should have someone who has the responsibility for understanding its CAD/CAM requirements. This includes both the requirements for accomplishing the work at hand on a day-to-day basis and the larger requirements for deliverables, information management, and exchange. Companies should invest the time to fully understand the potential impact of STEP on their business. Only with this knowledge can a company make a well-founded decision on implementation.

22.3.3   Implementing STEP

To fully implement STEP, many difficult problems must be overcome. Perhaps the most difficult is accomplishing the cultural change that is required. Historically, drawings are king. Drawings are the means and basis of information. With STEP, the status of drawings is reduced to derived supporting information. This is a tough concept to impart, let alone implement.

Suppliers will not solve the CAD/CAM interface problems without incentives. Customers must first characterize their interface problems to their software suppliers. This can be accomplished by documenting interface requirements and then contractually requiring suppliers to strictly adhere to those requirements. Of course, this is very difficult for all companies—especially small ones. Small suppliers do not have the economic clout of larger corporations; however, suppliers can contribute by documenting customer needs to them in terms of costs.

22.4   Benefits and Pitfalls of STEP

The most important potential impact of adopting STEP is that it may improve a company's competitive position. This can occur if internal processes can be improved at lower cost. However, this requires that commercial software is available that meets the company's needs. On the other hand, there may also be the potential that some business opportunities may be lost due to nonsupport of STEP.

22.5   Life After STEP

Program and standard names may evolve, but the PDES/STEP concept will live on. The need to improve communication of computerized information between diverse organizations will increase. The geometry and information-relational concepts in STEP are sound technology. Whatever the national standard of the future is, manufacturers should carefully consider its impact on their business.

22.6   Conclusions

In summary, the STEP standardization effort is a fairly unique experience. The promoters recognize that a change is required and that a standard is required to implement that change. STEP is being devised to lead CAD/CAM product development.

An initial version of the STEP standard was released in early 1993 and was registered as an International Standard (IS) in 1994. It remains to be seen if it will become a workable standard. An even greater challenge lies ahead: culture must change to implement STEP.

Note: Here are some of the organizations currently contributing to the development of PDES/STEP. There are many interested parties. This growing awareness will help to supply the initiative necessary to solve the problems related to information exchange.

Contacts

SMA.22.1   PDES, Inc.

PDES, Inc., was established in April 1988 to accelerate the development and implementation of PDES within the United States. Twenty-four companies presently contribute resources to further this effort. PDES is pursuing a two-phase program, with Phase I emphasizing data exchange implementation for mechanical parts and rigid assemblies. Phase II will focus on a database implementation and will broaden the scope to include such areas as electronic components and assemblies. Contact:

PDES, Inc.
Trident Research Center
5300 International Boulevard
North Charleston, SC 29418
(803) 760-3200

SMA.22.2   NIST and NIPDE

The United States Department of Commerce, National Institute of Standards and Technology (NIST), hosts the National Institute for Product Data Exchange (NIPDE). NIPDE is an industry-led, government-facilitated organization established to accelerate product data exchange development and implementation in industry. NIPDE is designed to help participants develop common requirements, set priorities, and develop schedules. Some of the participants are:

1. American National Standards Institute (ANSI)

2. CALS Industrial Steering Group

3. U.S. Departments of Commerce, Defense, and Energy

4. Electronic Industries Association (EIA)

5. Institute of Electrical and Electronics Engineers (IEEE)

6. IGES/PDES Organization (IPO)

7. National Aeronautics and Space Administration (NASA)

8. National Center for Manufacturing Sciences, NIST, PDES, Inc.

9. The Society of Manufacturing Engineers (SME)

There are also several participants representing major manufacturing corporations. NIPDE reports are available on written request and include information on the status of digital product data exchange in the United States. Contact:

NIST and NIPDE
B102 Radiation Physics Building, NIST
Gaithersburg, MD 20899
(301) 975-3982

SMA.22.3   The European Community

The European Community is developing a network of STEP centers to ensure that their countries have a means to focus their efforts. One example of this effort is ProSTEP, sponsored by the German Federal Ministry of Economics and member companies. The goal of ProSTEP is to develop methods and tools for computer-aided design and production facilities using STEP. ProSTEP will develop interface processors, database interfaces, STEP-related software tools, and will form a German STEP center. Participation criteria for associated partners are similar to those of PDES, Inc., in the United States, and Japan's STEP Center. Contact:

(Continued)

Contacts
(*Continued*)

ProSTEP (German STEP Center)
Post Fach 40 02 40
8000 München 40
Kurzzeich, Germany
Ph: 49 61 51 928713

Japan STEP Center
Computer Science Division
Physics Information Department
Mechanical Engineering Laboratory
MITI
1-2 Namiki, Tshukuba-shi
Ibaraki 305 Japan
Ph: 81 298 58 7054

SMA.22.4   The European Commission

The European Commission (EC) has established the Product Data Technology Advisory Group (PDTAG). PDTAG will provide recommendations to the EC as an advisory group. The group has members from approximately 12 EC countries, and includes representatives from many industrial disciplines. Their goal is to work to create a greater level of awareness of STEP, and of product data technology in general, in European industry.

SMA.22.5   Other Contacts

Industrial Technology Institute
PO Box 1485
Ann Arbor, MI 48106
(313) 769-4000

International TechneGroup Incorporated
5303 Dupont Circle
Milford, OH 45150
(513) 576-3900

STEP Tools, Inc.
1223 Peoples Ave.
Troy, NY 12180
(518) 276-2848

IGES Data Analysis, Inc.
2001 Janice Ave.
Melrose Park, IL 60160
(708) 344-1815

Good to Know

SMA.22.6   Growth Path to STEP

There are IGES-to-STEP and VDA-FS-to-STEP data converters under development that will provide a smooth growth path to STEP. *Examples:* ProSTEP, Germany; PDES, Inc., and International TechneGroup, Inc., USA. See Fig. 22.2.

Hermann Ruess
Hewlett-Packard Co., Mechanical Design Div.,
Boeblingen, Germany

SMA.22.7   Application Protocols

With STEP, the most important dogmatic shift in comparison to previous data exchange standards is its emphasis on product data, not just data. The transfer of a solid all by itself will not be sanctioned. The entire product and configuration context will also be required. Those individuals who

(Continued)

Good to Know
(Continued)

believe they will be involved in SM exchange through STEP should pay particular attention to the models called *application protocols* (APs). These APs will be the endorsed way to transfer information between systems. Their purpose is to interpret the core STEP models with the context of specific application activity; for example, AP203 Configuration Controlled Design (Table 22.1).

Mark J. Silvestri
Life Cycle Solutions, Inc., Avon, Mass.

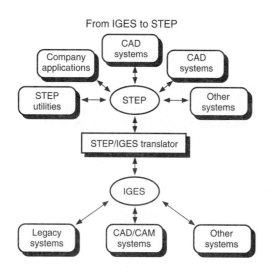

FIGURE 22.5   STEP doesn't mean the end to IGES. In fact, IGES can help users move into STEP. *(Courtesy of International TechneGroup, Inc.)*

SMA.22.8   Know Your Process

Know your process and how it may be helped or hindered by standards. Industries will be affected differently by this standard. The initial work has been aimed at the mechanical structure aerospace industry but has also received support from the mechanical structure automotive industry. The standards organizations hope that these industries will lead the way to general applicability and acceptance.

SMA.22.9   Highly Integrated STEP (HISTEP™)[4]

Since STEP represents a dramatic technological advance, the Industrial Technology Institute (Ann Arbor, Michigan) has developed a method for understanding the impacts of STEP-based technologies on the operations and human resources of an organization.

A structured analysis approach called HISTEP™ utilizes cross-functional teams to identify, plan, and deal with potential impacts of the new technology on people, jobs, and the organizational environment. This process helps an organization to understand STEP and what it takes to optimally implement it. Figure 22.3 illustrates the HISTEP™ process.

Part of the HISTEP™ process is determining how to use "organizational levers." These are aspects of an organization that can be modified to impact the way work is done. Examples of organizational levers are work and information flow, reporting relationships, leadership, team staffing, culture, and values and reward/incentive systems. They are called *levers* because a small change in one of them can have a large impact on how work is done. For more information on HISTEP™, contact the Industrial Technology Institute.

SMA.22.10   Important Technology Characteristics of STEP Tools[4]

A STEP-based technology tool can be rated according to how much it embodies a set of Important Technology Characteristics (ITCs). An ITC is a characteristic of an information technology which

(Continued)

both research and experience have shown to have an impact on organization and people. Eleven ITCs are listed here. Others may be added or subtracted as needed to suit a given application.

1. Range of information
    a. Depth and diversity of information
    b. Extent of the archived database
    c. Existence of information libraries
    d. Applicability across the life cycle

2. Reliability
    a. Consistency of the tool across time and applications
    b. Stability, resists minor changes
    c. Consistency of meaning and use of data boundaries
    d. A reliable system rarely fails

3. Self-sufficiency
    a. Can be used alone, without other systems to back it up
    b. Need to interface with other systems
    c. Completeness of the database
    d. Extent of needed utilities to avoid relying on external software

4. Fault tolerance
    a. Able to tolerate mistakes through internal features to protect against human or systems errors
    b. Has backup options to recover from operator, software, hardware, or power failures
    c. A fault tolerance tool is not subject to harm from its own mistakes

5. Maintainability
    a. Easy to keep the system operating
    b. Includes ease of maintenance, serviceability, vendor support

6. Flexibility
    a. Adaptable to multiple uses
    b. Variety of application protocol (AP) use
    c. Modularity of the software
    d. Options available
    e. Can upgrade without loosing existing information

7. Information integration
    a. Can exchange data with other systems, coordinate shared data, and interrelate APs
    b. Able to work with legacy systems

8. Data integrity
    a. Able to protect the character and meaning of data shared across applications
    b. Open, interoperable communication systems

9. Access control and configuration management
    a. Maintains secure, current, and consistent database
    b. Files and data version control, access control, and modification control

10. Ease of human use
    a. Easy to understand and learn
    b. Ease of work tasks for which the tool is used
    c. Ergonomic soundness

11. Efficiency
    a. General operational efficiency
    b. Includes required user training and ramp-up time, ongoing operational requirements

Michael T. Wood, Principal Member Technical Staff
and Mitchell Fleischer, Scientific Fellow
Industrial Technology Institute, Ann Arbor, Mich.

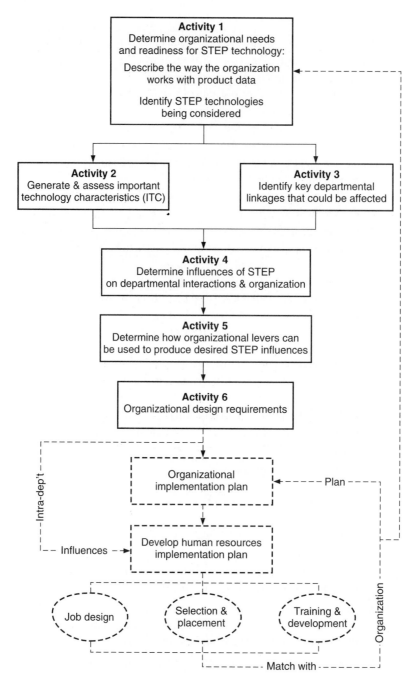

FIGURE 22.3 Six activities combine to make up the HISTEP™ process. *(Courtesy of the Industrial Technology Institute.)*

References

1. Adapted from: "Passing the Torch in Product Data Exchange" by David Mattei, International TechneGroup, Inc., Milford, Ohio, appearing in the September 1993 issue of *Computer-Aided Engineering* magazine. Reprinted with permission.

2. Adapted from: "Using STEP Application Protocols to Enable Concurrent Engineering in Real World Pilot Implementations" by Bill Anderson and Steve Ryan, PDES, Inc., Trident Research Center, North Charleston,

S.C., *Proceedings, The First International Conference on Concurrent Engineering,* Research and Applications (CERA), Pittsburgh, Pa., August 29–31, 1994. Reprinted with permission.

3. M. Palmer and M. Gilbert, "Guidelines for the Development and Approval of Application Protocols," Working Draft, Version 1.1 ISO TC184/SC4/WG4, Document N66, November 30, 1993.

4. Adapted from "Organizational Implications of STEP-based Information Technologies," by Michael T. Wood and Mitchell Fleischer, Industrial Technology Institute, Ann Arbor, Mich., *Proceedings, CALS Expo '92 Conference and Exposition,* San Diego, Calif., December 7–10, 1992. Reprinted with permission.

Section 5
Implementation

Chapter 23

Solid Modeling Implementation Strategies*

Victor Bradley
Mechanical Consulting Services Coordinator
Intergraph Corporation

Thomas Riddle
Independent Consultant

Implementation strategies are the substance from which you will either make or lose money with computers for your company. Computer and software technology is continually evolving. Your company will replace/upgrade your existing computers and software many times over the next decade. The single thread which will bind your management and design efforts together in a cost-effective manner during these changes is clearly defined implementation strategies. Any comprehensive definition of implementation strategies will account for change. The implementation strategies described in this chapter will continue to help you measure and improve your success with ever-changing computer technology over the coming years.

23.1   Who Should Read This Chapter, and Why?

This chapter is intended for three groups who are responsible for product development and production within your organization:

1. First-line managers—Technical implementation
2. Middle managers—Tactical implementation
3. Executive managers—Develop implementation strategies

23.1.2   First-Line Managers

Because those reporting to first-line managers are the designers and engineers using SM, they need to understand not only the technology, but also how it is implemented and how its use affects other departments.

---

*Portions of this chapter are adapted from: Victor E. Bradley and Thomas Riddle, "The Productivity Equation," *Computer-Aided Engineering,* Sept. 1992 edition.

23.1.2 Middle Managers

Middle managers are responsible for the tactical implementation of the SM system and its ongoing management across departmental boundaries. This is because multiple technology groups reporting to them often have conflicting goals and interests. Middle managers must make informed decisions about conflicting priorities concerning the use of SM as well as other technologies.

23.1.3 Executive Managers

Upper or executive managers approve the purchase of new technology such as SM for many and various reasons. All of these reasons assume one or more of the following tangible benefits will ensue:

1. A reduction in costs
2. A compression of development and/or production time
3. Improved quality

Executive managers must understand the potential benefits, limitations, and major implementation and management issues well enough to effectively develop an implementation strategy. Without understanding, there can be no genuine commitment. Without commitment, any assumed benefits will be elusive. Thus, this chapter is intended especially for executive managers.

23.2 Solid Modeling and Change Management

Solid Modeling is both driven by and a driver of change. For companies in the design, engineering, and manufacturing business in today's global economy, a productive and efficient CAD/CAM/CAE system is a key element in maintaining or gaining competitiveness. This we all know. This need for adopting new technology for competitive reasons is an example of technology usage being driven by change.

Perhaps less understood is the fact that technology is also a driver of change. To take advantage of the potential benefits of SM, a fundamental change in the concept of product development and production is often required. Before the advent of effective SM software, the need to make fundamental conceptual and operational changes to the traditional way manufacturers developed and produced products simply did not exist.

23.2.1 Moving from 2D Drafting to 3D Solid Modeling

The operational changes alluded to assume that your organization is currently in one of the following situations with regard to CAD technology:

1. Using manual drawing board design (no CAD)
2. Using CAD system for 2D design only
3. Using CAD system for 3D (wireframe, surface, or solid) but using it essentially as you would a 2D only CAD system
4. Using a CAD system for 3D SM but aware (or perhaps unaware) that you are underutilizing this capability

Many organizations in these categories are unaware of the fundamental operational differences between a 2D drafting system and a 3D SM system. The techniques used in SM and its integrated applications are discussed in Secs. 2 and 3 of this handbook. These are generally technology-focused discussions of issues to be faced when transitioning from 2D design to 3D SM.

An SM system includes hardware, software, and liveware (people). This chapter addresses more of the liveware issues of an SM system: the part you cannot buy, plug in, and allow to run on autopilot. This requires guidance, direction, and management during implementation, ramp-up, and production phases, as well as the inevitable expansion phases which follow as other technologies and applications are implemented. (See Fig. 23.1.)

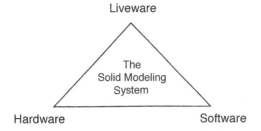

FIGURE 23.1 SM system components. Any computer system implementation is made up of three major components: hardware, software, and liveware (people). Of these three components, liveware is the most important. *(Courtesy of Intergraph Corporation.)*

23.2.2 The Emotional Cycle of Change

In order to manage change as it effects the individual worker, understanding the ABCs of human behavior is helpful. In this case, ABC is a literation of the three major components of human behavior: (1) *A*ttitude, (2) *B*ehavior, and (3) *C*onsequences. (See Fig. 23.2.)

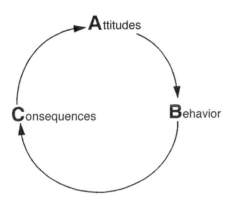

FIGURE 23.2 The ABCs of human behavior. Understanding the interaction of an individual's attitudes, behaviors, and consequences is essential for managers attempting to implement change in the workplace. A manager's most direct way of effecting a positive change in human behavior is through administration of consequences, both good and bad. *(Courtesy of Intergraph Corporation.)*

Anyone who has attempted to raise a child knows how difficult it is to change a human being's attitude. Neither attitudes nor behaviors can be directly affected by individuals other than themselves. However, in business, the consequences of individuals' behaviors can be directly addressed by their respective managers. When consequences change for individuals, their attitudes change. When attitudes change, behaviors change. When behaviors change, this directly affects consequences. This is the cycle of human behavior that, when understood by managers, is useful in helping individuals adjust to change. Opportunities to manage change arise from a variety of sources:

1. Engineering
2. The work force
3. Regulatory controls (EPA, OSHA, etc.)
4. Customer requirements
5. New programs and products
6. The work environment (new tools, software, hardware, etc.)

Easily identifiable personality characteristics emerge while implementing change related to computer systems. It should be noted that these personality characteristics are transitory. It is incumbent upon management to help individuals over come any negative reactions to change.

During the early stages of a given change, individuals often experience a disinterest in the occurring change. This disinterest is demonstrated as behavior referred to as *bailout,* and may be either internal or external in nature. Common bailouts are:

1. *This does not apply to my work.*
2. *This is too complicated.*
3. *This is too expensive.*
4. *This is not productive.*

5. *We have never done it this way before.*

6. *I'm too busy doing the work to consider doing the work better.*

7. *I'm too old to learn new ways.*

8. *We tried it before and failed.*

9. *It is not applicable to our industry.*

10. *It applies to their job, not mine.*

The period of time required for an individual's behavior to return to normal, if it does at all, is referred to as the *cycle of change.* There are four phases in an individual's cycle of change (see Fig. 23.3):

1. Uninformed optimism

2. Informed pessimism

3. External or internal bailouts

4. Informed optimism

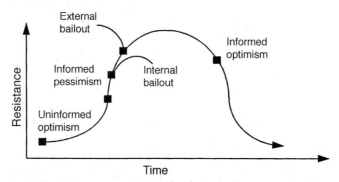

FIGURE 23.3 The emotional cycle of change. Individuals experience several emotional phases as resistance to change takes place over a given period of time. Management's opportunity to affect this cycle occurs when external and internal bailouts take place. Without management's intervention, the implementation of the change will stall and eventually fail. *(Courtesy of Intergraph Corporation.)*

Uninformed Optimism. A brief period of euphoria occurs when individuals first discover that change is in progress. This euphoria can and does result in increased productivity.

Informed Pessimism. As individuals learn more about the change, resistance occurs. The resistance is directly proportional to their understanding of how this change will impact their tasks.

External or Internal Bailouts. Individuals who express bailouts externally are normally informal leaders. They are willing to openly take a verbal stand, recruit converts, and lead others in the revolt against the change.

Individuals who express bailouts internally are most susceptible to the informal leader. Of the two behaviors, these are the most difficult for management to identify. They do not express their discontent unless cross-examined. To prevent a revolt by informal leaders, management must take corrective action to discourage this behavior.

Informed Optimism. Individuals who have reached this phase are now on the downside of the slope of resistance. They are aware that the change is continuing to impact them, but they are able to cope with the change because of their knowledge of the change itself.

23.2.3 How Long Should the Implementation Take?

By now, you may be thinking that the implementation of an SM system is not as simple as once believed. Indeed, the effective implementation of SM as part of an integrated CAD/CAM/CAE system is not a "plug and play" proposition and should not be undertaken lightly. *But,* it is not as complex as it may seem if you take it one step at a time. Don't try to do too much too quickly.

To answer our question, *if* the following are true:

1. Your company is comfortable with 3D wireframe or surface design.
2. Downstream operations are using design geometry directly.
3. File management is under control.
4. Version and configuration management is done reasonably well manually.
5. You have effective communication among various departments.
6. Your entire organization is eager to make the move.

Then you can probably move fairly quickly into SM.

On the other hand, *if* the following are true:

1. Your company is designing using 2D only.
2. Manufacturing uses paper drawings as their data source for creating NC programs and tooling design.
3. You are having trouble with drawing and file management.
4. You have little or no experience with computer graphics.
5. You have undefined goals and objectives concerning the use of SM.
6. You have organizational or personnel problems in adjusting to changes.

Then the implementation of SM is going to take longer and the cultural and operational changes required will be greater. However, the ultimate benefits from making such changes will be far greater by comparison.

Change Management

SMA.23.1   Implementation and Effectiveness

Without implementing conceptual and operational changes, the effectiveness of SM technology will be severely limited, resulting in unrealized expectations and undeserved placement of blame.

SMA.23.2   Look Inward as Well

It is human nature to first look outward for answers to problems. However, many companies implement SM expecting (hoping) that the technology alone will solve operational or management problems. This is not always true and one should look inward as well to effectively utilize in-house expertise. You may be surprised at how many answers can be found.

SMA.23.3   A Case in Point

Consider this. A company uses 2D CAD for design and drafting and produces paper drawings for manufacturing to use in producing numerical control (NC) toolpath programs. If this manual method is not changed, a great deal of the potential benefits of SM will be missed. The direct use of design geometry by manufacturing and other downstream processes is a fundamental operational change which must be made to reap the benefits which SM promises.

SMA.23.4   A Cultural Mind-Set

To effect fundamental operational changes, a change in culture or mind-set on the part of both management and designers must also take place. If management continues to provide a feedback mechanism (consequences, rewards, etc.) which does not take into consideration operational changes and new company and departmental goals and objectives, the operational change will not "take" or become a permanent part of the new way of doing business.

SMA.23.5   Easy for Change

It is management's responsibility to make a change transition as easy as possible for the very pragmatic reason of business expediency. A fundamental truism for managing change is that if management makes it relatively easy for their people to make the desired change, then it has a fighting chance of success; if not, the likelihood of successful change is low.

**Change
Management**
(*Continued*)

> ### SMA.23.6 Marketing SM Internally
>
> Be prepared to continuously "market" and justify front-end project expenses due to the implementation of SM techniques. Managers rarely understand the concepts and benefits. When a period of understanding and support is finally reached, these managers are often promoted to other positions inside or outside the company, thus necessitating repetition of the whole process for the new replacements.
>
> *Brian Ruuska, CAD/CAE Applications Engineer*
> *3M Co., St. Paul, Minn.*

23.3 Preparing for Solid Modeling

Companies will at times require assistance from outside consultants to objectively evaluate current work flow and make comprehensive recommendations regarding the reengineering of the design process. The most common and cost-effective method to accomplish this task is either a needs or productivity analysis performed by an outside consultant or group of consultants.

23.3.1 Needs and Productivity Analyses

A *needs analysis* is a preacquisition evaluation of a company's computer needs. Management will normally use the results of such analysis as a basis for the decision-making process, which includes the hardware and software purchase and implementation.

A *productivity analysis* is a postacquisition evaluation of a company's computer implementation and its future needs. The results of this analysis is used to evaluate productivity improvement opportunities. The results from a productivity and a needs analysis are very similar. However, a company will require a needs analysis only once, while the same company may require a productivity analysis on a periodic basis.

Planning

> ### SMA.23.7 Needs and Productivity Analyses
>
> In order to effectively evaluate current and future implementation needs, it is recommended that an expert or group of experts be charged with the responsibility of conducting the needs or productivity analysis. The analysis team should have:
>
> **1.** Experience with the implementation of current computer systems
>
> **2.** Experience and knowledge of currently available software and hardware
>
> **3.** Objectivity (politics can cloud the vision of internal evaluators)
>
> **4.** Anonymity from consequences
>
> It is recommended that an outside consulting firm perform this type of analysis. The investigation itself will involve a variety of aspects of the company, including the current staff's ability to successfully implement a computer system. This type of consulting service should be available from any major software or hardware vendor and from a variety of third-party consulting firms.

The need for today's managers to avail themselves of the information and expert advice provided during these types of consulting services is acute. Some of the many factors which affect SM strategies are as follows:

1. Computer technology is constantly evolving.

2. Individual companies' production needs are ever changing to meet current market demands.

3. The turnover rate of personnel has an impact.

23.3.2 Topics for Analysis

Just what aspects of the company are investigated during this type of analysis? The actual list of areas will vary depending on the analyst(s). However, the following list represents the minimum areas which any qualified analyst should investigate during the analysis effort:

1. Current and future systems application support staffing requirements
2. The end product and the design and production methods used
3. Current number of engineering designers and drafters
4. Current level of computer literacy of management
5. Current source and form of design data transfer between departments (work flow)
6. Current hardware and software (if any) used
7. Current database software (if any) used
8. Hardware and software currently under consideration for purchase
9. System performance issues (current and planned) as compared to usage
10. Ease-of-use issues with current hardware and software (if any)
11. Data storage, backup, and archive procedures (current and planned)
12. Current level of computer experience of the design and supporting staff
13. Current monitoring methods used by management to evaluate designers (if any)
14. Current type(s) of computer graphics created (if any)
15. Current and future applications for graphical data generated
16. Current modeling methods such as wireframe, surfaces, and/or solids used (if any)
17. Current standards and procedures (if any) and how they are applied
18. Barriers which may hamper a successful implementation of the computer system

23.3.3 Three Phases of Analysis

Needs and productivity analyses are performed in three phases: (1) fact finding, (2) evaluation of information, and (3) presenting recommendations. A discussion of each follows.

Phase I: Fact Finding

The evaluation of the preceding analysis topics is normally conducted on-site. The evaluation may include several techniques: (1) group meetings, (2) plant tours, and (3) individual interviews and/or questionnaires.

During this phase, activity is restricted to the gathering of facts. Qualified analysts should never attempt to interpret or make suggestions during this phase. They (the analysts) should understand that providing quick responses and suggestions during the fact-finding phase will make it more difficult to uncover real opportunities for improving productivity and/or current need. Phase I of the analysis may require 2 to 4 days to complete.

Phase II: Evaluating Information

The information gathered during Phase I is compiled and evaluated by the analyst in his or her office. Issues and trends within the information gathered provide a telling story to the experienced analyst. These impressions and suggestions become the rough draft of the recommendations for a given organization.

Final recommendations become formalized in a written report. The report is a high-level tactical plan addressing the current strategic goals of the company. Since this report will be reviewed by several levels of management, it should consist of at least three sections: (1) an executive summary, (2) compiled facts and information, and (3) recommendations. Phase II of the analysis may require several work-weeks to complete.

Phase III: Presenting Recommendations

The analysts report mentioned in Phase II should be presented to the company's management in person during a brief presentation. Phase III normally requires only one day.

23.3.4 Implementation Planning

Once all three phases of the needs and productivity analysis are complete and the resulting analyst's report has been reviewed and accepted by management, the next step is formal implementation planning regarding the tactical issues addressed. This process may require a significantly greater amount of time.

A typical implementation (including analysis, implementation planning, and the execution of the implementation plan) for a small installation (as few as 10 workstations) will require a management commitment of from six months to over two years, depending on the level of computer graphic experience of the company.

23.4 The CIM 12 Productivity Indicators and Benchmark

The CIM 12 is a group of productivity indicators used as a standard or benchmark to quickly determine where you are on the road toward full productivity with SM (see Fig. 23.4). In fact, it is strongly suggested that the CIM 12 be used by the analyst or consultant as a guide for performing the needs and productivity analyses discussed in Sec. 23.3.

The CIM 12 are arranged in three distinct groups to make them more understandable and manageable. These are (1) competence, (2) integrity, and (3) management. Each are discussed in detail.

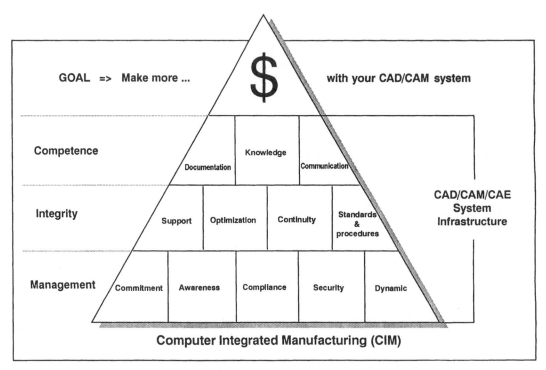

FIGURE 23.4 The CIM 12 productivity indicators. These indicators are specific standards which can be used to evaluate the productive success of an SM or CAD/CAE implementation. Management is the foundation on which successful implementations are built. *(Courtesy of Intergraph Corporation.)*

23.4.1 Competence

Without competent people, much of the money invested in new technology is wasted. Even with the latest technology, the human element is still very important. State-of-the-art technology does not eliminate the need for competence in any given field; this includes the disciplines of design, engineering, and manufacturing. CAD/CAM/CAE technology does not replace competent individuals but merely enables them to be more productive and better at their work.

Three of the CIM 12 productivity indicators are grouped here. In this context we speak of competence with respect to use of SM technology, not competence in the design, engineering, or manufacturing disciplines. Competence in these disciplines is a prerequisite to productivity, but does not guarantee it.

CIM 1: Documentation

All pertinent system and application documentation is kept current and made easily accessible to all operators and managers. When easy access to current documentation is made available, it is more inclined to be used and learned from.

CIM 2: Knowledge

All designers have sufficient knowledge of the SM system and software operation to efficiently perform all functions required by their specific application and understand the requirements of all downstream applications which use their data. There is only one way to ensure the adequacy of knowledge for both operators and their managers. Training classes led by competent instructors are the proven best method of achieving the goal of sufficient application knowledge.

CIM 3: Communication

An effective method for communicating and sharing knowledge and information among all designers, system managers, and application support personnel is established and maintained.

Planning

> ### SMA.23.8   Aiding Communication
>
> One of the best methods for aiding communication is by holding monthly internal user group meetings. These meetings should be across disciplines and should include designers, engineers, and managers.

23.4.2 Integrity

The word *integrity* (rather than *integrated*) was chosen to head the next group of CIM 12 productivity indicators due to the more comprehensive nature of the term. Integrity implies not only completeness (as the term *integrated* does), but also soundness and adherence to a code of values which include honesty, sincerity, and candor. The essence of integrity (other than completeness) is realism as opposed to fantasy.

CIM 4: Support

An effective internal application support capability is developed and maintained. Developing internal support capabilities can save a lot of time by reducing the number and frequency of external support calls and waiting for answers.

CIM 5: Optimization

Hardware, software, and procedures are configured for optimum performance, including providing immediate access to all in-process and released data as required. This implies a network and adequate file storage capacity as well as an easy-to-operate network file management system.

CIM 6: Continuity

Solid Modeling geometry is used directly by all appropriate downstream activities, including analysis, design documentation, and manufacturing operations.

CIM 7: Standards and Procedures

Comprehensive standards and procedures for system and application operations are documented, implemented, and updated on an ongoing basis. When one designer has to take over from another and there are no company or group-specific standards used for the creation of solid models, it can take hours or even days just to determine what and where everything is in the file.

23.4.3 Management

The remaining five CIM 12 productivity indicators represent management issues. Good management is the foundation of all prosperous businesses. It is no different selecting, implementing, operating, and maintaining high-technology CAD/CAM/CAE systems than with any other aspect of business management.

CIM 8: Commitment

Upper, middle, and line managers understand the capabilities and limitations of the SM system, are committed to its use in pursuit of business objectives, and provide strategic direction and oversight for all departments which use the system or the data generated by it. There seems to be a common perception at some levels of management that CAD/CAM/CAE systems are "plug and play" devices that you unpack and turn on to generate profits. To make a system work (i.e., to generate profits for the company), management at all levels must understand the capabilities and limitations of the system.

CIM 9: Awareness

All line managers are aware of the SM system and the application knowledge level of each designer reporting to them, and they encourage designers' efforts to improve their knowledge and utilization of the system.

CIM 10: Compliance

All line managers fully understand and ensure compliance with company standards and procedures for system operation on an operator-by-operator basis.

CIM 11: Security

Design and downstream data is secure from accidental loss. The likelihood of loss from fire or water damage depends upon many external variables, and may be quite low. However, the engineering, design, and manufacturing data is a company's single most valuable asset, other than highly skilled personnel. The risk may be low but the impact of data loss can be absolutely devastating. Do not be unnecessarily subjected to this potentially crippling risk.

CIM 12: Dynamic

All aspects of SM system operation are dynamic and should be reviewed regularly and upgraded as required. Changes in business, personnel, organization, technologies, and operations are ongoing in competitive companies. As a consequence, all issues discussed here should be conscientiously reviewed periodically.

Planning

SMA.23.9   Internal Application Support

The loss of productivity due to total reliance on external support systems can be significant. Develop an internal application support system. For medium to large operations a company's productivity can be greatly enhanced by dedicating a person (full or part-time) to the task of becoming a true expert in one or more applications, thus providing effective internal support. Do not expect those performing this responsibility on a part-time basis to be personally as productive as others not assigned this responsibility.

SMA.23.10   Configuration and Performance

Find out if the sizes of SM files being handled are too large to fit within available memory along with operating system and applications software. If so, portions of required data are stored out of memory on the system's hard disk. This information takes significantly longer to access. Adding more memory (RAM) to the system can result in dramatic performance gains. Likewise, the configuration of various software operating parameters can have dramatic effects on performance.

SMA.23.11   Modeling Precision

Make sure that the geometry created in the design stage is "good" geometry. Make sure that arcs (fillets and rounds) are actually tangent to adjacent straight edges and that they actually connect. One would be surprised to learn how often geometry intended for downstream use is totally unusable for the intended purpose due to modeling imprecision. If a little more care is taken to ensure accuracy of design geometry, downstream operations may be able to make better use of it.

SMA.23.12   Modeling Notes Improve Communications

A method of improving continuity between consecutive operations is to improve documentation of designs for downstream applications, particularly if design geometry is used directly by others. Consider including a notes-to-engineering or notes-to-manufacturing layer in each SM model file.

SMA.23.13   Methods and Performance

Certain ways of doing things can create more data or take more CPU or I/O time than other ways of accomplishing the same task. Knowledge of these details, and implementing standards and procedures based on this knowledge, can ultimately have a measurable effect on performance, and thus on productivity.

SMA.23.14   Lack of Commitment

Lack of real commitment is the number one reason for not achieving productivity from any CAD/CAM/CAE system. Real commitment comes from understanding system capabilities, limitations, and benefits, as well as which productivity issues are most important.

SMA.23.15   Executive Understanding

Interdepartmental conflicts frequently occur and must be solved at the executive level in light of the company's business objectives. Executive management cannot make these types of informed decisions without at least a conceptual understanding of the SM system and how its use benefits the company. Also, lower-level management will embrace the system only if it is clear that executive management is committed.

SMA.23.16   Proficiency Tests

When human skills or limitations pertain to a specific technology, there must be some explicit method of determining knowledge and level of proficiency in the use of such technology. One of the best ways to do this is to develop CAD/CAM/CAE system knowledge and proficiency tests for each application package. These tests should be customized for relevance to your type of work.

(Continued)

Planning
(*Continued*)

All current and prospective designers should be given the appropriate application-specific tests. This will help screen prospective employees and will aid management in determining upgraded training requirements for specific designers. They can also become one of the criterion for performance evaluation and motivation of current employees. Operator proficiency has a direct impact on a company's bottom line and should be recognized and rewarded.

SMA.23.17   Do Not Lose Sight of Goals

When evaluating the effectiveness of SM on operations, do not lose sight of the company's overall goals and objectives. After all, the SM system is a tool intended to aid in achieving business objectives, not an end unto itself.

SMA.23.18   Backup and Archive Procedures

Appropriate backup and archive procedures should be implemented to prevent accidental loss from system crashes, viruses, and inadvertent file deletion or corruption. Backups and archives should be stored in a disasterproof vault. Furthermore, a database identifying each stored item's location is required to facilitate quick and easy access and retrieval of data.

23.5   Training and Continued Education

In today's market, hardware and software vendors offer a variety of training options. These options include computer-based training (CBTs), self-paced manuals, and instructor-led training. The training solution chosen should be based on a knowledge of issues surrounding each option. For most companies, the training solution chosen may be a combination of these three options.

23.5.1   Computer-Based Training (CBT)

CBT is very useful in helping individuals understand basic operating procedures regarding specific software products. Most leading software vendors offer CBT in one form or another and some courses are more extensive than others. This form of training is highly goal-oriented and effective as an introductory training tool.

The initial start-up costs related to CBT as a training option are low. However, training requirements which extend beyond basic introductions to the software are better addressed with one of the other two available options.

23.5.2   Self-Paced Manuals

Software vendors, as a rule, offer manuals with their products and some offer self-paced training guides. This type of manual offers the ability to follow step-by-step instructions through simple labs and exposure to the functionality and commands within a given software package. The aid of self-paced manuals is beneficial to the new computer users. The labs within these manuals will guide the designer through a variety of simple and complex design tasks.

The initial start-up costs related to the use of self-paced manuals as a training option are minimal. However, state-of-the-art SM software evolves very rapidly. Improvements and changes are introduced every three to six months. Comprehensive, accurate documentation, such as self-paced manuals, require three to six months to complete. Thus, it is very unlikely that self-paced documentation will address all current functionality within a given SM system.

23.5.3   Instructor-Led Training

Most SM software vendors offer instructor-led training classes. These classes may be taught at the customer site or at a vendor training center. Many vendors offer both standard and custom classes. Standard classes are prepackaged, using standard outlines and labs. Custom classes are tailored to meet the individual customer's needs and requirements. Labs associated with custom classes normally address products specific to the individual company.

Instructor-led training classes are considered the most effective and cost-effective training option offered by software vendors. Instructors can remain current with changes and improvements within a given software package and will incorporate this information in training classes and related labs. Students of instructor-led training classes can expect to become productive within three to six months after completion of the training.

Of the three training options discussed here, instructor-led training is the most expensive. However, this type of training is the most flexible and comprehensive. The training option selected should match a company's specific training needs. Individuals who require simple introductory training, such as managers and supervisors, should consider either computer-based training or self-paced manuals. Full-time users, such as engineers, designers, and drafters, will need to attend instructor-led-training classes.

23.6   Continuous Improvement

Continuously improving your SM implementation is essential to maintaining relative productivity (see Fig. 23.5). Three primary areas for continuous improvement again are (1) software, (2) hardware, and (3) liveware.

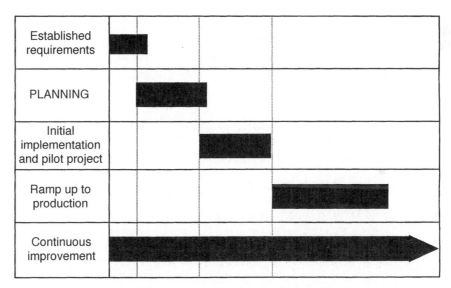

FIGURE 23.5   Continuous improvement should be the focus of all efforts—from the establishment of requirements, planning, initial implementation and pilot project, and through ramp up to production. *(Courtesy of Intergraph Corporation.)*

23.6.1   Software

Solid Modeling software is currently evolving, with significant changes occurring every three to six months. Most vendors' marketing efforts include trade shows and local demonstrations of their software. These vendor-sponsored shows are an excellent source of information concerning current software capabilities. Other excellent sources of information include independent analysts and other companies who have implemented current versions of particular SM products.

23.6.2   Hardware

The primary considerations for improving hardware are matching performance and configuration to SM software requirements, since the obsolescence of hardware is inevitable. Expect workstation and related hardware speeds and processing capabilities to advance significantly every six to ten months.

Planning

SMA.23.19 Your Hardware Budget

The average life span of computer hardware is three years until reaching obsolescence. New versions of software will always require faster hardware. Experienced users become more sophisticated over time and consume increasing CPU resources. Continuous hardware replacements should be regularly budgeted.

Brian Ruuska, CAD/CAE Applications Engineer
3M Co., St. Paul Minn.

23.6.3 Liveware

Liveware is people—both designers and managers of SM software. Management support for the continuous improvement of the current SM implementation is essential to maintain productivity. A company's largest investment is in training the people who perform the actual work. This training can be the result of formal or informal efforts. The need for training and retraining of individuals working with computer software is a given requirement. Both management and designers should be involved in the continuous improvement of their SM implementation through the following activities related to education and communication:

1. Attending formal update classes and seminars
2. Attending conferences, presentations, and related trade shows
3. Joining vendor-sponsored user groups
4. Participating regularly in internal SM software user groups
5. Reviewing SM-software-related trade journals

Continuous improvement of your SM implementation is essential to maintaining productivity with a focus on optimization. Without this effort, a company may inadvertently automate inefficiencies.

23.7 Opportunities and Potential Benefits

In today's economy, market pressures to respond to ever-changing consumer needs have never been greater. These changes shorten product life cycles and increase the need for customized products. Companies who respond to these consumer demands will be more successful than those who do not.

The potential benefits to companies moving to SM technology are extensive and meaningful to the bottom line—more profit for the company. Some of these benefits are:

1. *Concurrent engineering (CE).* Engineering and manufacturing processes are enabled simultaneously from shared SM data. (See Chap. 27 for more on SM and CE.)
2. *Higher quality.* Quality improves due to increased efficiency resulting from the ability to explore a greater number of design iterations during product development.
3. *Lower unit costs.* Due to reduced development and prototyping expenses, costs are reduced.
4. *Rapid prototyping (RP).* Solid models can be used to produce prototypes from StereoLithography and other RP technologies. (See Chap. 19 for more on SM and RP.)
5. *Personnel development.* SM technology provides a challenging environment for employees.
6. *Personnel advancement.* Job opportunities related to the management and supervision of SM become available to advance employee careers.
7. *Identification and elimination of inefficiencies.* SM develops opportunities for the elimination of inherent inefficiencies in existing work flows and/or practices.
8. *Increased workload capacity.* Efficient use of SM allows the production of more work while maintaining current staff levels.
9. *Greater feedback and control of production operations.* SM enables NC toolpaths to be generated, updated, and verified automatically with little human intervention.
10. *Improved overall communications.* SM enables a shift from the traditional paper-based design and manufacturing system to an electronic paperless one.

11. ***Increased accuracy of MRP data.*** SM data files can be easily linked and managed by MRP software.

12. ***Increased design flexibility.*** SM offers a more robust set of tools and methods to modify designs.

13. ***Increased design data integrity.*** With a single solid model supporting all downstream processes, changes are reflected quickly and accurately.

23.8 Where Can the Implementation Go Wrong?

The ways to cause an SM implementation to fail are fairly straightforward:

1. Ignoring changes (both internal and external to your company) affecting your current SM implementation

2. Underestimating the negative impact an individual user can have on your overall implementation

3. Underestimating the time and funds required to fully implement SM

4. Understaffing your computer system support efforts (system management, application support, and database management)

5. Poor training (improper, limited, or dated training of the users and system support personnel)

6. Failure to reinforce training with hands-on experience (minimum of 20 hours per week)

7. Limited or incorrect management feedback based on the lack of objective methods for the measurement of individual user's abilities with the system

8. Lack of or poorly defined standards and procedures

9. Well-defined standards and procedures which are not implemented through custom software (seed files, programs, and menus)

10. Closed communication lines between management and computer system users

11. Middle management not committed to the implementation

12. Poor or improper software-to-task selection and/or grossly undersized/oversized system producing low return on investment (ROI)

To summarize: low management involvement and understanding during the beginning phases of your SM implementation will limit the ability to affect the overall success and will increase the need for management intervention later, during the implementation cycle. (See Fig. 23.6.)

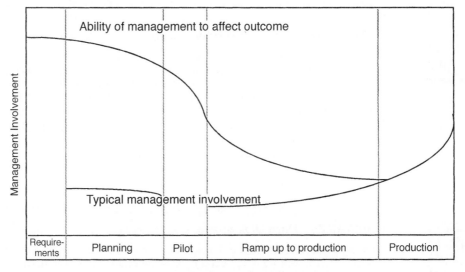

Phases of Implementation

FIGURE 23.6 Profile of typical "problem implementation." Problem implementations typically have a common trait: low management involvement during the beginning phases. The opportunity for management to affect the implementation diminishes over time. *(Courtesy of Intergraph Corporation.)*

23.9   Conclusions

When developing implementation strategies for SM technology, the issues are numerous, but not insurmountable or unintelligible—with proper assistance and support. Although it is not necessary for management to understand SM technology as thoroughly as must designers, it is essential that they base their decisions on such knowledge. Management can effectively leverage its knowledge by employing the expertise of outside analysts and consultants to make suggestions and recommendations on which to base their decisions concerning implementation strategies.

No CAD/CAM/CAE system implementation is perfect, including SM, nor are the people or organizations who develop, sell, support, operate, and manage it. Fortunately, to be truly productive, perfection is not required of the system or of the people involved with it. Other than appropriate technology, there are only two absolutely essential prerequisites for CAD/CAM/CAE system productivity: good information and good management. If you are not satisfied with your system's productivity, you must look both inward and outward for the solutions.

Good Practices

SMA.23.20   Documenting Project Costs

Documentation of project costs before and after SM implementation should be maintained. Values should be placed on both tangible and intangible benefits if at all possible. This will help to justify the SM system, its continued use and future expansion, and identify results for rewarding users, implementors, and managers alike.

SMA.23.21   Sharpen the Axe

Never lose sight of the balance required between process and product. Investment in the "process" of design must be just as important as the end "product" of design. You must make time to "sharpen the axe," even though you've got too many "trees" to cut down today.

SMA.23.22   Cross-Fertilization

Experienced and beginning users should be physically located in adjacent work areas for cross-fertilization of SM techniques, functions, and shortcuts.

SMA.23.23   For Designers and Engineers

Employing "CAD operators" simply to input graphical data increases design cycle time and reduces design quality. SM tools should be placed directly in the hands of designers and engineers.

SMA.23.24   Avoid a Poisoned Attitude

Bad early experiences with just a few users can poison a whole department's attitude toward SM. Early users should believe in the system and have patience while implementation bugs are weeded out. They should be your "high-flyers," have reputations for creativity, be willing to take chances, and be receptive to learning new systems. Their enthusiasm will spread to other employees and help alleviate resistance.

Brian Ruuska, CAD/CAE Applications Engineer
3M Co., St. Paul, Minn.

SMA.23.25   Hard Disk Space

Determine how much hard disk space you think you will need over the next three years and then double it! You will want and need it. Remember, the larger the hard disk, the lower the cost per megabyte of disk space. Be generous.

Don LaCourse, President
The Solid Modeling ExChange, Algood, Tenn.

Good Practices
(*Continued*)

SMA.23.26   Monitoring Productivity

If you wish to dramatically improve your system's productivity, record and monitor the CIM 12 productivity indicators outlined in Sec. 23.4. Focus your efforts on the optimization of processes instead of automation. Your SM system's vendor can provide advice and assistance with your efforts.

SMA.23.27   Supported Functions

Determine if the SM software under consideration supports all of your required engineering design and analysis functions.

SMA.23.28   Implementation Investments

The best way to ensure an efficient move to SM is to invest heavily in the acquisition and implementation planning stages. You should get the best professional help money can buy. The investment in professional consultants who know how to make your chosen system really productive is some of the best money you will spend in acquiring and implementing SM.

SMA.23.29   Implementation Guidelines

1. Implement modules, such as modeling and NC in a logical and progressive manner until the basics of the whole package are understood.

2. Software and documentation, either electronic or hardbound, should be kept up to date to ensure full support from your software vendor.

3. Target dates for implementing key aspects should be developed early and actively enforced.

4. Standards should be developed up front and modified as the need arises.

5. Components viewed as standard should be modeled as soon as possible to test the developed design standards.

6. Periodic meetings with the key SM designers can lead to valuable ideas for enhancing productivity.

7. The system administrator should be someone who communicates well with the daily users of the system.

8. Performance reviews should be a part of the ongoing process to keep SM designers moving in a positive direction.

Kevin P. Alexander, CAD/CAM/CAE System Administrator
Littleford Day, Inc., Florence, Ky.

Good to Know

SMA.23.30   A Never-Ending Story

The implementation process never ends. Hardware, software, companies, and people are ever changing.

Brian Ruuska, CAD/CAE Applications Engineer
3M Co., St. Paul, Minn.

SMA.23.31   Software Considerations

Before considering which SM software to purchase, there are several questions to ask yourself:

1. What type (injection molded, machined, cast, etc.) of parts do you make?

2. Does your company plan to use the SM design for downstream processes and, if so, which processes?

(*Continued*)

3. How much time will your current personnel require to become productive with SM software?

4. Will the purchase of SM software require your company to purchase new hardware?

5. How will your existing designs be maintained?

6. Will your existing staff be sufficient to support the new software and hardware?

7. What is the cost per seat?

SMA.23.32　Order of Accuracy

Determine the level of accuracy (third-order and/or above) in the wireframe, surface, and solid geometry required to produce your designs. Find out if the software under consideration supports this level of accuracy. (See Chap. 4 for more on the degree of defining equations of certain geometry in an SM database.)

SMA.23.33　Cost Per SM Workstation

Be careful! The cost per SM workstation can be very misleading. Most SM software is packaged in some modular fashion. When comparing SM costs, be sure to compare apples to apples.

SMA.23.34　Benchmarking

One of the most telling ways of comparing software is through benchmarking. A benchmark produced by several software vendors can better determine which product has features most applicable to the type of work required. Caution should be exercised when defining which SM products are to be benchmarked. Some vendors may attempt to limit benchmarks to their most robust software. The benchmark should simulate a real-life implementation of the intended software.

SMA.23.35　The Right Tool for the Right Job

Lately, we have been involved in some gear consulting projects and have come across gears designed using SM software. In these cases, our customers had wrongly assumed that these were trouble-free designs because they had gone through the SM phase. The problem is that the crucially important aspects, such as the optimum design of geometry for proper kinematic action, were skipped. The optimum design of geometry and other crucial aspects should be checked with software specifically designed for that need.

Thus, it is important to note that a good concept such as SM can be misapplied. This should be avoided. Let's use the right tool for the right job. Remember the saying: "If all you have is a hammer, everything in this world begins to look like a nail."

Jack Marathe, President
Universal Technical Systems, Inc., Rockford, Ill.

SMA.23.36　Factors to Consider

Following are 20 factors to consider when comparing CAD/CAM systems:

1. Dimension-driven

2. Parametric modeling

3. Integrated solid, surface, 2D modeling

4. Model-drawing associativity

5. Instancing

6. Automatic hidden-line removal

7. Assembly modeling

8. On-demand mass properties

(*Continued*)

Good to Know
(*Continued*)

9. Interference detection

10. Feature substitution

11. Object-oriented database

12. Advanced visualization

13. Hardware independence

14. Standard data formats

15. User programming

16. Single data structure

17. Integrated applications available—NC, sheet metal, FEM/FEA, plastics, mechanisms, etc.

18. Distributed data management

19. Bill of materials

20. Modular architecture and pricing

George LaBlanc, Director Marketing
Matra Datavision, Tewksbury, Mass.

Chapter 24

Solid Modeling and Design

Lawrence L. Barinka, Ph.D.
President
Interactive Computer Modelling, Inc.

Design applications are one of the major areas in which use of Solid Modeling (SM) technology has made giant inroads over the past decade.

The purpose of this chapter is to provide an overview of some of the ways in which SM is being applied throughout various design disciplines. The goal is to spark and spread new ideas for ways in which SM may be applied in the workplace.

Our intent is not to provide a tutorial on SM and design, but rather to provide information via actual end-user success stories of SM in various design applications. In particular, success stories are provided for government, academia, and industry environments to see how SM technology has been implemented and successfully used for design applications in such varied environments.

24.1 Introduction: Solid Modeling Becomes *the* Mechanical Design Tool*

In the second issue of *Computer-Aided Engineering* (November/December 1982), we outlined the state of the then-nascent technology of Solid Modeling as it applied to mechanical design. At that time, the technology had just begun to coalesce, and manufacturing companies were just beginning to think about giving SM a try.

In this article, we said the next generation of software would cost less, that SM and drafting would be combined, and the biggest improvement would be in more interactive interfaces. We also listed 15 different commercial solid modelers, most of which could be more accurately characterized as research projects.

Today, some 10 years later, those predictions, by and large, have come to fruition. Costs plummeted, perhaps more thanks to hardware than software. Associativity between the solid model and a drawing can virtually automate drafting. Variational and parametric modeling techniques, along with advances in graphical user interfaces, made SM a design tool and not just an arcane computer technology.

But perhaps the biggest difference has been in the acceptance of the technology among industry. Even as recent as the late 1980s, many believed drafting was here to stay as the primary design and communication tool for mechanical design. Solids were just too difficult to use, and besides, 3D modeling caused a disruption in traditional design processes.

Then came the 1990s. Competition, from around the block and around the globe, applied huge pressure, while recessions led to massive corporate downsizing. Today, the push is on for reengineering, creating new, streamlined processes—leveraging computers and networks—that drastically reduce times to market and allow companies to do more with less.

For mechanical engineering and design, the foundation for such efforts is typically SM. For all companies wanting to improve product development, whether they are working toward concurrent engi-

---

*Contributed by Robert Mills, Editor, *Computer-Aided Engineering Magazine.*

neering, reengineering their processes, or whatever, solids have become the center of attention. Solid models are the basis for conceptual design, visualization, detailing, analysis, NC programming, verification, rapid prototyping, and virtual prototyping.

This shift from drafting to SM has been pushed by great advances in commercial software. Today's SM software is built on standards, runs on multiple hardware platforms, and provides tight links to numerous engineering applications.

At the same time, today's users are more demanding: they require standard interfaces, quick implementation of new technology, and robust, bug-free code. In short, because SM is part and parcel to their competitive strategy—rather than merely an interesting technology as it was in the early 1980s—they expect SM not only to work, but to work efficiently.

24.2   Solid Modeling in Government

24.2.1   PRC's Project 2851

PRC, a government contractor in Northern Virginia, has successfully used and integrated SM in a simulation database production system known as Project 2851. Project 2851 is a Department of Defense (DoD) program managed by the Air Force. It is intended to support DoD training simulators using digital cartographic data, imagery, and 2D and 3D models for visual and sensor image generation. Project 2851, developed by PRC, is a database production system which produces these types of simulator data. The databases provide for realistic portrayals of various geographic areas around the world. Realism is required in order to achieve a positive training experience for military aircraft pilots, tank drivers, and other vehicle operators. The databases are distributed in standard simulator database formats defined and produced by Project 2851.

Solid Modeling has been effectively used to produce 2D and 3D models as part of the Project 2851 simulation databases. One reason it was chosen was based on its dual model descriptions in both CSG and polygonal form. The CSG form is important in the training simulation application because it allows for changes to be made to a model in a timely fashion. Time is a priceless commodity in large database production. Often, models need to be "tweaked." In such cases, the ability to make rapid changes is key.

Using the CSG form is also important when making multiple levels of detail (LODs) of a model. In visual simulation, several LODs of a model are typically used. An LOD is simply a representation of a model. For example, a low LOD of an aircraft model might contain 30 polygons, while a high LOD version of the same aircraft might contain 200 polygons. In the simulation, the low LOD would be used when the aircraft is far away from the viewer's eyepoint (thus revealing less detail). The high LOD would be used when the aircraft is much closer and more detail is evident to the eye. Thus, during the simulation, the LOD representation of an object is switched depending on the distance of that object from the eyepoint. By using the CSG form during model creation, small changes can be made to the CSG description to quickly make multiple LODs of the same model.

The polygonal model form provided by SM is important because nearly all training simulators process polygons for rendering their scenes. Thus, the CSG version is useful in the creation and modification of models and their many LODs, while the polygonal version is the real output that is later used. PRC then performs some postprocessing of the SM polygonal models to make them more compatible for simulation.

The modeling process within the Project 2851 system consists of several steps. First, the geometry of the model is defined through SM and its CSG commands. Next, the polygonal version is produced. The model's polygons are then logically grouped into objects known as *components*. A component is a collection of polygons that represent a part of a model that is homogeneous; that is, all of a component's polygons have the same attribute values, such as color, surface material, etc. Attributes are then assigned to the model. Information is then added to the model to help speed up visible surface calculations for some simulators' image-generation systems. Next, the Project 2851 modeling system removes some polygons that are not necessary, such as the polygon representing the bottom of a house model. Since the bottom of the house is never seen, the simulator's image-generation system does not need to spend valuable processing time on it. Finally, the model and all its associative information are stored in the Standard Simulator Data Base repository, where it can be retrieved on demand for producing databases meeting a customer's specific needs.

Many different types of solid models have been built by the Project 2851 modeling system using SM. They include airplanes, helicopters, tanks, trucks, a variety of houses, barracks, towers, road intersections, and many others. They have been successfully used in training simulation image-generation tests. It is safe to say that SM is a useful and valuable tool in supporting the training of our nation's military.

Figure 24.1 (see color insert) is an example of one of hundreds of simulator LOD models built by Project 2851 using SM.

24.2.2 Fairchild Space Improves Speed and Quality of Proposals with SM

Developing the initial proposal for a new satellite compresses a great deal of design work into a matter of weeks. Despite the speed of the process, some critical design decisions may be locked in at that point and the company making the proposal is often required to commit to certain performance and cost specifications. Fairchild Space has dramatically improved proposal performance by switching from wireframe modeling to SM.

Solid Modeling provides greatly improved visualization of the design concept. This has made it possible to integrate the maximum amount of payload into the satellite and to ensure that the satellite will fit inside the launch vehicle shroud. In addition, almost instant generation of center-of-gravity and moment-of-inertia data allows quick determination of guidance system requirements for various design concepts. As a result, the need to add large uncertainty factors has been eliminated, making design more competitive. Finally, SM technology has tripled engineering productivity, resulting in reduced proposal costs.

Fairchild began its involvement in the space industry with the development of Pegasus, ATS-6, Sert-II, and ISEE-3 in the early 1960s and, in recent years, the Multi-Module System bus (MMS) which consists of power, guidance, communications, and data-handling systems for a satellite—everything except the payload.

The MMS has served as the bus for a large number of commercial, scientific, and military satellites. The MMS is an off-the-shelf system, which reduces its cost and increases its reliability; yet it can easily be adapted to serve a wide variety of missions. This is accomplished by changing the various plug-in modules which perform the satellites' major functions. Another advantage of the modular approach is that the MMS bus provides the only satellite platform which can be repaired in space, as was demonstrated in a widely publicized Space Shuttle mission in 1988.

The company's current projects are NASA's and Jet Propulsion Laboratory's TOPEX/Poseidon satellite, designed to perform precision mapping of the ocean's surface. A second project is Explorer Platform which is designed for in-orbit payload exchange. Fairchild recently won a contract to build the Navy's PROFILE satellite and is presently involved in a large number of projects in the proposal and development states, including TOMS-EP (Total Ozone Mapping Spectrometer Earth Probe), OSL (Orbital Solar Laboratory), SPAS (Shuttle Pallet Satellite), and the Gravity Probe B satellite.

The Gravity Probe B is a relativity gyroscope experiment being developed by NASA and Stanford University to test two rather extraordinary, unverified predictions of Albert Einstein's Theory of Relativity. The experiment will precisely measure tiny changes in the directions of spin of four gyroscopes contained in an Earth satellite orbiting at a 400-mile altitude directly over the poles. The gyroscopes used in the probe are so free from disturbance that they will provide an almost perfect space-time reference system. They will measure how space and time are warped by the presence of Earth and how Earth's rotation drags space-time around with it. These effects, although small for the planet Earth, have far reaching implications for the nature of matter and the structure of the universe.

To meet the complex scientific requirements of the mission, the spacecraft requires a highly precise guidance system. In developing the proposal for the Gravity Probe B, one of the important technical issues faced by Fairchild engineers was developing a mass-trim mechanism to maintain the correct center of gravity. Developing the satellite model required, as usual, a very large number of iterations, and for each iteration it was necessary to calculate the amount of correction that the mass-trim system would be required to perform, as well as the most efficient method of generating these corrections. These calculations are extremely time-consuming to accomplish by hand and are also subject to inaccuracies. With the original solid model of the probe, calculations were performed precisely within a few seconds, making it possible to quickly update the mass-trim system. Within a few minutes, the effectiveness of the iteration in correcting the center of gravity of the spacecraft, and also packaging considerations, were easily evaluated. The proposal developed by three Fairchild engineers has over 100 components and occupies 30 megabytes of computer storage space. Fairchild's proposal for Gravity Probe B was one of two accepted by NASA and Stanford University to proceed to the study and development phase.

In more conventional satellite systems, the primary consideration in designing the guidance system is the weight of the fuel required for propulsion. Fuel typically makes up 20 percent of the launch weight of the spacecraft and every extra pound of fuel must be subtracted from the payload. Several years back, when Fairchild had a group of engineers dedicated to this function, it still took so much time to perform center-of-gravity and moment-of-inertia calculations that these figures were not available during the proposal stage. Even during the later design process, these calculations were usually out of date by the time they were completed because of the speed with which new design iterations were created. The ability to calculate center-of-gravity and moment-of-inertia data instantly during the proposal stage now allows the design team to quickly evaluate alternate design concepts in terms of propulsion system weight requirements. In many cases, this makes it possible for payload weight to be significantly increased. In addition, knowing the center of gravity and moments of inertia makes it possible to determine the type and size of control equipment, reaction wheel, thrusters, etc., which will be required to control the satellite, thus allowing far more accurate cost estimates.

In addition to weight, packaging is another critical factor in nearly every spacecraft design. When initial design concepts were created as wireframe models, packaging studies were fraught with the potential for costly errors. The use of SM has helped Fairchild engineers deal with this type of difficulty on many occasions. Nearly all of Fairchild's conceptual work now utilizes SM technology.

Another important aspect of satellite design is ensuring that the spacecraft will fit inside the shroud of its launch vehicle. This is very difficult with a wireframe approach because the conical configuration of the shroud can be very deceptive. It may look perfect from one view but still have hidden interferences which can be detected only if the model is rotated to exactly the right view. Another problem is that vibration of flexible appendages on the satellite cause it, as it undergoes the forces of lift-off, to have a dynamic envelope that is larger than its normal static envelope. The only way to calculate the dynamic envelope is to perform a dynamic finite element analysis. Using previous methods, this meant creating a finite element model, which took far too long to perform in the proposal stage.

Now, solid models of the shroud and spacecraft are created so that interferences in static conditions are easily detected. Then the solids are converted into finite element models using automatic meshing capabilities. Fairchild then attaches loads and boundary conditions directly to the model. The results of the finite element analysis provide the dynamic envelope which then compares to the shroud model for final interference checks.

In conclusion, the use of SM technology has dramatically improved Fairchild's design engineering operations. Validating designs in the concept phase and being able to easily modify the concept based on the results has increased the productivity of their engineering staff. Engineers are retrained in SM, further increasing the staff's productivity. New engineers are trained in about 20 hours to the point where they can use the software on their own, and in another two weeks they are usually fully proficient.

24.3 Solid Modeling in Academia

24.3.1 Solid Modeling in Education at FAMU/FSU

The FAMU/FSU College of Engineering has been using SM in several undergraduate Mechanical Engineering (ME) design courses for many years. Initially, PC-based SM systems were used to generate simple models of parts designed in class. Recently, workstation-based SM systems and mechanisms packages have been introduced into the design courses.

The SM software packages in use today are reasonably priced and offer good performance on low-cost workstations. In addition, the systems are sufficiently powerful and user-friendly for students to develop sophisticated solid models without long training periods. The solid models provide students with excellent tools to aid in the visualization of their designs from concept to final design. The solid models also serve as excellent aids in the presentation of their design projects and enhance the educational experience of the student, since there are no facilities for students to build physical models of their designs at the college.

An additional benefit of integrated mechanism analysis is that students can create a solid model of a mechanism, define all the joints and connectivities graphically, and then watch the model being animated in a single session. Previous nonintegrated mechanism analysis systems used on PCs and Microvaxes had adequate performance, but lacked graphical methods of creating the model. This meant that students had a difficult time debugging their work. One incorrect joint definition or data statement could take several hours for the student to locate. The integration of SM with mechanism analysis has eliminated the problem and allows the students to create more realistic models with fewer problems.

For the future, there is a great potential for use of SM software in other courses such as Vector Dynamics and Solid Mechanics, since it is much easier to visualize a system if you can examine it and watch it move as a true solid. Additional information, including velocity and acceleration vectors, force and moment vectors, and stress fields, help the student gain a much better appreciation for the behavior of systems.

24.3.2 The Purdue Quick Turnaround Cell: Integrating Design and Process Planning with Solid Modeling

The Quick Turnaround Cell (QTC) project began in 1986 as one of a number of research projects in Purdue's Engineering Research Center for Intelligent Manufacturing Systems (ERC). The original goals of the project were to design and implement a working prototype of a system for the design, automatic machining, and inspection of one-of-a-kind prismatic parts. The QTC system, first demonstrated in 1987, closely couples feature-based design, automated process planning with fixture planning, automated numerical control (NC) programming, and direct NC machining into a fully integrated CAD/CAM environment.

The intelligence of the QTC system is based on the use of geometric features and geometric reasoning. The design module provides object-oriented, graphical, three-dimensional design based on a small number of form features, basic volumetric shapes used to construct parts. Each feature, such as a hole, circular slot, or a NURB surface, is easily positioned, oriented, and sized on a work face of the stock (which is also an editable feature) with graphical interaction. Characteristic positions and dimensions of features are displayed as graphical icons called *handles*. Features are positioned with respect to other features, with toleranced vectors between position handles. Features also have dimension and form tolerances. The resulting part model is a high-level representation of the design containing all feature information, including the position and feature tolerances.

The QTC process planning system reads the part model created by the design system and produces a complete process plan file that includes tools, toolpaths, and fixturing information. The system performs geometric reasoning on a specially annotated boundary representation (B-Rep) of the part to translate the design features into machining-process features using a computation method called *Feature Refinement*. During Feature Refinement, a global precedence graph of feature relationships is created. This graph represents significant geometric relationships between features, such as intersections and containment, that are used to determine correct process sequences.

If the design model contains a hole feature, for example, that intersects a slot feature, the process planner will determine the appropriate machining sequence by reasoning about the precedence information for these features. The process planner then selects tools, determines approach directions, computes fixture setup information, and finally creates cutter location data for each fixturing configuration. Once the process planning is completed, the designer can choose to machine the part using the cell controller module, graphically simulate the machining using the NC verification module, or edit the part further based on the machining information now available.

The QTC project is an evolving research effort in quick turnaround manufacturing. Related research projects include frameworks for multiple-domain feature modeling, assembly modeling with QTC parts, five-axis sculptured surface finish machining, and intelligent fixture configuration planning.

Collaboration Project QTC Testbed

In 1990, a collaboration project between the Redstone Arsenal Production Engineering Division (PED) and the Purdue ERC was established to adapt, extend, and apply the research demonstrated by the Purdue QTC system for the PED environment. This project complements the ongoing QTC research program by extending it toward industrial applications, thereby providing PED with the newest technology in quick turnaround manufacturing, and providing the Purdue research team with critical feedback regarding industrial needs. The QTC system and research has seen significant enhancements due to this collaboration.

For Use by the Army Missile Command

Developing a next-generation design and process planning system which improves producibility of early designs and allows rapid functional prototyping of weapon system components is the objective of a partnership between the Army Missile Command (MICOM), Purdue University ERC, industry partners, and the National Science Foundation (NSF). From the MICOM perspective, the QTC project addresses producibility issues (e.g., tooling, tolerances) during the design of components, permits rapid prototyping of components without tedious NC programming, reduces cost of transitioning from development to production, and provides technology applicable to military research and development and private industry.

For Use in Desert Storm

During Desert Storm the need arose to modify the TOW missile launcher brake mechanism to perform better in the dry desert climate. MICOM engineers responded to the challenge and demonstrated the utility of the QTC system by utilizing QTC to design and prototype six variations of a braking mechanism for the M83 launcher. These functional prototypes were tested at the Redstone Arsenal Range by firing dummy missiles and monitoring transients in the braking mechanism. The design and prototyping of parts required three days, and testing was completed within three weeks. The QTC system continues to provide the MICOM with the ability to respond rapidly to the need for functional prototypes in order to test research and development concepts.

24.4   Solid Modeling in Industry

24.4.1   Solid Modeling and Analysis Contributes to Better Convertible Top Stack Design

Convertible folding top frames are one of the more complex auto body mechanisms. They are usually designed concurrent with a new vehicle body. In the past, top frame designers relied upon "intuition" and graphical analysis to visualize position and movement of the stack components. Designs were verified by construction of prototypes built to body dimensions. More often then not, design intent was not met, resulting in modifications and additional prototypes. Engineering change letters often exceeded the alphabet prior to production.

In 1990, Dura Convertible Systems, a leading design and manufacturer of top stack frame assemblies, installed SM, visualization, and dynamic/kinematic analysis. Interfaces were established to provide 2D and 3D plotting as well as superimposed force vectors, acceleration, and velocity information for on-screen operating models.

The system provides CAE support to Dura's other CAD systems for FEA (finite element analysis) and problem solving. Problem linkages for a complete top frame assembly can be modeled with changes evaluated in 3D wireframe or solids in a relatively short time period.

In one application a foreign convertible top frame with kinematic problems was analyzed and solutions determined. The top frame was modified and installed in a vehicle. Performance of the modified frame was as predicted. This was accomplished in one-fourth of the time required prior to the installation of the SM and analysis system.

Solid Modeling and analysis at Dura Convertible Systems has made a significant contribution in reducing the time required to design and develop a new convertible top as well as providing a useful tool for fast, accurate analysis of field and production problems. Figure 24.2 (see color insert) illustrates a sequence of positions for a complex convertible top stack design.

24.4.2   Solid Modeling Aids Development of New-Generation Amtrak Passenger Seating

The spring of 1992 witnessed the introduction of a new generation of mass-transit seating when Amtrak installed the first prototypes of seats that will, over the next few years, be installed throughout its fleet. The new seats provide dramatic advances over past models with features such as the following:

1. Retractable personalized food trays that can be cleaned in their stored position.
2. Adjustable leg and foot rests
3. Adjustable lumbar and headrest cushion assemblies

4. Ergonomically designed recline mechanisms that adjust both backrest and seat-bottom cushion positions

5. Capabilities for both audio and video service

Manual drafting techniques, long used in the transit vehicle seating industry, would have been overwhelmed by the complexity of the new design. Fortunately, when selected as one of three prototype suppliers for the project, Coach and Car Equipment Corporation had previously installed Solid Modeling and mechanical computer-aided engineering (MCAE) software. This installation allowed Coach and Car designers to produce solid models of the seats, allowing packaging and performance issues to be resolved on the computer screen rather than with expensive and time-consuming hardware prototypes. Stress analysis and mechanism kinematics issues were also addressed and evaluated in the concept phase. As a result, the new seats were designed in four months compared to the estimate of more than one year that would have been required using conventional methods.

The new Amtrak seat design is the initial effort to revamp their existing seat inventory. The current seat design has not changed significantly in 20 years because of the requirement to maintain commonalty among existing stock. Three companies were awarded design contracts by Amtrak after detailed presentations and capabilities analysis. After the designs had undergone many Amtrak reviews, the companies were asked to build prototypes which were installed in regular passenger service. Amtrak solicited comments from passengers before making a final determination of which design to select and which features were preferred.

Coach and Car, one of the three finalists, is the largest supplier of rail transit vehicle seats in North America. In addition to passenger rail car seats, the company produces seating for passenger buses, locomotives, off-road equipment, military, and commercial vehicles. The privately owned company has been in business for 67 years and maintains complete design, analysis, test, and manufacturing capabilities.

The basic concept behind Coach and Car's new rail seat design is to provide an environment that passengers can change to increase comfort on trips which typically last from several hours to several days. Because the definition of comfort differs for each passenger, and most likely changes during a trip, the passenger should be able to adjust the seat in order to achieve comfort.

The cushion and recline systems are good examples. Headrest and lumbar cushions are separate assemblies that can be adjusted on a vertical track-and-glide system to meet passenger desires. As the trip progresses, and as the passenger's definition of required headrest and lumbar support changes, this seating system allows the passenger to reorient the feel of the seat to his or her liking. The seat recline mechanism utilizes a unique geometry which pivots the seat-bottom cushion precisely with the seat backrest cushion such that the relationship between the two planes moves in concert with the human hip joint. This relationship minimizes the untucking-of-the-shirt-upon-recline problems, and ensures that the selected headrest and lumbar cushions provide the same support as the recline angle increases.

The seats also incorporate a new food tray system. On current seats, the food tray folds out from the seat back facing the passenger, similar to most airline trays. The disadvantage of this design in a rail environment includes the fact that the seats facing bulkheads require separate tray assemblies, resulting in loose components and additional service to these seat locations. Also, the trays must be unfolded to be cleaned, and any residue on the tray is transferred to the back of the seat when the tray is stowed.

The new seat design uses a tray that retracts into the seat arm and thus can be used on every seat. The tray top is exposed to the aisle and can be easily cleaned without unfolding. Debris left on the tray after use is left to fall on the floor where it can be easily cleaned as part of the entire vehicle-cleaning procedure. The tray can also be adjusted, using sliding and rotation options to provide the most convenient position.

The seat also offers the ability to reposition legs and feet by the use of a leg rest with an additional barber-style feature. This type of adjustability allows the passenger to reposition feet and legs for increased blood flow through the legs, while still providing proper support.

All of these new features required a level of complexity that had never before been attempted in the transit vehicle seat business. Frankly, it would not have been practical for Coach and Car to attempt the changes using its previous engineering methodology. But, several years ago, the company committed itself to advancing technology in the seat business and decided to upgrade its engineering tools. Traditionally, when companies implemented a CAD system, the first and only step was to automate the drafting system. However, Coach and Car was determined that the real savings were in design and not documentation. Coach and Car made a commitment to the concept of MCAE in which engineering designs are generated as solid models rather than pencil sketches.

These solid models are realistic enough for engineering and marketing to evaluate the product's appearance and functions and to make critical early assessments and evaluations. The initial design can be refined with a variety of techniques such as finite element and kinematic analysis. The basic idea of MCAE is that the design is largely proven and optimized prior to the prototype stage. Physical testing is substantially compressed and few, if any, design changes need be made after prototyping. Another benefit of this approach is that the drafting and detailing process is reduced to generating views of the solid model, dimensioning, and cleaning up.

An example of an area in which SM proves invaluable is the seat recline mechanism. The system is far more complicated than traditional seat recliners. Trying to resolve the packaging issues using traditional manual drafting methods would have been very difficult. Instead, the designer modeled the recliner mechanism in SM and then transferred it to kinematics, which was used to step the recliner mechanism through its full range of motion. The kinematic model at each extreme of the motion range was then converted back to a solid, which made it easy to resolve control, linkage, and packaging issues. In particular, interferences as well as pinch points or small gaps between the cushions and frame were readily identifiable.

The first prototype fit perfectly. In the past, achieving a precise fit between the cushions and frame usually required several prototype stages because of the complicated three-dimensional angles and contours involved. The same solid model of the recline mechanism was also used to generate a finite element model. This analysis technique made it possible to reduce weight in many areas which previously would have been overdesigned. The result is an expected 10 to 15 percent reduction in weight and material cost relative to traditional designs.

Another very challenging design issue in the new-generation seat was presented by the knuckle mechanism on the food tray. This part uses three pivot joints and one sliding joint to allow the food tray to rotate, swivel, and slide. This part also would have been very difficult to accurately design on a drafting board. Instead, using SM, the designer rotated the component into each relevant plane of operation and verified its performance on the computer screen. Shaded solid images made it easy for the designer to understand what was going on and also to communicate the concept to others for comment.

Once the design process was completed, selected views of the new seat were transferred to a CAD drafting package using the IGES neutral file format. These CAD views merely needed to be dimensioned, cleaned up, and formatted to complete the detailing process. Again, the design process was completed by one person in four months compared to an estimated one year which would have been required using previous engineering methods. The first prototype performed exactly as expected.

The design will become even more complex as additional safety features are added to the seat after the prototype phase. Dynamic testing has shown that a sudden change in vehicle speed of as little as 15 mph can cause severe injuries to passengers impacting traditional fixed, rigid seat assemblies. In response to this problem, Coach and Car has developed an energy absorption system that allows for controlled and predicted articulation of the backrest structure. This design provides for predicted passenger deceleration over time, significantly reducing the impact the passenger actually experiences. Tests have shown that in a 15-mph occupant impact, the resultant force level is reduced from in excess of 8 g's to less than 4 g's, greatly reducing the possibility of serious injury. The safety benefits of such a system are even greater as impact speed increases. A major obstacle in the past to incorporating safety features such as this into passenger train seats has been increased engineering cost, which must be built into the seating cost. The use of advanced design methodologies at Coach and Car substantially eliminates this concern.

All in all, the use of advanced software tools at Coach and Car has substantially streamlined design and prototype operations and significantly improved the company's competitive position.

24.4.3 Computer Modeling Produces World's First Artificial Ear by Machine

Until recently, patients who lost an ear through cancer or trauma had to wait for a professional trained in maxillofacial prosthetics to painstakingly create an artificial ear. Hand sculpting an artificial ear is an expensive and lengthy process, requiring that a wax model in the form of a mirror image of the patient's existing ear be created. Additionally, there are not many properly trained sculptors available, so the wait for an artificial ear or prosthesis is sometimes as long as a year.

The technology of developing an artificial ear for a patient has been limited to hand sculpting because the intricate folds and cavities of the ear make it impossible for a conventional machine tool, such as a multiaxis CNC mill, to reach all of the surfaces involved. But a new process, which generates a plastic prototype directly from a solid model, has accurately reproduced the complex shape of a patient's ear, leading to the production of the world's first artificial ear by machine.

The patient's existing ear was digitized and the data was then transferred to an MCAE system to generate a solid model. The refined solid model geometry was in turn transferred to the Stereolithography Apparatus (SLA) from 3-D Systems (Valencia, California), which generated a plastic prototype based on the geometry (see Chap. 19). The 3D acrylic polymer model was then used to make a Room Temperature Vulcanization (RTV) silicone mold of the ear. By shortening the development process with computer modeling, the development of prostheses can be much less expensive and available to more people than ever before. The key to success in this application was the ability of MCAE software to quickly generate an accurate solid model of the ear and to convert it into the format required for SLA.

Several alternative methods for digitizing the ear were considered. Laser scanning was rejected because the shape of the ear was too complex (with its many undercuts and hidden pockets) for the scanning laser beam to reach all areas. Additionally, there would be a shadowing effect in some areas of the model. MRI (magnetic resonance imaging) and CT (computerized tomography) scanning, which would have enabled the generation of cross sections at very small increments, were also rejected due to concerns about distortions in the scanning process.

It was decided to digitize the ear manually with a coordinate measuring machine (CMM). The ear cast was milled in 1-mm increments, resulting in a series of 64 cross sections, which were then digitized on a digitizing pad to create the 2D splines that would form the template of the ear's shape. This approach allowed the digitization of difficult areas that the other scanning technologies could not have reached. The CMM data was than transferred to SM via IGES.

Blending the various cross sections into one solid body was a challenge because the entire surface of the ear had to be generated in the SM system. The surfaces were created piece by piece from portions of the ear that resembled basic geometrical shapes, such as polylines, arcs, splines, or lines.

Solid Modeling was also used to build a solid model of the SLA support structure for the ear. When the supports were completed, files were created in the STL format which could be read by the SLA. The resulting 3D polymer model was then used as the basis to make an RTV silicone mold of the ear. With the silicone mold, a wax master model was cast, which served as the basis to produce the mold for the artificial ear.

A future medical use of computerized modeling will be in the reconstructive surgery of the ear and other body parts. Currently, the approach in reconstructive surgery of an ear, for example, is to harvest a block of rib cartilage from the patient. The surgeon carves the cartilage into a framework, over which skin is grafted to create the ear shape. The success of such surgery is dependent on the surgeon's sculpting ability and how much time the surgeon has to work, which is limited to the length of time that the patient can safely be kept under anesthesia.

One way to sharply reduce the time to reconstruct an ear would be to digitize the ear and have the geometry present in a CNC milling machine stationed in the surgery area. When the rib cartilage is harvested, it can be milled on the machine, saving a considerable amount of time. An even more efficient option will come in the future when the SLA process will be able to create an implant to serve as the framework of the ear. Current polymers used in SLA are not biocompatible, and would be gradually rejected by the body. Hip implants made from a medical-grade silicone elastomer have been successfully produced using the same technique detailed here. However, the biocompatibility of the ear framework is more critical because it serves as the foundation for grafted skin tissue. When this milestone is reached, computerized modeling will produce implantable foundations for virtually any body part.

24.4.4 MCAE Helps Ford Motor Company Compress Product Development Lead Time

Alpha Simultaneous Engineering is a 450-person organization within Ford Motor Company whose mission is to develop improved products and processes that can be transferred to the rest of the company. One of the key functions of Alpha is to evaluate the effectiveness of advanced computer-aided engineering tools prior to their implementation in the operational divisions. Another is to determine the most effective methods for applying these tools to real-world engineering tasks. An important current goal at Ford is to bring new car programs into production 36 months or less from the time engineering begins.

As a demonstration project to help accomplish this goal, Alpha engineers recently designed a new lower control arm in 95 workdays compared to the 229 workdays that would have been required using conventional engineering methods. The traditional approach is as follows:

1. The design engineer develops the concept model on paper.

2. He or she hands off the concept to a CAD operator who defines a detailed model on a CAD system.

3. The design engineer turns the model over to an analyst for finite element analysis.

4. The analyst returns the refined geometry, meeting design objectives, to the design engineer and to the CAD operator for final modifications.

The key to improving this process was the use of Solid Modeling software, which makes it possible for the design engineer to develop the baseline model, analyze its performance, and make necessary refinements without involving other individuals. Additional timesavings results from the ease of visualizing complex components in solid geometry form, and from automatic meshing procedures which greatly reduce finite element modeling time, allowing manufacturing to review the results at the concept level of design.

Alpha Simultaneous Engineering was conceived in the middle 1980s as a response to increased competitive pressures being felt by all major automobile manufacturers. Its purpose is to serve as a laboratory for the development of advanced technology and operating methods and to speed their transfer to the operating divisions of the company. The basic concept is to give star performers in Ford the chance to make advances which cannot be accomplished in the operating divisions due to the time pressures of ongoing projects.

Alpha is organized like a microcosm of the company, with departments dedicated to Product Engineering, Business and Product Strategy, Manufacturing, Sales, Quality Assurance, etc. Employees rotate into Alpha on two-to-three-year assignments from other divisions of the company.

Employees are encouraged to take projects which they have begun in Alpha with them to their home divisions when they return.

Today, the automotive engineering process typically begins with the design engineer assigned to the project generating a series of sketches to explain his or her concept of the part design. These sketches are turned over to a CAD operator working on a mainframe CAD system. The CAD operator provides the precise 3D definition of the part geometry which is needed to advance to the next stage. Obviously, a considerable amount of consultation is required between the design engineer and CAD operator to ensure that the design intent is preserved in the finished CAD model.

Once complete, the CAD model is transferred to an analyst with specialized training in the use of mainframe stress analysis programs. The analyst converts the CAD model into the format required by the analysis program, creates the mesh needed to model the part, and then runs the analysis and views the results to determine failure points. In a series of iterations, the analyst then modifies the part to eliminate weaknesses and reruns the analysis to see if the modifications have worked. During this process, the analyst must again maintain close contact with the designer to ensure that changes do not impair functionality. Once analysis is complete, changes to the model are given back to the CAD operator for modification and used for approvals and manufacturing.

The product chosen by Alpha engineers to prove the value of new MCAE methods is a rear lower control arm for a current production model vehicle. This part was selected because engineers felt that it would be possible to realize substantial weight reduction. The most prominent feature of the original forged-steel design is the bucket, a tapering cylindrical section near the center of the part that rests on top of a spring. Radiating out from the spring are several attachment points for the shock absorbers and kingpin bushings and also the tow links, which are tension bars designed to absorb reaction forces experienced by the bushing during transverse motion. The area between the bucket and attachments was covered by approximately ½-inch-thick material with a series of ribs to provide the necessary stiffness.

In developing the replacement, Alpha engineers conceived a radically different approach. They envisioned the use of a vacuum casting, which allows considerably thinner sections and details, thus increasing design flexibility. The proposed new material also had a yield strength of 95,000 psi, approximately twice that of the original material. Their basic design concept was to alter the part geometry to a space-frame approach, maintaining the bucket and attachment points in the same position, but eliminating most of the material in between to reduce weight. The geometry of the space frame was to be optimized to take up the loading previously handled by the walls and ribs.

With SM, the concept development was a rather simple process. One reason was that the design engineer could formalize ideas with three-dimensional shaded solid images. A key factor is that complicated shapes can be quickly generated and modified using SM software. The resulting 3D images are so clear that they leave no doubt about what has been created and are presented to other engineers and less technically oriented managers and marketing personnel in order to get conceptual feedback. By contrast, performing similar tasks on a shared-host CAD system would be impractical because of the difficulty involved in creating and manipulating the model and understanding the wireframe geometry. The process of developing the 3D baseline concept took only 15 days, compared to approximately 33 days that would have been required using conventional methods.

It is also important to note that with the conventional approach, engineers would probably not have used the space-frame design because of the difficulty of communicating the details of such a complex shape to all the parties involved.

Once the baseline model had been completed and reviewed, the project moved into the analysis phase. An automated modeling tool that generates a finite element mesh for even the most complex parts without user intervention was used. This saved considerable analysis time. Additional timesaving was experienced by eliminating the need to translate the CAD model, bring the analyst up to speed on the project, consult the design engineer on the analysis, and change the CAD model.

The SM software produced an input file for the finite element package which was used to perform the actual analysis. The design engineer used a series of load cases based on physical test data which included: spring load, load on shock mount, lateral load across bushing tangs, horizontal load, and the vertical load in reaction to spring through the tangs. The loads were applied in a series of combinations to model different operating scenarios.

The first iteration met the yield strength requirement of the new material but localized hot spots presented potential fatigue life concerns. The design engineer reinforced the tang sections at the front. Also, the orientation of the shock mount was changed with a reinforcing rim around the outside diameter replacing the previous radius. Material was removed from the tow link and bushing mount sections where the analysis showed that stress was at very low levels. These modifications brought the part within specifications and it was released for prototype build and testing.

As a result of the timesavings provided by MCAE on this application, 20 iterations of analyzing and changing the model were performed in just 80 days. Using the conventional approach, 196 days would have been required to perform a similar analysis. In addition, weight savings of approximately 40 percent were achieved by the new space-frame design.

After this analysis was completed, fatigue life requirements for the new design were increased beyond those used for the original part, making it necessary to further change the design. Late specification changes of this type, which occur by the hundreds in a new car program, illustrate the advantages of the MCAE method. Using the conventional approach, the design engineer, analyst, and CAD operator would all have become involved in the redesign process. It would have taken several weeks just to communicate the necessary information among the various parties and to resolve scheduling conflicts. In conclusion, MCAE is becoming an important part of Ford's effort to meet the competitive challenges of the 1990s. This technology is being transferred to operating divisions so that front-line design engineers can greatly reduce component design time requirements and thus reduce program lead time to world-class levels and beyond.

Manufacturing is more than pretty pictures...

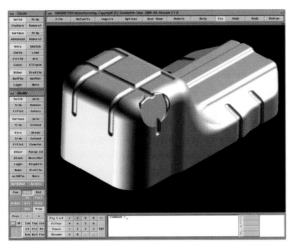

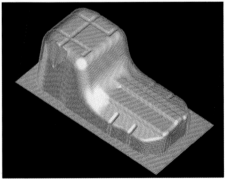

photo courtesy of YOROZU MFG. CORP.

VARIMETRIX VX

THE BEAUTY OF MANY MODELERS IS SKIN DEEP.
They were created for imaging, analysis, or drawing generation and don't have the accuracy or robustness to support integration of design and manufacturing. When data is transferred between multiple products to satisfy requirements, associativity is often lost.

Varimetrix VX is the first solid modeling system designed to address the entire manufacturing process. Our hybrid variational/parametric approach integrates solid, surface and wireframe geometry as well as process and tool path information in a single database. Unique gouge-free machining algorithms leverage the fact that geometric data is represented using state-of-the-art NURBS technology.

Don't settle for promises and excuses. Manufacturing is tough enough without the constraints of an inadequate CAD/CAM system. Software from Varimetrix bridges the gap between design and manufacturing at a surprisingly affordable price.

By the way, we also generate those pretty pictures when you need them.

VARIMETRIX

2350 Commerce Park Dr., Ste. 4
Palm Bay, FL 32905
voice 407.676.3222 • fax 407.723.4388
email info@vx.com

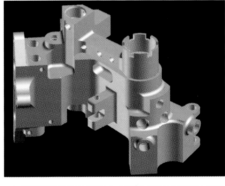

MODELING

All the basics, plus sophisticated functionality for filleting, blending, defining free-form shapes, creating thin-shelled parts, applying draft and generating parting lines.

MACHINING

Fast, gouge-free machining with no limitation on the cut pattern, number of surfaces or size of tool paths. 5-axis programming with unsurpassed tool control.

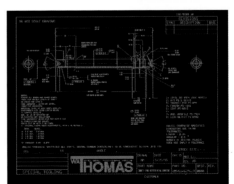

DRAFTING

Full-featured traditional drafting tools complement automatic generation of associative layouts from 3D models. Dimension and annotate to ANSI, ISO, or JIS standards.

(CIRCLE READER SERVICE NO. 213)

Chapter 25
Solid Modeling for Manufacturing

Robert J. Byrnes
Vice President
Varimetrix Corporation

The goal of computer-aided manufacturing (CAM) is a manufacturing process plan: the complete description of all processes, equipment, and materials required to manufacture a product. CAM software traditionally emphasizes NC toolpath computation. Today, more powerful computers and more capable software are fulfilling the CAD/CAM promise of automating manufacturing planning. Solid Modeling (SM) and the related technologies of feature-based, variational, and parametric modeling are leading the way. They promise the greatest boost to manufacturing productivity since CAM was introduced in the 1960s.

The most straightforward method for proceeding from a solid model to a manufacturing plan is to provide the model data to manufacturing engineers so that they may apply their expertise and knowledge of materials, equipment, and processing. However, not all product information is ordinarily contained in the SM database. Such information includes tolerances and manufacturing constraints. Although this method of proceeding from part to plan in isolated stages has a historical basis and is well entrenched in industry, it is no longer considered the most effective way to do business.

25.1   Product Design

The design of a product includes the shape created by the designer in order to achieve desired performance and aesthetic goals. However, shape is just one aspect of product design. Materials, production methods, special tooling, and relative costs must all be factored in. The appearance of more sophisticated software tools to assist engineers has accelerated over the past decade, largely spurred on by the advent of SM and integrated manufacturing applications.

25.1.1   Solid Modeling

Solid Modeling technology provides a number of benefits which are of particular importance to manufacturing. These include the following:

1. An SM part's shape is always geometrically valid.
2. Mass-properties and engineering analyses are more easily performed.
3. Some SM operations are easier to perform and are more reliable than those in wire frame or surface modeling. These include:
   a. Parting line analysis
   b. Filleting
   c. Shell operations
   d. Global operations such as adding or removing large amounts of geometry from the part

4. The unambiguous definition of solid models is superior to wireframe and surface models which allow misinterpretation by other operators and software.

Of the different SM database formats (CSG, B-Rep, Octree, Faceted, and Hybrid—see Chap. 4), the B-Rep and Hybrid modelers tend to dominate in most manufacturing applications. The primary reason for this is the importance of an accurate boundary representation for numerical control (NC) software. For many other manufacturing-related tasks there is no strong advantage to any specific SM database format.

For example, CSG modelers have limited usefulness in manufacturing. The boundaries needed by NC tasks (faces or surfaces) are implicit in CSG modelers, and do not provide the information necessary to compute cutting tool positions. However, for modeling basic shapes and industrial plant layouts CSG is capable and fast. For simpler parts, CSG even has some advantages over some B-Rep SM systems since there are some commercially available products which can analyze CSG models and automatically generate process plans.

25.1.2   Feature-Based Design

The need for critical information required by manufacturing goes beyond the shape of the part. Unless this information is incorporated into the product's SM database, engineers will need to communicate it through some alternate means. Automation of process planning would remain elusive.

Fortunately, there is a powerful SM technique which can incorporate manufacturing information into the SM part database and allow for easier and more effective part definition. This technique is *feature-based design*. Feature-based design is a modeling technique which allows product shape to be defined through form features (see Fig. 25.1) and provides for communication of critical information to all applications through a shared database. Feature-based manufacturing is a technique for assigning manufacturing operations to feature types, and then utilizing the information contained in the features to assist in toolpath and process plan generation (see Sec. 25.2.2). When feature-based design and manufacturing are combined, they provide a powerful environment for an unambiguous part design which naturally incorporates all product information necessary for manufacturing.

25.1.3   Starting with the Assembly

The assembly design consists of the individual components as well as how and where they fit together. In a top-down assembly hierarchy (see Chaps. 6 and 11), once the conceptual design of the assembly is complete, individual components can be addressed. From a manufacturing point of view, the assembly design also consists of tolerances and fit requirements for adjacent components. This data can be propagated throughout the assembly and also used to guide manufacturing in specifying the operations necessary to produce each component.

One of the advantages of beginning with the complete assembly design is that when a component is designed, the mating faces of adjacent components can be designed from it. Some SM systems are capable of symbolically representing components within the assembly; this allows partial analysis before all components are fully defined. These SM systems are well suited to conceptual design and provide the additional benefit of allowing the designer to reduce screen and database clutter by temporarily removing components from the active database.

25.1.4   Design for Assembly (DFA)

Design for assembly is a discipline which attempts to reduce the costs of manufacturing a product by reducing final assembly costs. These costs are directly related to the complexity and difficulties of bringing all parts together into a final product. Further, it is through analyzing the assembly that a designer can determine the necessary constraints and tolerance requirements to provide to manufacturing.

DFA complements and generally precedes other forms of design for manufacturing (DFM). In design for assembly, the manufacturing engineer is concerned with issues that arise after parts are already created and must be brought together into the final assembly. Therefore, from a planning perspective, any issues concerning assembly should be decided before detail design is complete.

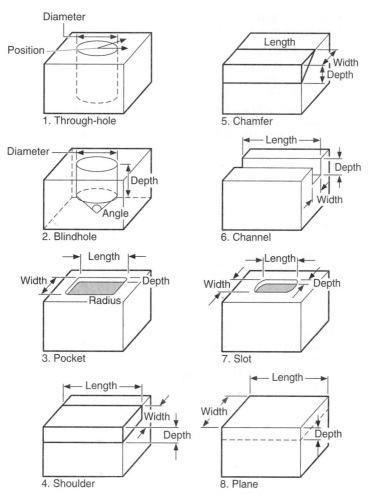

FIGURE 25.1 Part features provide shape and attribute information for manufacturing applications. *(Courtesy of Caroline Hayes, Robotics Institute, Carnegie Mellon University, 1987. Reprinted with permission from Wright and Bourne, Manufacturing Intelligence, Addison-Wesley Publishing Company, p. 222.)*

The first objective in reducing assembly costs, is to reduce the total number of components in the product. There are examples of extraordinary cost savings through reducing complex assemblies into much simpler designs. Often this will allow more cost-effective manufacturing techniques (for example, casting instead of milling). Beware, however, that there are exceptions and that some products are more efficiently obtained (and maintained) with a greater number of components.

Other problems that can arise during assembly are as follows:

1. Identical parts may become entangled if stored together.
2. Similar parts may be mistaken for each other.
3. Discerning part orientation may be difficult.
4. Assembly may be difficult in certain orientations.
5. Assembly may be difficult if critical features cannot be seen because of lack of visual contrast.
6. Parts may be too difficult to handle because of:
   a. Weight and balance
   b. Being too small or too large
   c. Residue, such as powders or liquids
   d. Parts being too awkward to grasp easily
   e. After machining, parts potentially having points or sharp edges

25.1.5   The Principal Axis

Products generally consist of assemblies of parts (individual components) which fit together to form a whole. Each of these parts is the result of one or more manufacturing processes. Some parts are machined directly from stock, some are purchased, and others are created from tooling. Common tool types are forgings, plastic or die molds, and stamping dies.

Parts are assembled by people or robots. The efficient design of parts to be assembled falls within the domain the DFA discipline (see Sec. 25.1.4). When parts are being assembled, the components must be held securely and brought together. Each of these assembly operations can be thought of as taking place along a *principal axis* (see Fig. 25.2).

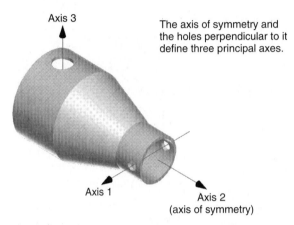

FIGURE 25.2   Features on the different faces of this part each have a different principal axis. *(Courtesy of Varimetrix Corporation.)*

Parts which are machined directly from stock can be described as falling into different categories according to shape (see Group Technology in Sec. 25.2.3). If a part is axially symmetric it is likely to be machined by a lathe. In this case the axis about which the rough material (the stock) is spinning is the principal axis. For parts which are cut on mills, the principal axis is the axis of the cutting tool (see Fig. 25.3).

Tool components of forgings, dies, and molds also operate along a principal axis: the axis along which the tool components move and along which the part material is extracted.

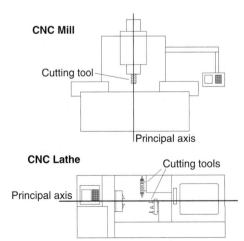

FIGURE 25.3   A lathe and a mill, each with the principal axis identified. *(Courtesy of Varimetrix Corporation.)*

Design

> ### SMA.25.1   Principal Axes
>
> A part may have a number of principal axes, each of which will require special attention during manufacturing. Major cost savings can be realized if a product and its parts are designed with the concept of principal axes in mind.

25.1.6   Design for Manufacturing (DFM)

DFM is a discipline which promotes optimal efficiency in bringing a product to market. DFM compels the involvement of manufacturing expertise in the conceptual and detail design phases of product development. DFM is often put into place with concurrent engineering (CE) programs to further enhance cost effectiveness. DFM and CE complement each other, but they are truly different methodologies. Design for manufacturing emphasizes overlapping and combining applications during each phase of product development. Concurrent engineering emphasizes overlapping of resource scheduling in order to compress the production schedule. (See Chap. 27 for more on SM and CE.)

DFM facilitates communication between different departments. Because DFM requires that traditional barriers between departments be removed, many companies have not embraced it as rapidly as they have other disciplines. DFM increases time spent in the design phase but decreases time spent in other phases and greatly reduces time spent on correcting problems. The use of DFM techniques can provide vast improvements in process planning, NC programming productivity, and machine tool utilization. This is in addition to the significant reduction in errors in the design and process.

25.1.7   Design for Cost Reduction

The discussion of SM for CAM should be done within the context of the design and manufacture of a complete product. It is at this high level of product concept that all aspects of design and production should converge. This is natural, because it is the entire final product which is sold; therefore, production costs and methods should be determined with the whole product in mind.

To determine all costs associated with a given product, the entire life-cycle cost must be considered. This would include all costs that an organization will incur as a result of pursuing a given path of product-related decisions. Life-cycle costs include:

1. Concept design
2. Detail design
3. Process planning
4. NC toolpath development
5. Part routing
6. Machining
7. Inspection
8. Quality assurance
9. Product maintenance
10. Product servicing
11. Product disposal or recycling

The more consideration given to the results of decisions made toward the front end of the life cycle, the more benefits will be obtained throughout the product's life. Once a part is released to production, there is little that can be done by the manufacturing engineer to cut costs. It is more effective to modify the detail design in order to reduce costs. Best results are usually obtained by involving manufacturing engineers in the concept design phase.

25.1.8   Data Management

Software tools are required to manage changing data in environments where these changes will affect other departments. Dynamic modelers are SM systems which automatically propagate changes in the design to ensure that all design constraints are satisfied. Some CAM products share these capabilities and automatically respond to changes in the design. In order to comprehensively manage changes throughout all aspects of product design, some CAD/CAM systems have an integrated product data manager (PDM) to manage changes through all applications.

The capabilities provided by dynamic modelers and CAM software are the basis for modern sensitivity analysis. Sensitivity analysis is used to determine the effects of changing constraints and tolerances on the final part cost. Because tighter tolerances are directly related to greater cost, analysis tools can help determine how large these values can be made without degrading product performance (see Fig. 25.4).

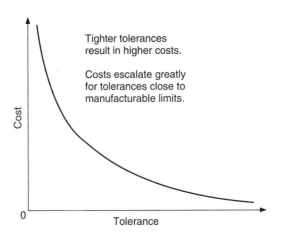

FIGURE 25.4 Graph of manufacturing costs versus manufacturing tolerances. *(Courtesy of Varimetrix Corporation.)*

25.2   Product Manufacturing

The manufacturing engineer's task is to translate the product design into the necessary manufacturing operations needed to create the physical product. The engineer's goal is to produce the part to the designer's specifications within the cost and time constraints.

25.2.1   Manufacturing Operations

This section provides a brief introduction to manufacturing methods, focusing primarily on more traditional techniques.

There are two broad categories of manufacturing operations: (1) material shaping and (2) material treating. The operation types selected for a given job result from the materials used, design tolerances, availability, cost, and other factors. Following are examples of operations which fall into these two categories.

Operations That Shape Material

1. Mechanical material removal
   a. Cutting (drilling, milling, turning)
   b. Abrading (grinding)
   c. Shearing (blanking, nibbling, piercing)
2. Chemical material removal
   a. Chemical milling
   b. Etching

3. Electro/thermal material removal
   a. Wire EDM
   b. Plasma, laser, or ion beam cutting
4. Mechanical material shaping
   a. Forging
   b. Rolling
   c. Extruding
   d. Drawing
   e. Shearing
5. Powder/granular material forming
   a. Compaction
   b. Laser sintering
6. Liquid/plastic material forming
   a. Die casting
   b. Sand casting
   c. Injection molding
   d. Blow molding
7. Joining operations
   a. Electron beam welding
   b. Laser beam welding
   c. Friction welding
   d. Adhesive bonding
   e. Infrared soldering
   f. Wave soldering

Operations That Treat Materials
1. Hardening operations
   a. Cold treatment
   b. Nitriding
   c. Curing
   e. Glazing
2. Softening operations
   a. Tempering
   b. Annealing

The majority of SM and CAM systems available tend to focus on shaping through material removal. This is the area addressed in Chap. 15, SM and numerical control (NC). However, the development of the process plan requires consideration of all manufacturing operations performed, as well as the handling of the part material between operations.

25.2.2 Feature-Based Manufacturing

Features are named entities that encapsulate geometry and constraints as well as allowed behavior and appropriate attributes. This information can be utilized by operators and software. Features are higher-level constructs; that is, they not only group information but they attach an abstract meaning as well. This higher-level meaning allows software to intelligently manage and analyze the feature contents. If the SM and manufacturing software can communicate through features, a great deal of the repetitive CAM tasks can be automated.

When presented with the shape of a part, the manufacturing engineer will focus on regions which will need specific operations for manufacture. They will appropriately refer to each of these regions as features in the part shape. They may be standard features (holes, slots, etc.) or they may be custom shapes, particular to that manufacturing environment.

The manufacturing engineer will specify which operation types should be used to obtain each feature. If feature families are correctly defined, operation types can be assigned which are appropriate to all their members.

Features

SMA.25.2   Knowledge Utilization

Feature-based manufacturing allows organizations to obtain greater benefits from their experienced manufacturing personnel. Those who possess the knowledge for optimally creating parts can be used to identify feature classifications and the operations to manufacture them. Once features are identified, the appropriate operation sequences can be retrieved for each new part design.

Features can be identified through any of several methods:

1. *Interactive:*   The designer identifies the geometry and assigns feature types.
2. *Automatic:*   SM software performs an analysis and assigns feature types.
3. *Capture:*   If the SM system provides feature-based design, features are defined as the designer creates the part geometry.

For all applications to work effectively together, they should be able to communicate feature information. This usually requires an integrated database. IGES and other traditional exchange specifications do not adequately address features. Fortunately, the Product Data Exchange Specification (PDES) and the Standard for the Exchange of Product Model Data (STEP) do address features. A feature-based PDES/STEP file can contain complete product data to provide for the exchange of feature information between software products which are not integrated. (See Chap. 21 for more on SM and IGES and Chap. 22 for more on SM and STEP.)

25.2.3   Process Planning

The creation of an ordered schedule of manufacturing operations to create a product is known as *process planning*. The plan is a fully inclusive document which takes into account all details of the manufacturing environment and specifies every stage of the manufacturing sequence (see Fig. 25.5).

The manufacturing process plan should be an optimal distillation of the relevant information about the part shape, materials, tolerances, and about the capabilities of the manufacturing facilities which will be used. This optimal plan traditionally requires a good deal of human expertise. This is because the many variables which affect the decision-making process have not been available in a form to allow automation by software. Further, this expertise is not easily identified and transferred from experienced to inexperienced personnel.

In response to the greater competitiveness between manufacturing companies and the concomitant demand for experienced manufacturing engineers, a number of solutions are evolving. Although many companies still rely on traditional "from scratch" methods for creating process plans for new products, some are exploiting various technologies to improve competitiveness. These include:

1. Variant Process Planning (VPP)
2. Group Technology (GT)
3. Generative Process Planning (GPP)

Variant Process Planning (VPP)

Variant process planning relies upon the existence of previously used process plans. An archived plan for a part similar to the new part is retrieved. The older plan is then modified to account for the differences between the older and newer designs. The use of existing process plans can be very cost-effective. However, there are a number of concerns. The pattern matching necessary to find appropriate plans to retrieve can get complicated. Also, plan modifications in response to changes in materials or manufacturing capabilities are not easily incorporated.

In order to search for appropriate plans, some form of data encapsulation is needed. That is, a compact description of the parts shape is needed. This description should be simple enough so that a computer can find probable matches quickly, yet allow for enough differentiation so that the plans found are likely to be useful. The most popular methods involve assigning numerical categories to shape attributes of the part in order to obtain a numerical code. This code is then compared to the codes generated for other parts in order to find matches (see Fig. 25.6).

Group Technology (GT)

GT uses numerical coding techniques to describes the part shape. For example, the first digit might describe the part as being axially symmetric, the next its length, and the next its greatest diameter. The code can be shorter for simple parts and longer for others. The GT code is the type of mechanism used in many VPP systems to retrieve process plans.

```
                                Operation Sheet

Plan Name: CK_TR_001.PLN

Part Name:   Avd. Tray                        Date: Apr. 28, 1994
Material:    Steel                            Release Number: 010-CK-092
Part Number: AT-007                           Order Number:   9400322

Planner:     KMB
Approval:    MCB

Lot size: 5

Raw Material Dimensions:   90 x 120 x 60 cm
```

Op. #	Feature	Process	P_type	Tl_name	Tl_ind	FEED	SPEED	Notes
1	Top Face	Face Mill	Rough	Flat_10	1	0.900	250	
2	Bowl	Drill	Rough	Drill_05	4	1.250	300	
3	Mounts	Drill	Rough	Drill_004	5	1.250	300	
4	Bowl	Pocket	Rough	End_05	2	0.900	250	
5	Bowl	Pocket	Finish	End_05	2	0.500	200	
6	Bowl	Swarf	Finish	Taper_02	3	0.500	200	
7	Boss	Swarf	Finish	Taper_02	3	0.500	200	
8	Mounts	Bore	Finish	Bore_005	6	0.250	120	

```
   Total Processing Time : 3.58 minutes
```

FIGURE 25.5 Sample operation sheet showing the manufacturing plan for the creation of a simple part. *(Courtesy of Varimetrix Corporation.)*

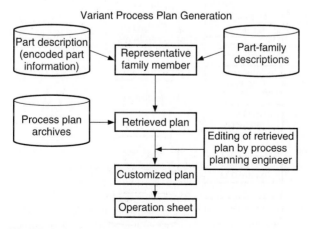

FIGURE 25.6 Data flow for the retrieval of process plans using VPP. *(Courtesy of Varimetrix Corporation.)*

GT codes are derived by analyzing the part shape. This analysis most frequently involves some interaction from an engineer to guide the GT code generation. In order to automate code derivation, software automatically classifies part shape so that the need for human interaction is reduced (see Fig. 25.7).

GT code for this axially symmetric component

1–3–3–0–0–0–2–71–6

Digit	Meaning
1	Shape
2	Length
3	Ratio of maximum diameter to length (shine axially symmetric)
4	Grooves/threads
5	Center hole
6	Holes
7	Material
8,9	Tolerance
10	Finish

FIGURE 25.7 Simple part and GT code assignment. *(Courtesy of Varimetrix Corporation.)*

Generative Process Planning (GPP)

In GPP, analysis is performed on the part shape, similar to that derived to support automatic GT applications. However, the middle steps of encoding and decoding are bypassed. When shapes are recognized, appropriate manufacturing operations are selected. When this task is completed, the operations are ordered into an appropriate process plan. Software utilities which perform this function are known as Generative Computer-Aided Process Planning (GCAPP) systems. Some GCAPP products require a heavy initial investment of manufacturing and GCAPP software expertise in order to prepare the rule base used to select and sequence operations.

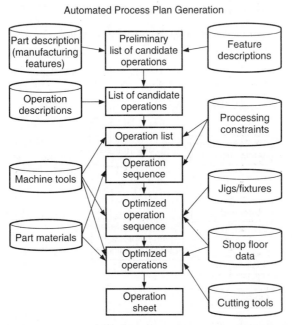

FIGURE 25.8 Data flow in a GCAPP system. *(Courtesy of Varimetrix Corporation.)*

An SM and CAM system that combines variant as well as generative planning techniques is generally more effective. These planning systems allow quicker usability and payback without compromising long-term benefits.

Both planning techniques have been developed to the point where certain categories of parts can have their process plans selected or generated automatically. However, these are usually special part families such as prismatic shapes requiring only 2½-axis milling. The greatest difficulty involved in progressing beyond this phase is in identifying and classifying more complex shapes and features.

This is where feature-based SM technology removes the ambiguity. If a part is designed from features, there is no need for software to perform shape analysis. At the time the feature is added to the part, the shape is automatically categorized and can have very specific meaning to the designer as well as other application engineers.

One area of active research is the interpretation of features from one application domain to another. Although a through-hole is a through-hole to both the designer and the manufacturing engineer, the designer may create a rib, while the machinist is interested in the pockets the rib separates. Solutions to problems like this have had limited success. In the worst case, however, the CAD/CAM software can ask either an expert system or the operator to reclassify the geometry into features.

Process Planning

SMA.25.3 Exception Handling

Exception handling is critical in any automated process. Designer's should always have the ability to guide the software or override any automated decisions.

SMA.25.4 Operational Sequence

The sequence of manufacturing operations may be predefined in the software, or selected through a rule-based expert system. The order of the operations can be critical. As a result of dynamic forces and material properties, the reordering of operations can make the difference between successful manufacture and failure. A change in material can invalidate the sequence because of the interplay between cutting tool and material deflection (bending).

25.2.4   Machining Considerations

As mentioned previously, most manufacturing operations (NC in particular) are best analyzed with respect to a principal axis. In the case of a lathe the principal axis is usually the axis about which the stock rotates as material is removed. In most milling applications, the principal axis is that of the cutting tool (see Fig. 25.3). The case of multiaxis machining (wherein the tool axis can change) is discussed later in this section.

When parts are cut on machine tools, they must be anchored rigidly, but without excessive force which might deform the material being cut. Depending on the part shape, it may be possible to use clamps. If the part shape is irregular, it may be necessary to design a fixture to hold the piece during machining. Clamp and fixture design is a job well suited to SM techniques. The part model can be combined with standard shapes in order to arrive at a fixture design with considerably less effort than would be needed using wireframe or surface modeling.

When a part is to be cut on a machine tool, rough stock is locked rigidly in place. The orientation of the part on the machine is sometimes referred to as the *setup*. Either the stock or the tool is then moved so that material can be cut away until the remaining material accurately represents the desired part. Of course, the material must be removed with sufficient accuracy so that not too much material is removed or remains. These are, in fact, two of the greatest sources of error in machining environments: (1) gouging, or removing too much material from the part or (2) undercutting, requiring the part to be brought back to the machine tool for further cutting.

While the stock is locked in place, machining can take place to the maximum accuracy of the machine and the tool. Each time the workpiece (the partially machined stock) is refixtured, greater inaccuracy is introduced. Also, greater expense is introduced whenever the machine is not actively removing material. Similarly, each time the part is moved from one machine to another, inaccuracy will increase. Moving the workpiece from machine to machine in the factory can introduce other problems as well. Complex routing of the workpiece through the shop invites a cascading of schedule delays if there is a hold-up at any point in the process.

If a part is designed so that all features lie along one principal axis, then they might all be machinable in one setup on a single machine. This is considered optimal for NC. As a rule, the fewer principal axes, the fewer setups are required. However, for large parts there is also the issue of features which share the same principal axis yet cannot be simultaneously accessed by the machine because of travel limits (the free range of motion through which the tool can be moved).

To further analyze efficiency on the machine, let's consider the tool itself. The tool is the physical structure which contacts and removes material. Each time the tool is changed to cut features of different sizes or to retrieve a fresh tool, time is wasted and no material is being removed. Also, some inaccuracy may result from minor differences in the length and shape of the different tools. By striving for uniformity in features, the number of different tools used can be minimized and machining costs can be further reduced.

Some machines are capable of changing the machining axis. If the tool axis is kept fixed while machining, it can then be changed to cut another region on the part. This eliminates the need to refixture the material. There are parts that are so complex that the tool must change orientation while material is being removed. The added degrees of freedom that these machines provide can translate into less cost-related restrictions on the designer (see Fig. 25.9). Of course, there are always limits on the allowable motion along each degree of freedom. The accessibility of the features by the tool is still an issue, as there is always the potential that features may be mutually inaccessible (see Fig. 25.10).

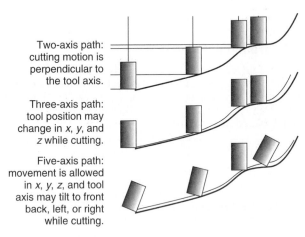

Two-axis path: cutting motion is perpendicular to the tool axis.

Three-axis path: tool position may change in *x*, *y*, and *z* while cutting.

Five-axis path: movement is allowed in *x*, *y*, *z*, and tool axis may tilt to front back, left, or right while cutting.

FIGURE 25.9 Two-, three-, and five-axis tool motion. *(Courtesy of Varimetrix Corporation.)*

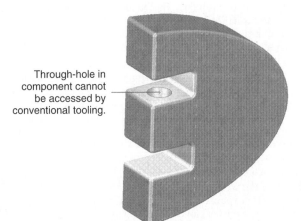

Through-hole in component cannot be accessed by conventional tooling.

FIGURE 25.10 An inaccessible (unmanufacturable) feature. *(Courtesy of Varimetrix Corporation.)*

Manufacturing

SMA.25.5   Standard Parts

The best way to reduce manufacturing costs is to use standard parts. Once the process for manufacturing a standard part is optimized, all products using it will reap the cost benefits. It has been estimated that 8 percent of all parts are exact duplicates of existing designs—the duplicate effort could be better invested elsewhere.

SMA.25.6   Lowering NC Costs

Reduce NC costs by reducing (in order of decreasing importance):

1. The number of machines used

2. The number of setups on each machine

3. The number of tools required

SMA.25.7   Work in Progress

SM is useful for communicating work-in-progress information between departments. Work-in-progress models are also useful for interim mass-properties calculations to estimate material removal and also handling characteristics (see color insert, Fig. 25.11).

SMA.25.8   Billet and Stock Management

SM can be used for billet and stock management. The NC operator cannot complete the toolpath generation unless accurate knowledge of the stock shape is known (see Fig. 25.12).

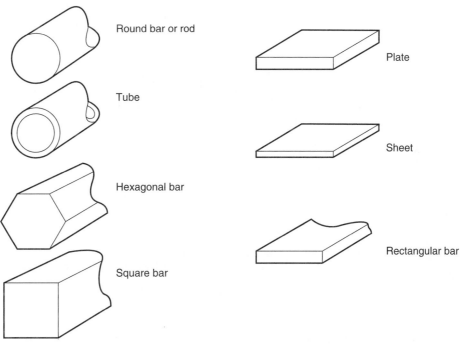

FIGURE 25.12   Common raw stock shapes.

25.3   Solid Modeling Applications

The familiar schematic of the flow of design from concept through detail design and then through to manufacturing is entirely deceptive of the role of the manufacturing department within an organization. Rather than being only recipients of SM data, manufacturing engineers are often involved in the modeling of machines, tooling, support structures, patterns, and stock for machining. The leverage provided by SM to designers is also of advantage to manufacturing personnel.

25.3.1   Robotics

Robots have become commonplace in many manufacturing settings. They perform tasks too repetitive, strenuous, precise, or dangerous for humans. Common tasks include welding, painting, and material handling. Although the capabilities of a robot are quantitatively different from those of a human, they are similar in many ways. The differences in capabilities mirror those found from human to human, varying only in degree.

If material handling involves robots, the in-process material shape should be easily grasped; the weight and balance should be within appropriate parameters, and the surface should not be slippery. For robots involved in assembly, part shape should meet the same criteria for symmetry or exaggerated asymmetry as noted previously. For those using optical sensors, visual contrast should be maximized (see Sec. 25.1.4).

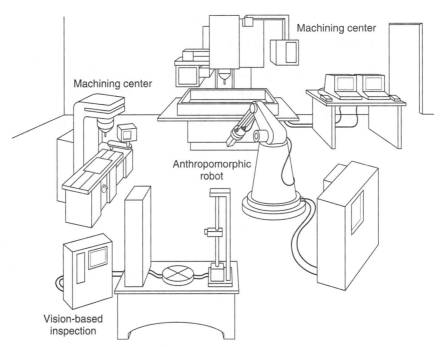

FIGURE 25.13   Work cell with robot in place. *(Reprinted with permission from Wright and Bourne, Manufacturing Intelligence, Addison-Wesley Publishing Company, p. 29.)*

Robotics

SMA.25.9   Part Handling

SM is useful in planning part handling and provides an accurate 3D layout of shop environments. Mass-properties calculations such as part weight and center of mass are useful for analyzing how parts can be manipulated.

25.3.2   Inspection

Part inspection is performed at various stages of manufacturing. The desired part shape, engineering constraints, and tolerances are used, along with measurement data, to determine if the physical part lies within the acceptable bounds of the designed part. The inspection process is often considered to be an after-the-fact application. However, as one of the processes involved in the life-cycle costs for manufacturing (see Sec. 25.1.7), it should be considered early in the cycle—about the time detail design is being implemented.

As with any other task, the implementation of a manufacturing plan should have an associated mechanism for determining if the goal has been successfully obtained. It is of questionable value to manufacture parts that cannot be confirmed as correct.

Just as there are manufacturing applications which are appropriate for different feature types and tolerances, there are different inspection methods as well. Further, the inspection might involve more than a single feature. For example, an individual hole might be inspected for roundness, whereas multiple holes might need to be checked for parallelism. Table 25.1 provides a list of geometric dimensioning and tolerancing (GD&T) characteristics and their symbolism.

Also, just as we have a process plan in manufacturing, there is also a plan for inspection. Instead of managing data and instructions in the form of toolpaths for NC machines, inspection data is created and sent to coordinate measuring machines (CMMs). (See Sec. 25.3.6 for more on SM and CMMs.)

TABLE 25.1   Geometric Dimensioning and Tolerancing (GD&T) Values and Symbology Which May Be Inspected

Refer to ANSI standard Y14.5M for recommended usage.

Symbol	Geometric characteristic	Symbol	Geometric characteristic
—	Straightness	⊥	Perpendicularity
▱	Flatness	∠	Angularity
○	Roundness	◎	Concentricity
⌭	Cylindricity	═	Symmetry
⌒	Profile	↗	Runout
//	Parallelism	⊕	True position

Inspection

SMA.25.10   Rigid Is Not Reality

SM systems, like their predecessors, design parts in rigid form. That is, modeled parts generally do not bend and flex. In the real world thin parts are not as well behaved, such as large sheet-metal stampings for auto bodies. If the part designed is so thin that it cannot assume a rigid position for inspection, a support structure will need to be built to hold the part.

25.3.3 Physical Modeling

Some parts are still created the old-fashioned way: through physical modeling techniques. This is not because of a rejection of newer technologies. It is simply the case that for some applications there is no computer interface as effective as an actual physical model.

For example, you probably have seen designers modeling full-scale automobile bodies in clay. The final clay model is inspected (measured) and the data read into a CAD/CAM database. Surface and solid geometry is modeled to duplicate the data so that the product can be analyzed, modified, and manufactured.

In this example, the desired physical model is the result of the ideal human interface between designer and clay which is not yet obtainable by computer-aided means. However, once the data is stored in a geometric database, all the advantages of the software environment are then made available.

Another example of physical modeling is the design of tubing and hoses in confined spaces. An effective method for obtaining an appropriate design for the molds is to lay out hoses in a prototype part and then measure the shape to have a CAD/CAM model created.

There are other parts which begin through modern SM techniques: the manifolds on automobile and truck engines are modeled to meet performance and shape constraints. However, because software simulation for flow analysis of the gases is not perfect, a physical model is also made. The physical model is then tested and modified until performance goals are met. Finally, to allow for accurate reproduction, the model is then measured and the data is read back into the CAD/CAM database.

25.3.4 Rapid Prototyping (RP)

Rapid prototyping is a collection of technologies for creating physical prototypes of parts from 3D surface or solid models. (See Chap. 19 for a more on SM and RP.) A 3D surface or solid model is analyzed to a desired tolerance and sent to an RP machine which will create a solid version of the part in any of several materials. Such prototypes are valuable to engineers and managers in the early design phase to ensure that design intent is satisfied.

RP prototypes are also valuable to communicate intent to purchasing and manufacturing. There is nothing quite like a physical model for communicating intent and to assist in the visualization of the final part. The RP prototype is representative of the final part. Yet the manufacture of that part may require the fabrication of intermediate tools. The RP process can be a valuable aid in tooling design, as discussed in the following section. (See color insert, Fig. 25.14*a* and *b*.)

25.3.5 Tool Design

Although the most common manufacturing application for CAD/CAM systems is NC toolpath creation, only a small minority of parts are actually machined. Usually, it is a tool to make the part that is machined. Tools of this sort include forgings, molds, and dies.

It is very important to note that the tool is not just the complement or the reverse of the part design. The following characteristics must also be considered:

1. For stamping, the material thickness must be taken into account.
2. For almost all tools there must be a positive draft angle so that the part can be easily removed from the tool after forming.
3. The tooling may need to account for material shrinkage.

Usually, the tool's shaping region can be made by starting with the part geometry. Many SM utilities such as filleting, adding draft, and offsetting are ideal for tool development.

Also, beyond the shaping region of the tool, other geometry must be added. The design of the tool surfaces which control the stretching and flow of part material are critical to the success of the tool, but are not included in the part design and are not present in the final product.

Sometimes intermediate tooling must be created in order to manufacture the tool. SM is a simple and effective method for generating the necessary geometry. This is especially true for the uniform and scalable structures which hold and move the tool components. The following considerations may be taken into account:

1. Parting lines and parting surfaces must be defined.

2. For stamping dies, binding surfaces (to hold material in place) and the die base must be designed.

3. For molds, the mold base, cooling passages, and passages for the material to be injected must be designed.

4. Pins and holes are added to mating faces to ensure alignment and to eject the part after molding.

Occasionally it is necessary to perform geometric operations on surfaces and then combine the resulting surface shapes with solid entities. Once the geometry is in solid form, the engineer can be assured of the geometric validity of the part. The advantages obtained from the solid form are then available to the manufacturing engineer to compute mass properties which are useful when computing volumes for injection molds.

Recent advances in materials allow some tooling to be created without the need for NC toolpath creation. If the geometry for the tool shape has been modeled as a solid it can be output directly to an RP machine so that a prototype can be created.

At one time, RP prototypes were useful for reference only. However, spray-metal forming allows an RP prototype to be converted directly into a tool capable of creating runs of plastic parts into the tens of thousands. A hard metallic coating is applied to the prototype, allowing it to act as a standard tool within a limited range of performance. If the limitations of a spray-metal mold are unacceptable, the tool's shape may still be proven and then a conventional tool can be machined to the same shape.

Patterns

SMA.25.11   Casting Patterns

SM techniques are a powerful tool for creating patterns for casting operations. These patterns can be created far more easily than traditional modeling techniques. The casting which results might require further machining. If so, the pattern can be used by NC operators as a model for the stock to be machined.

25.3.6   Coordinate Measuring Machines (CMMs)

CMMs are employed in order to obtain accurate and precise information about the shape of physical parts. CMMs gather position data from physical parts and feed that data into a computer. There are two varieties: those that use optical methods for measuring the part, and those that use a probe to touch the part (see Fig. 25.15).

There are many similarities in the methods used for manufacturing and for inspection. A plan is generated to guide the CMM, inspection operations are applied to each feature, and inspection coordinates are generated and output in a specified format. The inspection data is downloaded to the CMM and the physical part is measured.

If the intent of the inspection is to verify the manufacturing plan, the coordinates taken from the physical part must be mapped back onto the original design. The amount of error is determined and usually presented graphically (see Fig. 25.16). The CMM analysis results can then be distributed back to the manufacturing and design departments so that the most appropriate modifications can be made to the design or the manufacturing plan.

Another reason to measure physical parts is for reverse-engineering. In this context, we refer to measuring a physical part so that a computer representation can be generated. In this case the designer will need software tools to convert the measurements into surfaces and then into solids. The solid data can then be used for geometric analysis, rendering, animation, scaling, other geometric modifications, and CAM.

25.4   Solid Modeling Improvements Needed

The continuing evolution of SM technology is testimony to the demands of industry and the creativity of software engineers who compete to bring the best products to market. The vision and potential for future developments, however, often precedes product by many years. There are excellent SM/CAM

FIGURE 25.15 Coordinate measuring machine (CMM). *(Courtesy of Brown and Sharp.)*

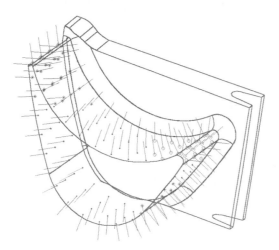

FIGURE 25.16 CMM inspection data superimposed on original SM part. *(Courtesy of Varimetrix Corporation.)*

systems available today, but it would be difficult to find one product which encompasses all of the newest technologies. Newer systems can be far more reliable, user-friendly, and cost-effective than those of only a few years ago.

25.4.1 Integration

High-end SM systems are now incorporating features and manufacturing attributes in their product design capabilities. The results of this progress are put to best advantage when the SM and CAM software form an integrated system. The shared database of design and manufacturing data should allow all departments access to the total product definition.

Unfortunately, if the SM and CAM systems are not well integrated, designers are likely to find dead ends in the data flow between design and manufacturing. Further, some of the newer-generation modelers, which are impressive in their modeling capabilities, seem to lack the geometric accuracy necessary to adequately support CAM applications.

25.4.2 Automation

The next stage of SM/CAM development will concentrate on utilizing the information in the SM database to automate some manufacturing tasks and optimize the manufacturing process. Also, manufacturing software which will advise conceptual and design engineers will be integrated into SM software. In concert with manufacturing advice, cost-analysis software will become a more common integrated component of modelers—as the decisions made in the early stages of design are those which are likely to have the greatest effect on product life-cycle cost.

SM/CAM systems which have attempted significant automation are hindered by being able to handle parts of only limited complexity. When part shapes fall outside the capabilities of the software, either unrealistic plans are created or the designer must intervene. In most CAM software, when the designer overrides the automated CAM utilities, the ability to automatically regenerate CAM data is limited or nonexistent. Very few of the current generation of SM products were designed as part of an integrated SM/CAM system. Therefore, it is the case that not all competent SM products are well suited for DFM.

25.4.3 Design for Manufacturing (DFM) and Concurrent Engineering (CE)

Improvements to the current generation of SM systems will be of greatest benefit to those organizations which utilize DFM and CE techniques. The free flow of information and expertise between departments at multiple stages in the product life cycle will greatly determine the competitiveness of manufacturing organizations. This, in turn, will further promote the market demand for more sophisticated SM systems.

Good Practices

SMA.25.12 The Overall Design Process

Is your organization new to SM for manufacturing? If so, rather than automating and improving existing processes, consider modifying the overall design process.

SMA.25.13 Modeling Advice

1. Solid models can be used to check fit, relative sizes, interferences, and range of motion of components in assemblies (see Chap. 11).

2. If modeled as a solid assembly, work cell components and machine tools (with clamps in place) can be checked for possible interferences.

3. Reduce production costs by following design rules:

    a. Work along a principal axis—the fewer in number the better (see Sec. 25.1.5).

    b. Gravitate toward standard shapes and components.

    c. Keep tolerances (fit, position, orientation, etc.) as large as possible.

Chapter 26
Volumetric Solid Modeling

Donald J. Meagher, Ph.D.
President
Octree Corporation

Solid Modeling (SM) was originally developed for the design of mechanical parts using geometric models (i.e., shapes defined mathematically). There also exists a second type of solid, a *volumetric* solid, defined by a large number of volume samples. Sources of volumetric information include medical and industrial computed tomography (CT) scanners, confocal microscopes, laser scanners, and computer simulations such as finite element modeling (FEM) analysis. Volumetric information is used in part design (e.g., custom medical implants), analysis, manufacturing (e.g., robotics and rapid prototyping), quality control (inspection and nondestructive testing), and in nontraditional CAD uses such as designing medical procedures (e.g., radiation therapy). This chapter will discuss volumetric methods and its use in FEM, robotics, and medical applications.

26.1 Geometric versus Sampled Information

For illustration, the nature and use of sampled representations will first be considered in 2D. In a CAD database, a curve is defined mathematically. When displayed, this geometric model is sampled, becoming a set of *pixels* (picture elements) on a raster display screen. While the mathematical description has essentially unlimited resolution, the sampled model (image) is an approximation. The number of samples per unit of area (the *sampling frequency*) must be sufficiently high to faithfully represent the smallest detail that must be viewed.

Next, consider the reverse operation: generating a geometric model from a set of samples. Paper drawings are often digitized (sampled) using a 2D scanner. Since the resulting images are an approximate representation they cannot, in general, be exactly translated into the original geometric model, at least not automatically. However, if the characteristics of the underlying model are known (i.e., that a particular set of samples represents a line), it may be possible to re-create at least part of a geometric model to the accuracy of the scanner. Often, manual intervention is used to improve on this (e.g., keying in exact coordinates).

A popular alternate strategy is to allow both a sampled model and a geometric model to coexist in a combined model. On a practical level, this eliminates the need for an initial conversion effort. To make a change, the appropriate raster pixels are erased and any new information is entered into the geometric model. The sampled model is thus gradually replaced by the more flexible and accurate geometric model.

There is a similar situation in 3D. For display, geometric models are sampled in 3D and projected onto a plane (the display screen) for shaded images. And, like drawings, physical objects can be scanned to generate a 3D set of samples. If the underlying model is known (e.g., that surface samples form a quadric surface), it may be possible to extract a geometric model. Again, this may require some amount of manual effort, depending on the complexity of the object, the sophistication of the geometric model, and the intelligence of the conversion program.

26.1.1 Volumetric Datasets

Let's discuss the various forms of raw volumetric data before they have been processed and encoded into a specific representation. The spatial arrangement of 3D volumetric datasets varies considerably but can usually be classified into one of three categories:

1. Regular array
2. Semiregular array
3. Irregular grid

Regular Array

As shown in Fig. 26.1a, a CT medical scanner generates images of thin slices through a patient. Each contains a 2D array of pixels. With most scanners, each pixel contains a 12-bit value that represents the average material density within a small, approximately cubical, region of space. Since each pixel actually represents a volume rather than a 2D area, it is often called a *voxel* (volume element). As shown in Fig. 26.1b, multiple slices can be assembled to form a 3D array of voxels. A typical CT study might consist of 100 slices of 512 by 512 voxels or 26 million voxels. The density value for each voxel usually requires 2 bytes of storage, resulting in a volumetric data set of over 52 Mbytes.

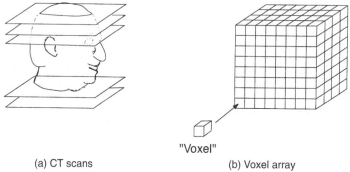

(a) CT scans   (b) Voxel array

FIGURE 26.1 Volumetric information from a CT medical scanner. (*a*) Slices of a patients's head; (*b*) multiple slices form a voxel array. A single voxel is shown bottom left. (*Courtesy of Octree Corporation.*)

Semiregular Array

Laser scanners often sweep in a regular pattern but, as illustrated in Fig. 26.2a, the precision of the distance measurement from the laser to the object is often much higher than the distance between sample points. Because of time and storage considerations, the total number of measurements is usually limited. The dataset is thus a regular array in two dimensions and a high-precision distance measurement in the third, forming a "semiregular" array of samples. In many cases scans are performed in a cylindrical coordinate system with either the object or the scanner rotating (see Fig. 26.2b).

Irregular Grid

In computer simulations it is often desirable to perform computations on irregular grids specially generated for each object or situation. This is done to meet accuracy and computational constraints. In finite element modeling, for example, objects are decomposed into cells that may form a complex, irregular 3D mesh that fills the object's volume (see color insert, Fig. 26.3). Similar grids are used with scientific simulations (weather, electric fields, fluids, etc.).

Often, special programs are developed to process and display irregular grids, but they can be complex, difficult to maintain, and costly to extend. Therefore, they are often resampled into a regular grid for input to a general-purpose volumetric SM program. Depending on the underlying model, sophisticated interpolation methods may be required to compute the best estimate of property values at the sample points in the array. With geological information, for example, samples often form layers, requiring special techniques to preserve the information content of the dataset. In the remainder of this chapter it will be assumed that datasets are regular arrays (or have been resampled into regular arrays).

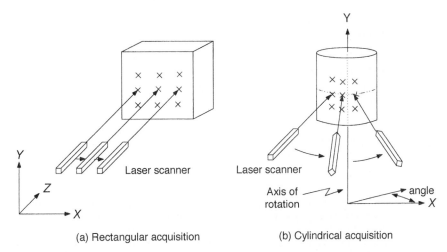

FIGURE 26.2 Semiregular grids from laser scanners. (*a*) Rectangular acquisition (note the linear translation of the laser scanner); (*b*) cylindrical acquisition (note the radial translation of the laser scanner). *(Courtesy of Octree Corporation.)*

26.1.2 Properties

The data contained in a voxel is called *property information*. A single-bit property can indicate if the voxel is solid or empty. While this may be usable in some situations, additional data is usually needed. This can include color, density, a local surface normal or gradient, stress, material type, thermal or stress coefficient, part number, and so on. The amount of property information per voxel varies by application and usually ranges from 1 to 64 bits (8 bytes). The memory required for various array and property sizes is presented in Table 26.1. It shows that volumetric arrays can place major demands on the computational and storage capabilities of a computer system.

TABLE 26.1 Memory Required to Store Voxel Arrays

Note the geometric growth of data storage requirements. (*Courtesy of Octree Corporation.*)

Properties	Voxel Array Size					
	128^3	256^3	512^3	1024^3	2048^3	4096^3
1 bit	256 KB	2 MB	16 MB	128 MB	1 GB	8 GB
2 bits	512 KB	4 MB	32 MB	256 MB	2 GB	16 GB
4 bits	1 MB	8 MB	64 MB	512 MB	4 GB	32 GB
1 byte	2 MB	16 MB	128 MB	1 GB	8 GB	64 GB
2 bytes	4 MB	32 MB	256 MB	2 GB	16 GB	128 GB
4 bytes	8 MB	64 MB	512 MB	4 GB	32 GB	256 GB
8 bytes	16 MB	128 MB	1 GB	8 GB	64 GB	512 GB

In some ways, volumetric and geometric objects have opposite characteristics. Geometric objects typically consist of a relatively small number (100s to 1000s) of mathematically complex shapes (spheres, cylinders, surface patches, etc.). Volumetric objects, on the other hand, usually have a large number (tens of millions) of very simple shapes (e.g., cubes). Handling volumetric models thus calls for a substantially different processing strategy. Various mechanisms are used to minimize the number of voxels processed and reduce the computations required. Also, operations are often implemented in hardware for enhanced performance in specialized areas such as medicine.

26.2 Volumetric Methods

As with geometric SM systems, volumetric SM must be able to perform a variety of operations on models. Such operations include:

1. Format translation
2. Object storage
3. Display
4. Measurements
5. Dataset processing

26.2.1   Format Translations

Volumetric objects must be translated from the formats generated by specific scanners or computer simulations into an internal representation. This may be a simple conversion or involve advanced, source-specific processing. Resampling, filtering, interpolation, and compression techniques are often involved. New properties may be computed during the translation. This could include, for example, determining the direction of maximum density change (the gradient vector) at each sample point for a CT dataset. Translation must be performed with great care and understanding, however, because any modification to the source information can have a profound impact on the success or failure of a volumetric modeler in a particular application.

26.2.2   Object Storage

Because volumetric datasets are so large, storage becomes a major consideration. Compression methods are often used. Also, it may be possible to compute certain properties (e.g., gradients) when needed rather than storing them permanently.

26.2.3   Display

Viewing volumetric datasets, as with geometric datasets, is by far the most common operation requested, and is also one of the most difficult to accomplish efficiently and with high image quality. Some of the considerations are listed and discussed here:

1. Random viewpoint
2. Display properties
3. Surface shading
4. Depth cueing
5. Isoproperty surfaces
6. Cutting planes
7. Radiographic viewing
8. Time-varying objects

Random Viewpoint

Generating an image of a voxel array from a viewpoint that lies on an axis of the coordinate system is relatively simple because the voxels line up perpendicular to the display screen. In most uses, however, it is important that display be available from any random viewpoint, requiring more sophisticated methods.

Display Properties

The transparency of a voxel (invisible, translucent, or opaque) and its color are usually based on property values. A lookup table is typically used to determine these characteristics independently for each property value. A table with 64K locations, for example, can be used to independently select transparency and color based on a 16-bit property. Selecting visibility in this way is called *property thresholding*. Changing colors or intensities to emphasize certain property values is called *property windowing*.

Surface Shading

Shaded surface images require the use of local surface orientation information. Two schemes are commonly used: (1) the Z-Buffer method and (2) the Surface Normal method.

The Z-Buffer Method. A 2D array (Z-buffer) containing the depth (from the observer) is computed for each pixel in the image. After the initial rendering (but before viewing), a filter is applied to generate a shading value for each pixel. (See Fig. 26.4 for a 1D example.) If all neighboring pixels have about the same depth, the corresponding surface has a normal approximately pointed at the observer (Fig. 26.4a).

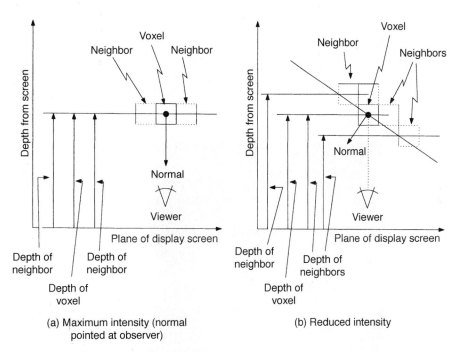

(a) Maximum intensity (normal pointed at observer)

(b) Reduced intensity

FIGURE 26.4 Z-buffer shading—1D example. (a) Maximum intensity when normal is pointed at observer. Note the equal depth of the subject voxel and its neighbors; (b) reduced intensity when normal is pointing away from observer. Note the varying depth of the subject voxel and its neighbors. *(Courtesy of Octree Corporation.)*

Assuming the illumination source is located at the observer, the visible brightness would be the greatest in this case, and the pixel is therefore given a maximum illumination intensity. On the other hand, if the neighboring depth is substantially different, the surface normal is oriented away from the observer and the associated pixel shading value is smaller (see Fig. 26.4b). This method is fast and simple but the shading is of relatively low quality (although still usable in many applications). One problem is dark bands that appear on the visible edges of objects caused by the fast drop-off of depth.

The Surface Normal Method. With this, an actual 3D surface normal vector is computed for each voxel by examining neighboring voxels. For example, with laser scanned surfaces, patches can be fit to points and used to mathematically generate surface normals. Volumetric datasets often do not have easily computed surfaces, however. In such cases, the maximum gradient vector can be computed from a property such as density. This is determined by examining the property values of neighboring voxels. It can be precomputed and stored with each voxel (as a property) or computed on the fly.

Depth Cueing

The perception of 3D is enhanced if objects become progressively darker at greater distances from the observer. This also helps the user to distinguish the front of an object from the back in visually ambiguous cases.

Isoproperty Surfaces

In some situations, the visualization of a volumetric dataset may be enhanced if points with only a particular property value are visible. It might be desirable, for example, to view all the regions of a plastic mold that are at a specific temperature. Simple property thresholding cannot be used, however, because very few voxels would, in general, have a property value precisely at the desired value. Most would be above or below it (samples near the value would typically be slightly above or below). A solution is to make a voxel visible only if it is above the value and it has a neighbor below it or it is below and a neighbor is above (and is therefore on or near such a surface). More sophisticated methods can be used to interpolate more exact isoproperty surfaces between voxels based on the actual values. One such method is called *dividing cubes*. It generates a large number of points estimated to be on such a surface. Cloud-of-points methods (see Sec. 26.2.6) are often used for display.

Cutting Planes

The interactive movement of a cutting plane can enhance the understanding of volumetric datasets (it is made invisible on one side). Properties are usually viewed on the cutting plane in color or shades of gray. Figure 26.5 shows a medical dataset with the interior exposed using three cutting planes. This can sometimes be generalized to a cutting object of any geometric shape.

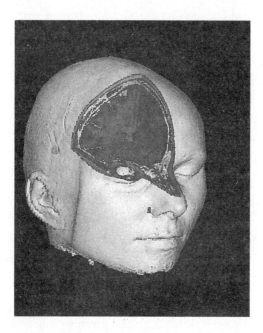

FIGURE 26.5   Medical data set with interior exposed, using three cutting planes. *(Courtesy of Octree Corporation.)*

Radiographic Viewing

As voxels are projected onto a display screen, they can be rendered opaque or translucent. If translucent, then color and intensity based on a property value can be added (rather than written) into the pixel location. When all voxels have been rendered, the result is a radiographic or summation image (sometimes called a *volumetric image*). With CT objects the result is similar to a conventional x ray but selected densities can be modified to emphasize or attenuate them. For example, a major motivation for the development of CT was improved visualization of brain tumors. They are obscured by the skull in conventional x-ray images. With radiographic viewing of a CT dataset, a "synthetic x ray" can be generated with the skull removed.

Time-Varying Objects

Sometimes it is possible to acquire multiple datasets for one object. A medical scanner, for example, can be synchronized to a patient's heartbeat. It can then be *gated* to generate multiple volumetric datasets corresponding to various phases of a heart cycle. Another source is FEM analysis. Multiple datasets can be generated, perhaps with increasing loads. Such time-varying datasets can be interactively viewed in sequence (e.g., a beating heart or deforming mechanical part).

Display

SMA.26.1   Display Interactivity

Some volumetric modelers require a long period to generate each image and therefore use a "movie-loop" sequence of pregenerated images. This is limiting, however, because design and analysis are iterative processes. Productivity is enhanced if imaging can be performed interactively.

26.2.4   Measurements

It is often important to measure volumetric objects (location, distance and angle measurements, mass-property calculations, etc.). Geometric surfaces can also be extracted automatically or manually for analysis, machining, etc.

26.2.5   Dataset Processing

Volumetric datasets are notoriously difficult to view because of the need to extract specific subsets of voxels corresponding to desired objects (e.g., anatomical organs) or features (e.g., cracks in a part). This is called the *segmentation problem*. While there is no universal segmentation algorithm, a number of tools and methods have been developed for use in procedures developed for specific situations. These include:

1. *Voxel type:*   Voxels often have a "type" value that is used for subset identification during segmentation. For example, in medicine a specific type value could be given to all voxels that were found to be part of a specific anatomical structure such as a heart.

2. *Masks:*   These are objects with either solid or empty voxels without properties (binary objects). They are used to select spatial regions of other objects. A solid sphere mask, for example, could be used to remove everything within a spherical region of an object.

3. *Property segmentation:*   Voxels are separated into sets based on property values. Various 3D filtering and processing operations are also usually available.

4. *Region segmentation:*   Voxels are selected by masks or geometric objects.

5. *Connectivity:*   Voxels are identified based on their connectivity to one or more reference points (often called *seed points*) in or on the object. Seed points can be generated automatically based on some situation in the dataset (all points above a density threshold, a landmark point such as the tip of the nose, etc.) or manually entered by the user. Connectivity between two voxels is determined by spatial relationships (i.e., face-connected, edge-connected, or vertex-connected), voxel type, property values, and other factors.

6. *Fill:*   This floods a bounded region with voxels containing a specified set of properties.

7. *Morphological operations:*   These include various low-level operations such as *dilation* (growing an object at its surfaces) and *erosion* (reducing an object at its surfaces).

8. *Cutting:*   Operators visually cut an object using an "electronic scalpel." This usually involves changing the type of all voxels that intersect a projected curve drawn visually. Structures can then be separated based on connectivity.

9. *Alpha processing:*   A voxel represents a volume and very often contains part of two or more structures (or tissue types such as bone and muscle). Usually such a voxel is classified as part of the structure that occupies the largest part. This is not strictly correct and causes small errors in analysis and display. This is called the *partial volume* problem. In some cases an estimate can be made of what fraction of the volume is part of a particular structure. This fraction is called the voxel's *alpha value*. When structures are displayed in different colors, alpha values can be used to improve image quality in a process called *alpha blending*.

Data Processing

SMA.26.2   Critical Trade-Offs

With volumetric datasets there is often a critical trade-off that must be made between spatial resolution and dataset size (and processing time). Individual applications should be studied to determine an optimal compromise. This can result in datasets that vary in resolution (higher density of samples where needed).

(Continued)

Data Processing
(Continued)

SMA.26.3   Acquisition Parameters

The ability to successfully process a volumetric dataset is often strongly influenced by the parameters used during data acquisition. This could include the orientation of the scanner, settings that control contrast, etc.

SMA.26.4   Segmentation Procedures

Some structures, such as a bone in a CT study, can be segmented relatively easily by density thresholding and perhaps connectivity analysis (to remove extraneous pieces). Most situations (e.g., involving soft organs) are much more difficult, however. A robust set of segmentation tools should be available for constructing custom procedures. A scripting language and tools to quickly build a user interface can help facilitate this process.

SMA.26.5   Database Access

In some situations it is important to be able to access the volumetric dataset in order to perform custom processing in an external program.

26.2.6   Representations

Various methods have been developed for representing volumetric objects:

1. Contours
2. Polygons
3. Voxel arrays
4. Clouds of points
5. Octrees

Contours

Contours are used with slice information (e.g., CT scans). Objects are represented by a set of lines in each image plane. First the images are thresholded (see Sec. 26.2.3) to generate binary images (each pixel is either solid or empty) and then lines are fitted to the exterior edges of solid areas. Each slice contains an independent set of contours (there are no connections between slices that would define surfaces).

A contour object can be considered a series of planar wireframes stacked in space. While contour methods are simple and reliable, and computer graphics systems can readily display contour datasets, images of contours are of limited value because hidden lines cannot be removed (there are no defined surfaces to hide them). Images become hopelessly confused for all but the simplest datasets. Also, except in relatively simple situations (e.g., bone from CT), structures cannot be extracted by simple thresholding.

Polygons

Polygons are an extension of the contour representation. The contours are connected between slices, forming polygons. While they can be displayed with popular polygon graphics systems, surfaces often bifurcate (split), causing uncertainty and errors where contours are connected.

Rather than fitting surfaces, individual voxels could be represented by six rectangular polygons. Unfortunately, the number of polygons quickly becomes astronomical (a voxel array with 256 voxels on each edge would require over 100 million polygons).

Voxel Arrays

The entire array of voxels is simply stored in memory. It is not necessary to force the extraction of edges or surfaces before display and processing; all of the original information remains available. Brute-force algorithms have been developed for display but sophisticated methods are needed for high-quality images and fast operation. Performance cannot be improved by polygon graphics accelerators since polygons are not normally used (there would simply be too many). Also, large memories are required, especially when multiple property bits are used (see Table 26.1). Rendering time can be excessive because all voxels must be accessed and processed for each image (inefficient if only a small fraction are visible or contain information of interest).

Cloud of Points

In this representation method, a large number of points are stored in a list, each point containing its x, y, and z coordinates and perhaps property information (e.g., surface normals). The primary advantage is that point projection hardware in polygon display systems (the "transformation pipeline") can be used to quickly project the points onto the display screen. If the density of such points is high, they visually merge on the screen and appear to be a solid.

Clouds can be divided into two types: (1) surface and (2) volumetric. Each is discussed.

Surface Cloud. A surface cloud contains points only on surfaces. For the surface defined by a fixed property value (an isoproperty surface), point generation begins by assuming that each property value represents a single point in space (the center of its voxel). Then, in effect, an isoproperty surface is mathematically interpolated and the points are sampled from it. Surface normals are usually generated locally and attached to the points for shading.

A conventional Z-buffer scheme (see Sec. 26.2.3) can be used to remove hidden points. Often the image is presented to the user while it is being generated. If the points have been spatially randomized, a crude image of the entire object appears quickly, followed by progressively improved renderings as more points are projected. A disadvantage is the high density of points required over the entire surface. Also, the user cannot zoom in on details because the surface would separate into points. And, since it is a surface representation, the interior information is lost.

Volumetric Cloud. Each voxel of interest (not every voxel) is represented by a point located at its center. This is conceptually similar to a voxel array, except that points are stored in a list (not a complete array). This requires more memory for each represented voxel because each must store its 3D coordinates. This is not needed with a regular array because the location of each voxel in space is implicit in its storage location.

Octree

Octrees are hierarchical tree structures (see Chap. 4) that result from a recursive subdivision of a finite universe. With volumetric datasets the bottom-level nodes represent individual voxels. Upper-level nodes represent large regions (8 voxels, 64 voxels, etc.). They are usually given a property value that is the average over the region that they represent. Unlike voxel arrays, it is not necessary to retain information in regions that are not of interest. Also, in some applications large homogeneous regions (all voxels having the same property value) exist and can be represented by high-level nodes. These characteristics can greatly reduce storage requirements.

Display is efficient since only the outer visible voxels (from any viewpoint) need to be accessed. And, since octrees are a solid representation, geometric objects can be readily intermixed with volumetric objects using boolean operations.

Data Representation

SMA.26.6 Disadvantages of Volumetric Clouds

At certain angles, gaps can show up, allowing voxels beneath the outer surface to show through. This can result in unexpected spots, often in annoying patterns. To avoid this, volumetric clouds are often summed into the display screen to form an image similar to that of a conventional x-ray image (radiographic image). Since all points are visible, gaps and patterns either do not occur or are less noticeable. Color is often used to enhance specific property values.

SMA.26.7 An Octree Disadvantage

Because octrees use specialized data structures and display algorithms, they are unable to use popular graphics accelerators, a disadvantage in many applications. Also, maintaining and processing octree structures can require a substantial amount of overhead processing.

(Continued)

Data Representation
(Continued)

SMA.26.8   Choosing a Representation Method

The choice of volumetric representation can be difficult. Here are some things to consider:

1. Contour methods may be sufficient if the dataset is relatively small, the structures can be readily determined, and the resulting display will not be complex. This is especially true if the results are to be used by a CAD system.

2. Polygon methods can improve visualization over contours but polygon generation (fitting surfaces to the data) can be difficult, large numbers of polygons may be generated, and the process is not 100 percent reliable (small errors often occur).

3. For large datasets, other methods are more practical. Point clouds can be displayed rapidly on existing graphics accelerators, but image quality is limited for some uses and sophisticated processing is difficult because voxel connectivity (e.g., neighbor information) is lost.

4. Voxel arrays are simple and effective for large datasets, and have been successfully used in a number of applications.

5. Octree methods are more complex and difficult to implement, but provide fast display with very large datasets, can handle multiresolution information, and support interaction with conventional SM systems.

26.3   Volumetric Applications

Currently, specialized applications take advantage of volumetric SM technology. These are listed and discussed in more detail in the following sections.

26.3.1   Finite Element Modeling (FEM)

FEM is used for analyzing stress, temperature, or other characteristics of a model (see Chap. 14). Volumetric methods are employed both in preprocessing (defining a mesh) and in postprocessing (displaying results). These methods are discussed here.

Preprocessing

In an FEM preprocessing step, the model is subdivided into geometric elements or cells that fill the object. In 2D, the elements are usually triangles or four-sided polygons. In 3D, tetrahedral elements (polyhedron formed by four triangles) and polyhedra with six rectangular faces (sometimes called *deformed bricks*) are usually used.

The generation of an element mesh can be difficult. It must trade off the high accuracy possible when large numbers of small elements are used with the speed of using small numbers of larger elements. The result is usually a custom-tailored mesh with small elements in critical areas (e.g., high curvature or expected high stress) and larger ones elsewhere.

An FEM mesh has both geometric and volumetric characteristics. While defined geometrically, its function is to strategically position sample points or volumes for simulation. Volumetric methods can be useful in mesh generation. Octrees are sometimes used, for example, because the regular subdivision into smaller elements along surfaces tends to place smaller elements in regions of high curvature. Likewise, *quadtrees* (the 2D equivalent of octrees) are used in 2D mesh generation.

Postprocessing

After analysis, in the postprocessing stage, the mesh elements contain computed values that are usually displayed with color. In 2D, viewing is straightforward because all elements can be viewed at once. In 3D, however, viewing can be very difficult because interior elements are hidden by outer layers of elements. To take advantage of volumetric SM systems, the geometric mesh and its properties can be converted into a regular array. Stress or other values can be computed for each voxel, and volumetric display tools can be applied (see Sec. 26.2.3). Such tools could include:

1. *Thresholding:*   To make only regions of high stress visible.
2. *Cutting planes:*   To show internal stress patterns in any orientation.
3. *Time-varying objects:*   To show temporal changes.

As FEM and analysis moves from 2D to 3D and meshes become more complex, it is expected that volumetric methods will be increasingly applied.

26.3.2   Robotics

Volumetric SM can be applied to controlling robots. Path planning, for example, requires fast collision detection. Conventional SM methods are slow in this role, at least partly because the entire work space is modeled to the high precision normally required for part design. Since the absolute accuracy of robot movement is limited because of mechanical tolerances, substantial "guard bands" must be maintained around potential collision objects. In many robot work spaces, for example, a modeling resolution of one part in 4000 in each dimension would be sufficient for collision detection. This tends to favor the speed of volumetric methods.

Volumetric SM can also effectively implement various "geometric reasoning" operations used in the optimization of robot movements. This could include, for example, finding the minimum distance between two moving objects, or determining if pushing on an object would cause it to slide or topple over.

Mapping Hostile Environments

Volumetric SM can represent unknown robotic work spaces. This is especially important with mobile robots that venture into unmapped, perhaps hostile, environments (contaminated sites, the ocean floor, etc.). Figure 26.6 illustrates the use of a laser scanner to generate a volumetric model of a work space and its contents (Fig. 26.6a). It starts as a completely unknown volume. Because of the need to avoid collisions, it is initially assumed to be completely solid (Fig. 26.6b) and therefore not safe for robot movement. A scan is then made from an initial location outside the work space. The spatial region from the laser to any surface detected by the beam must be empty and is cleared in the model (changed from solid to empty), as shown in Fig. 26.6c.

Empty regions of the work space that were not actually scanned remain unknown and therefore solid. A second set of sample points then partially removes the solid region behind the object (see Fig. 26.6d). Additional scans can further refine the work-space model as needed. This method can be fast and, while not exact, may be sufficiently accurate for visualization and planning purposes.

Robot Control and Safety

Volumetric SM can be used in the comparison of expected and actual work-space situations to enhance robot control and safety. In one scheme, a model of the work space is maintained internally as objects are repositioned. It is then tested against the real world using visual, laser, ultrasound, or other sensors. If the two versions (model and reality) are found to be different, an error has been detected and appropriate action is taken (e.g., all movement stopped and an alarm sounded). This could result from a broken tool, an object that has fallen over, or perhaps someone has inadvertently entered the work space.

26.3.3   Medical Applications

Because of the critical nature of the application, the development of 3D medical scanners has had a high priority over the years. This has led to the proliferation of computed tomography scanners in the 1970s. Later developments include magnetic resonance imaging (MRI), positron-emission tomography (PET), and 3D ultrasound. All of these applications generate large amounts of volumetric information.

Often the resulting voxels are brick-shaped (rectangular parallelepipeds) rather than cubical. With current CT scanners, for example, the resolution within a slice is usually much higher than the distance between slices (achieved by moving the patient in the scanner). Additional slices are often generated by interpolation to equalize the resolution for improved image quality.

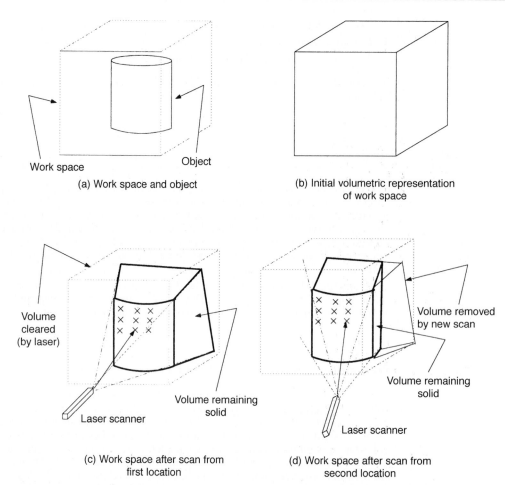

FIGURE 26.6 Volumetric representation of unknown work space. (*a*) Coexisting work space and object; (*b*) initial volumetric representation of work space; (*c*) work space after initial scan (note volume cleared by laser and volume remaining solid); (*d*) work space after second scan (note new volume cleared by laser and volume remaining solid). (*Courtesy of Octree Corporation.*)

There are a number of applications where volumetric SM is used in medicine:

1. Diagnosis
2. Surgical planning
3. Radiation therapy
4. Custom implants

Diagnosis

Although early enthusiasm for 3D modeling as a diagnostic tool was not realized, it has been found to be effective in analyzing certain situations such as spinal problems and head injuries. In recent years the diagnostic function of medical scanners has been extended by the development of "interventional" MR scanners. They provide an open area for a physician to conduct a procedure on a patient while still in the scanner. For example, real-time or near-real-time 3D information can be used for guidance.

Surgical Planning

Early use of volumetric SM was primarily reserved for the most difficult cases (e.g., craniofacial surgery) but is now more widely used. In facial trauma, for example, the ability to spatially locate and measure fractures and bone fragments allows the surgeon to optimize corrective procedures. This could include, for example, the elimination of multiple exploratory incisions. The extraction of measurements and the introduction of geometric shapes to represent manufactured objects (e.g., clamps and surgical instruments) can also be important. Advanced modeling features (e.g., cutting) are beginning to be used to actually simulate surgical procedures.

Radiation Therapy

Traditional methods of directing radiation beams for cancer treatment can be very inaccurate. In practice, a surprisingly large percentage of a dose is misdirected because of a lack of accurate spatial information. One of the difficulties of delivering "intelligent" radiation therapy is in modeling complex anatomy. With a tumor, for example, the goal is to control a radiation beam that will deliver a lethal dose to the tumor while subjecting surrounding tissue, especially vital structures, to a much lower dose. To accomplish this, the beam may need to be continuously moved to spare neighboring tissue while remaining focused on the target. In some cases the cross section of the beam can be modified to match the cross section of the tumor.

First, the tumor must be positioned within the coordinate system of the therapy machine. This is normally done by locating landmark points on the patient, often using small permanent tattoos. Sometimes tiny metal balls that will show up in scans are glued to the patient. For brain tumors, establishing a patient coordinate system can be accomplished by attaching a metal frame to the patient's head. The frame contains calibration structures that can later be found in the volumetric dataset and used to register the patient when he or she is moved to the therapy machine. A recent development is the incorporation of CT scanners into therapy devices specifically for patient positioning.

Tumors can have highly irregular shapes and be in difficult locations. For example, they can branch into adjacent regions or wrap around vital structures such as arteries. By effectively and accurately modeling them, volumetric SM promises to make radiation therapy safer and more effective.

Custom Implants

Volumetric SM is used in the design of custom prosthetic devices based on the patient's actual anatomy. Such devices exhibit enhanced operational characteristics (comfort, mobility, etc.) because of the improved fit, and are generally more reliable, especially over long periods (e.g., 10 years).

A custom hip design, for example, begins by acquiring a set of CT scans from the upper leg and pelvic regions of the patient. Various segmentation tools are then used to remove soft tissue and extraneous bone. Because of variations in scanners and patients, plus the possibility of bone disease and injury, the designer usually fine-tunes the range of densities that is considered "good" bone to be saved within the femur (the thighbone that will hold most of the implant). The remaining space within the upper part of the femur is to be filled by the implant.

Once satisfied with the bone model, various cuts are made to reveal important locations and surfaces. Geometric information is extracted and used to define the shape of the implant. The resulting model can then be entered into the volumetric SM system as a geometric object to check the fit. For example, the implant can be unioned into the bone and examined with cutting planes.

Overlapping spatial regions can be color-coded to facilitate visualization, and cut planes can be made selective (to cut only bone but not the implant). When an intersection operation is performed, the overlap region can be displayed directly as an object. This represents the bone that must be removed to insert the device. If needed, the shape or location of the device could be modified.

When the design is satisfactory, the geometric model is machined in a metal such as titanium. A custom cutting tool is often fabricated to aid the surgeon in removing exactly the intended interior part of the femur. Robot arms are now being used in the operating room on an experimental basis to perform this removal automatically. Figure 26.7 shows an actual implant embedded in a femur (selective cutting planes have been used to reveal it).

Suggestions for Further Reading

Kaufman, A., Cohen, D., and Yagel, R., "Volume Graphics," *Computer,* vol. 26, no. 7, Computer Society of the IEEE, 10662 Los Vaqueros Circle, P.O. Box 3014, Los Alamitos, CA 90720-1264, July 1993.

Udupa, J. K., and Herman, G. T., *3D Imaging in Medicine,* CRC Press, Boca Raton, Fla., 1991.

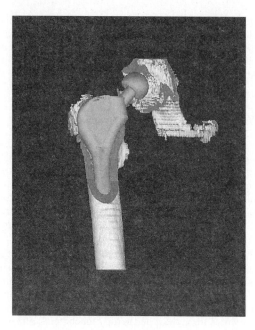

FIGURE 26.7 Medical implant (hip prosthesis) shown embedded in a femur (thighbone). Note the use of selective cutting planes. *(Courtesy of Techmedica Inc.)*

Samet, H., *The Design and Analysis of Spatial Data Structures,* Addison-Wesley, Reading, Mass., 1990.

Samet, H., *Applications of Spatial Data Structures,* Addison-Wesley, Reading, Mass., 1990.

Laurini, R., and Thompson, D., *Fundamentals of Spatial information Systems,* Academic Press, London, England, 1992.

Nielson, G., Shriver, B., and Rosenblum, L., *Visualization in Scientific Computing,* IEEE Computer Society Press, Los Alamitos, Calif., 1990.

Kaufman, A., *Volume Visualization,* IEEE Computer Society Press, Los Alamitos, Calif., 1991.

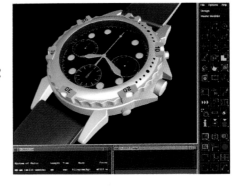
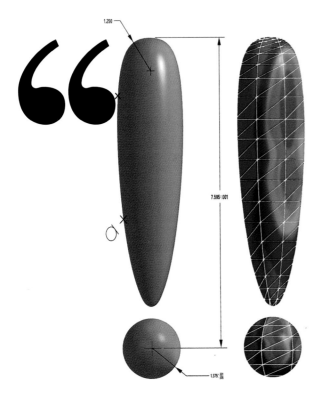
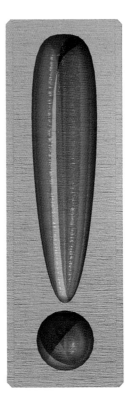

Chapter 27

The Role of Solid Modeling in Concurrent Engineering

Peter Marks
Managing Director
Design Insight

Concurrent engineering (CE) is one way of describing far-reaching changes in the way companies interact with customers and suppliers, organize their people and processes, and communicate between functions. Properly implemented and aided by Solid Modeling (SM), these changes can dramatically improve customer satisfaction, market share, and profits. Improperly implemented, CE becomes just another failed buzzword.

This chapter serves three purposes. First, it outlines a framework for understanding and implementing CE. Second, it illustrates how SM, when properly implemented, supports CE processes. Third, it provides specific advice for planning and implementing CE.

27.1   The Road to Concurrent Engineering (CE)

The answer to the question "What is the best road?" depends on where you want to end up. The biggest mistake companies make in implementing SM with CE is assuming that they will perform the same tasks, by the same people, in about the same way as before. The goal of CE is to leap beyond traditional methods. It changes everything in the pursuit of higher customer satisfaction, market share, and profits.

When SM systems are implemented based on past practices, the effort is only partially successful. Certainly, some gains are achieved by using SM instead of 2D and 3D wireframe systems. Many companies eventually discover better processes. Yet the result of going to SM while conducting business as usual is that companies end up with about the same market share and profits as before. The situation can be even worse—if competitors make gains.

Today, we have many ideas on how to achieve a competitive edge. Such ideas include: design for manufacturing, cycle-time reduction, total quality management, reengineering, business process improvement, cross-functional teaming, and CE. There is significant overlap between most of these ideas, and this chapter might have been titled "The Role of SM in Creating Better Products and Earning Higher Market Share and Profits."

Concurrent engineering, for example, is based on reengineering various design, manufacturing, and customer support processes. It involves teams, cycle-time reduction, and close attention to do-it-right-the-first-time quality. Many companies start with one theme, such as total quality management, and soon realize they must touch upon all the others.

Whatever the names used to describe process improvement, the requirements for success are similar. To use our road metaphor, a company must first understand where it wants to go and the paths it must take to reach that destination. A worthy destination will include targets for customer satisfaction, market share, growth, and profits.

Many paths must be taken to reach this destination. SM is not so much "the answer" as it is a powerful new vehicle to travel many of these paths. It enables new ways of interacting with customers and suppliers. It also improves communication between functions and makes new processes possible.

27.2   Effective Implementation

The simple story is that SM and CE should journey together. However, effective implementation is more complex. Indeed, CE faces a crisis of credibility. It is in danger of becoming a meaningless buzz-word through careless use.

Some managers talk of revitalizing the design process through concurrent engineering—as if the two words were a prescription for success. When pressed for details, they mumble something about putting everyone into the same room and doing designs concurrently. This turns out to be easier said than done for larger organizations which have the most to gain from CE. Concurrent engineering requires a clear and credible road map for implementation.

27.3   The Road Map for CE

The "map" we use here for CE is based on extensive new work sponsored by CASA/SME—the Computer Automated Systems Association of the Society of Manufacturing Engineers. It reflects the best thinking of many experts in design and manufacturing and provides a framework for understanding and implementing CE.

27.3.1   Six Perspectives on CE

The New Manufacturing Enterprise CASA/SME Wheel views manufacturing from six perspectives, each a level or ring as shown in Fig. 27.1. Each of these six levels must be considered in planning for CE. Working from the center out, they include:

1. Customer Focus—Level 1
2. People and Teamwork—Level 2

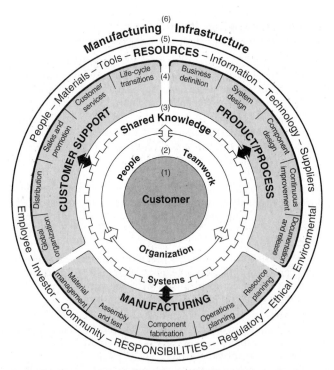

FIGURE 27.1 The CASA/SME new Manufacturing Enterprise Wheel. *(Courtesy of the Computer Automated Systems Association of the Society of Manufacturing Engineers, CASA/SME. Reprinted with permission.)*

3. Shared Knowledge and Systems—Level 3
4. Processes—Level 4
5. Resources and Responsibilities—Level 5
6. Manufacturing Infrastructure—Level 6

Customer Focus—Level 1

This includes the central role of the customer and evolving customer needs. Design, manufacturing, and support must be aligned to meet customer needs. This is the bull's-eye to hit, the hub of the wheel, the vision and mission of the enterprise. SM and related tools such as rapid prototyping (RP) enable new ways of interacting with customers, determining customer needs, and developing better product specifications.

People and Teamwork—Level 2

This includes the role of people and teamwork in the organization. Included are the enterprise's means of organizing, hiring, training, motivating, measuring, and communicating to ensure teamwork and cooperation. This is the soft side of the enterprise, captured in ideas such as self-directed teams, teams of teams, the learning organization, quality circles, and CE. One common issue in cross-functional teaming is that different functions communicate with different tools. Designers have their engineering drawings, accountants have their spreadsheets, manufacturing engineers have their process plans, while customers have their partially explained needs. SM is a tool for better communication between all these functions.

Shared Knowledge and Systems—Level 3

This includes the revolutionary impact of shared knowledge and systems to support people (level 2) and processes (level 4). Included are both manual tools and computer systems to help plan, do, check, and refine work—and then communicate results. SM is today's most powerful tool for sharing essential geometric knowledge and then driving automated systems.

Processes—Level 4

This includes key processes from product definition through manufacturing and customer support. There are three main groups of processes: (1) product/process definition, (2) manufacturing, and (3) customer support. Within these three groups, 15 key processes complete the product life cycle (see Sec. 27.5.4). The goal of CE is to work on these key processes in parallel rather than in a purely sequential process of trial and error. SM plays a key role in both automating individual functions and communicating between functions.

Resources and Responsibilities—Level 5

This includes enterprise resources (inputs) and responsibilities (outputs). Resources include people, materials, tools, information, technology, and suppliers. Reciprocal responsibilities include employee, investor, and community relations, plus regulatory, ethical, and environmental obligations. With CE, administrative functions are a thin layer around the periphery, bringing new resources into the enterprise and supporting key processes within.

Manufacturing Infrastructure—Level 6

While a company may see itself as self-contained, success depends on customers, competitors, suppliers, and other factors in the environment. The typical manufacturing company purchases 50 to 70 percent of a product's total value from outside suppliers in the form of raw materials, energy, specialized services, components, and subassemblies. Without world-class suppliers providing this 50 to 70 percent of value, how can any company offer the quality and value it needs to compete? Thus, today's suppliers and manufacturing companies must increasingly link design and manufacturing. Solid Modeling—even across company and national boundaries—is the best method for sharing much of this product data.

27.4   Processes Before Tools

Plans for CE should consider all six perspective levels of the CASA/SME Wheel outlined earlier. Companies should clearly identify the desired product outcomes, organizational structures, and processes before, or at least in parallel with, major new investments in SM technology. This is the process mapping and process reengineering part of CE.

A detailed examination of process reengineering is beyond the scope of this chapter, and is the subject of many books. Note, however, that the CASA/SME Wheel provides an excellent map of the territory and is a useful tool for communicating with all who are involved in process improvement.

27.5   The Role of SM in the New Manufacturing Enterprise

Your company has examined its products, benchmarked its processes, and established a clear map of where and how it wants to move ahead. Now, where does SM fit in?

Using the CASA/SME Wheel as a reference, SM has a key role to play in many aspects of CE. In part, this is because people process more information visually and physically than verbally. Most potential customers, for example, would rather see and touch a product than hear a salesperson talk about it. SM is our most powerful tool for digitally representing the visual and physical aspects of the real world. Let's look at each level of the CASA/SME Wheel and see how SM can play a role.

27.5.1   Customer Focus

The customer is level 1 and at the hub of the CASA/SME Wheel. This is the bull's-eye to hit and the focus for CE.

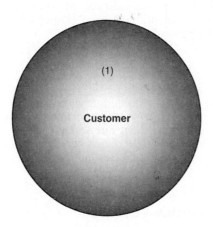

FIGURE 27.2   Level 1 of the CASA/SME Wheel. A customer-centered mission helps align activities and empowers the work of teams in CE. *(Courtesy of the Computer Automated Systems Association of the Society of Manufacturing Engineers, CASA/SME. Reprinted with permission.)*

While most companies give lip service to the importance of understanding customer needs, more products fail due to an imperfect understanding of those needs than any other single cause.

Clearly, the customer should be part of any successful CE process. SM technology can help companies stay closer to their customers in at least three ways:

1. Customer needs
2. Customer communication
3. Customer relations

Customer Needs

Solid Modeling is an ideal tool to help determine customer needs prior to full engineering design. Questionnaires and verbal methods of interaction are notoriously inaccurate in determining customer needs. Customers say one thing, designers hear another. Simply put, it is usually more useful to see things through the "eyes of the customer" than to hear the "voice of the customer."

SM is an ideal tool to evaluate proposed concepts in customer interviews and focus groups (see color insert, Fig. 27.3). Even better, it can drive rapid prototyping (RP) processes to give customers something to see and touch. Developing a series of such soft and hard prototypes, and using them to engage customers in a meaningful dialogue, is almost always better than trying to write the perfect product specification. SM makes this kind of customer interaction possible, affordable, and (in the long run) faster.

Customer Communication

Solid Modeling is also ideal to help entire teams, including customers, communicate during the engineering process. Companies are making extensive use of visual tools to keep customers informed (see color insert, Fig. 27.4). There are may success stories, from aerospace, automotive, and machine tools to physicians and patients involved in the design of new medical prostheses.

Customer Relations

Solid Modeling can be an ideal tool to maintain an ongoing relationship with customers after initial design, especially in build-to-order situations. Already, computer technology is being used to let customers see and choose options. Producers of standard parts are providing on-line access of CAD models for their customers to use in such areas as tool design.

Companies talk about staying close to customers, yet rely upon old methods of determining customer needs. This results in needless change orders, missed schedules, and added costs. Remember, the number one cause of products that fail to earn a profit is the misunderstanding of customer needs.

27.5.2 People and Teamwork

The central role of people in the organization forms the inner circle of the CASA/SME Wheel. The benefits of CE are paced by the ability of people to share knowledge and work together. Companies that are stuck in rigidly hierarchical and functionally isolated patterns of work need to change the organization to achieve even moderate levels of concurrency. This involves a culture change, with higher levels of trust between functions.

The steps required to build effective cross-functional teams are many and, again, beyond the scope of this chapter. Some teams have had good success in team-building exercises. Others take personality tests to better understand one another. Still others carefully craft team metrics and rewards.

Most people have good intentions about working together. Certainly there is likely to be some level of politics and selfish thinking driven by imperfect reward systems. Yet people basically want to satisfy customers, help their colleagues, and do their best. What thwarts the best of intentions is often a failure to communicate.

Solid Modeling can help with the good-communication part of the equation. If engineers walk into a cross-functional group with engineering drawings in hand and stacks of computer printouts ready to prove their points—just who will really understand? Accounting may come similarly equipped with spreadsheets; marketing with customer surveys; and manufacturing with process capability charts. Each function manages to communicate and prove its points only to its brethren. And after the meeting each function talks about the idiots in accounting, engineering, manufacturing, sales, purchasing, and so on. This is not CE; it is concurrent failure to communicate.

Psychologists note that we have many different modes of communication. Some of us prefer to touch and feel, others to add up the numbers, others to listen, and still others (including many engineers) to see it first, then build a real or mathematical model.

Successful cross-functional teams work a bit like the United Nations, with simultaneous translation to meet the learning styles of all team members. Over time, team members will even learn to speak more of one another's language. In practical terms, this means that each discussion is translated into words for the word people, renderings (and solid models) for the visual people, analyses for the numbers people, and real objects (rapid prototypes) for the hands-on people.

Computer technology linking product specifications, CAD models, financial data, simulations, and rapid prototypes makes such "simultaneous translation" affordable. And, yes, SM is often the key technology—the backbone of effective systems to clearly communicate between functions as different as industrial design, engineering, purchasing, accounting, manufacturing engineering, union labor, quality assurance, safety, distribution, sales, and maintenance. Lower-cost hardware and software, and the availability of SM based on popular operating systems, will accelerate its widespread adoption as a communication tool.

27.5.3   Systems for Shared Knowledge

Level 3 of the CASA/SME Wheel involves planning communication systems (see Fig. 27.5). In ages past, we named epochs by the dominant materials and technology of the age; the Stone Age, the Bronze Age, the Iron Age. Materials and processes are still evolving. Today, the dominant "material" of civilization is information; and the dominant technology is the computer. We are in the Information Age. Solid Modeling, as noted earlier, is the leading tool to represent the *material* of products-to-be in unambiguous computer models.

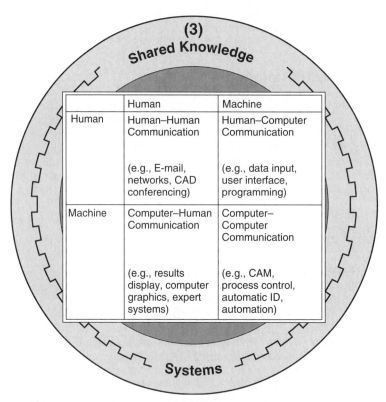

	Human	Machine
Human	Human–Human Communication (e.g., E-mail, networks, CAD conferencing)	Human–Computer Communication (e.g., data input, user interface, programming)
Machine	Computer–Human Communication (e.g., results display, computer graphics, expert systems)	Computer–Computer Communication (e.g., CAM, process control, automatic ID, automation)

FIGURE 27.5   Level 3 of the CASA/SME Wheel involves planning communication systems for shared knowledge. *(Courtesy of the Computer Automated Systems Association of the Society of Manufacturing Engineers, CASA/SME. Reprinted with permission.)*

27.5.4   Processes

Processes are the life of the manufacturing enterprise, the fundamental work to be done. In level 4 of the CASA/SME Wheel, there are 15 key processes in three main groups—a trinity of actions focused on customer satisfaction, each of which should be considered in planning for CE (see Fig. 27.6). Each of these processes are discussed here.

Product Definition and Design

1. *Business definition.*   SM is seeing use in business definition to quickly visualize new product ideas. For example, a computer-aided focus group can give prospective customers a much better understanding of alternatives and trade-offs. This helps avoid the usual market research problem of customers voicing one set of values, while behaving differently later, when the reality of the choices are clearer. SM is also a powerful tool for communicating and selling a business vision.

2. *System design.*   System design sets the overall product architecture. Sometimes described as engineering concept design, system design defines:

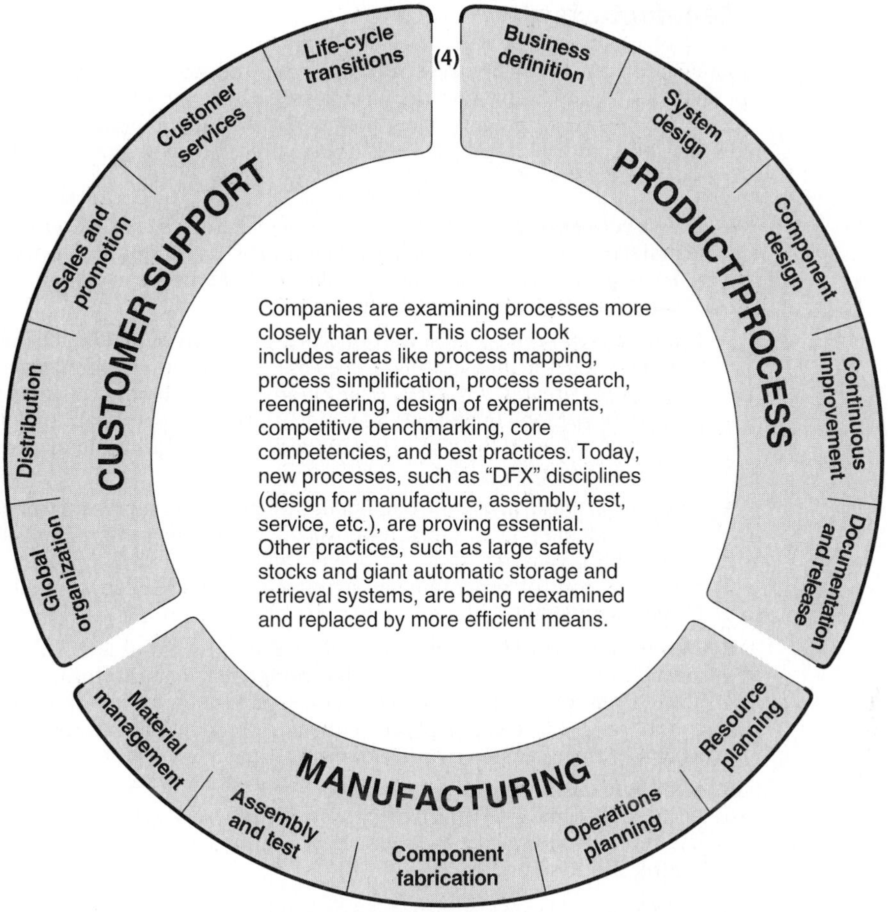
Life-cycle transitions
(4)
Business definition
System design
Component design
Continuous improvement
Documentation and release
Resource planning
Operations planning
Component fabrication
Assembly and test
Material management
Global organization
Distribution
Sales and promotion
Customer services
CUSTOMER SUPPORT
PRODUCT/PROCESS
MANUFACTURING
Companies are examining processes more closely than ever. This closer look includes areas like process mapping, process simplification, process research, reengineering, design of experiments, competitive benchmarking, core competencies, and best practices. Today, new processes, such as "DFX" disciplines (design for manufacture, assembly, test, service, etc.), are proving essential. Other practices, such as large safety stocks and giant automatic storage and retrieval systems, are being reexamined and replaced by more efficient means.

FIGURE 27.6 Level 4 of the CASA/SME Wheel—15 key processes. Companies are examining processes more closely than ever. This closer look includes process mapping, process simplification, process research, reengineering, design of experiments, competitive benchmarking, core competencies, and best practices. Today, new processes, such as "DFX" disciplines (design for manufacture, assembly, test, service, etc., see Chap. 25), are proving essential. Other non-value-added practices, such as large safety stocks, are being reexamined. These trends, taken together, are a part of CE. *(Courtesy of the Computer Automated Systems Association of the Society of Manufacturing Engineers, CASA/SME. Reprinted with permission.)*

a. Minimum functional and performance requirements
b. Initial layout and packaging
c. Boundaries and descriptions of major subsystems
d. Priorities for optimization

SM is an ideal tool for systems verification, interference detection, and team communication.

3. ***Component design.*** Component design proceeds within the context of system design and includes all the traditional design, engineering, analysis, and testing functions. It may proceed at one or more levels, with one or more design teams, depending upon the complexity of the product. SM has emerged as a superb tool for component design, especially when there is added value in linking geometry to various forms of structural, thermal, kinematic, dynamic, ergonomic, etc., analyses. (See color insert, Fig. 27.7.)
4. ***Continuous improvement.*** Product/process improvement steps include assembling components into system mock-ups—evaluating the result and striving for continuous improvement. The evaluation may include design reviews (words), drawings (renderings), simulations (analyses), and physical mock-ups (prototypes).
5. ***Documentation and release.*** The customers of design are manufacturing and customer support. Documentation processes include final checks and shipping of complete, easy-to-use, product/process definitions. Solid models are replacing drawings (either paper drawings or 2D and 3D wireframe representations) among leading companies. The emergence of STEP (see Chap. 22) will accelerate this trend.

Manufacturing

Manufacturing is much like reverse-engineering the steps of product definition. Just as each step in product definition builds upon the former, so each step in manufacturing begins to translate product requirements, first to process plans, then to individual components, and finally to finished products. Given a good product definition—and capable processes to manufacture the product—the result should be a satisfied customer.

6. *Resource planning.* This includes critical make/buy decisions, outsourcing, global organization of manufacturing facilities, supplier relations, and any required proofs of manufacturing feasibility. SM has proven an ideal communication vehicle between design and manufacturing. In CE, it allows early consideration of trade-offs.

7. *Operations planning.* Just as products are built from individual components, factories are built from individual manufacturing processes. Component suppliers must periodically revamp entire facilities for greater throughput, and more frequently make minor modifications for individual product runs. Many operations' planning tools have used less complete forms of CAD data. Now the use of SM is on the rise in a variety of manufacturing simulation and planning applications. (See color insert, Fig. 27.8.)

8. *Component fabrication.* Component design usually represents most engineering design expenditures, and component fabrication usually represents most manufacturing costs. SM is now providing the geometric basis for a wide variety of fabrication simulation programs, including numerical control programming simulation, plastic injection-molding simulation, sheet-metal-forming simulation, and many others. (See color insert, Fig. 27.9.)

9. *Design for assembly.* Finished components are next assembled and, often, tested for conformance to product specifications. Like component manufacturing, assembly may include several levels, from subassembly to final assembly. SM is now being used extensively to analyze assembly considerations (see Chap. 11) such as static and dynamic interference detection and the physical assembly process. (See color insert, Fig. 27.10.)

10. *Material scheduling.* Material scheduling controls the day-to-day flow of supplies into manufacturing and the flow of finished goods to customers. The best home for these processes is shipping and receiving. Reducing the number of components is another powerful aid to simplifying flow control. These steps are aided by SM.

Customer Support

Design and manufacturing are like two legs of a tripod: essential but not sufficient for total customer satisfaction. The third leg is customer support. This includes aspects of customer satisfaction such as distribution, sales, services, and life-cycle support.

11. *Global organization.* The global economy is changing the way business is organized. For example, most major companies must now support design, manufacturing, and customer-support organizations in the Americas, Europe, and the Pacific Rim. SM systems are especially useful in overcoming difficulties of communication across national and language boundaries.

12. *Distribution.* Distribution systems and channels are frequently a key to competitive success. Design and manufacturing must often serve several masters. For example, products are designed not just for the end customer, but for the needs of the distribution channel and the opinions of influencers as well.

13. *Sales and promotion.* "Build a better mousetrap and the world will beat a path to your door," say design and manufacturing. "But only if the world knows and cares . . . ," says the sales and marketing communications team. Salespeople in many companies tap directly into shared databases, giving their customers a clear view of product options, costs, performance, and delivery times. Sales, in turn, can provide a wealth of knowledge for product design and manufacturing.

14. *Customer services.* Products are now being designed with service and support systems built in. For example, new aircraft carry on-line service documentation. High-end copiers diagnose their own problems. New software packages have on-line help systems and tutorials.

15. *Life-cycle transitions.* No product lasts forever. For both the individual user and the market as a whole, each product comes to the end of its life cycle. Design and manufacturing are coming to grips with life-cycle transitions beyond the intended life of a product. Two examples of such "green engineering" include the design of products for disassembly and design of processes for recycling. Here again, solids are beginning to play a key role.

27.5.5 Resources and Responsibilities

The CASA/SME Wheel views resources, corporate responsibilities, and related administrative functions as a thin layer around the wheel. Resources come into the company and finished goods are sent to distributors and customers through this layer.

The resource layer manages the flow of inputs from the manufacturing environment. These include:

1. People and skills (human resources, leadership)
2. Materials (purchasing, inventories)
3. Tools (equipment, machinery, workstations, facilities)
4. Information (on customers, markets, trends, etc.)
5. Technology (internal and external R&D)
6. Suppliers (components, special knowledge, services)
7. Investors (capital converted to needed resources)

Resources flow into the enterprise, where value is added. Then finished goods and services flow out of the enterprise, to customers, and to other stakeholders. In addition to its customers, the enterprise has responsibilities to maintain its infrastructure. These include:

1. Employee (wages, benefits, security, worthwhile jobs)
2. Investor (return on investment, stability)
3. Community (support of infrastructure)
4. Regulatory (government regulations)
5. Ethical (moral responsibilities)
6. Environmental (minimum wastes, sustainable ecology)

Solid Modeling is not yet widely employed in administrative functions such as purchasing, equipment design, or environmental management. However, increasing application can be expected as systems become easier and more affordable to use.

27.5.6 Manufacturing Infrastructure

Outside the nominal bounds of the enterprise is its environment. The final aspect of CE is interaction with suppliers, regulatory agencies, and other "partners" in meeting customer needs.

Solid Modeling has a key role in streamlining many of these interactions and assuring unambiguous communication. An obvious example is the use of solid models to communicate with suppliers of tools, dies, molds, machined parts, and other purchased components. This already strong trend will accelerate with improved product data exchange standards, higher bandwidth information highways, and an increasingly capable network of global suppliers.

A related trend is toward the "virtual enterprise," with key processes subcontracted to other suppliers. For example, some computer companies design their products (processes 1 through 5), but outsource manufacturing (processes 6 through 10), and rely upon value-added resellers for customer support (processes 11 through 15). Strong companies exist with core competencies just in design, or manufacturing, or customer support.

Unambiguous product definition, primarily solid models plus related data, often binds such virtual enterprises together. SM is emerging as a communication tool in other areas between companies and their manufacturing infrastructure. Such areas include:

1. Virtually integrating suppliers
2. Linking distributors
3. Improving shipping processes
4. Coordinating research and educational institutions
5. Better communication in community relations
6. Speeding regulatory approvals
7. Encouraging new capital investment
8. Attracting and educating skilled workers

When CE is practiced not just within a company, but with external partners as well, customers and suppliers participate in design. Competitors, research institutions, and even communities and governments become partners.

27.6 Summary

The effective implementation of SM and CE go hand in hand. Companies must start with a road map of the desired change. The CASA/SME Wheel provides a starting point for tailoring such a CE road map to individual companies, based on the experience of successful companies from many industries.

Once the "main highways" are understood, new and highly effective applications for SM become clear in each of the six levels of CE discussed here, from better understanding of customer needs to better coordination with external suppliers.

For More Information: Further information on the CASA/SME Wheel is available from The Society of Manufacturing Engineers, One SME Drive, Post Office Box 930, Dearborn, MI 48121, phone: (313) 271-1500.

Customer Focus

SMA.27.1 A Shared Vision

Make sure team members in CE have a shared vision of customer needs. Use methods such as focus groups, "$APPEALS," and "QFD" to define customer requirements.

SMA.27.2 Customer Contact

Provide frequent customer contact with the CE team to maintain a focus and understanding of customer needs.

People and Teamwork

SMA.27.3 Cross-Functional Teams

Use cross-functional teams, with members selected to represent high-priority customer needs in such areas as performance (design engineering), cost (as a function of manufacturing), responsiveness (as a function of distribution), and so on. Team membership is driven by customer needs and competitive positioning.

SMA.27.4 A Supportive Culture

Build a supportive culture for CE through the addition of team metrics and rewards.

SMA.27.5 Multiple Cycles

Keep the core members of product-focused CE teams together through multiple product development and launch cycles. Make sure that team members follow products through to customer use and that they learn in a continuous improvement environment.

SMA.27.6 Take Ownership

The high level of cooperation and teamwork required for CE can be accomplished only by training employees and managers to take ownership of the entire design process rather than their traditional areas of responsibility.

SMA.27.7 Optimize the Design Process

A firm using CE must be committed to optimizing the entire design process at the expense of traditional functional roles. It also must be committed to continual improvement in the engineering design process, the technology, and tools used to automate this process and the products being designed.

(Continued)

People and Teamwork
(Continued)

SMA.27.8   Organizational Barriers

Though physical walls do not exist in all engineering organizations, cultural or organizational barriers do. The initial task in any CE implementation is to provide an environment that encourages communication. Locating all members of the design team in a common location is desirable, but not always feasible.

Keith Campbell, Engineer, VP Marketing
American Small Business Computers, Pryor, Okla.

Systems

SMA.27.9   A Voice in the Process

Build systems that support teaming. Provide design and manufacturing teams that give all stakeholders—especially the customer—a voice in the process.

SMA.27.10   Handbook of Solid Modeling

Consider the majority of this handbook as a tool to help build a solids-based system for enterprise integration. All the information contained in this handbook applies here.

SMA.27.11   Support Human Communication

Support human communication. Consider: multiple media to match different human communication styles; words and databases; visual images and computer graphics; abstract thinking and analyses; physical things and automated processing. Use simple and powerful tools to help teams and team members understand one another.

SMA.27.12   Get Physical Fast

Use rapid modeling, visualization, simulation, and prototyping methods for early mock-ups of the product. Use the models for design walk-throughs, and include representatives from design, manufacturing, sales, customers, and others.

SMA.27.13   Synchronization

Synchronize the work of individual teams and process owners with integrated systems based on widely supported data exchange standards. Make sure the three main areas play together. Product/process defines what to build; manufacturing builds it; and customer support conveys and ensures value to the customer.

SMA.27.14   Product Data Management (PDM)

Use simple but effective engineering PDM systems to track work in progress, changes, and effectivity.

Processes

SMA.27.15   All Things Considered

Consider all key value-added functions from the initial concept through customer use. Know what's critical to your customers—and thus to your success. The 15 key processes identified in level 4 of the CASA/SME Wheel are a good place to start.

SMA.27.16   A Value Chain

Think about your processes as a value chain. Who are your suppliers? Who are your customers? Which steps add value? Which steps can be simplified or eliminated? How might the transfer of information or products from one step to another be improved for instant, accurate, and complete transmission of value?

SMA.27.17   Look Ahead and Behind

Consider ways to help functions look ahead and behind, to communicate outside the sequential value chain. SM is a key tool. Anticipate problems down the road. The new manufacturing enterprise doesn't drive with its eyes fixed just 10 feet ahead—or in the rearview mirror. Each key process communicates as required to other processes.

(Continued)

Processes
(*Continued*)

SMA.27.18 Support Best Practices

Benchmark and support best practices, especially in the DFX domain (design for manufacturing, design for assembly, design for X . . .). These are best practices that allow an individual process to better tune its results for higher throughput, quality, customer satisfaction, market share, and profits.

SMA.27.19 Capture Process Knowledge

Capture process knowledge using tip sheets, checklists, databases, engineering standards, hypertext systems, expert systems, and other systems and tools.

SMA.27.20 Seek and Use Appropriate Metrics

As far as possible, track the impact of systems and processes on customer-oriented goals rather than internal measures. The customer doesn't care how many hoops you've jumped through—or how elegant your new parametric solid models have become. The question is, are you helping to build products that customers want to buy?

Resources and Responsibilities

SMA.27.21 Administrative Functions

Include administrative functions, such as purchasing and human resources, as a resource for CE teams.

SMA.27.22 The Total Product Life Cycle

Recognize special employee, investor, and community relations, plus regulatory, ethical, and environmental obligations, early in the process. An example is the trend toward "green" engineering, where products are designed for recycling and the total product life cycle.

Manufacturing Infrastructure

SMA.27.23 External Resources

Include external resources, such as academic, consulting, research, and government institutions, to add value to CE teams.

SMA.27.24 Computer-Based Tools

Use computer-based tools to understand and track new technology, customer needs, competitors, new regulations, changing demographics, and other competitive factors. Filter this information for best use by CE teams.

SMA.27.25 Integrate with Customers

Maintain close integration with customers and prospective customers; the goal of CE is to serve their needs. Use solid models, rapid prototypes, and similar tools to ensure clear communication.

SMA.27.26 Invest in Special Relationships

Invest in special relationships, such as supplier programs and cooperative work/study programs, to maintain top quality in the human and material resources for manufacturing.

SMA.27.27 Old and New

Replace slow, ambiguous, paper-based communications with customers and suppliers with fast, unambiguous, computer-based communications.

Implementation

SMA.27.28 No Walls—One Team

We have given our design engineers, manufacturing engineers, and QA engineers each workstations. All three groups are trained on SM and are expected to share files. A weekly meeting to review progress is held by the project manager to ensure that CE is implemented and conflicts resolved. Our emphasis is on training on one side and changing culture on the other. No walls, but *one* team! SM becomes just one of many tools for communication.

Eldad Cohen, Engineering Consultant
Brookline, Mass.

Implementation
(*Continued*)

SMA.27.29 CE Design Tips

1. Expect the whole product team to be SM-literate so that they can review and check designs early in the process (i.e., at the layout stage, before prototypes are made). Early evaluation is critical to design manufacturability and cost effectiveness.

2. Allow time in the project schedule for tolerance checking and the time to make corrections.

3. Perform design checking on SM geometry before making prototypes. This is critical. Check for conformance to industry standard practices (e.g., constant wall thickness for plastic parts).

Howard W. Stolz, Product Designer
Sun Microsystems, Mountain View, Calif.

SMA.27.30 Hardware Capabilities

Provide SM workstations with sufficient power. SM technology demands large main memories, larger data files, and powerful workstations. Vendor-suggested minimums may not optimize your productivity and overall costs. Designers should benchmark various configurations—or consult experienced users—to determine the best configuration.

SMA.27.31 SM Sells Ideas

Do not underestimate the power of SM to communicate and sell your ideas. To gain the most from this aspect of SM, buy at least one workstation with "the works" to use for customer, management, and team reviews.

SMA.27.32 SM and X Terminals

Consider the use of SM and shared "X" (X terminals) to help geographically dispersed users communicate (see color insert, Fig. 27.11). This is referred to as *virtual teaming*.

SMA.27.33 SM, Customers, and Suppliers

In selecting an SM system for use in a CE environment, consider your key customers and suppliers as part of the selection team. For example, substantial reductions in time to market are often possible when key suppliers use the same system.

SMA.27.34 Data Exchange

Because heterogeneous systems are a way of life despite SMA.27.34, demand superior data exchange tools from your vendors. A complete set of tools might include extensive and accurate IGES support, specialized packages to exchange surface data if required, and close involvement with STEP (see Chap. 22).

SMA.27.35 Not Just Geometry

Complete product definition requires both unambiguous geometry and a database of attached textual and numeric information. Perhaps the simplest yet most powerful tools emerging on this front are for industrial strength hypertext. The idea is to attach searchable (associative, object-oriented) data to features of the solid model. Less complete geometric representations (such as 2D sections or bit maps) can be extracted from the solid and used in parts catalogs, etc. Use these tools to build and share product and process knowledge.

Common CE Pitfalls

SMA.27.36 Information Explosion

There are some hard lessons to learn from CE. If your organization is not equipped to simultaneously process a large set of information, it may clog up information storage or degrade the turnaround time.

SMA.27.37 Spurts Are Not Desirable

Release of large amounts of information in spurts is also inappropriate for this mode of operation. Cross-functional teams require continuously updated information.

(Continued)

Common CE Pitfalls
(Continued)

SMA.27.38   Risk of Wasted Effort

With CE there is a greater degree of risk of human resources doing something in parallel that's not required, and therefore creating intellectual inventory which clutters up the working environment. Intellectual inventory is also created in serial design processes but, with a CE program where the goal is to halve or quarter product development lead times, the consequences could be far more taxing.

SMA.27.39   Possible Increase of Iterative Costs

In certain circumstances, CE can probably increase some of the design costs because it is an iterative process and some portions of the work will have to be redone as better ways are found to configure the product and as manufacturing discovers the need for changes in product design to enhance manufacturability. There is a slight possibility that one can go overboard in iterations, especially during early phases, thereby taking more time than necessary.

SMA.27.40   Errors May Build Up

There is a concern that one can go overboard and engage in more simultaneity than necessary. As more and more key activities which lie on the critical path are done in parallel, there may be no slack time left. There are more risks of committing errors. It may take valuable time away from key activities to correct errors, leading to the possibilities that corners will be cut, and overall quality of the end product may suffer.

Dr. Biren Prasad, Sr. Engineering Consultant, EDS
General Motors Corp., Warren, Mich.
also Managing Editor
Concurrent Engineering: Research & Applications (CERA),
W. Bloomfield, Mich.

Chapter 28
Managing Solid Modeling Data

Joel N. Orr
President
Orr Associates International

Solid Modeling (SM) data differs from other computer files in two important ways: it is extensive and, generally, mission-critical. Installed in its proper role, an SM system contains the central information of the organization: the geometry of its products. All other information refers to the solid model.

Looking at it another way, however, SM data is simply data. The usual data processing needs and precautions can be profitably applied to it. In this chapter, we touch upon the main concerns of managing SM data.

28.1 Maintaining Standards

Not all SM systems verify objects as solids or check them in other ways. It is important that standards be maintained if parts are to be reused. Problems caused by imperfect models will propagate throughout the manufacturing process—especially if electronic communications with customers and suppliers are in use.

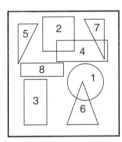 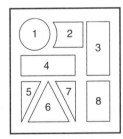

FIGURE 28.1 Uniform standards and procedures throughout an organization will assist in proper data management and in troubleshooting problems.

With a growing number of organizations desiring to share engineering and manufacturing data, there has emerged a need for standard file formats. The Initial Graphics Exchange Standard (IGES) and Product Data Exchange using STEP (PDES) have been refined as the generally accepted formats. IGES deals only with geometry, and is widely used and well understood (see Chap. 21). PDES contains considerably more information, and is only now beginning to be applied, with government agency encouragement (see Chap. 22).

28.2 Component Libraries

Unlike internal drawing objects, which are generally tied in by their geometry to a particular drawing and are hence difficult to reuse, solid models are very much like the objects they represent. It is there-

FIGURE 28.2 An off-the-shelf library of standard parts are modeled once and reused many times as needed. Database size is kept to a minimum because the component model is an instance of the model stored in the library.

fore possible and desirable to build component libraries to be "off the shelf" so that a part, once modeled, need not be modeled from scratch again.

Solid Modeling systems generally offer facilities for the management of component libraries. Naming conventions, access provisions, and viewing capabilities are peculiar to each system. But all facilities have this in common: they do not work automatically. Security, access, naming, and maintenance are performed by people operating under a set of procedures, much as they do under manual arrangements. The main difference is that a single person manages much more data in the computer environment than in the manual environment, so the cost of a mistake in a computerized situation is much higher than in a manual one. That is why procedures and standards are particularly important.

How these libraries are organized and how they are searched will determine their utility. If a designer is trying to determine if a given kind of component already exists, finding the class of component must be made easier than designing a new one. Otherwise, designers will not be motivated to use existing components.

There are many ways in which such components can be indexed and organized. At one extreme, complete group technology classification schemes can be applied (see Chap. 25); at the other, simply being able to list and search names and associated comment fields may suffice if the library is small. Intelligent consideration during the planning phase will yield great productivity benefits in the use of the component library.

28.3   Database Organization

The nature of assemblies conforms nicely to hierarchical data structures. Many SM systems are implicitly hierarchical, in fact. Even at the graphics-library level, hierarchies have been implemented in support of assembly-type structures, as in PHIGS, the Programmers Hierarchical Interactive Graphics Standard, or HOOPS, the commercial Hierarchical Object-Oriented Programming System.

But hierarchies can be very constraining because, in them, each "child" can have only one "parent." So, for large assemblies, multiple copies of a part are often required. Network-structure databases overcome this limitation, with many-to-many associations permitted; but, for various technical reasons, they are not popular.

28.3.1   Relational Databases

Relational databases, which have tables as their units of structure, have become very popular in commercial computing environments. Most SM systems have interfaces to one or more relational database management systems such as ORACLE® or INGRES®.

28.3.2 Object-Oriented Database Management Systems (OODBMS)

Software design in general is going in the direction of objects. Object-oriented programming and databases are becoming increasingly popular, and with good reason.

Programming before objects was like building an apartment building. Object-oriented programming resembles the construction of a residential subdivision. Think about the differences between a 10-story apartment building with 10 apartments on each floor and a development with 100 individual houses. The apartment building has centralized utilities.

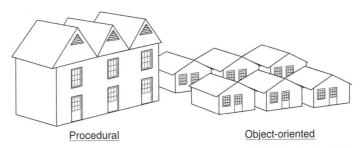

Procedural   Object-oriented

FIGURE 28.3 Comparing procedural to object-oriented programming is like comparing an apartment building to a residential subdivision. A procedural program has central services and utilities while an object-oriented program consists of self-sufficient units.

The development is more expensive to construct than the apartment building because each house has its own utilities and more walls per dwelling unit. In the apartment building, units share walls, and the ceiling of one level is the floor of the next.

On the other hand, adding a dwelling unit to the apartment building is difficult and expensive, while an additional house in the development costs no more, in principle, than any of the first hundred.

Another way of comparing procedural and object-oriented programs: Procedural methods require the programmer to immediately become involved in implementation details; object-oriented techniques encourage the programmer to think about what needs to be done rather than how to do it—the creation of a good model of the problem is paramount. Procedural programs are verb-oriented; object-oriented programs focus more on nouns.

A Short Course

Here is a very short course in object-oriented programming. Objects are grouped into classes and have methods associated with them; an object belonging to a class is said to be an *instance* of that class. Such systems are also *event-driven;* all actions are the result of *events,* such as mouse-clicks and key entry. Events generate *messages,* which activate objects. For example, *mouse-click* could generate a message that would activate a method associated with a *button* object in a graphical user interface program.

To be formally considered *object-oriented* (a term developed at Xerox's Palo Alto Research Center along with the first object-oriented language, SmallTalk®), a programming environment must support four behaviors:

1. *Inheritance:* New objects in a class "inherit" the characteristics of the class—although those characteristics can be individually modified by the programmer.
2. *Encapsulation:* Objects contain both data and methods—behaviors that are triggered under certain conditions.
3. *Information hiding:* An encapsulation in which certain details are not visible; for example, when you think of a car you don't think of all its components, or necessarily how it works.
4. *Polymorphism:* The ability of a single message to "mean" different things to different objects.

Programming in an object-oriented environment consists of the creation of classes of objects that will collaborate to produce the desired effects. Debugging object-oriented programs can be very simple or terrifyingly complex, depending on how well they are written.

Object-oriented programming is not harder than procedural programming, but it is very different; many programmers find it difficult to "unlearn" the procedural approach. "The object-based approach promises to make software easier to reuse, refine, test, maintain, and extend," says Brian Wilkerson of Apple Computer. "But simply implementing an application in an object-based language does not guarantee these benefits. They can only be achieved if the implementation is based on a sound object-based design."

Enhancements

Adding capabilities to properly designed object-oriented programs is much easier than enhancing procedural programs, for many of the same reasons that it is easier to add another house to a development than to add an apartment to an apartment building. Houses and objects are largely self-contained; apartment buildings and procedural programs are completely determined by their original plans.

The qualities of object-oriented programs make possible the creation of software components—pieces of code that can be used in many programs with little integration effort. It is this promise more than any other that has attracted adherents to object-oriented programming.

As mentioned previously, OODBMS store items as objects, rather than hierarchically associated records or rows in tables. Thus, new data types (classes) can be added at any time, without affecting the preexisting structure or methods.

OODBMS Topology

The topology of the object metaphor—the way in which its components are interconnected—is very simple; in fact, relational and hierarchical structures can be emulated or embedded in it. The self-contained nature of objects is responsible for this strength.

Moreover, this topology is well suited for implementation in client-server networks, which represent an important trend in engineering systems. Like such networks, OODBMS are extensible and modular; they can grow or shrink to adapt to new demands.

The power of objects is in their robustness, extensibility, flexibility, and modularity. And, for SM, there is the additional benefit of a natural mapping between the solid models and the objects of an object-oriented database.

28.4 Network Considerations

While a tutorial on network structures is beyond the scope of this book, it is useful to note that the data volumes induced by SM files affect different types of networks in different ways. In peer-to-peer network arrangements, which are common in small installations, data flows only between pairs of computers, not on a network at large; thus, volumes are not cumulative. But in ring- or bus-topology networks, all of the data traverses all of the network wires, so quantities are aggregated.

Product Data Management (PDM)

SMA.28.1 PDM Is Imperative

A good product data management (PDM) system for controlling and maintaining the database of SM information is imperative. Many of today's systems link a database module such as Informix®, Oracle®, or Ingres® with their modeling software via a user interface. These systems can be tedious and difficult to use if caution is not used in their initial implementation.

SMA.28.2 Who Will Benefit Most?

Companies that create small lines of similar products stand to benefit the most from PDM systems. Some of today's PDM systems handle individual parts well but fail to address the needs of companies utilizing large assemblies.

Kevin P. Alexander, CAD/CAM/CAE System Administrator
Littleford Day, Inc., Florence, Ky.

**Product Data
Management (PDM)**
(Continued)

SMA.28.3   A PDM Assessment

The effective implementation of a PDM solution starts with an assessment of the enterprise legacy and needs. This assessment should focus on the business processes, the people, and the technology in order to optimize the current processes and prepare the environment for a successful implementation of an integrated product development solution.

Michael Legros, PDM Marketing Manager
Digital Equipment Corp., Marlboro, Mass.

SMA.28.4   Nine Things PDM Can Do

1. PDM can manage SM part files through the entire development, release, and sustaining phases of a project.

2. PDM can relate files by project. SM analysis files can be linked to their SM part files.

3. PDM keeps SM part files in single location throughout the life of the product. It controls the ownership of the file.

4. PDM can be set up to require approvals before revision or release.

5. PDM can automatically notify a group whenever a change (or request for a change) is made.

6. PDM can force geometry file names to be revised with each change.

7. PDM can automatically archive all changed files daily.

8. PDM allows down rev files to be retrieved instantly.

9. PDM does not allow down rev files to be changed after they are released.

Howard W. Stolz, Product Designer
Sun Microsystems, Mountain View, Calif.

SMA.28.5   Knowledgeable Assets

A person knowledgeable in database terminology and structure will be a valuable asset during this time of implementation. Some companies may be able to use a person from the MIS department to eliminate the need to hire outside help. Consulting is also another option available from many software vendors and third-party consulting firms.

SMA.28.6   Attributes

The PDM system must be configured to allow designers to define key attributes for future retrieval of parts. The attributes should provide a logical grouping of components to reduce the shear number of parts that must be sifted through to find a desired one. Designers must adhere to the procedure of assigning good values to attributes without feeling they are wasting valuable design time. Supply default values wherever possible to reduce the amount of data input. These attributes can also be used to create the necessary bills of material for production control purposes. The download of the bills of material to the company's MRP system can be done electronically to reduce the exchange of paper.

SMA.28.7   If PDM Is Not Used

If a PDM system is not be used, the system administrator must use directory structures to logically separate components or projects. Each designer can have project directories listed under his or her login directory. The designer then places all project-related files in the appropriate subdirectory.

(Continued)

**Product Data
Management (PDM)**
(Continued)

SMA.28.8   For Multiple Users

If access is required by multiple users, a project directory with a login known by the appropriate users can be created. Utilize a server, if at all possible, to centralize the storage location of files. The type of database management implemented may prove to be the most important decision impacting long-term success of the SM system.

Kevin P. Alexander, CAD/CAM/CAE System Administrator
Littleford Day, Inc., Florence, Ky.

**Network
Considerations**

SMA.28.9   Network Bandwidth

SM data tends to be more voluminous than that of simple drawings, so network bandwidth can become a constraint in an intense modeling environment. This is a factor that must be taken into account in the design of the network. Estimates of average model sizes should be used to gauge the amount of network traffic that will appear under normal working conditions.

SMA.28.10   Networking Voice and Video

As voice and video become more widely used in conjunction with solid models, the demands on networks will rise precipitously. Network planners should be careful not to underestimate the medium- and long-term requirements in this area when planning capital-intensive network infrastructures.

Needed

SMA.28.11   Database Editing

Most SM systems do not provide a good set of tools to guide you through the process of deleting and/or compacting the SM database. Some sort of a graphical tree representation of the relationships of the operations would be helpful.

A technique that could reduce this problem is the frequent use of the UNDO capability. Instead of keeping all your trial-and-error operations, UNDO the undesired operations as soon as you evaluate them and decide that they will not work or are unwanted. This will keep the database size to a minimum on most SM systems.

SMA.28.12   UNDO Applications

Some SM systems that provide full UNDO capabilities still regenerate all undone operations when a parametric edit is performed. Also, some SM systems allow you to delete operations and objects, but they never actually remove them from the database.

George E. Mock, Member Technical Staff
AT&T Network Cable Systems, Norcross, Ga.

SMA.28.13   Information Hooks

SM systems should provide hooks into knowledge bases, expert systems, databases, and other specialized software. Uses include:

1. Design-rule checking
2. Cost estimating for material and labor
3. Design-alternative analysis
4. Planning and scheduling
5. Project-status reporting

(Continued)

Needed
(*Continued*)

6. Procurement

7. Regulation compliance

8. Object linkage to various external corporate databases

9. Process hazards and operability analysis

10. Process safety management

SMA.28.14   Database Searches

SM systems should allow comprehensive database searches via multiple criteria. For example, in plant design, it should be able to answer questions such as: "What pipelines are constructed of 316 stainless steel?" "How many are there?" "How many pressure vessels have a capacity over 5000 gallons?" "When were they purchased?" "What did they cost?"

Brian Ruuska, CAD/CAE Applications Engineer
3M Company, St. Paul, Minn.

Good to Know

SMA.28.15   Smart Part Libraries

If your SM system allows the attachment of attributes to a solid object or face, use of these attributes can let you build "smart" part libraries. This gives the ability to create programs that will automatically fill out a bill of material and to create detail views and layouts of each solid in an assembly and place them on the proper layer. These attributes can also be used for cost and productability programs.

Richard A. St. Arnauld, Sr. Tool Design Engineer
Pratt & Whitney Aircraft Div. of UTC, West Palm Beach, Fla.

SMA.28.16   SM Database Management Tips

1. Do not allow multiple copies of an SM part to exist. Allow only one version of an SM part file to be edited at a time.

2. Create layouts by inserting parts. Initially, a layout contains all the parts in a project. As soon as possible, write out all the parts as separate files and insert or "view" them back into the layout as necessary.

Howard W. Stolz, Product Designer
Sun Microsystems, Mountain View, Calif.

SMA.28.17   Using Alphanumeric Terminals

Object-level data should be accessible from nongraphic alphanumeric terminals. Not all users of the project data need graphical capability. Not all companies or departments can afford high-end graphic workstations.

SMA.28.18   Data Access Management

SM systems should provide multiuser access facilities to manage the project database within work groups and across disciplines. This improves communications and establishes the manner in which project data will be shared. Access management should address the extent of sharing based on such concepts as geographical areas, process systems, or design discipline. In addition, data access management should address the following:

(*Continued*)

Good to Know
(Continued)

1. Networked environment management with regard to work groups

2. Database partitioning for multiuser access and cross-functional data sharing

3. Management of change: How does a design change affect the designs produced by others in the work group? How is the change communicated?

4. Cross-functional data sharing: How does each member of a work group view the team's data during a given work session? Each work session should provide a consistent view of the project.

5. Remote access: How do remote users access the project? The SM system should provide for remote dial-in capabilities.

Brian Ruuska, CAD/CAE Applications Engineer
3M Company, St. Paul, Minn.

SMA.28.19   Data Links

Look for ways to link SM data to internal or external (to the SM system) management tools such as spreadsheets (see Fig. 28.4). Such tools allow the manipulation of large amounts of data from a single interface and are particularly useful for the production (as needed) of a family of similar parts.

Don LaCourse, President
The Solid Modeling ExChange, Algood, Tenn.

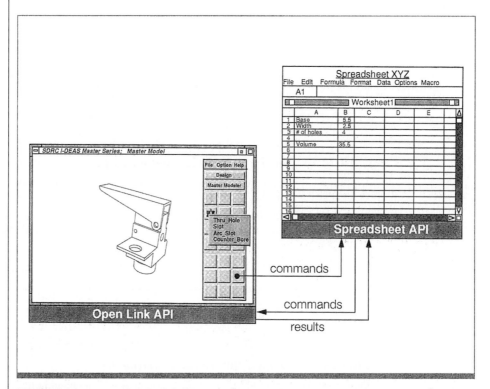

FIGURE 28.4   In this example, I-DEAS Open Link® is used to link a spreadsheet with the I-DEAS® SM database. You can modify values in the spreadsheet which directly update the solid model. The resulting changes are then fed back to the spreadsheet. *(Courtesy of SDRC, Structural Dynamics Research Corporation.)*

Section 6

In the Field

Chapter 29

Solid Modeling at Sony Corporation

Seiji Ito
Manager
Planning and Control Dept.
Management and Engineering Information Systems Div.
Sony Corporation

Hajime Ikeda
Assistant Manager
Design Innovation Dept.
Management and Engineering Information Systems Div.
Sony Corporation

Sony Corporation is one of the world's leading manufacturers of video and audio equipment, televisions, displays, semiconductors, computers, and information-related systems, such as micro floppy disk systems. Keenly aware of the interrelated nature of software and hardware, Sony is bolstering its presence in the music and image-based software markets through Sony Music Entertainment, Inc., and Sony Pictures Entertainment. A firm commitment to research and development has helped Sony build a reputation as a pacesetter in the electronic equipment industry. Having also garnered recognition as one of Japan's most international corporations by manufacturing in the markets where its products are sold, Sony is expanding its other corporate functions, such as management and R&D, on a global basis.

29.1 Innovation

In recent years, the manufacturing industry in Japan has become intensely competitive, especially in the electronics and automotive markets. To address tough issues such as faster development cycles and diversified customer needs, Japanese manufacturers are moving away from traditional engineering methodologies.

Sony Corporation acknowledges that innovation in engineering and the way companies do business will help manufacturers reduce time-to-market challenges. Undoubtedly, traditional engineering environments have limited companies from meeting customer demands. Today, with the availability of lower-cost computers, advanced CAD/CAE/CAM software, and an innovative approach to new product development, manufacturers are capable of delivering high-quality, low-cost products more quickly than ever before.

As Fig. 29.1 shows, there are two elements to this innovative approach to new product development: added value and development efficiency. Sony is committed to applying a computer-aided engineering (CAE) approach to the enhancement of these elements concurrently.

Innovation in manufacturing can be accomplished through computer integrated manufacturing (CIM), which maintains a systematic relationship with design innovation, creating a process that implements engineering expertise through CAD/CAE/CAM technology. Sony plans to build a new-generation design environment that centers on 3D Solid Modeling (SM) design, simulation, and test analysis techniques. Figure 29.2 (see color insert) shows a typical solid model developed at Sony.

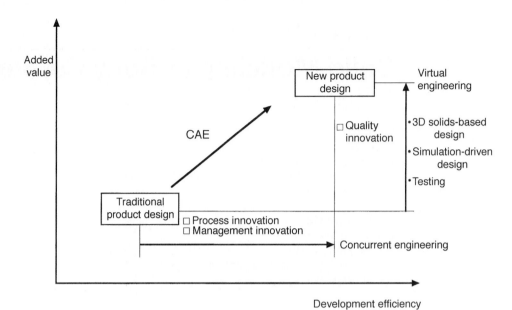

FIGURE 29.1 CAE design innovation. As compared to traditional product development, it is necessary to develop a more-value-added product early in the design process. Innovation in the quality and design process, concurrent engineering, SM, simulation, and testing are necessary to meet CAE goals. *(Courtesy of Sony Corporation.)*

29.2   Design Process

29.2.1   Traditional Design Process

Figure 29.3 illustrates the flow of information in the traditional design process. As you can see, the following stages in new product design are occurring consecutively.

1. Product planning
2. Industrial design
3. Concept design
4. Basic design
5. Detailed design
6. Evaluation of functionality by building a prototype
7. Prototype testing
8. Reentering results in the basic or detailed design several times as required
9. Release to production

Many problems have been discovered in our traditional design process, including the following:

1. There are no real models within processes from product planning through detailed design.
2. Lack of early visualization initiates low confidence levels when the design is still in the conceptual stage.
3. Many times, there is a big difference between what designers imagine the design to be and the finished product. This includes not only aesthetics, but also mechanics, packaging, and the manufacturing processes involved.
4. Expensive physical prototypes are built and tested in order to gain a better understanding of the design.
5. Problems often occur further downstream when drawings are created due to discrepancies between what was originally conceived and what really exists. These discrepancies are due to the degree of difficulty in designing complex shapes and components.

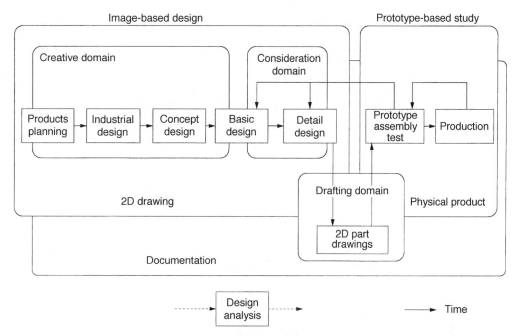

FIGURE 29.3 Traditional design process. The traditional design process sequentially proceeds from product planning, industrial design, concept design, basic design, and detail design to prototype evaluation. There are actions required between processes based on the results of each. *(Courtesy of Sony Corporation.)*

6. When evaluating prototype and test performances based on physical models, it is difficult to capture and document important criteria as well to solve problems that arise.

7. The analysis process is performed separately by analytical engineers (see Fig. 29.3). Although helpful, the analysis results never fully reflect the current state of the design.

29.2.2   New Design Process Based on CAE

It is CAE that helps solve the preceding problems and enables design, process, quality, and management innovation to meet the needs of a changing engineering environment.

This innovation means adjusting to a concurrent engineering (CE) approach to new product development. Figure 29.4 shows Sony's new design process based on CAE and how the performance of various product design stages concurrently eliminates the visual gap between what is perceived as the design and the actual product. This is especially true in early design when product planning and concept design can enable engineers to develop a product efficiently within a shorter cycle time. By interacting concurrently, engineering teams can investigate a range of implications that impact mass production of a new product.

CAE increases the initial quality of a new product by integrating product data definition from the design to prototype stages. This is accomplished by utilizing a single 3D solid model for analysis—such as finite element modeling, test analysis, simulations, and rapid prototyping techniques.

29.3   Case Study Application

Application: The development of a Rotating Drum Evaluation Device (RDED) for Digital Audio Tape (DAT) equipment assembly.

It is very important during the development, design, and manufacture of videocassette recorders (VCRs) and digital audio tape (DAT) equipment to show how the recording and subsequent playback of signals for picture and sound are performed. The rotating drum (also referred to as the *rotating head, rotating head cylinder,* and *rotating head drum*) is the device which performs the recording and playback

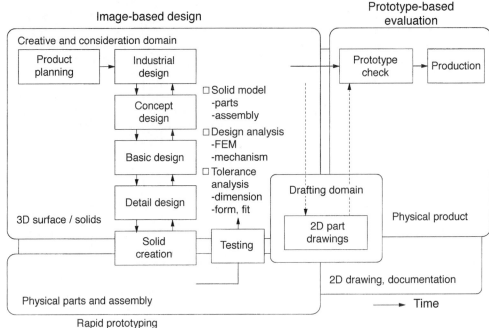

FIGURE 29.4 The new design process based on CAE. All key development processes are performed in parallel. Notice that assembly modeling, analysis, and rapid prototyping are all performed early when a product's performance and quality are more easily influenced. *(Courtesy of Sony Corporation.)*

of these signals to a tape while rotating. Because the rotating drum is the key contributor to the performance of a VCR and DAT, quality management is extremely important. Therefore, the rotating drum's performance must be evaluated as it is incorporated into the VCR or DAT mechanism assembly.

Accordingly, the RDED must be equal to the mechanism of the actual product for proper performance evaluation (see Fig. 29.5). In other words, it is necessary to confirm the characteristics which satisfy the specifications when performing the recording and playback of the signal in the actual tape. Because the recording pattern of the VCR and DAT signal is written obliquely on a tape, the tape path system of the evaluation device must be designed as a tape moving correctly and obliquely against the rotating drum.

The RDED and the tape path system become very complicated 3D SM structures because they are designed obliquely and must avoid any interference among mechanical parts. The schematic diagram in Fig. 29.6 illustrates the RDED system.

29.3.1 Objective

The objective is to develop a device that will evaluate rotating drum characteristics by measuring the recording and playback signal within one minute during production.

This test device will also enable engineers to perform lapping (grinding of the drum) at the optimal tape-to-drum head contact shape. This helps guarantee that the characteristics of the rotating drum will meet desired specifications.

29.3.2 Rotating Drum Evaluation Device (RDED)

The characteristic results of the RDED are processed and evaluated by the host computer. The resulting graphical information is judged GOOD or NO GOOD as compared to the measurement of elec-

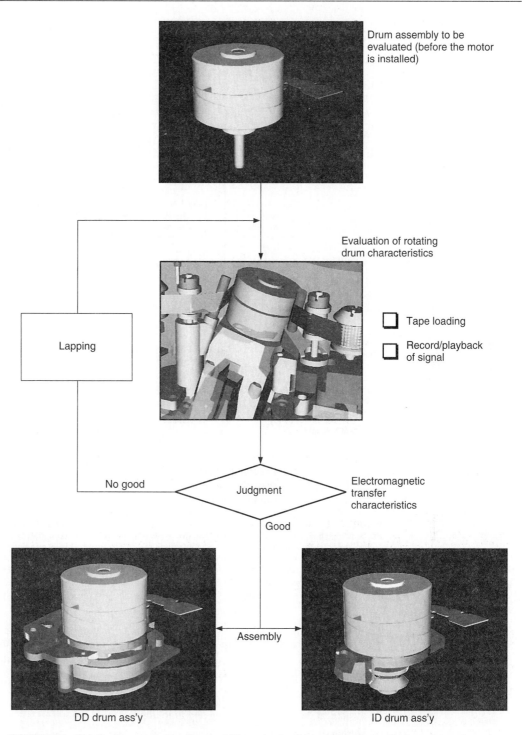

Drum assembly to be evaluated (before the motor is installed)

Evaluation of rotating drum characteristics

☐ Tape loading

☐ Record/playback of signal

Lapping

No good

Judgment

Electromagnetic transfer characteristics

Good

Assembly

DD drum ass'y

ID drum ass'y

FIGURE 29.5 Rotating drum evaluation flowchart. The evaluation drum consists of two cylinders: one rotating and one fixed. Unlike the final drum assembly, the evaluation drum configuration does not incorporate a motor. Testing the evaluation drum includes measuring electromagnetic transfer characteristics obtained by tape signal recording and playback under the same mounting conditions as actual product use. The drum assemblies judged as "good" are completed for final drum assembly. The drum assemblies judged as "no good" require reevaluation after modification. *(Courtesy of Sony Corporation.)*

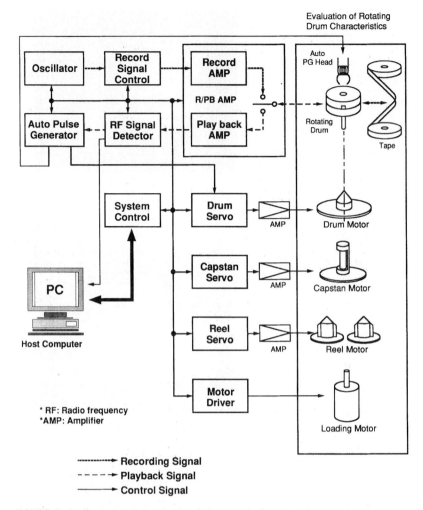

FIGURE 29.6 Rotating drum evaluation device system diagram. A host computer processes the control and signal tests conducted during drum evaluation. Other host computer functions include: generating recording signal waves, controlling signal currents, and inspecting playback signal waves. These refer to the signal system. For the mechanism system, the host computer controls each motor and the start position on the tape for evaluating signal recording and playback. *(Courtesy of Sony Corporation.)*

tromagnetic transfer characteristics and measurement data obtained under the same conditions as mounting the rotating drum and recording/playback components of an actual assembly.

Therefore, it is extremely important that the same issues be addressed in the design and development of the RDED as in the actual assembly. These issues include:

1. Geometric design of the tape path system
2. Structural design of the loading and unloading of tape
3. Design of tape drive system
4. Part mounting without interferences

The following summarizes the RDED specifications:

1. Uses a digital audio tape (DAT) cassette tape
2. Has a tape loading mechanism which mounts a DAT cassette
3. The ability to evaluate subassembly characteristics without a drum motor
4. Has an auto pulse generator (PG) which enables the test device to select a PG setting that connects the drum motor topology servo (lock) automatically
5. Has an adjustable tape path mechanism

6. Must perform evaluations at a tape-to-drum contact angle of 182° in the tape path mechanism
7. Drum loading mechanism allows for fast drum contact
8. Time frame for a characteristic evaluation: within one minute
9. Two drum rotation modes: 2000 and 4000 rpm

29.3.3 Tape Path System and Feedback Loop

The design of the tape path system of the RDED begins with the use of an optimized design tool called Tape11. Tape11 automates the following procedures for tape path system design:

1. Selection of rotating drum and tape specifications
2. Selection of tape loading type
3. Arrangement of the tape path configuration elements
4. Calculation of the relationship of geometric position for the configuration elements in a 4×4 (4 lines × 4 rows) matrix operation
5. Review and evaluate the calculated tape path system
   a. Balance, distance between configuration elements, and the package size of the tape path system evaluated by numerical values
   b. Manufacturing feasibility
6. GOOD or NO GOOD judgment

In the tape path system, the optimized design solution will be obtained by the preceding selection process (steps 1 through 4) and iteration process (steps 3 through 6). We call this iteration process the *feedback loop* (see Fig. 29.7). In the traditional design process, physical prototypes were to be created in step 6 in order to judge the 3D structure for possible interference conditions.

Tape11 is used by designers throughout the entire tape path layout design. The data derived from this process allows the input of numerical values to alter the design interactively, revise the 2D layout review drawing to visualize the results in real time, and to react to it. Tape11 has all the necessary capability to automatically generate solid models from the final design data.

Solid Modeling is especially helpful for the concept and evaluation of the tape path system and for designing the feedback loop for optimization. In the past these processes were executed separately. There were problems, including the inefficient use of design data between each process. Additionally, the processes are very complicated and it is difficult to express the results of the matrix operations with only a mental image. The design data includes not only the relationship between the design geometry, but also complex 3D orientations.

Today, the use of computers, SM and related software, design expertise, and the development of 2.5D design algorithms have improved design, increased efficiency, and improved manufacturability.

29.3.4 Avoiding Interference Problems

Solid Modeling allows Sony engineers to avoid many interference issues in the early design stages of the tape path system, as in the case of the rotating drum evaluation system. Mechanical interference problems were recognized as a major concern early in the development of this device. SM helped significantly in avoiding interference conditions, especially for the structure and configuration around the rotating drum.

29.3.5 Checking Manufacturing with Solid Modeling

In the case of the RDED it was necessary to review whether we could actually manufacture the device, even though we could visually create it as an idea. We could avoid failure beforehand by determining

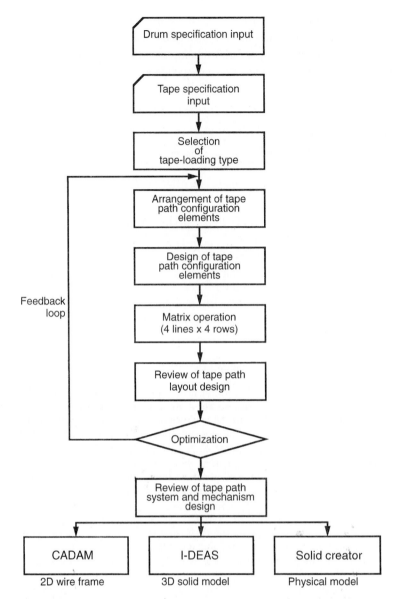

FIGURE 29.7 Tape path system design flowchart. The design of the tape path system starts with input from the drum and tape media specifications. After design specifications are approved (loading type and tape path configuration elements), the geometric design data is generated through a matrix operation (for visualizing a design review). The design is evaluated repeatedly to determine opportunities for optimization. This data is used for reviewing a detailed mechanism design as a 2D wireframe model, 3D solid model, and/or (when required) a rapid prototype model. *(Courtesy of Sony Corporation.)*

whether the parts themselves met functional requirements at the design concept stage. To accomplish this task, we checked every section of the solid model using the continuous model-clipping functionality without machining the parts.

29.3.6 Conclusions

For the development of the RDED, we have been able to reduce optimization time for the feedback loop and improve design quality. We can also avoid interference problems in the design review stage, and develop a design that meets functional specifications early in the development cycle.

29.4　Solid Modeling Payoffs

The tape path system design illustrated in Sec. 29.3 is a typical application of 3D SM design at Sony Corporation. This technology can be used in a range of consumer electronics, such as VCRs (8mm, Beta, VHS, etc.), commercial VCRs (Omega, Beta-Cam SP, Digital, etc.), and audio equipment such as digital audio tape systems.

Similar to the tape path system design, Sony engineers integrate their 3D designs using SM, FEM, and modal test analysis. Sony has applied experience from previous SM applications to disk systems design and has obtained significant success. Currently, disk systems products include CDs, MOs, and VD. Soon, other products will follow, such as displays (TVs, computer monitors, etc.), video cameras (Handycams, digital VTRs, high-resolution VTRs, etc.), and optical products.

It is somewhat difficult to show numerical performance results for these applications. However, in a single prototype it took 30 percent less time to mold a single part with a complex shape. This success is a direct result of designing with SM. These results are significant because it takes approximately 1.5 months and several million yen to produce one prototype. As SM data defines our products and is used consistently from design through manufacturing, benefits will dramatically increase.

29.5　Future Goals with Solid Modeling

Sony's next-generation design environment will promote virtual and concurrent engineering using SM in a networked environment. It is within this realm that all can commonly share knowledge-based technical information and the know-how of individuals, groups, and entire companies.

We define the integrated design concept in this new environment as advanced computer-aided engineering (ACAE). We also define virtual engineering, the core of ACAE, as the design concept that drives new product development, using SM throughout the process and eliminating the need for prototype-building as much as possible.

Our next-generation ACAE environment consists of the following elements, as shown in Fig. 29.8. (Note that the numbers shown in parentheses following each item refer to those locations in Fig. 29.8.)

1. Design integration environment by engineering workstations (EWS) (31)
   a. Multiapplications / single platform
      (1) Mainframe applications (2, 3, 4, 5, 6, 7, 8, 18)
      (2) Workstation applications (14, 15, 16, 17, 19, 23)
   b. Integration of mechanical, electrical, and administrative engineering systems
      (1) Mechanical applications (4, 7, 8, 14, 15, 17)
      (2) Electrical applications (22, 27)
      (3) Administrative applications (2, 3, 5, 6, 8)
2. Network environment (1, 24)
   a. Common ownership of technical information (20, 25, 21, 26, 22, 27)
   b. Easy access to information among engineers (23, 28)
3. Solid creation rapid prototyping (RP) system environment
   a. Network RP system (19, 29, 30)

Applications

SMA.29.1　Related Issues

In recent years, the function of SM has been greatly enhanced from its use for visualization of 2D design to detailed 3D design. There are, however, various related issues that need attention, such as implementing SM throughout an engineering organization, training 2D CAD operators to become proficient SM operators, acquiring additional computer memory, accelerating computer response times, and justifying additional hardware and software costs.

SMA.29.2　Where Used

We propose the use of SM where its functionality can bring about the greatest productivity: at the early stages of product design. SM is a big advantage over traditional 2D design, as well as an effective tool for showing designs with analytical elements, complex 3D shapes and layouts.

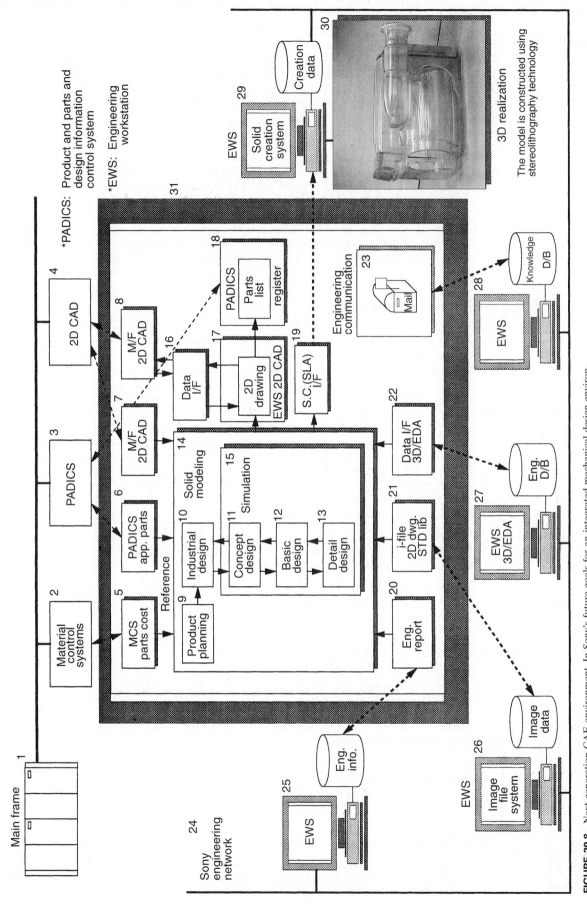

FIGURE 29.8 Next-generation CAE environment. In Sony's future goals for an integrated mechanical design environment, designers will use various applications based on a network infrastructure without reference to mainframes or workstations. Communication and the common use of information among designers is given top priority. (*Courtesy of Sony Corporation.*)

Optimum System Configuration

SMA.29.3   Exceed Minimum Requirements

Currently, most SM applications operate on a UNIX workstation environment. In many cases, hardware vendors list only the minimum specifications required, which typically are not satisfactory for optimal system performance, and capabilities that allow for efficient SM functionality.

SMA.29.4   Performance Resources

A workstation's performance depends on its central processing unit (CPU) speed as well as its random access memory (RAM) volume. Designers must also consider adequate hard disk space since many applications open temporary files during a modeling session.

SMA.29.5   RAM Disks

Applications that create temporary files on the system's hard disk during a modeling session and access graphic data from it can sometimes dramatically improve performance by preparing a RAM disk for the temporary file system.

File Management

SMA.29.6   File Directories

It is good engineering practice to create product file directories. By selecting a product file directory as the working directory, one can avoid losing files or having numerous files exist under the same or similar names.

SMA.29.7   Backup Files

It is highly recommended that a backup should be made of system and data files as often as possible while designing with any SM or CAD system. Many SM programs consume vast amounts of computer resources. A crash (internal system error) can occur at any time due to external system or internal application errors. Therefore, we recommend that designers back up files prior to operations that involve large loads and consume extended amounts of CPU time.

Data Management

SMA.29.8   Naming Files

One neglected area in the SM design process is naming files. It is best to assign file names that are easy to understand and to remember since the SM process can generate numerous files. A separate log of file names is recommended. It is especially helpful that the file names be understood by everyone on a project team.

SMA.29.9   Managing Objects

When designing parts in SM, it is rare to design only one object. Generally, it is more realistic to work with tens or hundreds of objects. It is best if these objects are designed and managed using assembly modeling and object library techniques so that the engineering team can quickly search for and use the required objects at the necessary time. (See Chap. 11.)

3D Orientation

SMA.29.10   Local Coordinate Systems

Some SM systems can perform assembly operations without considering a coordinate system. However, a concept of coordinate systems is convenient for designers who will migrate from 2D CAD to 3D SM. Local coordinate systems aid in the development of complex shapes by handling a parts coordinate definition as opposed to the global coordinate system when needed. For example, a local coordinate system allows an operator to set up an inclined coordinate system on the surface of the part. It helps to reduce the amount of modeling by knowing these functions beforehand.

(Continued)

3D Orientation
(Continued)

SMA.29.11 Orienting Objects

In the design process, much time is spent orienting multiple objects in a 3D environment. One effective means for orienting objects is utilizing a point-and-line method. Before arranging objects, create a point at the position where you plan to place an object. Then, create a line in the direction of orientation of the object.

By using these points and lines, operators can orient objects more easily. Moreover, it is easy to review values if the point is made a datum for the design of the object. Object orientation by absolute value input is not desirable because it is difficult to capture the value later, and also becomes an obstacle for intuitive operations.

It is always necessary for designers to capture the datum setup position of an object. The preceding orientation method will be effective especially when designers cannot get the information about a setup point from the object.

Display

SMA.29.12 Wireframe Displays

One issue facing designers who have migrated from a 2D CAD system is the significant increase in the amount of information displayed on the screen. Design data is typically displayed in 3D space as wireframe images. Working in this new 3D environment can be intimidating. It is only a matter of practice and time, however, until shape recognition will improve, especially with the supplemented use of shaded SM displays.

SMA.29.13 Shaded Displays

Many times, shading speed depends on the computer and graphics hardware speed. Displaying shaded images is much slower than when working with wireframe images. Consequently, it is very important to use wireframe and shading functionality properly to design efficiently. It is possible to conduct shading without specialized graphics hardware, but at significantly reduced performance.

SMA.29.14 Color Management

Designers can create an understandable model for design review by changing colors of objects for alternate functions as the parts are assembled and the design proceeds.

SMA.29.15 Display On/Off Functions

With an increased number of displayed objects, it can be difficult at times to select lines and points because of the overlap of objects. We recommend using the display on/off function for groups of objects. The on/off function makes the object you are currently working on clearer, and also improves the overall display speed. It is best to select and apply this function according to the state of a given design.

Systems Information

SMA.29.16 X-Windows System

Today's UNIX-based SM systems are compatible with the X-Window operating system standard, a multiwindow computing environment. If system resources permit, we use XBiff, Xclock, Xload, Xcalendar, talk, etc., and combine them with the underling UNIX environment. This makes it possible to build a more effective mechanical design environment.

SMA.29.17 Determining Machine Status

It is important to visually check the status of the computer during operations since SM consumes large amounts of CPU and related resources. Make it a routine to check at least the following:

1. Memory status

2. Guaranteed open hard disk space

3. Current CPU load

These items help decide whether the next operation can be executed efficiently. Most important, be cautious of available hard disk space to ensure that no errors occur during important operations and that your model is being saved properly.

Good to Know

SMA.29.18   Fillets and Chamfers

We do not recommend creating detailed fillets and chamfers at early stages of design. These shapes are not complicated, but the data contained in them can become quite large, which can slow computer performance and engineering productivity.

SMA.29.19   Less Is Good

Since many changes are anticipated early in the design process, it is much more efficient to design with less data and without detailed features until the design fundamentals are decided.

SMA.29.20   Feature Functions

For SM software lacking feature functions, boolean operations should be used frequently to define shapes. It is important that frequently used shapes are stored within component libraries for easy retrieval.

SMA.29.21   Optimization of Facets

Setting up facets will be a problem when using a polygonal or faceted-based modeler because the data becomes unwieldy and slows computer performance. There are trade-offs to be made between system performance and model accuracy when selecting default facet values.

Higher-level modelers also use facets to display surface and solid data even though the underlying geometry is mathematically correct. Trade-offs which involve model clarity and display speed are also to be made here.

SMA.29.22   Performance Evaluations

It is important during product development that actual performance evaluations be done on the software model. This significantly shortens design cycles and improves quality. The evaluation should be executed before drawings are created, when the design impacts 80 percent of manufacturing costs.

SMA.29.23   Management Reform

There is a need to reform the traditional management system from one that concentrates on drawing output to a new management style that facilitates design definition and analytical data evaluation.

SMA.29.24   Interference by Offset

Interference checking is an important factor in the design of complex 3D layouts. It is important to capture a gap clearance on oriented objects in 3D space. Generally, the dimension function is used for measuring the gap, but it is not easy to determine the shortest distance between faces in SM systems.

By offsetting geometry by the allowable gap clearance, one can easily recognize if the gap is acceptable. If surrounding objects interfere with your offset, your allowable gap has been violated. In many situations, measuring the actual distance between objects may not be necessary as long as allowable gaps are considered.

SMA.29.25   Hand Operations

It is important to clarify hand operations. For example, the right hand is typically used for drawing with the mouse or other peripheral, while the left hand selects functions.

Some SM systems require that the right hand draw and select functions. This hinders efficient model production because one is continuously returning to the menu for option selections then to the display for modeling. If the SM system has shortcut functions, they can be much more effective because the assignment of functions with keys within the range that the left hand can manage is made possible. *Example:* CRL + 1 = line function.

Suggestions for Further Reading

Seiji Ito, "How CAE Technology Is Changing Mechanism Development," *2nd Design Engineering Plaza,* Japan, 1992.

Jun Numata, "Product Design in the Age of Intellect: Virtual Engineering," *Conference of Japan Techno-economics Society,* Feb. 24 Japan, 1993.

Yukio Hasegawa et al., "What Is CIM?," *T.IEE Japan,* vol. 109-D, no. 3, 1989.

Shuhei Kuriyama, "Big Impact in the Manufacturing Industry: The Implementation of Solid Lithography," *CAD & CIM,* no. 26, 1991/5.

Hiroshi Yokoi et al., "The Status and Tendency of CIM," Hitachi Hyoron, 71(6), 1989.

Eijiro Tagami et al., "The Current and Future of Rapid Prototyping Techniques," *CAD & CIM,* no. 26, 1991/5.

Yoshinori Okada, "How to Build CIM," *CAD & CIM,* vol. 3, no. 1, 1989.

Yasuhiko Matsuoka, "The Method of Vacuum Forming," *CAD & CIM,* no. 26, 1991/5.

Wayne McClelland, "Concurrent Engineering for Mechanical Design," Structural Dynamics Research Corporation (SDRC), *Technical Management Seminar,* Japan, June 1991.

"Survival of the Fastest II—Streamlining Product Development with Simulation Tools," SDRC Japan K.K., 1991.

Virtual Product Development Engineered with Intergraph

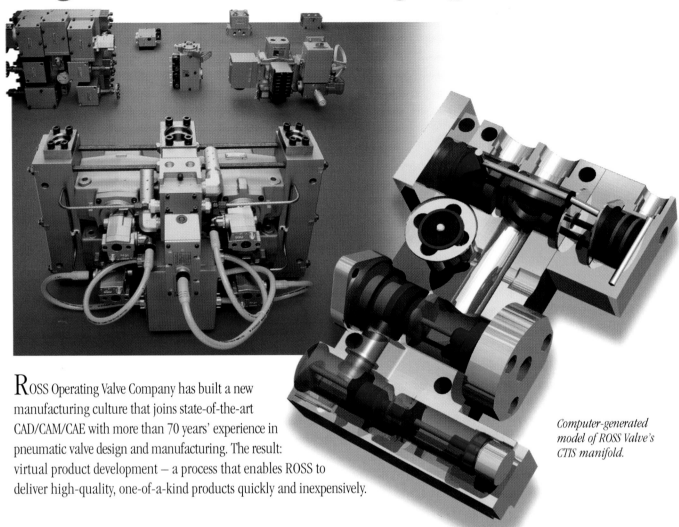

Computer-generated model of ROSS Valve's CTIS manifold.

Ross Operating Valve Company has built a new manufacturing culture that joins state-of-the-art CAD/CAM/CAE with more than 70 years' experience in pneumatic valve design and manufacturing. The result: virtual product development – a process that enables ROSS to deliver high-quality, one-of-a-kind products quickly and inexpensively.

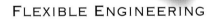

FLEXIBLE ENGINEERING

"Intergraph's Engineering Modeling System is a significant factor that enables us to combine design, manufacturing, and marketing into one holistic function," says ROSS's chief operating officer. "It allows us to use time as a competitive element. We can develop a unique design to customer specifications, and deliver a working prototype in as little as 72 hours."

MANUFACTURING INTEGRATION

Intergraph CAD/CAM/CAE software brings together more engineering tasks than any other concurrent engineering solution available. To find out how manufacturers worldwide are using integrated automation to re-engineer their product development processes, call 800-345-4856 and ask about our Virtual Product Development seminars.

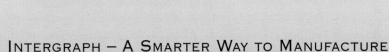

INTERGRAPH – A SMARTER WAY TO MANUFACTURE
For seminar information call 800-345-4856

INTERGRAPH

Solutions for the Technical Desktop
(CIRCLE READER SERVICE NO. 215)

Chapter 30

Solid Modeling at Volkswagen Automotive Group

Dr.-Ing. Peter Kellner
Dr.-Ing. Viet Vu-Han
Systems Analysts
Volkswagen Automotive Group

What is the relative importance of SM for a car manufacturer? When is it needed? Where are the difficulties of implementation? What are the benefits? What is recommended?

In 1981, these questions and others were addressed at Volkswagen. The following is a summary of our experiences with SM since this time.

One of the principal objectives in the car industry is to shorten the time it takes to get a new car design into production. Achieving this goal requires data continuity from concept design to the finished part. The research and development (R&D) division (Volkswagen's FE Division), begins a new car concept by developing a 3D computer model with all surface areas defined. The dies required for producing this new car are designed and manufactured in the production division. Experience has shown, however, that it is not sufficient to buy a computer, apply a CAD/CAM system and solve all problems that may arise.

As a rule, CAD/CAM systems are kept as general as possible because of the varied applications to which they may be put. Consequently, various steps must be taken if complex tasks are to be accomplished. The advantages of data processing as opposed to conventional and manual methods of work emerge only gradually due to the considerable initial input required by the system.

The first stage in reducing the amount of input required is to create parametric programs for specific applications. The designer enters the required parameters; then the computer calculates according to a fixed scheme and produces the result in a very short time. Standard parts can be easily retrieved in this way and incorporated into designs. These programs are effective and can be used in a variety of areas.

The next stage in reducing input is the use of a system in which the design and/or processing logic is stored and reused. With the use of an application system based on a 3D solid model, data can be included more rapidly and systematically with support from the system. This data can then be processed, extracted, and passed on in accordance with the specific requirements of production. This approach offers major advantages, particularly by saving considerable amounts of time during the process of creating new dies.

30.1 Company Background[1,2]

The Volkswagen Group consists of four independent companies: Volkswagen, Audi, Seat, and Skoda. In addition to these there are many other production, distributing, financial, and service-rendering companies within the group around the world. In the field of information systems, the Volkswagen Group is supported by its own division company, VW-GEDAS. With operations spanning the globe, the Volkswagen Group is today truly a European manufacturer, characterized by a division of market activities between the individual group companies.

Volkswagen Group spends approximately DM 2.5 billion annually on worldwide research and development and employs an R&D staff of approximately 12,300. The average number of employees is approximately 261,000. The group's investments remain at a high level totaling about DM 5.5 billion.

One aim of Volkswagen Group is to reinforce its position as a truly international enterprise in order to ensure that it will remain competitive in the next century, particularly in light of the opportunities offered by the Europe of the future. A few of the factors that will sharpen competition in the next decade are:

1. The emergence of Eastern Europe as a market and product base
2. Increased European and worldwide investment and no formal restraints on car imports into Europe in the near future
3. A probable shakeout among the big six European car makers
4. A necessity to develop "green" cars that are better for the environment, more efficient, and safer

These kinds of challenges place a high priority on innovative production processes. Time to market is a vital component for an automobile company's success, and SM is one of the efficient instruments used to reach our goal of achieving high quality and moving a new car from design concept approval to volume production in 32 months.

30.2   CAD/CAM Capability Review

If we look at the full range of mechanical design practices, beginning with conventional methods and finishing with CAD-style modeling, we have determined that only 3D surface and SM entails any notable benefits. The following benefits are included:

1. Opportunities to represent perspective views with concealed edges and, hence, 3D portrayal
2. Derivations of physical features such as weights, volumes, moments of inertia, or FEM calculations
3. The ability to obtain complete data continuity along the car body process chain

Volkswagen's body process chain includes the following segments:

1. Research and Development Division
   a. Design of the styling model
   b. Body design
   c. Proving center
2. Production Division
   a. Method planning
   b. Die design
   c. Work preparation and NC programming
   d. Model and template construction
   e. Machine tool center
   f. Workshop/tool construction and assembly
   g. Fitting/press shop and preparations for series operations

In principle, CAD/CAM data includes geometric and alphanumeric information. The geometric CAD information is generated on the basis of 3D surface area and solid models. Alphanumeric data, such as processing or structural information, has to be maintained concomitantly and allocated to the geometric objects. Design guidelines and standard parts must be taken into consideration. In some instances, these varied tasks cause conventional CAD applications to take as long as work performed on the drawing board. A forward-looking solution is the development of CAD systems which take a car manufacturer's specific requirements into account.

With the aim of shortening the time needed to develop a car, it was sought to accelerate die design using CAD systems. It is acknowledged today that SM entails major advantages for complicated tasks and is obviously preferable. We have determined that, for our applications, 2D CAD provides no significant advantages over drawing-board design work. The following aspects of our work may be cited as the disadvantages associated with 2D CAD design which have lead us to this conclusion.

1. The standard of work deteriorates because the focus of work is moved from a large drawing board to the small screen. In automotive design, our drawing boards can reach 2×5 meters in size.

2. An object has to be converted and drawn in at least three 2D views.

3. The use of 2D CAD data for NC programming or model construction is very limited.

The fundamental weakness of a conventional approach based on 2D drawings for complex objects lies in the fact that, having started with a 3D image of a design in one's mind, it is necessary to return indirectly to 2D drawings in order to produce the physical 3D object from them.

In addition to the benefits provided by CAD applications in data transmission, accuracy, and reproducibility, 3D SM has other advantages, which include:

1. Data consistency

2. Physically correct bodies are interlinked by means of solid theory (boolean) operations which supply consistent results

3. In visual terms, the design is enormously aided by representing geometric objects from every possible perspective and by creating intersections and views automatically.

4. The quality of the design is enhanced by utilizing specific functions during the modeling process; for example, by ascertaining the center of gravity of parts so that guide elements can be located (avoiding tilting) or by calculating weight so that transportation elements can be adequately dimensioned.

5. The specific characteristics of solid models make it possible to carry out further investigation, such as collision tests (e.g., for robot simulations, mechanical milling heads, and mechanization) and FEM calculations, etc.

The conventional 3D wireframe model will become less significant in the future due to its weaknesses in the representation area, particularly in the case of intersections.

30.3   Solid Modeling Applications

Since 1982 Volkswagen has employed Matra Datavision's EUCLID-IS® CAD/CAM and SM system for die design, 2.5D NC programming, and robot simulation. Over 100 SM terminals are currently operational, providing design support to over 150 operators, engineers, and managers. This CAD/CAM/CAE system operates on Digital Equipment Corporation (DEC) mainframe computers, terminals, and workstations using the VAX/VMS operating system, and on Silicon Graphics, Inc. (SGI) workstations with the UNIX operating system.

30.3.1   Die Design[3]

If a design is performed only interactively with the functions offered by an SM system, lengthy individual steps will be repeated and it will soon be obvious that the system's entire scope for automation is not yet being utilized. Variant or parametric programs can be regarded as a rapid solution. A further step is to create an administration system which provides designers with accompanying support during the design stage, ensuring that individual components adhere to design specifications. The need for design support has led to the development of the following on-line support systems, fully integrated as applications in EUCLID-IS®:

1. General Die Design System (AWK)

2. Large press dies (AWK-G)

3. Medium press dies (AWK-I)

4. Pressure cast dies (AWK-D)

5. Injection plastic mold dies (AWK-S)

Designers benefit from these integrated support applications during the design of dies for production components. During the design phase all standard features of EUCLID-IS® are available and complement such applications.

30.3.2 Part Transport Simulation

Automated sheet-metal processing has made it necessary for the manufactured parts to pass through a press and between presses under controlled conditions. The Simulation of Mechanization program (SPM), an application on EUCLID-IS®, simulates the various movements involved and supports not only press die design but also the layout, design, and production of the transport devices. AWK is used to prepare optimized layouts together with design and production data for the mechanization devices and relevant information on freedom of movement. Such information is represented in the form of path curves and "taboo" solids for die design and collision control.

30.3.3 Robotics

Benefits in collision control can be gained by utilizing SM for robot programming. The individual car components (e.g., body panels, support frames) are stationed at various locations along the assembly line. Here they are fastened or welded together into assemblies or to the car frame structure. The piling and withdrawing of the closely packed, large, and heavy sheet-metal parts requires machine power and assistance from robots. By developing solid models of the very narrow welding cells, the optimal movements of the robot arm and gripper can be generated without any collision with the environment.

The robotic environment for the production of a new car is designed with EUCLID-IS®, while the robot movements are programmed with the support of the robot simulation system ROBULA developed at Volkswagen. ROBULA has been integrated within EUCLID-IS®. Collision control, optimization of the working paths, and the conception of the entire robot work area are carried out on the CAD screen. With ROBULA and EUCLID-IS®, robots can be off-line-programmed in the field, and optimized placement of the robot and working arm paths can be determined before robot activation. This is a much needed improvement over the expensive trial-and-error methods of the past.

30.3.4 Numerical Control

Two-dimensional drawings alone do not contribute to the automation of NC programming. With SM, the model can be used as a reference for the direct input of NC manufacturing data. Collision control between workpiece and machine (five axes), generation of toolpaths, and optimization of manufacturing sequences can be carried out based on the solid model. If the solid model contains both geometric and attributed processing information, automation and computer integrated manufacturing (CIM) is then possible.

The SM system should provide the capability of assigning manufacturing and related information as attributes to geometry and make such information available for NC processing. NCPLUS is the planning and support system developed at Volkswagen based on EUCLID-IS®.

30.4 Information Systems Integration

Integrating information systems for SM design, manufacturing, and specialized applications accelerates the entire work process considerably. AWK-G (support application for large press dies) and NCPLUS will be used here as examples to portray the functional aspects which have so far been implemented and what development potential is still present. AWK-G is being developed in direct cooperation with experts from the Press Shop Design Department, NCPLUS, and with experts from the Work Preparation and NC Programming Department of the Central Planning of Volkswagen.

A complex die is created based on a network of interlinking factors. In order to represent all interdependent links, a relational database (RDB) is used in which alphanumeric data on the die and information on the die structure are stored and retrieved as necessary.

30.4.1   AWK-G Working Procedure

Work performed with AWK-G is divided into three phases, as follows:

1. Prepare geometric and numeric die parameters.

2. Create 3D solid models with necessary processing attributes.

3. Produce results.

   a. Automated creation of CAD cast model

   b. Automated creation of detail drawings

   c. Transfer of geometric and technical data to NC programming

R&D provides the description of the part to be produced as a free-form surface area for inclusion in the method planning stage, during which the initial design and sheet-metal retainer surface areas are generated. This data is then used as a basis for die design, the results of which are then passed on to the work preparation, NC programming, and other subsequent departments.

CAD surface area data is exchanged between CAD systems via VDA-FS (German Automobile Industry Association's surface area interface), and prepared for die modeling. Creation of the 3D solid model is supported by AWK geometry modules which help to generate all known background information on the die. If need be or in the case of special designs, it is always possible to access each of the basic CAD system's functions, thereby ensuring completion of the design in each case.

Once the 3D solid model has been obtained, detail drawings and CAM/NC information is compiled interactively or automatically as required.

30.4.2   Preparations and Parameter Assignment for Cast Parts

The die-cast solid model is completely parameterized. The first design phase in large press dies is preparing the die parameters or modifying default parameter values. Information on the part is contained in the punch-form contour, template contour, and the surface area, as provided by the aforementioned R&D and method planning departments.

The die designer retrieves the CAD data from R&D using the Design Data Administration System (KVS) internally developed by Volkswagen. KVS is an administrative on-line inquiry and archive system for technical information. Based on the punch-form contour retrieved from R&D, additional contours needed for modeling the die are produced by the die designer.

For example, if a draw die is required, punch and sheet-metal retainer surface areas for the appropriate cast parts are created from the surface area retrieved from R&D. Free-form surface areas can be converted into solids by means of special AWK surface functions.

30.4.3   Die Modeling

The strength of SM is evident in the design of complex models, where hidden lines and edges simplify viewing and support in the definition of objects. Dies are objects of such complexity that designers normally create many 2D cross sections in order to describe the 3D part accurately. The AWK-G support application was developed to make the process of designing stamping, edging, and cutting dies for sheet-metal body sections easier.

Based on the original surface area of the part, designers are guided through a series of menus to develop preliminary and finished die geometry. This menu structure largely corresponds to the structure of the die. By automating the generation of die components while taking the actual design process into account, a high degree of support is achieved. Attention is focused on a practical design procedure. A familiar self-explanatory user interface is available for the few inputs required by the designer.

Work using the AWK system is not subject to a rigid procedural layout. A flexible exchange between the different AWK menus and the interactive functions of EUCLID-IS® is made possible. This flexibility allows for the subsequent data transfer into CAM applications. The actual design status can be displayed and inspected at any time, and the process can be interrupted and continued as seen fit. Figures 30.1*a* (see following page) and Fig. 30.1*b* (see color insert) illustrate how AWK-G and EUCLID-IS® make it possible to design press dies for various types of presses and frames.

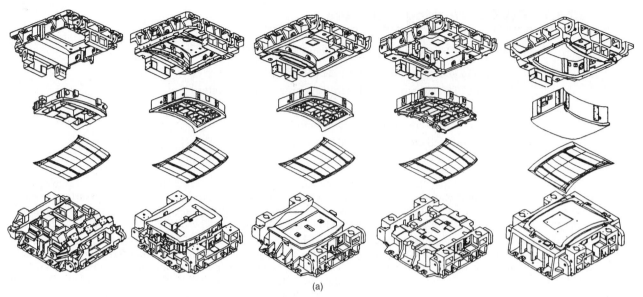

FIGURE 30.1 Die design with AWK-G and EUCLID-IS® by Matra Datavision. (*a*) Complete set of dies for a front hood. (*Courtesy of Volkswagen Automotive Group, Germany.*)

30.4.4 Creating Cast Parts

One main principle of SM is the intensive use of boolean operations (see Fig. 30.2). By selecting the press, AWK automatically assembles all data defining the press for the purposes of further processing. Data affecting the die's dimensions are based on design guidelines. The data is preset for standard dimensions and the designer modifies the relevant parameter values if necessary. The cast parts programs in AWK can be activated once part data has been prepared and the appropriate variables modified.

The way in which the four solids of Fig. 30.2 are linked on the basis of solid boolean theory results in the drawing matrix cast part. Interlinking of the basic elements that produce the cast part is shown

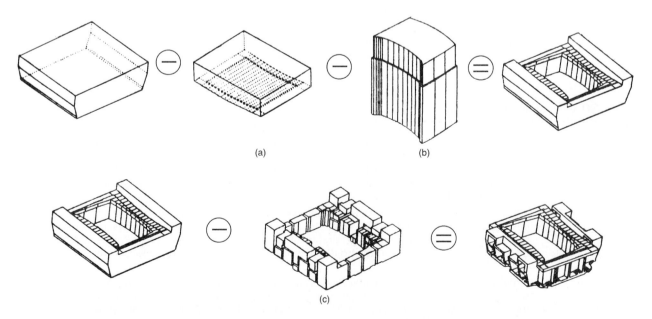

FIGURE 30.2 The AWK boolean process for cast parts. This draw die illustrates how cast parts are modeled from blank stock by removing the following: (*a*) external solid consisting of the cast part's external contour; (*b*) internal solid containing the punch contour; (*c*) the upper solid defining sheet-metal retainer path. (*Courtesy of Volkswagen Automotive Group, Germany.*)

as a CSG tree structure (see Chap. 4 for more on database structures). The structural information is interpreted and evaluated during the calculation. A cast part's structure can be modified or extended as seen fit.

Ultimately, a cast model is equivalent to a set of geometrical, numerical, and structural parameters.

30.4.5   The Standard Parts Concept

The employment of SM should take into account the entire design process. Standard parts, which may normally be described in 2D only, should be generated as 3D solids. In addition to the larger solid cast parts, die design entails a considerable amount of standard parts (e.g., guides, retaining devices). Some modification to the cast part is usually required to accommodate the use of standard part solids. The standard part and its surroundings (drilled holes, milled pockets, etc.) represent a logical unit (see Fig. 30.3).

Each standard part in the die is entered into the parts list database. Numerical inputs are frequently made either by selecting from a stored list offered by the system or by indicating a value, which is then checked within the system for consistency.

30.4.6   Using a Relational Database

AWK-G administration is based on a relational database (RDB). The history (or CSG tree) of a solid model like a die and its added technical information can be very large and complex. To support data

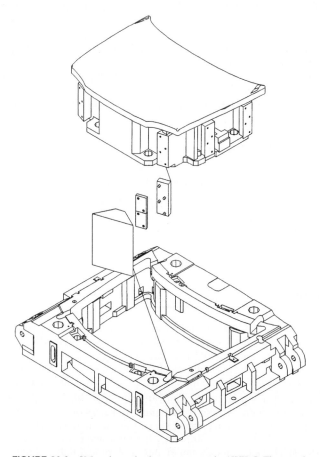

FIGURE 30.3   SM and standard parts concept in AWK-G. The punch guide plates shown here illustrate how the principle of standard parts and associated features are implemented. *(Courtesy of Volkswagen Automotive Group, Germany.)*

management, a relational database can be useful, particularly in the case of nongeometric data. All data known or specified in advance of a design process is stored in the database and retrieved as necessary. For example, alphanumeric data assigned to a standard part is stored and retrieved from the database when a geometry function is initiated involving that part.

The database also contains design logic in the form of a predefined die structure. The die structure can be modified and also stored in the RDB. This causes the system to become increasingly intelligent over time. Once carried out and judged to be useful, the structure of a design can be retrieved and modified later as the basis for new designs.

Relational database administration is responsible for two tasks:

1. The definition of data being stored and read
2. The management of data being produced and entered

30.4.7 Producing Drawings and Data Output for NC

If SM modules for the extraction of drawings and NC data exist, redundantly inputing data is not necessary. The principal objective of die design is to obtain a geometric die model supplemented by all technical information required for production. This data can then be converted into an NC topology model and a manufacturing procedure model. 2D dimensioned drawings and individual sections can also be extracted from the AWK model.

If data continuity is maintained on an interactive basis with the NC planning and support system NCPLUS and other computer systems, the process of creating press dies is particularly accelerated. In addition to parts list data, all NC information needed for production is made available for direct transfer to the subsequent departments.

Based on the attributed die model, automated technical drawings for the press shop department are developed by a Drawing Creation Module as needed at the nearest CAD terminal and then printed out. This type of die production minimizes the amount of paper-based information used and enhances the utilization of a single shared source of data.

The Drawing Creation Module performs the following functions, while necessary inputs are reduced to a minimum:

1. Decodes the geometrical objects
2. Notes the previous status of the drawing if alterations are to be made
3. Analyzes all processing information entered and recorded by the system
4. Checks information for consistency from the various sources (integrated by the system or interactively)
5. Compiles the workshop drawing

30.4.8 Making Patterns

One of the advantages of SM is the ability to create physical patterns directly from the solid model. Once NC processing information has been attributed, the solid model can be used to enable AWK to create a CAD cast pattern with allowance dimensions. This serves as a reference model for milling the polystyrene casting model from a solid block. In such applications, the use of SM makes it possible to shorten lead times considerably and minimize the extent of required input (see Figs. 30.4 and 30.5).

These results produce a pattern of much better quality with regard to precision, uniform allowance dimensions, and proportion of adhesive. Manual transmission errors are also minimized. The advantages become quite obvious when producing polystyrene edging cheeks and toolpaths. These small cast pieces of approximately 25×40 cm are very time-intensive to produce manually because they contain free-form surfaces. The solid models can be put in place and milled directly from a larger polysterene block. A small connection bridge holds the pieces together and can be removed manually after NC milling.

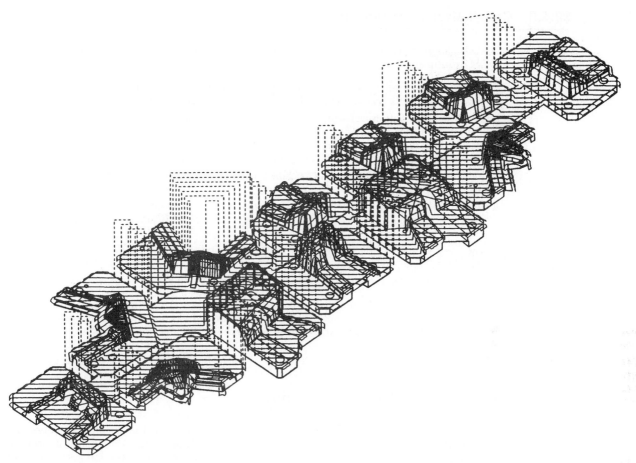

FIGURE 30.4 Simplified NC programming for polysterene casting pattern. This illustration shows how the polystyrene casting pattern is programmed on screen in a relatively simple manner. *(Courtesy of Volkswagen Automotive Group, Germany.)*

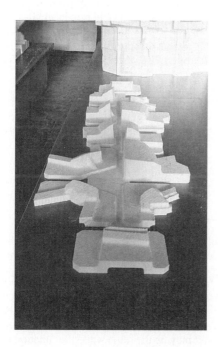

FIGURE 30.5 Similarity between the displayed polystyrene tool paths and the plastic models. *(Courtesy of Volkswagen Automotive Group, Germany.)*

30.4.9 Cost/Labor Calculations

The calculation of manufacturing costs and labor by the Work Preparation Department are enhanced by SM over the use of conventional 2D drawings. In the conventional approach:

1. Planning Department gives the Work Preparation Department a list of requirements containing administrative data (designation, material, etc.), a work order number, blueprints, and parts lists.

2. The Work Preparation Department then examines the drawings produced from the die design. As many as 40 sheets of drawings may accompany a single design. The work preparation employees must be familiar with all of them and assess them in technical terms. In other words, they have to list all the work to be carried out, calculate the necessary labor time, and determine production costs.

3. Individual costs, deadlines, and the machine tool group for production are established from material right through to placing orders for castings, etc.

4. Job cards that contain all machining steps necessary for production are created to accompany each workpiece. Machining times are calculated on the basis of REFA (German work-study organization) tables.

5. The Work Preparation Department's documents are then sent to Process Control, where machines are assigned. The work schedule drawn up is used as a basis for planning deadlines and capacity.

6. The documentation is then made available to NC Programming.

Today, with the use of SM and NCPLUS, the Work Preparation Department can efficiently calculate surfaces to mill, holes to drill, and all steps required for manufacture in an optimal order. Cost and labor are derived with higher accuracy. The job cards can be also punched automatically.

30.4.10 Numerical Control Programming

The primary benefit of designing with SM is seen in NC programming. The NC programmer receives a solid model based on the die design. Normally, they are also provided with detailed drawings with machining symbols (surface, reamed, and threaded symbols, etc.). With these two sources of information, an NC part program is created in sequence. Machining strategies must be considered (e.g., how a recess is produced: first roughing, followed by planing, then finishing the contour). The necessary tools are then created, technical features are determined (feed rates, cutting speed, etc.). However, if the same features appear in another workpiece, the sequence has to be repeated using conventional methods.

With NCPLUS and EUCLID-IS®, NC programmers do not need to reenter data already defined in the solid model through AWK. NCPLUS takes any special requirements of the Work Preparation and NC Programming departments into account. Work is greatly simplified as a result.

The 3D solid model and relevant NC processing information is read into NCPLUS and visualized on screen as shown in Fig. 30.6 (see color insert). The various machining objects are shown in different colors, which provides for a rapid summary of machining work.

Corresponding geometric and technical information is displayed graphically and alphanumerically. The machining time required is calculated by the system as a background operation and then displayed. Very accurate cost analyses are possible. Depending on the choice of NC equipment, the work schedule is automated based on the fully described solid model and defined production data (feed rates, speed, etc).

30.5 Solid Modeling Difficulties

Why was the application of SM not so widespread in the past? What are the difficulties of using SM? Here are some comments:

1. SM systems of the past did not offer the same high quality and reliability as traditional 2D CAD systems.

2. The use of SM is more difficult due to the higher complexity of working in 3D. However, such difficulties are evident in traditional 3D wireframe and surface modeling as well.

3. The current generation of conventional 2D designers have difficulty modifying their design methods. With SM, the end design result may be the same while the functional process is quite different.

30.6   Solid Modeling Benefits

1. The Work Preparation Department is now incorporated into the CAD/CAM process chain and works from the complete 3D solid model. Consequently, drawings are no longer necessary here.

2. The need for drawings has also been eliminated in pattern-making. Polystyrene casting patterns are of high quality. Manual transmission errors are minimized. Time to produce casting patterns is reduced by about 70 percent compared with the manual methods.

3. Machining strategies are enhanced. The necessary tools are created on the basis of production knowledge and stored as existing attributes. This greatly reduces the time involved in NC programming. Strategies devised with NCPLUS are transferred to the NC module of EUCLID-IS® to calculate movement paths, control collisions, and issue NC data.

4. Where possible, complete machining can take place on a single piece of equipment in order to avoid setup times. This objective is considerably supported by prior SM-related toolpath simulation.

5. The greater overall input required for detailed 3D SM proves worthwhile in various respects. As far as subsequent departments are concerned, the additional perspective of the 3D model on workshop drawings provides vital support comprehension.

6. Wireframe modeling produces so many lines that it is very difficult to visually assess a design to identify incorrect lines. Solid models, on the other hand, allow perspective representations of designs with concealed edges from all possible angles. This greatly aids visual comprehension.

7. In SM, only physically correct objects are modeled, and knowledge of solid and free space (inner and outer) is available.

8. Solid models can provide physical data such as:
   a. Volume
   b. Weight
   c. Moments of inertia
   d. Solid collision observations

It is also possible to calculate stress data by means of finite element analysis (FEA).

30.7   Future Goals

One of our future goals is to integrate more closely the design tasks associated with surface and solid modeling. Initial car body part design is described as surfaces. We then develop dies as solid models. In the future it is conceivable that SM will be responsible for devising basic geometrical conditions for method planning of car body parts. Examples here might include:

1. *Automatic part positioning.*   The most advantageous position for deep drawing is directly calculated and suggested by the SM system.

2. *Initial design support.*   Modifying a parts surface area requires considerable input when correcting the initial design, since it is currently created on a patch-type interactive basis. Functions developed specifically for the Method Planning Department can make work easier and reduce data input during interactive sessions. Developing associativity would cause the initial design to be updated automatically if a part were to be altered. This is currently integrated into the die design and NC programming stages.

3. *Work schedules compiled rationally by NCPLUS.*   The die construction department will have data transferred to the Integral Operating Information and Control System (IBIS). IBIS, which will be directly linked to NCPLUS, is used to plan deadlines and capacity (i.e., to control the workpiece's rational flow through the machine tool center).

Conventional model making is losing its importance to an increasing extent, since hard models are no longer needed for copy milling if SM is used. Conventionally, a plastic model or template is needed to assess the quality of the sheet-metal part and stamping die to demonstrate that the stamping process would be successful. Work is currently in progress to determine how best to dispense with the need for any physical models (e.g., visual model of reshaping processes right up to finished sheet-metal parts). Modern pattern-making will be equipped with SM workstations and NC milling machines.

Good Practices

SMA.30.1   Flexibility and Acceptance

Our most experienced designers were selected to use SM first. From the viewpoint of flexibility and acceptance of the new technology, this was not the best choice. We have found it better to train those that are younger and without technical prejudice.

SMA.30.2   Product Definition

It is highly recommended that products be described as complete, unambiguous 3D solid objects from the earliest stages of conceptual design. Each object can be created using a combination of solid, surface, and parametric techniques, producing a single model which serves as the base for all product development activities throughout the entire process chain.

SMA.30.3   Integrate a Relational Data Management System

The ability to store relations between basic elements in a database is normally needed. The structure of a complex product is not only hierarchical in nature. To maintain all dependencies it is wise to use a relational data management system where the alphanumeric information associated with the entire process chain is stored. The system should have the capability of recalling this information at any time when needed.

SMA.30.4   A Distributed Object-Oriented Database

This approach helps each department work concurrently with the same actual data, ensuring that all changes are automatically communicated to all departments. The entire organization, from designers, manufacturing engineers, and perhaps marketing and management, determines interactively, but under rigid organizational guidelines, the product's properties, performance, and manufacturability.

Recommended Guidelines

SMA.30.5   A Complete SM System

The SM system should have the ability to enhance the effectiveness of the entire engineering organization by using techniques to integrate design, analysis, drafting, and manufacturing with management information services.

SMA.30.6   Parameter Definition

The SM system should provide the capability to create both geometric and nongeometric parameters in a comprehensive database defined as a product model, including, for example:

1. Interior and exterior characteristics and surfaces

2. Manufacturing methods and processes

3. Functional relationships between features

4. Interference checking and mass-properties calculations

SMA.30.7   Standards

For dimensioning, drafting, and standard parts generation, the SM system should deliver current ANSI, ISO, DIN, and AFNOR standards, which should be easily customized to meet a company's specific needs.

SMA.30.8   CAE Tools

If required, the SM system should seamlessly integrate design, finite element modeling, analysis, and postprocessing activities. The direct use of SM data substantially reduces the time needed to analyze parts for structural integrity. The following tools and techniques for efficiently designing products should be made available as integrated applications:

1. Static and dynamic interference detection

2. Kinematic and dynamic analysis

3. Mesh generation, mesh editing functions, graphic aids, and mathematical-checking functions

(Continued)

Recommended Guidelines
(*Continued*)

4. Compatibility with industry standard analysis packages for solving structural and thermal problems

5. Postprocessing of the analysis results displayed on the design model

SMA.30.9   Solutions for Plastic Parts

The production of superior-quality plastic parts has become more and more important. Particularly critical is the area of injection molding, where production conditions can cause plastic components to distort and shrink in a seemingly unpredictable fashion. The following capabilities should be explored when choosing an SM system for the design of plastic parts.

1. Techniques for designing plastic parts and assemblies

2. Performing part-shape analysis

3. Generating mold cavities

4. Designing thermal and mechanical mold layouts

5. Designing mold assemblies with standard tooling

6. Predicting plastic material behavior under test molding conditions

7. Creating accurate machine tool instructions

Good to Know

SMA.30.10   What to Expect

What is to be expected with the introduction of SM? On the organizational side, a new working structure may be necessary to reach high efficiency levels with SM applications. Such a working structure may include:

1. Closer integration between all design disciplines, such as 3D wireframe, surfaces, solids, analysis, NC, and documentation.

2. Previously distant departments may be required to work more closely together. With the increased sharing of information, changes in one department will affect others more directly.

3. With less need for some intermediate processes, previously independent departments may need to be combined or eliminated.

SMA.30.11   Choosing Applications

Two-dimensional systems have the advantage of simplicity and are very suitable for prismatic objects (e.g., sealing strips) or rotating symmetrical elements (e.g., shafts, bearings). SM is in these cases not necessary for manufacturing. However, SM may be required if such parts are to made available as part of an SM standard parts library.

In the long term, it will be possible for the Workshop (die construction and assembly) and Fitting/Press Shop departments to use a remote station to retrieve SM and manufacturing data produced by departments at the front of the process chain. Data will be addressed, retrieved, and processed by the application systems on workstations set up at locations considered to be rational.

References

1. Volkswagen 1990 Annual Report.
2. Volkswagen 1992 Annual Report.
3. Vu-Han; Gruel; Ludwig; "Use of Applications in the CAD/CAM Process for Car Body," internal Volkswagen document, 1992.

Glossary of Terms

AFNOR Association Francaise de Normalisation (French Association for Standardization).

AWK Allgemeines Werkzeugkonstruktionssystem (General Design System for Dies).

IBIS Integriertes Betriebs-Informations und Steuerungssystem (Integral Operating Information and Control System).

KVS Konstruktionsdaten-Verwaltungs-System (Design Data Management System).

NCPLUS NC Planning and Supporting System.

REFA Ausschuss für Arbeitszeitermittlung; *today* Verband für Arbeitssudien (German Work Study Organization).

Chapter 31

Solid Modeling at Hewlett-Packard

Peter Zivkov
MCAE Technologies Consultant
Corporate Engineering
Hewlett-Packard Company

Hewlett-Packard (HP) is a leading producer of engineering workstations and mechanical computer-aided engineering (MCAE) tools. We are taking advantage of our own workstation and computer-aided design (CAD) technology and overcoming some of the limitations of 3D Solid Modeling (SM) with innovative engineering processes. As a result, we have been able to develop new products of higher quality, at lower development cost, and in half the time. This chapter describes methods of use, benefits, and some of the difficulties of SM we overcame in order to improve our mechanical engineering productivity. HP is unique in the MCAE industry in that it not only develops and markets mechanical engineering (ME) CAD and product data management (PDM) tools, but uses those same tools extensively to develop leading products in all areas of our hardware businesses. This advantage allows us to be an effective and responsive supplier and user of SM technology.

31.1 Mechanical Engineering at Hewlett-Packard

Currently there are several thousand ME CAD seats installed at HP. The majority of these are SM systems, while the rest are 2D drafting systems. These systems and the people using them are distributed over more than 70 sites worldwide. All are integrated through HP-Internet, one of the world's largest privately operated computer networks.

Because HP divisions share and exchange engineering data to develop and manufacture new products, we have converged on a minimal set of CAD tools across the entire company. This allows HP divisions to reuse data, training, integration, and expertise as required for all downstream processes such as drafting, analysis, and manufacturing.

During the last 5 years, HP has been making some significant and very important transitions. These are:

1. From paper and pencils to engineering workstations
2. From paper to electronic information and processes
3. From physical prototypes to software models and tools
4. From serial to concurrent engineering (CE) practices
5. From individual productivity efforts to automating the work group

These transitions have been important factors in improving HP's competitiveness and time-to-market capability. While these changes are by no means complete, there have been enormous improvements in our mechanical engineering process during the last few years. Affected areas of product development include:

1. Design
2. Analysis and simulation
3. Prototyping
4. Release to manufacturing

31.2   Design

Currently over two-thirds of HP's new product designs are being developed using SM systems. This is an unusually high percentage for any company, let alone for a company of HP's size. How did we get to this point? To answer this question, it may be helpful to discuss some of the reasons why we were able to adopt SM so successfully. These include:

1. Common design tools
2. Interactivity and visualization
3. Reduction in drafting effort
4. Completeness and reuse of design data

31.2.1   Common Design Tools

HP engineers and managers consciously chose to consolidate on the same 2D and 3D design tool for all HP divisions. Without this early decision, it would have been impossible to take full advantage of SM in design or to integrate other computer tools, such as FEA or CAM, in a uniform way across the entire corporation. In addition, we found that engineering data, good practices, training, integration to other tools, and expertise could more easily be shared and reused across the company if the same CAD tool was used.

31.2.2   Interactivity and Visualization

In addition to the use of a common SM tool for the entire company, HP has also standardized the use of HP workstation and graphics hardware to quickly display even very complex solid models. This allows our engineers to work continuously with a fully shaded 3D model, making visualization and design much more intuitive and productive. Figures 31.1 (see color insert) and 31.2 show typical examples of the type of solid models one can see at HP. The result of using 3D SM is an immediate understanding of the design by all people on the product development team.

FIGURE 31.2   SM example showing an exploded view of a palmtop computer. *(Courtesy of Hewlett-Packard Company.)*

With 3D shaded solids, designers and engineers can quickly understand new designs, identify errors, and improve the design's quality by altering the computer model. Engineering tools, such as SM, simplify communication among the product development team on large or complex projects. Some of the projects which are currently under way at HP today would be difficult to conceive or attempt without the successful use of SM (see color insert Fig. 31.1).

31.2.3   Reduction in Drafting Effort

A key factor in the acceptance of SM at HP has been the reduction or, in some cases, elimination of the kind of traditional 2D orthographic documentation shown in Fig. 31.3b. In many cases, HP engineers can have prototype parts and tooling made directly from the solid model. This is an important advantage since drafting, which includes adding dimensions, tolerances, and notes, usually requires as much effort as the initial 3D design. Any necessary 2D documentation is typically done only once, at the end of the project, when the part design has matured and is ready for release to manufacturing. In some cases, however, traditional documentation is still required for suppliers without CAM capability.

An example of a critical-to-function (CTF) drawing which would be sent to a manufacturer with the 3D model data in lieu of a traditional blueprint is shown in Fig. 31.3c. This simple drawing conveys all necessary information (critical tolerances, material type, and finish) which is not geometrically included in the 3D solid model shown in Fig. 31.3a. Once a solid model of the part exists, generating the CTF drawing is a fast and easy process.

31.2.4   Completeness and Reuse of Design Data

Unlike 2D CAD drawings, 3D solid models are precise and unambiguous. For this reason, they can be easily reused for downstream processes. HP engineers frequently reuse models from other design teams or even from other HP divisions in order to reduce development effort. Using solids, we create complete 3D models of entire products, eliminating the need for a physical prototype of a conceptual or initial design.

Using electronic 3D data, distributed computing, and networking allows distant development teams (in Colorado, Massachusetts, and California, for example) to communicate as if they were co-located (see Chap. 27, Fig. 27.11). Our philosophy at HP is that design data should be created once and reused as it moves from department to department, person to person, or tool to tool. We've found that 3D solid models can be integrated to many other tools and processes by using both standard (IGES, DXF) and custom applications or translators.

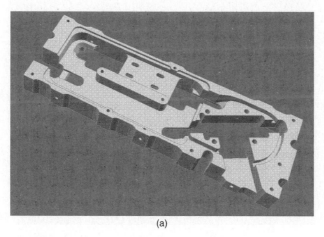

(a)

FIGURE 31.3   Typical HP design documentation. (*a*) Solid model of a mechanical part.

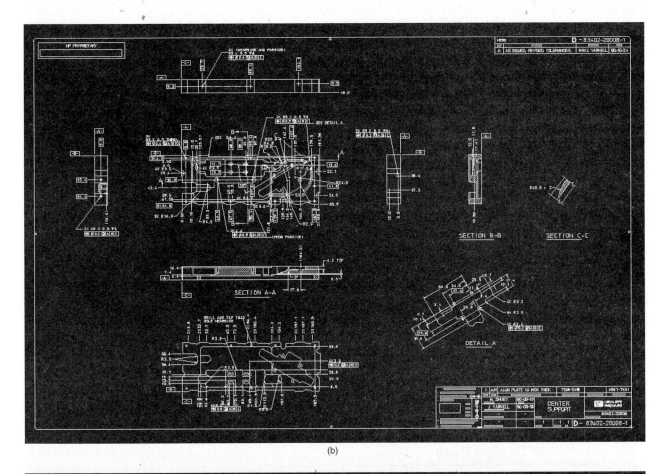

(b)

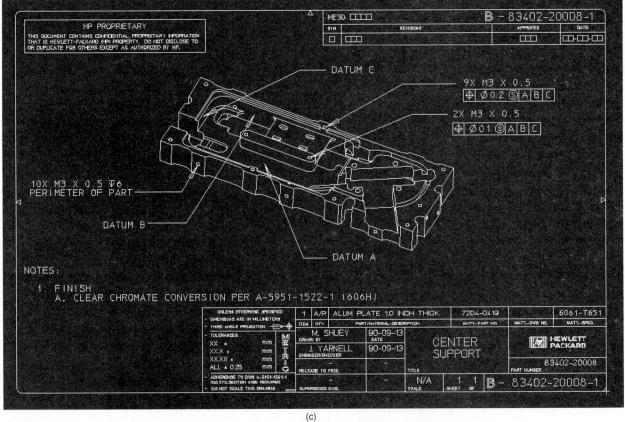

(c)

FIGURE 31.3 *(Continued)* (*b*) traditional 2D orthographic documentation for the same part; (*c*) simplified documentation for the same part. Note the absence of dimensions. The electronic use of the solid model eliminates this requirement. *(Courtesy of Hewlett-Packard Company.)*

31.4

31.2.5   Design Summary

At HP we've found that proper use of SM during design has yielded the following benefits:

1. Improved product design quality
2. Faster product development
3. Fewer physical prototypes during development
4. Improved communication among development teams
5. More creativity and innovation

31.3   Analysis and Simulation

Solid Modeling is a very simple form of simulation. Through its use, HP engineers can predict ease of assembly or identify potential interference problems between parts in a complex assembly. We are usually interested in more than just simulating geometry. Our goal is to predict product performance with additional analysis and simulation tools.

As with CAD, HP has tried to selectively limit the number of analysis tools to a manageable few. This makes training, reuse, leverage of expertise, and integration with CAD much easier. Currently, HP is using analysis and simulation tools to perform the following functions.

1. Computational fluid dynamics
2. Tolerance analysis
3. Structural analysis and shape optimization
4. Sheet-metal cost and manufacturability analysis

At HP, we've found it more difficult to implement analysis tools than 3D SM. Our difficulties to date have been:

1. Limitations in learning many new tools at once (including CAD, E-mail, X11, data management, etc.).
2. Infrequent or occasional use which is easily forgotten.
3. Unlike our SM system, which is a generic 3D design tool, we must use many specific analysis tools in order to simulate the performance (structural, thermal, dynamic, cost, etc.) of any given part.

However, the benefits from these analysis tools can be important factors in reducing the development time of new products. In summary, these benefits include:

1. More design iterations through the use of software models
2. Reduced need for expensive physical prototypes
3. Better product design quality and reliability
4. Improved engineering confidence during development
5. Reduction of warranty costs after product release

31.3.1   Computational Fluid Dynamics

Computational fluid dynamics software is used for predicting the flow and temperature of air through electronics enclosures. This tool is directly interfaced with our SM system, allowing SM data to be reused for air flow and thermal analysis. Without a direct interface with SM, building the analysis model can be a slow and sometimes tedious process. Figure 31.4 shows an example of computational fluid dynamics analysis results.

31.3.2   Tolerance Analysis

Tolerance analysis tools are used to simulate tolerance build-up of assemblies, identify the amount of variation that will occur, and flag the main contributors to critical assembly tolerances.

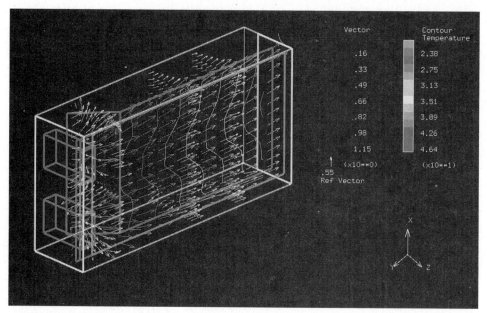

FIGURE 31.4 Simulation results predicting airflow, velocity, direction, and air temperature in a 3D analysis model of an instrument enclosure. *(Courtesy of Hewlett-Packard Company.)*

Currently, wireframe data from SM is passed to the tolerance analysis tool through an IGES interface. Simulation points, datums, features, assembly processes, and fits are defined before analysis is performed. Several reports can be generated displaying results. Currently, HP engineers must be specifically trained to operate the tolerance analysis interface. Our intention is to improve our process by customizing our SM system. This will allow our designers to specify all of the input parameters within the familiar work environment.

31.3.3 Structural Analysis and Shape Optimization

Surface data from SM is currently passed to structural analysis and shape optimization software through an IGES interface. Complete solid model definition for analysis and meshing of 2D and 3D elements is done within the analysis software. In addition to structural analysis, HP engineers are now beginning to use conductive thermal analysis as well as kinematic and dynamic analysis as a routine step in product development.

These analysis tools are currently being used at a leading minority of HP divisions. Our goal, however, is to improve their integration with SM and make them easier to operate. This will allow us to take greater advantage of analysis and simulation, rather than relying on building and testing physical prototypes during early design.

31.3.4 Sheet-Metal Cost and Manufacturability Analysis

In addition to these analysis tools, HP has developed and is successfully implementing a commercially available design for manufacturing (DFM) and cost analysis tool for sheet-metal part design and manufacturing. This software is integrated with SM and assists our design engineers by:

1. Making the design of sheet-metal parts in SM faster and easier

2. Providing a series of suggested sheet-metal features (holes, fold radii, offsets, etc.) for which tooling already exists

3. Flagging a part's features that are difficult or expensive to manufacture

4. Predicting the total manufacturing cost of a given part design

5. Automatically creating a 2D flat drawing of the 3D model

6. Automatically generating a manufacturing process for a given sheet-metal part design, including a flat pattern, tooling list, and folding sequence

31.4   Prototyping

Along with the reduction of drafting in design, the effective use of prototyping has been a major component in HP's drive to improve its mechanical engineering process. HP has again chosen a small set of common CAM tools which are very closely integrated with SM. HP is currently using CAM tools to perform the following functions:

1. Fast and simple machining on manual milling machines which have been retrofitted with two axis controllers.

2. 2.5 axis NC machining for more complex machining jobs which includes both milling and turning capability.

3. Flat pattern layout, punching, and forming of sheet-metal parts.

4. StereoLithography (SLA) for interfacing to rapid prototyping (RP) systems (see Chap. 19). HP currently operates an in-house SLA machine and uses a number of service bureaus for quick rapid prototypes. Our SLA parts are typically used for working prototypes or as patterns for molding a small quantity of plastic prototype parts.

The aforementioned software tools have been customized to interface closely and easily with 3D SM without traditional 2D drawings. In fact, SM systems are used on the shop floor to receive engineering data, visualize and understand the part to be made, and to prepare the 3D solid models for the CAM process. This has lead to high-technology HP shops, where visitors can see machinists using their CAD systems to interactively rotate, visually slice, or modify 3D solid models in order to prepare the designer's data for the NC process.

31.4.1   Typical Prototyping Process

From the designer's workstation, a design packet (including a 3D solid model and a CTF drawing) is sent electronically to one or several manufacturing sites. The designer is prompted for any other shop-specific information, and the data is sent transparently to the internal or external shop through Internet. E-mail messages confirming the delivery are sent to the shop, related engineering personnel, and anyone else who needs to know (managers or production buyers). The incoming order and a picture of the part is automatically printed on a laser printer which signals the shop to begin making the part. A model maker reviews the design on his or her SM system and retrieves the data necessary to make the part.

If there are questions from an internal shop, the model maker and the engineer can share the same GUI window on each of their workstations while talking over the phone to discuss the design. The model maker then converts the design data to the necessary manufacturing format and loads it into the CAM system to define the detailed processes used to manufacture the part.

31.4.2   Prototyping Summary

Using the 3D solid model to drive the manufacturing process has been a key factor in sharply cutting the cost and time required to manufacture high-quality parts. In summary, these are the benefits we've seen at HP:

1. Prototypes can be made in less than one-half the time compared to our previous NC process, which depended on 2D CAD drawings and manual NC programming. Even very complex designs, like the one shown in Fig. 31.5, can now be transmitted through the network, translated into the CAM system for NC programming and manufactured in just a few days.

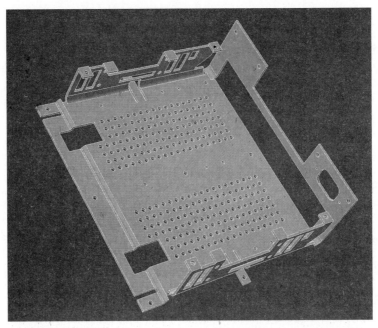

FIGURE 31.5 This sheet-metal part was designed in Waltham, Massachusetts, and manufactured in Santa Rosa, California. Time from electronic transfer to finished part: three days. *(Courtesy of Hewlett-Packard Company.)*

2. Improved part quality is attained, since the engineer's design data defines both the part geometry and the manufacturing process. Questions about missing dimensions or geometry from a 2D blueprint are no longer an issue. Ninety percent of prototype parts are now expected to fit the first time without any rework.

3. Time savings are realized due to the reuse of 3D models to design tooling or fixtures required for manufacturing. This is true for all types of parts including die-cast or molded parts. Some new prototyping methods, like SLA, are only possible when a 3D surface or solid model of the part is available.

4. Better and more frequent communication between designer and manufacturer is now possible since they both have the same tools and relatively more time to discuss "design for manufacturability."

Most of the prototyping methods discussed so far apply equally to external shops, which HP uses for some prototyping, and volume manufacturing. HP has teamed with suppliers which are capable and motivated to work with 3D CAD data and limited 2D documentation. HP engineers can now send CAD data electronically to a variety of external suppliers through high-speed modems, E-mail integration, or networks by using the same software interface used for internal manufacturing sites.

31.5 Release to Manufacturing

Each HP division has a Manufacturing Specifications Organization (MSO) which manages and archives engineering data after a product design is complete. At HP, this group has the same CAD capability and equipment that is found in R&D. As CAD data is released from design to manufacturing, this organization updates and maintains both 3D CAD models and 2D drawings, both of which are archived for future use.

In some cases, traditional 2D documentation is created at the end of a project's development if a valued supplier requires traditional documentation. In many cases the simplified 2D cover sheet is the only drawing that is archived and maintained with the 3D model through the entire life of the product. Having the same 3D CAD environment for both R&D and manufacturing has improved communication and has helped to break down some of the barriers that previously existed between these organizations. Our release process is now more continuous and error-free, resulting in faster and less costly product delivery.

31.5.1 Product Data Management (PDM)

PDM is a companywide database management tool and is a custom version of HP's commercially available data management product. PDM is used to collect, organize, and share critical electronic information that is created during product development. This information is used as a central pool of data which can be accessed and shared by anyone within the company. Currently, PDM is primarily being used by the MSO community to collect, control, and distribute all types of engineering data at each HP site. However, in the near future, PDM will play an increasingly important role in linking people at many distant HP sites who are all working on a distributed product development team.

31.5.2 Technical Illustrations

In the past, drafters or engineers spent a great deal of time creating complex isometric assembly drawings to illustrate how to put a product together, take it apart, or how to service it in the field. With the adoption of SM, creating this type of drawing from an existing 3D model of a product is very easy and is now frequently done to create illustrations for HP's technical documentation or product service manuals.

31.6 Hewlett-Packard's Vision for Better Mechanical Engineering

Traditional product development is a serial process and highly dependent on hardware (physical prototypes) and paper-based information such as drawings and material lists. Normally, each step must be completed before the next can begin. To communicate a design solution, it must be fully documented as a 2D drawing so that others can understand it in order to build or test a new part or assembly. Only after a product has been built can we see if the original design needs have been met. Traditionally, three to four costly and time-consuming prototypes were built and tested in order to develop a robust design.

Hewlett-Packard's new product development is a concurrent process highly dependent on the integration of software tools and the easy flow of electronic information between many people. Today, we use computer design and simulation tools to predict the performance of a new design without spending money on more than one or two physical prototypes. This way, a design engineer can make many improvements and design iterations on the solid model without committing to these changes in an expensive physical prototype. Periodically, a rapid prototyping (RP) cycle is used to verify the design and simulation models and to test manufacturing processes.

Traditional 2D documentation, if needed, is created only when the design is complete. Drafting, which used to be a major activity in the traditional process, has been taken out of the critical path and is now a one-time or optional last step in design before data is released to manufacturing. HP's traditional and current development processes are shown in Fig. 31.6.

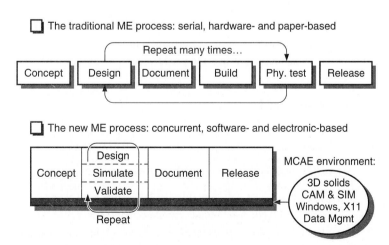

FIGURE 31.6 Comparing HP's traditional and improved ME development processes. *(Courtesy of Hewlett-Packard Company.)*

In the past, we had very specific tools for each serial step in the development process. Today we have a few common computer tools which are used from start to finish by all people working on a development team. In review, these common tools are: SM for design and review, networking, the X11 window interface for providing communication and access to others, and data management tools like PDM for the sharing of product development data.

31.6.1 Hewlett-Packard's Visionary Plan

Hewlett-Packard is developing a three-phase visionary plan for our mechanical engineering work environment. These visions were communicated, accepted and supported by engineers and managers throughout the company. This visionary plan was meant to be achievable but also very challenging in order to stimulate everyone in the company to improve our ME tools and processes. Here is a list of goals that define HP's visionary plan.

Phase I

1. Design all new products using 3D solid models.
2. Attain prototyping capability from 3D solid models without traditional 2D drawings.
3. Achieve commonplace use of StereoLithography (SLA) and desktop manufacturing processes.
4. Begin the use of selected ME analysis and simulation tools.
5. Release solid models of fabricated parts and assemblies to our MSO for long-term data archival and reuse.

Phase II

1. Tightly integrate ME and EE design systems and processes.
2. Make the use of software tools for ME analysis and simulation commonplace.
3. Achieve companywide use of PDM tools.
4. Provide a corporate 3D model library of frequently purchased parts and assemblies for design reuse.
5. Improve integration between ME design and manufacturing information systems.
6. Establish integration between computer-aided inspection and CAD/CAM.

Phase III

1. Provide all critical engineering information on-line between team members.
2. Establish paperless processes and information flows.
3. Integrate design, manufacturing, and procurement systems into one work environment.

Results of Phase I

As a whole, we have done very well in reaching our goals for Phase I of our visionary plan. Here is a review of how we progressed based on a survey of HP divisions.

1. The use of 3D solid models to create new designs has increased by 25 percent each year and is currently at 60 percent.
2. Over 70 percent of HP divisions have manufactured parts without traditional 2D drawings. All HP divisions send CAD data to manufacturing electronically.
3. 37 percent of HP divisions are using SLA and related desktop manufacturing processes.
4. 50 percent of HP divisions are using some type of ME analysis tools.
5. 56 percent of HP divisions have released solid models to manufacturing for archival and reuse.

Unfortunately, survey results for Phase II are not yet available. Obviously, there is a lot to be proud of in these achievements. However, there is still a lot of work to be done to reach our goals for the remainder of our visionary plan.

31.7   Conclusions

By sponsoring and guiding comprehensive changes in its MCAE environment, HP has significantly improved its product development processes. By taking advantage of SM, improving CAD integration, networking, data management, and ME simulation technologies, HP has been able to double its mechanical engineering productivity in many cases. These efforts have resulted in better-quality products, faster product delivery, and lower development costs. Our clear visionary goals and results demonstrate that HP is a world leader in the use of SM for mechanical engineering.

Hidden Limitations

SMA.31.1   Retraining

Hewlett-Packard engineers are some of the best and brightest, but many left universities before computers, CAD, and networking became prevalent. It is very easy to overlook training needs when investing in new CAE tools. If adequate training is not provided, engineers can easily waste as much as 50 percent of their time trying to learn new tools. An expected productivity gain can quickly become a productivity drain.

SMA.31.2   Expectations

Most people can intuitively see the advantages and power of using SM. Product demonstrations by SM suppliers always make it look so fast, friendly, and effortless. However, it is not nearly as easy to make all these new tools work when you are back in the office and there is a deadline to meet. SM is still an emerging technology. It can be very complex and occasionally very tedious. Managers and engineers must have realistic expectations of what is possible, or even the best SM tools will fail because people simply expect too much.

SMA.31.3   Information Overload

Computer-aided engineering (CAE) technology is advancing so rapidly that most design engineers cannot keep up with the latest tools, methods, and industry news. After all, their job is to design a new product, not to invent a new engineering process or make use of a new CAE tool. For this reason, it is important to adopt a new CAE technology only after it has been proven to work and add measurable value by CAD specialists or small leading-edge development groups. In fact, there is so much information and news available about CAD developments that we use several people and computer-based systems for collecting and distributing useful information within HP's mechanical engineering community.

SMA.31.4   Reengineering

Engineering tools and processes are inseparable. Changing one affects the other. Because of SM, HP divisions have had to radically modify their traditional engineering processes. In most cases, this has also given us the chance to simplify and streamline most key processes. However, many HP divisions are also still relying on older, 2D CAD or paper-based processes along with the newest SM methods. This can lead to confusion with nonengineering groups who are not aware of, or have not embraced, the use of these new methods.

SMA.31.5   Company Culture

Hewlett-Packard began as a small test and measurement company in the 1940s. In some ways, today's culture in HP still reflects this. Many people find it difficult to rely on a 3D model or a software prototype. They are much more comfortable building and testing prototypes that they can actually touch. In many cases, physical testing seems faster, since our company is already well outfitted with specialized test labs, equipment, and personnel. HP has had a long and successful tradition of rigorous physical testing. Because of our culture, it will be difficult to switch to a new paradigm of performance testing and evaluation using software tools.

Hidden Benefits

SMA.31.6 Creativity and Innovation

Because engineers are now working with computer models rather than physical ones, they are more likely to experiment and try new ideas. This has allowed HP's designers to work more creatively and apply new innovation to problem solving.

SMA.31.7 Teamwork

Improved teamwork has already been mentioned, but it should be highlighted as a significant hidden advantage. SM offers a new way to communicate designs through realistic and oftentimes beautiful pictures of complex engineering models. These pictures and the real-time animation that is possible promote understanding and are a good catalyst for getting people to discuss the product design.

SMA.31.8 Morale

Hewlett-Packard has been very successful in using MCAE technologies. Many HP people are very proud of the improvements we've been able to make in the mechanical engineering environment over the last 5 years. This progress has fostered an unprecedented sense of confidence, morale, and enthusiasm in HP's ME community. With this success has come more respect and even some admiration from HP's electrical engineering (EE) and software development communities about the effectiveness and productivity of HP's mechanical engineers. For many people it is simply fun and enjoyable to work in today's dynamic and high-technology environment.

SMA.31.9 Visionary Thinking

Even with the many changes that have occurred at HP, our people are still asking for further improvements. Why? Because they can envision an even better work environment in the future—one which allows them to work more productively and creatively. Their expectation is to take full advantage of emerging technologies in order to make their work easier and more interesting, as well as to develop even better new products at a lower cost and in less time.

Additional Limitations

SMA.31.10 Expenses

Even though the cost of using SM is justified, it is still an impediment for many companies. The price of SM software and hardware is dropping and is within reach of many companies, but the technical skills required to support, maintain, and effectively use these systems can be expensive to buy, difficult to find, or slow to develop.

SMA.31.11 Integration

Integration from SM to other systems like drafting, analysis, manufacturing, documentation, or information systems can be difficult or sometimes even impossible. Translators between systems vary greatly in their quality and their ability to share data effectively. IGES, DXF, HPGL and other standard file types can be useful, but they require additional work and special processes to set up and use.

SMA.31.12 Drawings versus Models

Solid Modeling provides the ability for design and manufacturing engineers to create and use 3D models which are very useful. However, nonengineering organizations in most industries still rely on traditional 2D drawings to communicate information. For the foreseeable future, engineers will not only have to create models, but drawings as well. Ideally, the 3D model would be stored in a standard format which would carry all the information found in a traditional 2D drawing and could be inexpensively viewed, rotated, interrogated for size and design intent, and printed on demand. This capability would eliminate the reliance on drawings and simplify the need for creating and maintaining both 3D models and 2D drawings.

SMA.31.13 System Performance

Engineers, by nature, seem to push their tools to the limit. Large, complex 3D models of assemblies are as big and as detailed as the performance of the hardware system will allow them to be. Because

(Continued)

Additional Limitations
(*Continued*)

of this, SM tools and their use can always benefit from more system memory, faster CPUs, or graphics hardware. With some simple modeling constraints, performance is usually satisfactory for most systems, but it would be ideal if SM designers were free of these constraints.

SMA.31.14 Networking and Communication

Once a company is successful in the use of SM, the next logical step is to communicate data directly to partners and suppliers outside the company. Until recently, the most practical way to do this was by mailing physical media (diskettes or tapes) or through the use of modems which provide point-to-point communication. Both of these methods can work well, but have significant limitations when compared to using commercial networks or the Internet. Networking for CAD/CAM transfer can offer instant access to both data and people as well as a simplified process for getting the data to the right location.

General Advice

SMA.31.15 Think Long-Term

Think long-term when choosing MCAE tools and suppliers. ME CAD tools, associated processes, and engineering data are difficult to change and expensive to replace (especially for larger companies). Choosing a popular tool with the latest features is great, but only if that supplier will still be in business 3 to 5 years from now. MCAE suppliers tend to leapfrog one another every few years. The key is to choose suppliers who will be competitive enough to be in your top 5 list for a long time to come.

SMA.31.16 Standardize

Standardize a few key CAE tools (hardware and software) and processes. It is much easier to implement, use, and support only one general-purpose tool than to try to use several tools with overlapping designers and features. Support requirements and complexity increases very quickly with each new tool. For example, if we used 3 CAD tools, we would need three times (or more) effort for each of these:

1. Training

2. Hardware support

3. Operating system support

4. Application support

5. Integration to manufacturing systems, analysis tools, informations systems, and other engineering systems

6. CAD tool customization

SMA.31.17 Modularity

Look for modular integration between MCAE tools in your engineering environment. If you were forced to, could you replace your SM tool in an emergency without totally disrupting your business?

SMA.31.18 Encourage Expertise

Identify, encourage, and support leading designers and engineers to become local experts on a particular tool, technology, or process of their choice. These people will have the satisfaction of learning something they are interested in and sharing their knowledge and enthusiasm with others. Not everyone can, or should, be an expert in all aspects of MCAE.

SMA.31.19 Keep It Simple

Always strive to simplify the engineering process. Some of the things we do as engineers and designers aren't really required, but are done only because "this is the way we've always done it." New technology like SM offers the opportunity to create new engineering processes which can be simple, effective, and efficient.

(Continued)

General Advice
(*Continued*)

SMA.31.20   A Dual Strategy

For the short term, encourage fast, dramatic, and revolutionary changes on small, focused, pilot projects with the best available people. For the long-term, promote evolutionary changes across larger multidisciplinary organizations. This dual strategy is effective because the small fast-track projects provide quick and valuable results to the entire organization which you may want to change over time.

SMA.31.21   Visionary Goals

Develop and work toward a desired future vision of your work environment. Take the time to define, document, and share this vision with everyone who can help you achieve it. This will put into perspective the many intermediate steps required and illuminate potential pitfalls as well as previous progress.

SMA.31.22   Measure Progress

Measure progress as best you can, whether improvements or difficulties. Engineering processes and productivity are very difficult to measure. However, any measurable aspect of these is useful in showing the progress made, or the need for new tools, methods, or resources.

SMA.31.23   Encourage Communication

Focus on and encourage the communication of best practices and success stories between peers. In most companies, people are simply too busy working to look around and talk with their peers from down the hall in order to find out what is new.

SMA.31.24   Ease of Use

Focus on ease of use for your average professional. Just because a few bright engineers like a particular tool or method doesn't mean it is the best solution for everyone in the company. Look for tools that allow easy customization and integration. Your needs and expectations are likely to change over time; your tools should be able to adapt.

SMA.31.25   Be Aware of the Learning Curve

Always give people adequate time to learn new tools and methods. SM technology and related processes can be complex and difficult at times. It can take a long time to completely understand and implement new ways of engineering.

SMA.31.26   Continuing Education

Plan for both formal and informal continuous training. Be sure to provide formal training when both designers and system (hardware and software) are ready. There is no use in getting trained if you won't have the opportunity to use what you have just learned for another month or two. Informal training is best done by local experts (peers) who can answer questions as they come up, or in small groups at weekly meetings.

SMA.31.27   Culture and Social Issues

Company culture and social issues are the most difficult to change in an engineering environment. Don't underestimate the power of social issues which occur in most working groups. Some typical examples: the "Not Invented Here" syndrome or the rumor mill, "I don't know much about it, but I heard that tool was really hard to use."

SMA.31.28   Expect Change

Continue to expect rapid change in the areas of hardware performance, design automation, SM, performance simulation, networking, multimedia, and even virtual reality. Workstations and PCs are doubling their performance every few years. The dynamic changes seen now will not stop after SM implementation, but will continue at an even faster pace in all of these areas.

Glossary of Terms

CFT drawing   An HP 2D drawing containing only information that is considered critical to function. CFT drawings accompany solid models to manufacturing.

HP-Internet   Hewlett-Packard Company's collection of interconnected computer networks, which join most all of the company's PC, workstation, and mainframe users.

MSO   Hewlett-Packard Manufacturing Specifications Organization

Chapter 32

Solid Modeling at Eaton Corporation, Supercharger Division

Donald N. Wentworth
Supervisor—Advanced Engineering
Eaton Corporation
Supercharger Division

This chapter will focus on the integration of Solid Modeling (SM) throughout Product and Manufacturing Engineering at the Supercharger (SC) Division of Eaton Corporation located in Marshall, Michigan. Discussions will begin with a brief company background and capability overview. We will then proceed with a detailed design process case study using SM technology. Following the case study we will discuss such topics as manufacturing, payoffs, pitfalls, and future goals with SM. Discussions will include underlying issues such as network structure and data management, as these are essential elements to building a successful SM system.

32.1 Company Background

With 38,000 employees in 20 countries, Eaton Corporation is a manufacturer of highly engineered products serving automotive, industrial, commercial, and military markets. Principal products include truck transmissions and axles, engine components, electrical equipment, and controls. The company's total sales for 1994 exceeded $6.1 billion. The SC Division, headquartered in Marshall, Michigan, designs and builds roots-type superchargers for OEM and after-market applications. The SC Division of Eaton is the *original equipment manufacturer* (OEM) of roots-type superchargers, and supplies them to automotive manufacturers. *After-market applications* refers to the supply of superchargers to wholesalers and distributors for retrofitting on vehicles after they have been marketed and sold.

Customers include Ford and General Motors in the United States, and Aston Martin, Jaguar, and TRW in Europe. All product engineering and development is done at the Marshall facility, with a dedicated manufacturing plant in Athens, Georgia.

32.2 CAD Capability and Network Overview

Current CAD/CAM/CAE software capability includes:

1. Computer-aided design (CAD) applications
    a. Pro/ENGINEER® developed by Parametric Technology Corporation (Waltham, Mass.), nine (9) floating network licenses
    b. AutoCAD® developed by Autodesk, Inc. (Sausalito, Calif.), nine (9) floating network licenses
2. Computer-aided manufacturing (CAM) applications
    a. SmartCAM® developed by Point Control Corporation (Eugene, Oreg.), one (1) floating network licenses each of Advanced Milling, Advanced Turning, and IGES CAM Connection

3. Finite element analysis (FEA) applications

   a. Patran® developed by PDA Engineering (Costa Mesa, Calif.), one (1) license

   b. Ansys® developed by Ansys, Inc. (Huston, Pa.), one (1) license

   c. Abaqus® developed by Hibbitt, Karlson and Sorensen, Inc. (Pawtucket, R.I.), one (1) license

4. Rendering applications

   a. The Advanced Visualizer® developed by Wavefront Technology (Santa Barbara, Calif.) one (1) license

Our existing engineering network consists of Unix workstations and servers manufactured by Sun Microsystems (Mountain View, Calif.). The SC division engineering and manufacturing centers are linked by a fractional T1 line between Athens Georgia, and Marshall Michigan. Plans are to upgrade communications to full T1 line capability. It is very important to have an adequate supporting network in place to move large SM files between design and manufacturing facilities. Also included in this engineering network are Eaton corporate R&D centers and world headquarters.

32.3 Why 3D Solid Modeling?

Considering the fact that we had a fully functional 2D CAD system in place, a fully trained user base, distributed database management systems with every drawing on-line, why move to 3D SM? The answer comes from the following directions.

1. Problems within the 2D database

   a. Traditional drafting errors from projection mistakes, changes to one view that weren't carried through to other views on other sheets, etc. There are no projection errors with SM and changes to the geometry are reflected in every drawing in which the model is used. One hundred percent confidence in views.

   b. When editing dimension text—right number wrong geometry! This leads to problems when giving IGES files (as we increasingly do) to customers and suppliers. This is impossible to do with a dimension-driven SM system. When you edit a dimension, the model regenerates to reflect new geometry.

   c. We did not draw surfaces drafted on our 2D drawings but, instead, used drafting symbols to depict a surface increasing or decreasing in draft. We now model draft on all surfaces. This takes longer but is worth the effort. By showing draft we are always certain of the wall thickness being correct and of the correct fitting of parts in fixtures.

2. Paperwork for engineering change notices (ECNs)

   a. Drafting errors = ECNs = non-value-added time. ECNs that are issued to fix, clean up, better explain details on a drawing do not benefit anyone. These are after-the-fact changes that result in lost time that could be better spent working on new designs.

3. Lack of 2D functionality

   a. Creating cross sections can be a major effort on a 2D drawing and can take considerable time. With SM we can cut sections quickly to examine internal features anytime and then remove them (see color insert, Fig. 32.1).

   b. Mass-property data is not automatic with 2D. With SM you can get this data whenever you want or need it.

4. Product structure not inherent within a 2D database

   a. Product structure is inherent in the SM assembly with an accurate BOM available anytime.

   b. With 2D, we had duplicate copies of the same part scattered everywhere. This made it a chore to update all the drawings when a common part was modified. With SM we have one part referenced many times. Therefore, changes throughout a design structure are simple.

5. Manufacturing engineering issues with 2D drawings

   a. Process sheets were created from product engineering detail drawings.

   (1) The correct view was not always available and, in many cases, there is not enough time to create new views. Any view of a part is easy to create with SM.

   (2) The lack of draft angles did not help with the design of machining and inspection fixtures.

   (3) No exploded views for assembly cells—Product engineering did not develop these 2D views because of the time involved. Manufacturing did not have the time either, even though they wanted them. This is very easy to do with SM.

   b. We design complex castings. This means that we frequently have complex fixtures. Our fixtures can hold from 4 to 24 nested parts. Trying to design fixtures in 2D just did not always get it right. In 3D SM we build the fixture around the model and, because of the interference checking within SM, we are certain that parts clear clamps; cutters only cut the part, etc.

   c. NC programming—2D does not complement four-axis machining. We now export 3D models with fixtures in place to SmartCAM® via IGES. We can estimate cycle times for customer quotes (this is great for historically tracking how you came up with the price you did), program proto- type and production runs, and free production machines from manual programming.

6. Customers and suppliers

   a. Both customers and suppliers are increasingly asking for 3D data exchange. Customers are exchanging data to package our designs on their engines. Suppliers want 3D for machining our parts, making tooling, and interfacing to their rapid prototyping systems.

32.4   Design Process Case Study

A typical application of SM technology in the design of a supercharger assembly will be discussed here, and includes the following topics.

1. Application overview
2. Initial design parameters
3. Developing the housing casting
4. Significance of application
5. Modeling related parts
6. Assembly modeling process

32.4.1   Application Overview

The primary design components of a supercharger can be broken down into three subassemblies: (1) cover, (2) rotating group, and (3) housing. Each of these three subassemblies is built around the cover casting (see color insert, Fig. 32.2), bearing plate casting, and housing casting (see Fig. 32.3). Of all the components in a supercharger unit, SM provides the greatest benefits in the design of the castings, as they are often complex and contain internal core features that must be carefully designed. Our casting designs are usually composed of more than one solid model; the external shape model and one or more core models. The combination of the external and core models yields the casting, The complete casting then serves as the parent for the machined model.

32.4.2   Initial Design Parameters

Our sales engineers work with engineers from our customer's design team to establish the basic design constraints. This often involves the back-and-forth exchange of wireframe IGES files and drawings. Sometimes designs are established from existing supercharger designs, but, in the case of the super- charger discussed here, a new design is required.

32.4.3   Developing the Housing Casting

First, an internal core model is created of the air intake geometry and the volume required for the rotor bores. Once the internal core shape is developed, a second model is begun of the external geometry. It is the external model that will become the complete casting itself. Various features are added to the housing casting, such as flanges to attach the bearing plate and the customers throttle body and intake manifold. As design information is passed to and from the customer, additional features are added, such as the PCV tower, water passages, and bosses for mounting accessory drives. Additional models

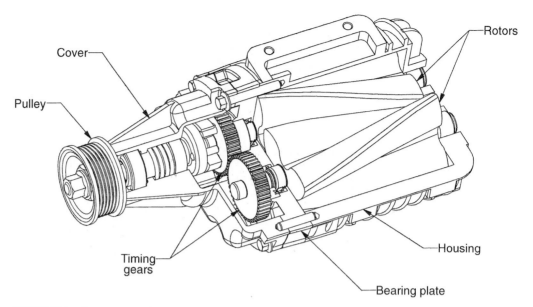

FIGURE 32.3 Cutaway assembled view of "generic" supercharger showing subject components. *(Courtesy of Eaton Corporation, Supercharger Division.)*

are developed and added to create a core assembly which, in turn, will be removed from the casting. Careful consideration must be given during this process to the following:

1. Making sure that there is adequate wall thickness between core features and exterior geometry
2. Ensuring that the cores can be removed
3. Ensuring that the part can be cast as designed

Once the casting model is partly developed, it is sent electronically across our engineering network to our manufacturing facility for a design for manufacturability (DFM) review. The manufacturing engineer will work with the tool designer to establish where they would like to locate and clamp the part by placing bosses and stops on the model. Manufacturing will send the model back and design engineers will review it with our supplier, who will build a prototype. If installation packaging is a concern, our customer may ask us to provide a packaging model to make sure the design fits their engine compartment. We have used the Laminated Object Manufacturing (LOM) Rapid Prototyping (RP) process developed by Helisys, Inc. (Torrance, Calif.) successfully for the rapid development of packaging models and prototype sand castings. (See Chap. 19 for more on SM and RP.)

As development continues, the internal core models are refined and external bosses adjusted until the design is complete. Detail drawings are then made from the solid model. These detail drawings are distributed to casting suppliers to obtain quotes for patterns and castings.

32.4.4   Significance of Application

A feature of SM is the ability to cut apart or merge together two or more models to form a finished part while maintaining reference to the original models. We utilize this technique to remove the core models from the exterior casting model. This allows us to constantly refine the internal core and see the effect immediately in the exterior casting model. If we add a new boss to the side of a core, that material will be removed from the exterior casting model.

We utilize a similar technique to create the finished machined model from the casting. Essentially, the very first feature of the machined model is the entire casting model. The casting model in turn references the internal core models. Using this technique we can remove material to represent machined areas without affecting the casting model. This is because the machined features belong only to the machined model. However, if a feature is modified or added to an internal core or the exterior model, that change will be included and displayed in the finished machined model. An additional benefit to designing castings this way is that we can create several machined models from one casting model.

Another issue to consider is that it is easier to model simple parts and combine them than it is to create a single complex model (see Chap. 6). SM also provides the ability to suppress (turn off) features. Because a core model is treated as one feature (even if it is made up of 100 features) it can be suppressed in the casting when it is not needed. This can accelerate display and model regeneration time.

32.4.5 Modeling Related Parts

The related components that make up the supercharger are fairly easy to model. For example, the input and rotor shafts (see Fig. 32.4a) are created by sketching their profile and revolving them about an axis (see Chap. 8 for more on the sketcher). For the bearings and seals we model only the profiles, since this is all that is necessary to define these shapes. The gears are modeled to their outside diameters with only a few teeth to show graphically what the gears look like on the drawing and in the assembly. Showing only a few teeth helps keep redisplay time down to a minimum. The pulleys are modeled with revolved profiles similar to the shafts.

The rotors themselves are quite complex and are constructed by first reading in point data that defines the rotor profile. The point data is generated from a rotor design program developed by Eaton. Splines are then constructed through the points to construct a 2D cross section of the rotor. This cross section is then swept along a predetermined vector while keeping the cross-section normal to a surface that defines the angle of the helix. Figure 32.5 shows the rotor construction geometry.

32.4.6 Assembly Modeling Process

There is little variation between one supercharger and another in terms of assembly. Because of this we have developed a simple system that employs named coordinate systems to assemble the solid model.

Rotor Shaft

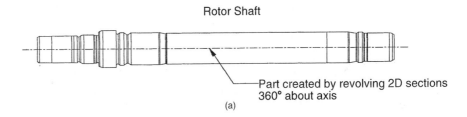

Part created by revolving 2D sections 360° about axis

(a)

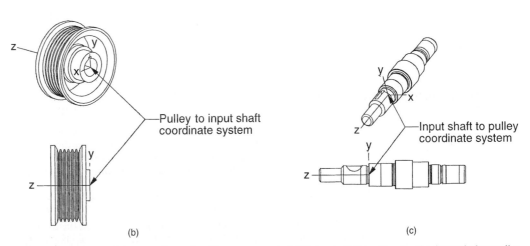

Pulley to input shaft coordinate system

Input shaft to pulley coordinate system

(b)   (c)

FIGURE 32.4 A few of the supercharger's subject components. (*a*) Rotor shaft; (*b*) pulley showing input shaft to pulley coordinate system; (*c*) input shaft showing pulley to input shaft coordinate system. (*Courtesy of Eaton Corporation, Supercharger Division.*)

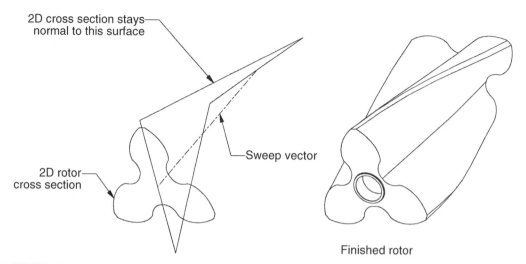

2D cross section stays normal to this surface

Sweep vector

2D rotor cross section

Finished rotor

FIGURE 32.5 SM construction of supercharger rotor. *(Courtesy of Eaton Corporation, Supercharger Division.)*

The rules are simple: the z axis always points toward the pulley and the y axis is vertical (see Figs. 32.4b and 32.4c). The coordinate systems are oriented at logical positions on the parts. For example, consider a pulley that is press-fit on a shaft and seated against a shoulder. The coordinate system for the pulley would have the z axis coaxial with the center line of the pulley and the x-y plane coplanar with a face on the pulley. Similarly, the z axis of the coordinate system would be coaxial with the center line of the shaft and the x-y plane coplanar with the surface that defines the shoulder of the shaft. Then, when assembling the pulley to the shaft, the designer simply selects the coordinate system on one part and the coordinate system on the other, and the parts go together.

What is important is how the coordinate systems are defined so that parts can be substituted for each other. Coordinate systems are defined similarly for all interfacing components (the housing and bearing plate, bearing plate and cover, etc.). The display of coordinate systems are managed by layers so we do not have to see them unless they are required. Because coordinate systems are features, they will regenerate their locations when the features that define them change; this in turn will effect how the parts are assembled.

If in the previous example (see Fig. 32.4) we change the location of the shoulder on the shaft to some other position, the coordinate system will follow it. In turn, the pulley will move to its new location as it is governed by the coordinate system on the shaft. Any part associated to the pulley would move, and so on throughout the entire assembly. This of course is the benefit of the associated database of a parametric relational SM system. Earlier we mentioned that the coordinate systems have unique names. This allows us to interchange similar parts and have various parts within the assembly retain their relation to each other. We can switch covers and input shafts in an assembly and be confident that the seals, pulley, bearings, etc., will still know how to go together. This is accomplished by defining an interchangeability record for each part that defines interfacing features between parts. Typically, these interfacing features are mating surfaces, common axes, and points. In our case, the interchangeability record references named *coordinate systems*.

32.5   Interfacing Solid Modeling with Manufacturing

After a solid model is completed in product design, a copy of it is transferred to the released design vault in the manufacturing database. The tooling designer will then work with this model, or assembly of models, to deign the various fixtures and gages necessary to produce the part. There are two reasons why manufacturing works from a copy instead of the same original model:

1. Product and manufacturing are 800 miles apart. Even though we have a high-speed line linking the networks together, it would still be too slow to reference a 35-Mb assembly.

2. Manufacturing does not want the model to update automatically without their knowledge, and currently we do not have a DBMS in place to handle this type of activity.

Engineering can give manufacturing a copy of a model at revision A, and manufacturing can start to build fixtures around this model. In the interim, engineering completes revision B of the same model and notifies manufacturing that B has been released. Manufacturing will then copy B to their database and replace A in the fixture with B.

By doing it this way there is no demand on the network to reference a large file, and manufacturing can update their work when they are ready. Another advantage to this method is that tooling design usually begins before the solid model is fully detailed. Thus, the tool designer will often begin work on a model that is only partially complete, usually the exterior packaging shape. Product engineering "officially" recognizes only the release model. Once the model is 100 percent complete, the tool designer will replace the partially complete model in the fixture design. This allows us to practice concurrent product development with the understanding that only the release design from engineering will be approved.

A typical fixture design begins by placing a solid model of the milling-machines table and a large slab of metal called a *tombstone* in an assembly (see Fig. 32.6). The tombstone is the main body of the fixture used to hold the parts. Manufacturing reviews the part and establishes how they would like it oriented on the tombstone.

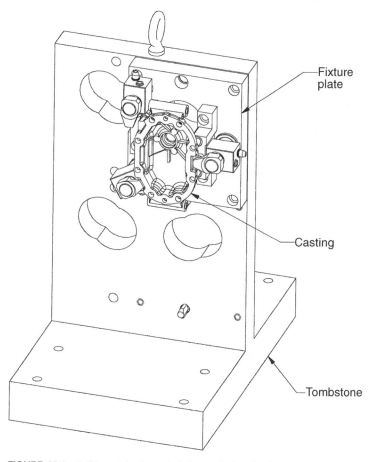

FIGURE 32.6 Solid model of a typical fixture design showing tombstone, fixture plate, and part casting. *(Courtesy of Eaton Corporation, Supercharger Division.)*

The tooling designer places the casting model in the assembly, offset from the tombstone and table-top, and begins designing the fixture. Stops, rest pads, and clamps are assembled to the casting model at the location of datum targets. When these components are in place, the tooling designer creates the necessary fixture blocks to tie the stops and clamps to the tombstone. After the first position on the fixture is complete, the components are translated to the next position, and so on, until the design is complete.

Once the fixture is designed with all the components fully assembled, it is checked to make certain that none of the machines' cutters interferes with it. This is accomplished by placing solid models of the cutters and their holders in the fixture assembly and moving them from place to place, while measuring interference between suspected parts. In the future we plan to implement NC toolpath verification and collision avoidance to replace this manual method.

32.6   Solid Modeling Payoffs

The implementation of SM technology in our organization has produced the following payoffs.

1. **Better tool, gage, and fixture design.** By having the actual part in the form of a solid model, and because tool gage and fixtures are built around the solid model, manufacturing has a much better feel and understanding of the part than was previously obtainable from 2D drawings.

2. **NC programming** is greatly facilitated by linking the fixture assembly via IGES to our CAM software. Previous methods relied on manual programming from 2D prints.

3. **A higher degree of confidence** in the design of complex castings is realized by utilizing cross-sectional analysis and surface-to-surface clearance checking. Complex cross sections through a part or an assembly that might have taken 2 days in a drafting system can be created in seconds with SM.

4. **SM moves our division in the right direction for the future.** As the demands of the industry force the reduction in the product development cycle, we need to take advantage of technologies that can assist us in compressing time to market. By designing with SM we can take advantage of various rapid prototyping services.

5. **Improve the quality of detail drawings.** With SM we are confident that the drawing views are always right and that dimensions and geometry are accurate. All too frequently, our drawings previously had views that weren't projected correctly: dimensions that had been edited and no longer reflected the geometry, a view updated on sheet 1 of a drawing that wasn't carried through to sheet 2 and to the assembly drawings. We do not have these concerns with drawings generated from SM.

Solid Modeling Caution

SMA.32.1   Associated Detail Drawings

Associated detail drawings do not mean 100 percent accuracy and automatic updates, however! If your model is incorrect, then your drawing is incorrect. After a change has been made to a model, the drawings still need to be checked as thoroughly as you would any drawing. You can expect to clean up the placement of text and dimension notes; nonmodel dimensions may no longer be attached if the feature they referenced was deleted or significantly modified.

---

6. **We can better promote the use of standard parts and features with SM.** Once a part is complete it can be used in many assemblies, and those assemblies will update if the model is changed. A standard feature that is used on many different but similar parts can be created on a generic model and copied to new models maintaining the same dimensioning scheme and tolerances as the generic.

7. **Color-shaded images** provide for almost immediate visual feedback to the designer. These images can be shared with engineering, sales, customers, and suppliers.

By combining items 1 through 7 one can see how concurrent engineering, or what we call "Simultaneous Product and Process Development" at Eaton, can be enhanced by utilizing SM.

32.7   Future Goals with Solid Modeling

The use of SM in our organization is by no means complete. There are many goals left to reach and others that are yet to be defined. A few of these goals are discussed.

32.7.1   Integration

One of our goals is to integrate SM with manufacturing for NC programming when workstations can process the necessary data in a short amount of time. We feel that this is still a ways off.

32.7.2 Four-Week Quick Delivery

We have a goal within Product Engineering to be able to deliver a slightly customized supercharger to a customer within 4 weeks. Slightly customized means we take a generic casting and perhaps add some weldments for mounting bosses, provide a specific-length cover, change the number of grooves in a pulley, or provide a specific pulley diameter.

We plan to do this by building models that have all the major features already constructed and detail drawings complete. From these models we'll build a set of castings. Within limitations, we'll be able to incorporate customer-specific installation requirements into these generic castings. We'll do this by adding features to the generic models and then updating the detail drawings. The drawings will be sent to the model shop and the necessary modifications can be made to the castings. It is our intent to have canned NC programs and common fixtures available to facilitate this process.

32.7.3 Rapid Prototyping (RP)

We would like to increase our application of RP technology such as LOM (Laminated Object Manufacturing by Helisys, Inc., Torrance, Calif.) to produce sand castings of our covers, bearing plates, and housings, plus build packaging models for customers. There is also some potential to create hollow rotors using the SLS (Selective Laser Sintering by DTM Corp., Austin, Tex.) for investment castings. (See Chap. 19 for more on SM and RP.)

32.7.4 Coordinate Measuring Machines (CMM)

As more companies are able to access feature information from the SM database for manufacturing, we can foresee linking CMM programming directly to our SM assemblies of inspection fixtures. For example, a part has ten 8-mm holes, 22 mm deep, and you already have the drill to machine them defined in your tool library. Because these holes are features, and features contain all the necessary information about diameter, depth, location on a surface, material type, etc., feature-based NC products automatically know how to machine the feature. We believe that feature recognition by software other than your CAD system is going to have dramatic effects on how parts are machined, inspected, and analyzed for cost.

Pitfalls

SMA.32.2   Organizational Culture

Many of the difficulties we experienced while implementing SM had nothing to do with how well the technology worked but was dependent on our ability to absorb it. Our design and engineering departments have always depended on 2D drawings, not 3D models. Initially, we did not change our attitudes to adapt SM into our design process. For example, a common complaint is, "It takes too long to get a drawing out for quotes because you have to create the 3D solid model first and then detail it."

Yes, in many cases this has been true, but what many fail to realize is that while that 3D solid model is being created much fine-tuning and many corrections to the design are being made to ensure its accuracy. This is one of the earliest benefits of designing with solids. This fine-tuning and these corrections represent possible errors that may not get caught in the 2D drawing, that may end up in a pattern, that may end up in a bad casting, that may end up on an ECN, that may end up back on the designer's desk for corrections to the 2D drawing. Then the ECN has to be routed throughout out the entire engineering department for approval and that can be (and, in most cases, *is*) a lengthy process.

(Continued)

SMA.32.3 Training in Techniques

Another training issue that we haven't resolved, and from my experience attending user groups no one else has either, is how to create a solid model. I'm not being facetious with this and it can be a very aggravating problem. To prove my point, have two designers experienced in modeling build the same part and you will see that they will be completely different from each other. To illustrate the problem further, have a third designer make some edits to one of the models based on a marked-up print of the design.

To us this is a very real situation and one for which we have only a partial solution. The supercharger housing shown in Fig. 32.1 was built by one person and contains approximately 500 features and 6 models. When that person goes on vacation or is sick, someone else has to work on it. How do they figure out the design without spending countless hours querying the model for feature construction information?

We don't have an answer for this particular case, but we have begun to address this problem in the following manner. All of our standard parts such as the shafts and rotors are either simple enough to figure out or they have a *cookbook* construction technique.

More complicated parts like our castings are built from what we call "generic" models. These generic models contain 50 percent or more of the standard features that this part would always have. When designers need a part like this, they copy the generic and use it as the basis for a new design. The initial features set is well understood, so anyone else working on the design would have to figure out the nonstandard features only.

Unfortunately, in the case of the housing shown in Fig. 32.1, it is a totally custom part and the knowledge of building it is in the hands of one person. Tools are provided that assist one in determining how the model was created, what features relationships are, and assembly constraints.

SMA.32.4 Lost or Corrupted Models

For one reason or another we have experienced lost or corrupted models. When this happens we first look for the part on backup. We have excellent utilities to manage backups. If we find the model in its uncorrupted state, then all is fine. If not, then we have to manually replace the part in the assemblies that reference it. In many cases, tools are provided to interactively replace parts in an assembly that can no longer be retrieved. Although this is a slow and frustrating job, it does allow an assembly to be repaired.

Make sure that the SM system you are evaluating is equipped to handle this type of failure. Keep in mind that any notes or dimensions that might have referenced the corrupted part may now be lost, and all associated drawings will have to be checked for errors. Assembly modeling and problems associated with doing a top-down design illustrate why this is so.

SMA.32.5 Training Requirements

Training for SM design was far more complicated than expected. Our initial training was held on-site at the Marshall, Michigan, facility. All designers and a select group of product engineers who were accomplished in CAD were trained during a week-long seminar.

The next week we were on our own, without a clue as to how we'd go about developing superchargers in SM. We didn't know all the little nuances of modeling (e.g., to add draft to the model before adding fillets). We didn't know about advanced functions that we'd need to make castings. To get around some of these start-up issues we arranged for some on-site consulting. This proved very worthwhile and we would advise anyone to set aside at least one week's worth of consulting time in their budget before launching SM.

SMA.32.6 Spot Training

Much of our ongoing training is on a case-by-case basis as the opportunity arises. A designer might have the need to design a certain feature but may not know the best method. We then work with them on some new techniques or perhaps show them several ways to approach the problem.

SMA.32.7 Associativity, Good and Bad

Managing the SM data we create has been a nightmare and took us totally by surprise. You could say that the best and worst feature of a parametric relational SM system is associativity. For example, we have a common shaft that is used in a dozen assemblies. This is one shaft being referenced

(*Continued*)

Pitfalls
(*Continued*)

by 12 different assembly models, assembly drawings, subassemblies, and detail drawings, etc. Now, we make a change to that shaft and the change is propagated to all associated models and drawings. That's great and exactly what we want—five days' worth of design changes updated in 10 minutes.

Now, despite proper security precautions, electronic data files are not immune to destruction. Somehow that shaft model becomes corrupted, misplaced, or accidentally deleted from the system. We now have 12 assembly models with a shaft missing. But even worse, we possibly have 12 assembly models that are subject to corruption because the system cannot link the proper associativity chain between other parts that were dependent on that shaft! All assembly models and drawings that reference that shaft could potentially be corrupted and rendered useless.

Note: Like any advancing technology, there are areas in which SM can benefit from improvement. Listed here are a few (certainly not all) needed improvements that we, as end users, highly recommend.

Needed Improvements

SMA.32.8   Faster Affordable Hardware

We feel that, as of this writing, there is not an affordable workstation available (less than 50K) that we could not bring to its knees with just one of our solid models. Processing capability greatly effects an operator's productivity. Too much time is spent waiting for display, model regeneration, and model retrieval from disk.

SMA.32.9   Increased Feature Modeling Capability

In our opinion, parametric relational SM systems still have a long way to go to make feature creation more intuitive, accurate, and in some cases even possible. Our most difficult task in modeling castings is getting all drafted surfaces, rounds, and fillets in place. We feel that today's SM software is a long way from being able to do what a pattern maker can do with his or her thumb when filleting the intersection between three surfaces (see Chap. 5 for more on curves and surfaces with SM). We also experience many inconsistencies when creating solid features. At times, you are amazed at the complexity of an intersection created by a feature in the model and, at other times, left dumbfounded because the system cannot create a simple hole.

SMA.32.10   Assembly Modeling

No matter what people say, it is still difficult to apply a top-down design approach with SM (see Chap. 11 for more on SM for assemblies). Even though the tools exist for designing in assembly mode, we feel it is still easier to model individual parts and collect them later in an assembly.

Author's Note: The author would like to thank Larry Larder and Dennis Strauch at the Eaton Corporate R&D Center for their assistance in producing the two color images shown on a Tektronic II SPX Dye Sublimination printer. Also a special thanks to Mike Sadger for his work on the housing casting and assembly models.

Chapter 33

Roundtable Discussion

Despite High-Tech SM Laurels, the Glory Remains in Making Parts

Laura Carrabine
Editorial Manager
SDRC

No longer touted as specialized software for an elite group of experts, Solid Modeling (SM) has become the core of many leading-edge CAD/CAM/CAE systems. Indeed, as power and ease of use have increased tenfold, SM systems can tackle most mechanical design tasks at a fraction of the time former 2D tools and techniques took. In the fiercely competitive global marketplace of the 1990s, manufacturers are driven by reducing production schedules, improving product quality, and gaining new market share. To meet these demands and remain successful as the next century approaches, companies are acquiring SM software at a brisk pace. Yet, implementing state-of-the-art tools is tricky business, and industry experts agree that in order to make SM applications successful, it takes a careful combination of tools, technology, training, and talent to create a winner.

Conversations with Dave Burdick, Program Director CIM Service, the Gartner Group; Marc Halpern, Research Director, D.H. Brown Associates, Inc.; Stephen Wolfe, Editor of the *Computer Aided Design Report;* and information from a survey titled: *The National Study of Solid Modeling User Expectations** from Gisela Wilson, Mechanical CAD/CAE/CAM Program Manager, CAD/CAM International Data Corporation (IDC), reveal careful scrutiny of the SM evolution—its impact on design for manufacturing and how trends will impact future engineering and technologies. Highlights include getting beyond all the bells and whistles to find out how high-tech solutions can help or hinder how engineers crank out new products.

33.1 Not *Who* Needs SM, but *Why?*

Every engineer who tells his or her manager, "Gee, we really need to do solid modeling!" should also propose reasons why implementing the software would benefit the overall organization, not simply an individual or small group. Careful scrutiny of internal operations should be considered as important as the software evaluation. For clients considering a change in technology, the experts agree that SM on its own is not a cure-all. Burdick says that SM isn't the biggest issue. "Users need to adapt a richer design representation."

To do so, engineers and designers need to move beyond the world of simply documenting design intent to *leveraging* design intent. And, to do that, they need a more robust fundamental set of tools and capabilities. So, instead of simply creating 2D drawings which just document intent, SM technology and

---

*Copies of this survey are available by contacting IDC, Framingham, Mass., (508) 872-8200.

more advanced modeling techniques, such as parametric and variational input and concurrent associativity, allow users to begin to leverage past design history. "It's very difficult to modify and create new designs," says Burdick, "when the design history is captured in the form of a drawing."

However, if engineers are working with a full design representation in the form of a 3D model, one with variables and constraints that can be altered to create new designs, it's much easier. It is more favorable to have a richer geometric description so analysis and manufacturing can leverage that data upstream more easily and more productively.

"First," continues Burdick, "consider the mind-set of the organization. If it is looking at SM technology as a means to attack the historic productivity issue, the effort is going to fail. The significant benefits from an SM system are not simply the ability to bolster the productivity of drafters and engineers. Rather, the biggest benefits are *capabilities*—the capability to reduce time to market, the capability to improve product innovation, the capability to build defensive market positions, and the capability to deal with all kinds of regulations."

The second issue to consider in order to take full advantage of SM is recognizing the need to reengineer processes. Halpern adds that companies should develop a rational strategy of how to change their processes. "There has to be a commitment to change," says Halpern, "and an incremental plan that is evaluated each step of the way. Committees have to determine which processes work and which ones don't and why they don't. It's not an overnight effort. It takes time, discipline, resources, and hard work. You can't just drop SM software on engineers' desks and expect big changes. That's not going to happen."

Generally, successful implementations of SM technology occur when companies have done their homework, which includes converging the information/technology infrastructure. It's not unusual that many large manufacturers that have been around for 20 or 30 years are now operating 10 or more different CAD/CAM/CAE and/or drafting systems. Burdick says such companies need to determine how to converge the underlying foundation technologies in order to reap the benefits of a new SM system. "This is paramount to truly take advantage of the elusive goal of integration. Companies need to seek a higher plane and look at these important issues before adding SM to the fray," adds Burdick.

According to the IDC survey, several reasons for selecting an SM system were noted. Most relate directly to features and functionality. They include:

1. Parametric capabilities
2. Availability of finite element and plastics modules
3. Ties to finite element analysis
4. Good translation to other software

33.2 Going Beyond Concurrent Engineering: Developing an Enterprise-Wide Vision

The Gartner Group considers an organization's psyche—the overall view of where the company believes it is today, where it wants to be in the future, and how it plans to get there. "Our approach," says Burdick, "is called Concurrent Art to Product Engineering (CAPE) to help clients achieve their goals. Many companies are recognizing that the tool-by-tool and department-by-department approach to adapting SM isn't hacking it anymore. Now, they are looking more strategically across the whole enterprise to see how they can thoroughly enhance engineering processes. Within any given organization, there are different groups of people with different attitudes about the CAPE approach. In many cases, there *are* people within these companies who have a corporate vision. However, if you talk with individual engineers in one division, they could care less about CAPE. They just want the tools to help them do their job better and faster."

Burdick sees three classes of companies that are changing from one technology to another:

Category One companies are typically operating a mainframe 2D drafting system and the organization decides to downsize in order to find a lower-cost way to continue to do 2D drafting. "These types of companies will probably not be very successful," adds Burdick.

Category Two companies may be operating an older system, such as a mainframe or minicomputer and using third-generation CAD tools. The company is investigating ways to begin using 3D, next-generation tools more productively.

Category Three companies are one step beyond, already using workstations running SM technology with success. These types of companies are fundamentally altering processes and beginning to link the technology not only internally, but also externally with their suppliers.

In many cases, in order to make these engineering process changes, companies have to create the need for change. In most companies, the scenario isn't someone who has a great vision of how things ought to be. Rather, the need emanates from competitive products getting to market faster. Burdick says, "The whole time-to-market issue is really coming to bear. Speed and innovation are becoming the watchwords for the 1990s, not simply increasing productivity."

33.3   Selecting New Technology: The Bait and the Benchmark

According to Wolfe, only 30 percent of those who step up to the SM bat hit a home run. "There are a lot of companies that consider implementing SM, believe everything vendors tell them, buy a system, then fail miserably. Take modeling and assembly processes, for instance. A company may find that the software they selected isn't really very good for assembly modeling. Once they get the assemblies modeled, they can't make drawings. Moreover, they can't do the things they need to do to manufacture parts. This exercise certainly isn't cost-effective, but it *is* an education."

Wolfe explains that companies should study how they can use SM to more effectively accomplish what they do. If it does not meet their needs and expectations, they shouldn't buy it. "People who do their homework correctly do not run into these problems. A lot of people go through the motions, but what they are really trying to do is justify an off-the-wall decision someone made along the way."

Wolfe and others strongly advise conducting benchmark testing and pilot projects in the SM decision-making process. Based on the results of a particular benchmark, however, it is wrong to expect the same system to be the universal system to do everything. "This strategy does not work," says Wolfe. "What happens is companies do a little homework in one area and then try to generalize the results across the entire product line, and it may not be feasible. Some SM systems are terrific tools for making plastic castings, but they aren't effective for designing complex assemblies or sculpted surfaces. If a benchmark does a beautiful job of designing a automotive doorknob, you cannot be sure the same package will work for designing the dashboard. One little piece does not tell the whole story.

"Unless companies take it upon themselves to assume a realistic view of what SM technology can and cannot do, they will continue to struggle. Once burned a couple of times, however, organizations are beginning to develop a foundation of what's necessary to remain competitive," adds Wolfe.

Halpern concurs and adds that many companies adopt SM as a panacea without changing the design process. "What we find is that if engineers work within a drawing-driven environment, SM never takes the leading role it's meant to play. Companies are not leveraging SM. Is there incremental change? Yes, but companies need to make a wholesale commitment to changing their design process in an evolutionary fashion in order to take full advantage of SM."

As an example, the D.H. Brown group recently interviewed 16 large companies using two leading SM packages. Over time, only two companies had eliminated the need to generate drawings. What differentiated these two companies from the other 14? Halpern says, "They changed the design process to the point at which they changed terminology to their own vocabulary, and eliminated old terminology. They also demanded that their subcontractors adopt SM or they would do their own in-house manufacturing."

Halpern notes that Japanese manufacturers, traditionally 2D engineering environments, define their processes *before* adopting any new technology, including SM. "The Japanese live by the process of continual implementation and constant evaluation." Halpern adds, "Manufacturing, engineering, and process engineers all work together in the same room. They didn't optimize their processes overnight. It's been over decades. Too many companies in the United States want to use SM technology as a "shrink-wrapped" solution and try to make a go of it. For many companies, the bottom line still relates to creating drawings for subcontractors who complete projects using different systems. So the improvement that SM provides is incremental and certainly not as widespread as it could be."

33.4   Out of the Mechanical Engineering Department

To be sure, a new wave of industries are jumping on the SM bandwagon. The benefits derived from 3D capabilities are spewing forth from a myriad of applications—from medical imaging to interior design to scientific visualization. For example, physicians and researchers using SM technology can design custom prosthetic devices and surgical equipment. Halpern believes SM may also play more of a role in molecular modeling. "The software can help scientists formulate the theoretical structure of chemicals, materials, and synthetic reactions. Molecular structures are so complex that it is difficult to capture the models with theoretical diagrams."

The IDC survey reports that SM systems can be used for a wide range of design and engineering tasks, ranging from preparing pictures for design reviews to engineering tasks such as mass-property calculations. When asked to rank the three applications that provide SM users with the greatest payback, visualization was ranked first, parts design was second, and assembly design was third. (Others in order of greatest payback include: industrial design, interference checking, drafting, input to finite element modeler, mass-property calculations, preparation of pictures, NC applications, stereolithography/desktop manufacturing, and kinematics.)

Among applications of SM systems used by survey respondents, visualization, parts design, and conceptualization/industrial design were the most popular. Visualization, for instance, allows everyone on a project team (mechanical engineers, manufacturing engineers, electrical engineers, packaging engineers, drafters, marketing staff, management, etc.) to envision what products will look like upon completion. Everyone can benefit from solid 3D representations of their work. The IDC survey shows that 85 percent of the survey respondents use the visualization capabilities of their SM systems.

The use of SM can also be found in the cinema, dentistry, jewelry design, and geophysical studies. Halpern notes that SM systems are still very demanding from hardware and ease-of-use points of view. "As the technology improves and the price/performance on hardware continues to explode, I expect to see SM taking off in the home markets someday."

Many engineering departments at colleges and universities throughout the world are teaching SM and using it as a research tool. Increasingly more manufacturers are coordinating efforts with leading engineering and research groups at institutions, such as MIT, Stanford, and the U.S. Naval Academy, to design new products using SM technology and techniques. As a result, more graduates have knowledge and experience with real-world design and manufacturing processes, as well as hands-on training with sophisticated CAD/CAM/CAE tools, largely due to cooperative relationships between schools and industry.

Wolfe believes that true SM will remain in the engineering department, at least for while. "SM is not going to apply to nonengineering fields because it's too cumbersome. Each model requires too many parameters to be described. Not only do users have to be very learned, they have to think in terms of procedures and analytical geometry. If you think about CAD/CAM in this way, you will be an effective operator. If you don't, you're going to have a lot of trouble."

33.5   What Technology Will Evolve from SM?

The experts' predictions were mixed. Wolfe says more advanced research needs to be devoted by the leading software vendors and universities in order for new technology to emerge. "If I was R&D director at a profitable CAD/CAM company, I would commit to advanced research for new technology and mathematics."

Halpern hopes that SM will evolve into standard high-level representations that can liberate designers from details of geometry construction demands on different systems. "These representations," says Halpern, "would provide robust semantics that will allow users to describe their designs through highly intuitive graphic gestures and expressions of design intent."

"Technology is a window," says Burdick. "People aren't paying enough attention to what they are trying to do. They need to learn how to balance people, processes, and technology to try to get their jobs done. We'll look back 20 years from now and see that the most successful companies are the ones that have done a good job of balancing these three elements.

"In the past, there weren't many compelling reasons to use an SM system. For certain applications, such as analysis and conceptual design, there were some benefits, but there wasn't a rich enough or easy enough SM system available which would allow users to do all their engineering work.

"Now, we see the emergence of what we call second-generation hybrid modelers which extend beyond parametric modeling. These systems allow for some very sophisticated modeling functionality and associative capabilities, so engineers can use it for analysis and conceptual design. The other big plus is that they are easy to use, easier to use than some drafting packages that people have come to love or hate over the years," explains Burdick.

Wilson adds, "At a current cost per seat of around $10,000 just for SM, however, this level of technology diffusion within a company and its extended enterprise is unrealistic, unless we are talking about high-end users such as Ford or Boeing.

"Hurdles to a broader use of SM are not only the software costs per se, but also the need to upgrade existing hardware and networking capabilities. Passing solid models around and viewing them goes beyond the capabilities of the average PC on most desks," continues Wilson.

Wilson expects SM to become a nonissue in the near term: as CAD vendors take their pricing down to commodity software levels. Wilson adds, "Users will no longer buy technology, but the most efficient standards-based tools for their product development work."

All the experts agree that SM systems should be less expensive and vendors should consider ways to make systems more affordable for more users. Purchasing an SM system means not only the up-front license fee, but also maintenance fees, upgrade charges, license transferability between platforms, education, and training costs. Burdick adds, "People are too preoccupied with the initial software price. If you look at the ownership of the system, *that* is such a small part of the what people actually pay. However, there is a mind-set in the marketplace that everything ought to cost just $500."

The IDC user survey reports that, although the increase in both active and casual users of SM will require a proportional increase in spending for SM software and training, the spending plans show that half of the survey sites spent less than $25,000 on SM and training in recent years. This low spending is expected to continue. It is interesting to compare the spending plans among sites with fewer than 50 engineers and drafters and sites with 50 and more such employees. Both groups plan to increase their SM spending at about the same rate.

IDC adds, "Lack of training is often cited as one of the explanations for the relatively slow acceptance of SM among designers and engineers. Therefore, the IDC survey tried to establish how SM users are trained, and which method they themselves consider to be the most effective.

"As it turns out, four-fifths of the SM users are trained by CAD/CAM/CAE software vendors themselves, either by attending the vendors' SM courses or through their user manuals and on-line help. About one-sixth of the users receive in-house training, and only 5 percent of the users attend college or university courses. Vendors receive high marks for their training from current SM users: almost three-fourths of them consider vendor training courses the most effective training methods. In-house courses are at the top of the second most effective training methods, and vendor manuals lead among the third most effective training methods."

The report continues, "On-line help does not score well at all. While the survey does not explore why certain training methods are more popular than others, it is clear that vendors need to devote close attention to this issue."

IDC's report shows that SM vendors should feel optimistic about the future because users are beginning to realize the benefits. And, as costs for hardware and software continue to spiral downward, the incentive to purchase is more enticing. According to the report, "Users are planning to design considerably more parts using SM technology and to increase the number of employees using SM tools." Indeed, this translates into increased revenues for vendors. Additionally, as increasingly more SM systems are easier to use, IDC expects that the time users spend on SM will increase. This coincides with increased pressure by manufacturers to improve design and engineering processes.

Advice and Observations

SMA.33.1 Meeting Your Needs

Companies should study how they can use SM to more effectively accomplish what they do. If it does not meet their needs and expectations, they shouldn't buy it. People who do their homework correctly do not run into these problems. A lot of people go through the motions, but what they are really trying to do is justify an off-the-wall decision someone made along the way.

SMA.33.2 Benchmarks and Reality

It is strongly advised to conduct benchmark testing and pilot projects in the SM decision-making process. Based on the results of a particular benchmark, however, it is wrong to expect the same system to be the universal system to do everything. If a benchmark does a beautiful job of designing a automotive doorknob, you cannot be sure the same package will work for designing the dashboard. One little piece does not tell the whole story.

Stephen Wolfe, Editor
Computer-Aided Report, San Diego, Calif.

SMA.33.3 A Plan for Change

Companies should develop a rational strategy of how to change their processes. There has to be a commitment to change and an incremental plan that is evaluated each step of the way. Committees have to determine which processes work and which ones don't and why they don't. It's not an

(Continued)

overnight effort. It takes time, discipline, resources, and hard work. You can't just drop SM software on engineers' desks and expect big changes. That's not going to happen.

SMA.33.4   Make a Wholesale Commitment

Many companies adopt SM as a panacea without changing the design process. If engineers work within a drawing-driven environment, SM will never take the leading role it's meant to play. Companies are not leveraging SM. Is there incremental change? Yes, but companies need to make a wholesale commitment to changing their design process in order to take full advantage of SM.

Marc Halpern, Research Manager
D.H. Brown & Associates, Inc. Port Chester, N.Y.

SMA.33.5   Balance People, Processes, and Technology

Technology is a window. People aren't paying enough attention to what they are trying to do. They need to learn how to balance people, processes, and technology to try to get their jobs done. We'll look back 20 years from now and see that the most successful companies are the ones that have done a good job of balancing these three elements.

SMA.33.6   Cost Considerations

Purchasing an SM system means not only the up-front license fee, but also maintenance fees, upgrade charges, license transferability between platforms, education, and training costs. People are too preoccupied with the initial software price. If you look at the ownership of the system, that is such a small part of the what people actually pay.

Dave Burdick, Program Director CIM Service
The Gartner Group, Inc., Santa Clara, Calif.

SMA.33.7   In Retrospect

Operators of CAD systems five years ago had enough to learn in simply grasping the 3D concept and utilizing their own design knowledge with that of the system. Now it seems as though designers must split their concerns between what the part design requires and what the SM system must have to allow the part to be modeled properly.

SMA.33.8   Drawings and Model Complexity

Those of us who have taken the technological leap forward into 3D SM sometimes forget that the majority of the CAD systems used today are mainly for 2D drafting. While we see the virtues of SM as much more than creating 2D detail drawings, those not directly familiar with SM often don't understand the complexity of the solid model required to generate that detail drawing.

SMA.33.9   Conventional Detail Requirements

Detail drafting is still a necessary evil in this day even with the advent of direct numerical control to download part information to machining centers. Customers often require "as built" drawings for their records. Purchasing departments sometimes require drawings be sent to vendors for adherence to specifications. Assembly personnel still require drawings to assist in building the components.

SMA.33.10   SM Flaws

There are some serious flaws in SM technology that must be addressed. The complexity involved due to the parametric and variational capability built into SM detracts from the ability of the designer to concentrate on the end product. Data management systems are cumbersome and often require more knowledge than many CAD operators possess. A new wave of users will eventually catch up with the requirements of the new SM systems and the ongoing efforts of vendors to supply more intuitive software will aid the process.

(*Continued*)

SMA.33.11   SM of the Future

SM of the future should allow designers to define attributes at the time of file creation and automatically track and store files. More flexibility in manipulating parametric and variational models must be made available. Modification to solids for downstream processes should be kept to a minimum or made easier.

In general, today's generation of SM systems has forced companies to hire more educated engineering personnel to replace the draftspersons generally using CAD systems of the past. The added intelligence required should be built into the system to reduce operating costs.

Editor's Note: Very good point!

Kevin P. Alexander, CAD/CAM/CAE System Administrator
Littleford Day, Inc., Florence, Ky.

SMA.33.12   More SM Flaws

Here are some negative aspects of SM technology. It should be noted that not all SM systems share these faults.

1. Conventional SM (nonparametric) makes the process of modifying solids extremely cumbersome.

2. Creates extremely large files.

3. Can overload the software (greater than maximum entity count).

4. Requires large amounts of memory (RAM).

5. Much more data to process; therefore, all operations become slower and slower as the design matures (see Chap. 6 for modeling strategies).

6. Limits the number of parts that can be inserted into a layout.

7. Can only transfer SM data to vendors with same software. Must extract surfaces or wireframe to transfer to vendors with different systems (see Chap. 21).

8. Parametrics:

   a. Cannot make some modifications depending on order of construction.

   b. Must remember how a feature was created in order to modify it. The construction method is not always obvious.

   c. Cannot (with come SM systems) rearrange the order of construction.

SMA.33.13   SM Hardware Selection

Purchase the most powerful hardware available and the largest screen possible!

Howard W. Stolz, Product Designer
Sun Microsystems, Mountain View, Calif.

SMA.33.14   The Rest of the Story

Graphical data is only a small percentage of a complete design package. The SM system must be able to manage and integrate the information accumulated during the entire process, including engineering, detail design, procurement, and production.

Brian Ruuska, CAD/CAE Applications Engineer
3M Co., St. Paul, Minn.

SMA.33.15   The Weakest Link

In the final analysis, a company's technology is only as good as its slowest component. SM is only one of the technologies required for faster time to market through concurrent engineering.

(*Continued*)

Advice and Observations
(*Continued*)

CAD/CAM International Data Corporation (IDC) recently conducted two focus groups of high-level technology decision makers in the automotive industry which pointed to the following hurdles on the road to faster time to market:

1. The need to develop a long-term CAD strategy that includes the company's subsuppliers

2. The need to optimize the entire product development process before automation can even begin to provide benefits

3. The need to break down the barriers between different functions of the product development process, so that product data developed through SM can actually be leveraged throughout the entire process, down to manufacturing

Gisela Wilson, Program Manager
CAD/CAM International Data Corp., Framingham, Mass.

SMA.33.16   Design Dependence

Many organizations are totally dependent on 3D surface and SM for the design of complicated geometric parts. Unfortunately, some design decisions are made based on a CAD system and designers' modeling ability.

In the days of traditional drafting techniques, producing a 2D detail drawing of a complex part was difficult at times, but allowed for insufficient geometric definition in noncritical areas that were best left to a talented model maker. SM will not allow such lack of definition. As designers with SM, we must now choose our design solutions carefully. Difficult geometric areas can add days to a part's modeling time. On a good note, this encourages us to find simpler solutions to complicated design situations.

Don LaCourse, President
The Solid Modeling ExChange, Algood, Tenn.

Glossary

Special appreciation is extended to the following organizations for their extensive contributions to this glossary:

Aaron Marcus and Associates
Autodesk, Inc.
CIMData, Inc.
Computer-Aided Design Software, Inc. (CADSI)
ICAD, Inc.
IGES Data Analysis, Inc.
Intergraph Corporation
Lowrey Consulting
Manufacturing and Consulting Services, Inc. (MCS)
National Institute of Standards and Technology (NIST)
Octree Corporation
The MacNeal-Schwendler Corporation (MSC)
Varimetrix Corporation
Volkswagen Automotive Group
Wavefront Technologies
Wohlers Associates
Wright Consulting

absolute coordinates   The location of a point in terms of distances and/or angles from a fixed origin.

absolute path name   Sequence of directories, beginning with the root directory (/) that locates a file. See also **path name** and **relative path name**.

acceleratio   A distributed body force such as gravity.

accuracy settings   Refers to system tolerances. All 3D objects, whether manufactured or computer-generated, are defined within acceptable geometric tolerances.

active coordinate system   Coordinate system in which key-in point coordinates and read-out coordinates are expressed. See also **coordinate system**.

active depth   Plane in a 3D design upon which you can place elements and perform manipulations.

ad hoc   For the particular case at hand, without consideration of a wider application.

AEC   Architecture, Engineering, and Construction.

AIAG   Automotive Industry Action Group.

algebraic function   A function $f(x)$ such that for some polynomial $P(x,y)$ it is true that $P(x,f(x)) = 0$.

algorithm   A mathematical procedure used to compute a desired result.

aliasing   Refers to the jagged lines or edges that can appear in computer-drawn images. Aliasing occurs when smooth lines or edges in an image are drawn with pixels. Aliasing can be eliminated automatically through a technique called oversampling (also called *antialiasing*), but at a cost of increasing the time required to create the image.

ambient light   Background light that is defined in rendered images or animations. Examples of ambient light are starlight and hazy sunlight.

angle bisector   Line dividing an angle into two equal parts.

angular acceleration   The rate at which a structure is accelerating in spin rate about an axis.

angular velocity   The rate at which a structure is spinning about an axis.

animation   To give life to. In SM, animations can either be real time or simulated. A real-time animation would consist of a macro actually executing commands to modify or move geometry. A simulated animation would simply be a slide show of captured images.

annotation   The text included on a drawing or model, such as notes, instructions, dimensions, etc.

ANSI   American National Standards Institute.

ANSI Y14   An ANSI subcommittee. Y14 (Computer-Aided Preparation of Product Definition Data).

antialiasing See **aliasing**.

antisymmetry surface restraint The restraint of a surface tangent to the surface. This implies that the structure is symmetrical about this plane, and the load on the implied symmetrical part is equal to, but in a direction opposite to, the modeled part.

API Application Programmer's Interface.

arc A curve segment defined by a start angle, end angle, and a constant radius.

array A rectangular or circular pattern of graphical objects.

ASCII American Standard Code for Information Interchange. A standard set of 128 binary numbers representing keyboard information such as letters, numerals, and punctuation.

ASME American Society of Mechanical Engineers.

aspect ratio The shape of the display device on which an image will be viewed. The aspect ratio of a rendered image is expressed as the width of the image divided by its height.

assembly A final gathering of piece-parts and subassemblies to make one unique assembled product.

assembly modeling The process by which individual solid models are brought together to form an assembly model.

associative geometry A system that lets you place graphic elements based on a relationship (for example, parallel to) with existing graphic elements. Elements placed associatively maintain the relationship when the existing graphic element is manipulated.

attenuation The gradual decrease of light intensity or fog thickness as it travels from its origin.

attribute Textual information associated with CAD geometry. Attributes can be assigned to objects and then later extracted. Applications include creating bills of material.

automatic mesh generation A process that uses geometry and topology of the solid model and mesh rules developed by analysts to allow computer generation of the mesh model.

auxiliary coordinate system A coordinate system defined in addition to the default coordinate system to provide an alternate, simplified way to express coordinates for specific geometric shapes. See also **coordinate system**.

axis An annotation tool that provides a model's orientation in 3D space.

axisymmetric A solid geometric entity that is symmetric and typically revolved about a common axis.

B-spline curve Parametrically defined curve where each pole influences a defined range of the curve.

B-spline surface Parametrically defined surface where each pole influences a defined range of the surface.

Bailout During the early stages of a given change, individuals often experience a disinterest in the occurring change. This disinterest is demonstrated as behavior referred to as *bailout* and may be expressed by the individual either internally or externally.

bandwidth The difference in node numbers or degrees of freedom for a stiffness matrix stored by numerical ascending order of the nodes.

batch-oriented programs Batch implies control is passed to another solver or program for solution at a later time. The alternative is to perform the solution interactively.

benchmark A test given to several SM software vendors usually in the form of a modeling task. A benchmark can be used to determine which SM product has features most applicable to the type of work required.

Bezier curve Parametrically defined curve where each pole influences the entire curve.

Bezier surface Parametrically defined surface where each pole influences the entire surface.

bicubic patch A surface element that is defined by cubic equations in two parametric variables on its surface (e.g., u and v).

bill of materials A tabulated diagram that shows the assembly hierarchy, the number of occurrences of each part in each subassembly, and the number of occurrences of each subassembly in the overall assembly.

binary A variable that can have one of only two values (e.g., 0 or 1, ON or OFF, etc.).

bit map The digital representation of an image in which bits are referenced (mapped) to pixels. In color graphics, a different value is used for each red, green, and blue component of a pixel.

bit plane Hardware used as a storage medium for a bit map.

bits A binary digit (1 or 0).

blend A solid transition of variable cross section swept along an arbitrary path. Its definition consists of two or more dissimilar closed planer profiles and a trajectory curve.

BOM Bill of Materials.

boolean Boolean algebra is named after the English mathematician George Boole, 1815–1864. Also refers to three CSG operations to construct solid objects: UNION, DIFFERENCE, and INTERSECTION. Any valid solid can be used in boolean operations, including primitives, geometric operations, or the result of previous boolean operations.

boolean DIFFERENCE One of three boolean operations that subtracts one solid primitive from another solid, such as the subtraction of a cylinder from a solid in order to make a hole. Also referred to as SUBTRACT or REMOVE.

boolean INTERSECTION One of three boolean operations where the resulting solid is defined as the volume common to the selected solids. Also referred to as COMMON, CONJOIN, or INTERSECT.

boolean UNION One of three boolean operations that combines two separate solids so that the space of the two solids becomes the space of the new solid. Also referred to as ADD, COMBINE, JOIN, or MERGE.

bottom-up design An approach to assembly modeling where the designer creates the part geometry as the first step, then combines parts into appropriate subassemblies and the final assembly. See also **top-down design**.

boundary A 3D outline of a data volume.

boundary evaluation An operation that generates a B-Rep solid from a CSG solid.

boundary representation (B-Rep) A database method that defines and stores a solid as a set of vertices, edges, and faces (points, lines, curves, and surfaces) which completely enclose its volume.

bounded objects In SM, an object is considered bounded if it has a complete set of bounding surfaces and is restricted to occupying a finite volume.

bounding box A box that encloses a 3D geometric object.

box A solid primitive defined as a right-rectangular hexahedron. That is, it has six rectangular faces. The typical input required is length, width, height, and location.

branch node A database tree structure in which a tree node is connected to two or more nodes below it (at a greater distance from the root node).

buffer See **frame buffer**.

bump texture A texture that modifies surface normals and is used to shade an object's surface.

bytes A computer value that consists of 8 bits.

cached value A value of an entity attribute that has already been calculated and is stored in the computer memory. The next time the value of the attribute is required, it does not have to be recalculated.

CAD Computer-Aided Design.

CAE Computer-Aided Engineering.

CALS Computer-aided Acquisition and Logistics Support. CALS is a U.S. Department of Defense and industry strategy to transition from paper-intensive processes to automated electronic data exchange. IGES is one of the neutral data exchange formats used in the CALS initiative. A proposed change of the meaning of the CALS acronym to Continuous Acquisition and Life-cycle Support is pending approval.

CAM Computer-Aided Manufacturing.

camera A term typically used in viewing and display applications. A camera is a means through which to view a modeled scene. You can move cameras, set near and far clipping planes, and set the focal length or scale.

cartesian coordinate system A rectangular coordinate system consisting of three mutually perpendicular axes: the x axis, the y axis, and the z axis.

cascading windows A GUI design where the windows cascade. This is a special case of overlapping window management in which the windows are arranged automatically in a regular progression that prevents any window from being completely obscured.

case loads Loads that are grouped to approximate a loading case on the structure.

CBT Computer-Based Training.

CE Concurrent Engineering.

cell Permanent association of elements that can be stored and placed as a group, and then manipulated either as individual elements or as a group. Also referred to as a *block* and/or *component*. See also **component library**.

centroid The center of mass of an object. If the object's density is uniform, the center of mass is also the centroid of the volume. A value calculated by the mass-properties analysis of a solid model.

CGA Color Graphics Adaptor.

CGM Color Graphics Metafile.

chamfer A beveled edge or corner between two otherwise intersecting lines or surfaces.

change propagation The changes made to a part's design as it is refined into a product, and as current products are evolved into new products. Also refers to the distribution of change from a root cause.

children (1) The components of a design instance in a product structure tree. Also referred to as *parts*. (2) Nodes in a database tree structure that have a parent.

choice attributes Engineering rules in which the user is prompted for a value.

CIM Computer-Integrated Manufacturing. Also, Corporate Information Management.

circle Element that is a closed planar curve, every point of which is equidistant from the center point.

clean modeling Refers to the practice of removing geometry from a model that is not wanted or needed. Also refers to the use of proper geometry construction techniques, such as creating continuous surfaces, minimizing narrow faces, and avoiding small corner angles, that facilitates downstream processes.

click To select something by positioning the cursor and pressing a mouse button.

client A piece of software on the same network that requests and uses the capabilities provided by a server.

client-server architecture A GUI design that allows a single instance of the windowing system software to be shared across entire networks of heterogeneous machines. Response times may be limited by the communication bandwidth of the network.

clipping plane A plane parallel to the camera lens (or current view) that defines the near or far boundary of what is displayed. Objects closer than the near **clipping plane** and farther than the far **clipping plane** are removed from the display. If an object is bisected by a **clipping plane**, it appears to be cut in two.

closed B-spline curve B-spline curve that effectively has no start or end.

closed B-spline surface B-spline surface that effectively has no start or end edges in either or both the U and V directions.

closed planar profile A profile defined by a completely closed area (no gaps) and where each entity in the profile lies on the same plane.

CMM Coordinate Measuring Machine.

CNC Computerized Numerical Control.

coincidence Refers to geometry that occupies the same spatial location. For example, coincident vertices are points that occupy the same x, y, z coordinates. Coincident lines can have differing lengths while one occupies the same location as the other.

color map   A range of colors associated with a range of scalar values. The scalar values can be assigned default rainbow colors or can be a custom RGB color mix.

color texture   A texture that modifies the color, ambient, highlight, dissolve, or reflection of a material.

compiling   The process of turning a programmer's code into a form the computer can understand.

compliant elements   A force element that applies a force between a pair of bodies. Examples of compliant elements often found in mechanical systems are springs, hydraulic and pneumatic actuators, and bushings.

component library   A collection of frequently used, previously modeled components, often stored in an easily accessible location for access by all users.

composite imaging   A process used to combine two or more 2D images to form a new image. For example, a rendered image could be composited over a scanned image to create a new image with a detailed background.

concentric   Having a common center or origin point with varying radii.

concurrent engineering   Engineering teams working in parallel on different aspects of the same product; for example, design and manufacturing.

concurrent intersections   Refers to an operation that would require the SM system to check for the validity of many intersecting entities during a single process.

conduction   A process that transmits heat through the solid; viewed more as a reaction than a load.

cone   A solid primitive geometrically defined with a base circle, a curved exterior surface tapering to a point, and an axis of revolution normal to the base circle.

configuration   A particular grouping of computer hardware as a functional unit. It may also include the allocation of hardware resources and sometimes refers to software parameter settings.

conic   Element having the form of a cone.

conic section   Curve formed by the intersection of a plane with a cone.

construction   Any portion of a solid model that can be developed or constructed separately from and joined to the solid at a later time. Using multiple constructions saves CPU time.

Constructive Solid Geometry (CSG)   A database structure which defines and stores a solid as a series of UNIONs, INTERSECTIONs, and DIFFERENCEs by boolean techniques. Also see **boolean**.

context-sensitive help   Refers to an on-line help capability that provides assistance on topics or specific functions when those functions are being used and help is requested. *On-line* refers to information that is available on screen during operation.

control key   A key on the keyboard used in conjunction with other keys to perform special functions.

control panels   In GUI design, control panels appear at the implicit or explicit request of the operator and provide information reflecting the current state of a number of related system parameters, any of which can be changed interactively while the panel remains on display.

control polygon   Polygon whose vertices define pole locations and from which a B-spline curve is calculated.

controls   In GUI design, any visually represented window component that can be manipulated directly with the mouse or keyboard.

convergence   The closeness of the approximate finite element analysis results to the actual solution.

convection   A process that transmits heat from a node or surface by the movement of constant-temperature gas or fluid over the surface. A heat convection coefficient is required.

Coons patch   Surface defined by four boundary curves, tangents, corner twists, and blending functions. Curvature and continuity can be maintained between patches. Named after developer Steve Coons.

coordinate frame   The origin location of a cartesian coordinate system and the orientation of its axes.

coordinate system   Geometric relation used to denote the location of points in 3D space. The most common is the rectangular coordinate system, whereby points are located by traversing the x, y, and z axes of 3D space. Normally, the origin of a coordinate system is defined as 0,0,0, though this is not required. Other coordinate systems are used to more easily express the coordinates of specific geometric entities. For example, a spherical coordinate system can be used to help define points on a sphere, and a cylindrical coordinate system to help define points on a cylinder.

coordinates   Ordered set of absolute or relative data values that specify a location in a coordinate system.

coplanar   Refers to two or more entities that lie on the same plane. Two planar surfaces, for example, that lie on the same 3D plane are considered coplanar. If these coplanar surfaces share a common edge, it is recommended that they be joined into a single surface. See also **clean modeling**.

corruption   A condition in which SM-related model files or the SM code itself becomes unusable. Corruption can occur from various causes, most of which are internal system conflicts.

CPU   Central Processing Unit. It is responsible for arithmetic computations, logic operations, memory addresses, and data and control signal traffic in a computer.

CPU time curve   If the Central Processing Unit (CPU) time required for a series of operations were charted, this would represent the CPU time required for later operations versus earlier ones.

cross section   View of the interior of an element as it is sliced along a plane.

crosshairs   A cursor usually made up of two perpendicular lines on the display screen used to select coordinate locations.

CRT   Cathode Ray Tube. Denotes the video display tube used with computers.

CSG   Constructive Solid Geometry.

CT   Computed Tomography.

cursor   A pointer on a video display screen that can be moved around; used to place textual or graphical information.

curve   A line that changes direction in a smooth, continuous fashion.

curve fitting   The process of passing arc segments through a number of control points to create a curve.

curve smoothing   The process of curve or surface approximation using polynomial equations to generate a curve that passes near, but not always through, a set of control points or mesh vertices.

curvilinear   Refers to a path or trajectory that contains both line segments and curves (arcs or splines).

curvilinear data   See **irregular grid**.

Cusp   Point or edge in a curve or surface.

cutting plane   A tool that slices through the 3D data exhibiting characteristics of a plane in the data, including scalar and vector measurements.

cycle of change   The period of time required for an individual's behavior to return to normal after a change, if at all. Includes four phases: uninformed optimism, informed pessimism, external or internal bailout, and informed optimism.

cylinder   A solid primitive defined as a right-circular cylinder. The ends are circular and of equal radius. The axis is normal to the ends.

data   Information used as a basis for reasoning or calculation.

data set   A computerized collection of data items that can be processed to analyze or visualize relevant information (e.g., a 3D array of density samples from a medical scanner).

Database   Related information organized and stored so that it can easily be retrieved and, typically, used by multiple applications. A noncomputer form of a database is the telephone directory.

datum   Point (or plane) of reference.

DBMS   Database Management System.

debugging   Act of removing flaws. In SM, the act of testing macros or programs to locate and remove sources of errors.

default   A parameter or variable that remains in effect until changed. It is what a computer program assumes in the absence of specific instructions.

default model   A solid model file that is loaded into memory when a new model is created. Default models are used to establish a predetermined operating environment. Sometimes referred to as a *start model* or *seed model*.

degree of accuracy   Refers to the degree (the largest exponent) of the equations used to define various geometric entities in an SM database. Linear elements such as lines and planes are of a lower degree, while sculptured and free-from surfaces are of a higher degree.

degree of equations   For single variable polynomials, the largest exponent applied to a variable. With multiple variables, the largest sum of exponents (including 1) applied to variables in a term. For example, $x^3 + ax^3 = 0$, $ax^2y + by = 0$, and $axyz + x^2 = 0$ are all third-degree equations.

Degrees of Freedom (DOF)   The individual coordinate directions in which a node is free to displace.

delete   To remove, destroy, eliminate, or erase.

dependent   Subordinate; relying on another item (root) for support. The position of a dependent element in a drawing file is determined by a predefined relationship with a root element.

depth cuing   When calculating a computer-generated image, it is the darkening of surfaces farther from the observer to increase the illusion of depth.

derived   Solid or surface that is generated from other elements.

descendant attribute   An attribute whose value is made available to all the parts in a branch of the product structure tree.

design file   File containing graphic and text data. Also called a *drawing file*.

design iteration   The cycle in which a Solid Model design is modified and evaluated. More design iterations allow more possibilities to be explored, thus resulting in a design of usually higher quality.

dialogue boxes   In a GUI, dialogue boxes provide a visual and functional context for presenting options from which to select. Any interactive exchange of information that takes place in a limited spatial context is considered a dialogue.

diameter   Straight line passing through the origin of an arc or circle, terminating at the point of intersection with that arc or circle.

differential equations   A mathematical relationship among a set of variables and their derivatives. In a mechanical system, the variables are positions and the derivatives are the velocities and accelerations. The independent variable in a differential equation for a mechanical system is time.

digitize   Entering graphical location points into a computer with a tablet, puck, stylus, or scanner.

digitizing tablet   A graphics input device that generates coordinate data. It is used in conjunction with a puck or stylus.

dimension   (v) To form to the precise scale; to place dimensioning information on a graphic element. (n) One of a group of properties whose number is necessary and sufficient to determine uniquely each element of a system of usually mathematical entities. For example, the numeric length of an axis; the collection of annotations placed on a part to display it in either 2D or 3D representation.

dimension-driven   A system in which exists the ability to modify the value of a dimension and have all affected geometry change.

dimensionally constrained   Refers to a state in which a design is controlled by the dimensions associated with the geometry of the design. Thus, when the value of a dimension changes, all affected geometry also changes. Typically, but not always, dimensionally constrained systems provide for bidirectional associativity and for topological constraints.

DIN   Deutscher Industrie-Norm (German Industry Standard).

directory, workstation   An alphabetical list of files on a computer.

DIS   Draft International Standard.

disk   Round, flat plate coated with a magnetic substance on which data is stored.

display What you see on your screen. Sometimes the display needs refreshing, which you can do manually or have set to happen automatically.

display curves See **isolines**.

display depths Physical range defined by the upper and lower points along the view axis, within which the active depth must be located, and which determines the volume within the 3D design that is displayed. See also **clipping plane**.

display list A secondary database used to display geometry on the screen. A display list contains all the display-related data of the geometry in such a format that it can be displayed quickly and efficiently.

display model A secondary model used to facilitate the generation of a wireframe, shaded surface, or other display.

display tolerance The resolution at which geometry is displayed in screen. This may differ from a system's modeling or geometric tolerance.

dissolve A property of a material that makes a surface appear transparent. The dissolve value is adjustable and usually varies between 0 and 1.

DoD Department of Defense.

DOS Disk Operating System.

double curvature Refers to a surface entity that curves simultaneously in two directions.

double precision Numbers are stored using two computer words, providing twice as many digits as single precision. Computational round-off errors are reduced in this way.

downstream process All subsequent operations or processes performed on or with a solid model. Downstream processes include (but are not limited to) analysis, NC code generation, and rapid prototyping (RP).

dragging Dynamically moving the virtual image of a graphical entity across the display screen to a new location using a puck, mouse, or stylus.

draw space As opposed to model space, an auxiliary electronic space that is defined in terms of two-dimensional coordinates where 2D text and conventional details are constructed.

DXF Drawing Interchange File.

dynamic analysis Determines the motion of a system due to the action of applied time-varying loads and/or restraints. Position, velocity, and acceleration are reported.

dynamic detection The act of analyzing the full range of motion of an assembly of solid models to determine if any will intersect each other or in fact share the same volume.

dynamics Animation that lets you see the creation or modification of elements in relation to the movement of the screen cursor.

EC European Community.

ECO Engineering Change Order.

edge A bounded line or curve that forms the intersection of two faces on the surface of an object.

edge precedence When solids are booleaned by ADD, SUBTRACT, or INTERSECT, edges (lines or curves) may become coincident (occupy the same space) as other lines or surfaces. Edge precedence refers to which solid will have its edges removed and which will stay.

EDM Electronic Discharge Machining. Also referred to as Engineering Data Management.

EGA Enhanced Graphics Adaptor.

EISA Extended Industry Standard Architecture.

element In *modeling,* the basic building block used in geometric modeling. Every modeled object created is assembled from elements. Elements include points, lines, curves, surfaces, solids, etc. In *analysis,* the lowest form of entity analyzed. In FEA this could be a mesh element. In kinematics this could be a single rigid body.

endpoint Data point that defines the end of a linear element.

engineering rules Representation of the strategy for designing or manufacturing a product. Rules describe how to divide the product into components, how to model the product's geometry, how to calculate various engineering attributes, or how to describe the process of manufacturing or testing, etc.

Enter key Also called the *return key.* It signals the computer to execute a command or terminate a line of text.

entity Anything which is being displayed on an interactive CRT which can be identified as a discrete "thing." Entities can consist of geometry (points, lines, circular arcs, conics, splines, surfaces, solids, etc.), as text items (notes, dimensions, lists, tables, etc.), or as "information-adding" things (coordinate systems, surface normal vectors, etc.). Menus, icons, prompts, tutorials, etc., are usually not considered entities.

entity map A list describing how entities are translated from a proprietary CAD/CAM format to and from a neutral format like IGES.

entity subsets Any collection that is less than the complete set of IGES entities. Entity subsets may be informally defined, as are the subsets of entities supported by a particular CAD/CAM system. They may also be formally defined as a way of improving data exchanges, as with the CALS IGES subsets.

environment variable A variable that acts upon the entire system. Environment variables may be stored with and applicable to a single model file, or they may be stored and applied globally to all model files. Also known as a *system variable.*

equations of motion A set of differential-algebraic equations whose solutions define the motion of a body.

errors, accuracy Refers to system errors caused by SM tolerance or accuracy settings.

errors, accuracy, large/small geometry Refers to system errors caused by the close proximity of very large and very small geometry coupled with SM tolerance or accuracy settings; for example, when a very large radius is required to be tangent to a very small radius.

errors, intersection Refers to errors caused by the SM system's inability to determine all intersections required to complete a particular operation such as a boolean ADD, SUBTRACT, or INTERSECT.

errors, modeling Refers to all SM-related system errors occurring during a modeling session, such as accuracy or intersection errors.

errors, system   Refers to all hardware-related system errors occurring during a modeling session, such as DISK FULL or OUT OF RAM errors.

Euler's formula   A mathematical equation that relates the number of topological elements in a polyhedron. In its simplest form it states that $V - E + F = 2$, where V, E, and F are the number of vertices, edges, and faces, respectively. Derived by the 18th-century Swiss mathematician Leonhard Euler.

evaluated representation   A solid model that has all face, edge, and vertex information explicitly represented.

exclusion list   A list of objects that a source object has no effect upon. For example, in viewing and display applications, if a reflection map is a source object, the objects in the exclusion list will not see the reflection map.

expert systems   Computer system that captures some amount of design knowledge in an automated decision-making format, generally in the form of "if-then" rules.

explicitly defined   Information that is directly represented (rather than implied). In SM, for example, an edge directly defined by an equation and two endpoints is explicitly defined.

export   Sending a scene or model to a file (IGES, DXF, TIFF, HPGL, etc.) so that it can be read or imported into another program.

expression   Algebraic expression for numerical entities (distance, radius of circle, and so forth).

external solver   A finite element solver residing outside the solid model-based analysis product. The mesh, loads, restraints, etc., must be exported from the solid modeler for use. Results may be imported to the solid modeler, but associativity required for model optimization may be lost in this process.

extract   To separate a part from the whole, to copy part of a surface without necessarily changing the location, thus creating a new element.

extrusion   A process used in geometric modeling to convert 2D shapes into 3D shapes. A 3D object is created by displacing a copy of the 2D shape, then linking the copy to the original to form a closed, solid object. Examples of extrusion are a cylinder and a prism.

face   A type of element used in geometric modeling. A face can be a flat, planar polygon or a curved, bounded surface. Some systems define a face as the bounded portion of an infinite surface region.

FEA   Finite Element Analysis.

feature-based modeling   Performs functions that were previously performed using primitive boolean operations. *Example:* A through-hole could be defined using a boolean difference operation and a cylinder of sufficient length. However, if the design became thicker and the cylinder was not long enough, the hole would become a blind hole. In contrast, the through-hole feature understands the rule that it must pass completely through the part and will do so no matter how the part changes.

features   Entities that encapsulate how geometry looks and how the geometry behaves using rules and attributes along with their defining constraints and geometry. Features impart not only geometry to a design but a set of associative, nongeo-metric attributes which aid in communicating the design to the manufacturing process. Features include holes, slots, ribs, webs, and user-defined features.

FEM   Finite Element Modeling.

fences   Temporary means of locating and grouping elements for manipulation.

field rendering   A technique used to improve the frame-to-frame continuity in a rendered animation. Field rendering combines interleaved portions of two consecutive rendered images to create a single image, which is then recorded onto video. Sequences of field-rendered images yield better continuity of motion between frames.

file   Collection of logical records stored as a unit.

file name   User-defined name given to an interactively created file. The name should be relevant to the contents of the file.

fillet   Arc that adds material to a part by rounding a corner and blending two lines, curves, or surfaces.

Finite Element Analysis (FEA)   An analysis technique that computes stress, strain, displacement, etc., using a continuum structure broken into discrete finite-sized pieces.

Finite Element Mesh (FEM)   The collection of elements approximating the actual structure. FEM is also short for Finite Element Model.

fitted text   Text that is automatically sized and rotated to fit between two points.

fixed restraint   The complete restraint of a surface (normal and tangent to the surface or any other coordinate system).

flat shading   A display technique used to shade the surfaces of objects quickly. Flat shading is slower than wireframe display and does not show smoothed edges. Also referred to as *polygonal shading*.

Flavoring   The process of improving CAD/CAM data exchange results by modifying entities during an IGES data transfer.

floating-point operations   A basic mathematical operation (e.g., addition or division) that operates on noninteger numbers (i.e., numbers with a decimal fraction such as 5.631).

floppy disk   A circular plastic disk coated with magnetic material mounted in a square plastic holder. It is used by a computer to store information for later use. It can be inserted or removed from a floppy disk drive at will. It is also called a *diskette*.

font   Complete set and style of the characters and symbols of a typeface used for displaying text.

form features   In Solid Modeling, parts of solid objects that can be specified in familiar engineering terms (e.g., fillets, slots, and through-holes).

formula-defined shapes   Shapes that are defined by using one or more equations. This includes complex shapes such as aesthetic bottles or simple shapes such hyperbolic paraboloids, oblate spheroids, prolate spheroids, or ellipsoids.

frame   The basic unit of time measurement in an animation. Instead of using seconds to tell time, a frame count is used. The duration of an animation is changed by increasing or decreasing its total number of frames. Typically, 30 frames of animation correspond to one second on NTSC videotape (25 frames for PAL videotape, 24 frames for film). Motion is created by storing object locations at every frame of an animation.

frame buffer A portion of a computer's memory that stores an image so that it can be displayed on the computer screen. The number of bit planes in a frame buffer determines the total number of colors that can be displayed on the screen simultaneously.

free-form geometry Geometry that uses curves and surfaces to define objects.

free-form surface Surfaces that are not limited to mathematically simple linear or quadric surfaces.

Fresnel reflection The reflection that results from light striking a diffuse surface at a glancing angle. Ray-tracing uses Fresnel reflection.

frustrum A solid primitive defined as the portion of a solid contained between two planes which are usually parallel.

full path name Name of the entire path or directory hierarchy to a file, including the file name.

function key A key on the keyboard that can be assigned to perform a task. A function key is typically used as a shortcut to a lengthy string of keystrokes.

Fused Deposition Modeling (FDM) A patented process by Stratasys, Inc. (Eden Prairie, Minn.) for producing a physical prototype directly from a 3D surface or solid model.

gamma correction A method of adjusting pixel values so they can be properly represented on an output device.

gap tolerance The allowable distance or gap between the edges of mating surface regions. A tighter (lower) gap tolerance will result in fewer and narrower gaps, but at the expense of increased processing times.

geometric data Data consisting of basic shape parameters of a solid.

geometric operations Refers to the group of SM operations that include but are not limited to blends, extrudes, sweeps, revolves, fillets, corner rounds, and local surface deviations.

geometric transformation Translation, rotation, and scaling.

geometry Elements that make up a model, such as points, lines, surfaces, solids, etc.

global coordinate system The coordinate system in which the geometry of the entire product is represented.

global coordinates The location of a point within the permanent coordinate system of 3D model space. Also known as *world coordinates*.

global modifications Modifications made to a solid model using global or boolean operations.

global origin Point in a model file from which its coordinate system is calculated (normally 0,0,0).

gouge-free Refers to toolpaths which do not gouge the part.

Gouraud shading A rendering process with blended colors based on light measured for each vertex in a polygon. Unlike Phong shading, the appearance of edges and the area of each polygon will remain flat.

gradient In a volumetric data set, a vector that points in the direction of maximum property change at any point. The magnitude of the gradient is the rate of change.

graph A diagram or data structure consisting of nodes representing items and connections that represent relationships between items.

graphical output Display of design-instance geometry.

graphics library A set of graphics functions that can be integrated into a program to provide graphics output. Graphics libraries can range from a simple TIFF or PCX image output to a complex 3D display list.

gravitational force A force which represents the attraction between a body and the earth. For bodies near the surface of the earth, this force is perpendicular to the earth's surface.

grid An area on the graphics display covered with regularly spaced dots used as a drawing aid.

group A collection of elements. For example, the elements that form a chair might be organized into groups that make up the legs, the back, and the seat. You can perform many operations on groups, including positioning, assigning materials and texture maps. Groups can form the individual components of an assembly model. Productivity is enhanced by modeling a group or part once and referring to its definition in many assemblies. This is referred to as *part instancing*.

group technology See **part classification**.

GUI Computer-generated Graphical User Interface consisting of windows, icons, and menus.

half plane A planer half-space (i.e., the space on one side of a plane that separates all of a defined space into two parts).

half-space The space on one side of a surface that divides all of a defined space into two parts.

halo In viewing and display applications, the special effect that results when dissolve is dependent on the surface face orientation relative to the viewer. Halo lets you see the boundary of an object that has a transparent interior.

hard disk A rigid metal disk covered with magnetic material. Mounted permanently in a hard disk drive, it spins at high velocity, is capable of storing large amounts of data, and allows information to be accessed faster than a floppy disk drive.

hard-coded features Features which are selected from a menu (choice list), icon, or other mechanism for identifying a predetermined geometric configuration, the methods for controlling its placement, and the types of variables it can contain.

hardcopy A paper printout or plot of information stored in a computer.

hardware The portion of the SM installation that supports and facilitates the use of SM software. This includes computers, monitors, input devices, printers, and plotters.

hardware rendering The interactive display and shading performed by the system workstation independent of but in conjunction with a software application.

heat flux Heat flux or flow transmits heat from a surface at a specified rate. Also referred to as *flow*.

heat source A heat load may be defined at a point, along a line, or through a volume to model heating or cooling devices.

A body heat source might represent a chemical reaction releasing (or collecting) a distributed heat.

hexahedron elements Finite elements that enclose solid regions of a structure with six (hexa) quadrilateral faces.

hidden line A wireframe display option that displays only the lines that should be visible from the current view. Lines that would be obscured by solid objects are hidden.

highlight In viewing and display applications, the color of an object where it directly reflects the light source. The size of the highlight is determined by the shininess of the material. In general modeling, elements change color when selected. This is referred to as the *highlight color*. The color used is typically a system variable.

horizontal Parallel to, in the plane of, or operating in a plane parallel to the horizon or to a baseline.

hot key Any keyboard key that has been mapped to execute a command or series of commands.

hybrid solid modeler An SM database that actively maintains two or more substantially different representations of solid objects such as CSG and B-Rep.

I/O Input/Output, a mechanism by which a computer accepts or distributes information to peripheral devices such as plotters, printers, disk drives, and modems.

icon Symbol that graphically identifies a command.

IEEE Institute of Electrical and Electronics Engineers.

IGES Initial Graphics Exchange Specification. Used to represent the two- and three-dimensional drawings of objects. (An ANSI standard.)

illumination model Mathematical equations that represent various material lighting and shading effects. The illumination model for a material is typically specified by a statement in a material library file.

image Information that can be displayed as an array of pixels on a video display terminal.

image file format Establishes the x and y resolution and the aspect ratio of the image file for a particular output device.

image file type Determines how the image is stored. An example of an image file type is .rla.

implicitly defined Information that is defined by a situation rather than by explicit definition. In SM, for example, an edge defined as the intersection of two surfaces is implicitly defined.

information-oriented Systematic Graphic Design 117 In GUI design, refers to the use of layout, typography, symbols, color, and other static and dynamic graphics to convey facts, concepts, and emotions.

initialization file See **start-up file**.

instancing The process of modeling an object once and storing it in a part library so that subsequent models that require that part need only reference the original model. The visual reference of the part is referred to as an *instance* of the original part.

interoperability Related to the examination of the information exchange between two specific CAD systems, and the ability of each CAD system to use such information.

interface Shared boundary through which the user and software communicate.

interference A condition of special intersection between two parts in an assembly; also their region of intersection.

interference detection The act of analyzing an assembly of solid models to determine if any of them intersect each other or in fact share the same volume.

internal solver A finite element solver residing inside the solid model–based analysis product.

interpolation The calculation of an estimated property value for a spatial location that is not a sample point.

intersection Boolean operator used to intersect solids and form a common volume.

intersection curve The curve computed at the intersection of two surfaces.

intersection search curve The intersection of an entity with other entities is checked for on lines between finite locations on the boundary of the entity. The straight line segments between points form the search curve.

inverse dynamic analysis A hybrid form of kinematic and dynamic analysis in which the time history of positions or relative positions of one or more bodies in the system is defined and the resulting velocity, acceleration, and reaction forces are calculated.

IPO The IGES/PDES Organization headquartered at the National Institute of Standards and Technology (NIST). A volunteer organization that develops and maintains the IGES standard and provides input to the International Standards Organization (ISO) for the PDES/STEP standard.

irregular grid A grid whose nodes are not evenly spaced in x, y, and z directions or even in a rectangular configuration. An irregular grid suits data with areas of interest that require finer sampling than other areas. The terms *curvilinear* or *structured* are sometime used synonymously with irregular.

ISO International Standards Organization.

isolines Lines displayed on a 3D surface showing mathematical definition between its boundaries. Also referred to as *flow lines*.

isometric (1) View shown from an apparent angle of 30°; the view is actually rotated 45°. The part is viewed from the top, front, right, and corner. (2) Relating to or being a drafting system characterized by three equal axes at right angles. A view in which the horizontal lines of an element are drawn at an angle to the horizontal, and all verticals are projected at an angle from the base.

jaggies See **aliasing**.

JOIN See boolean UNION.

justification Point of orientation for text placement.

KBE See **Knowledge-Based Engineering**.

kernel-based architecture A GUI design in which the windowing services are provided by some portion of the operating system itself, or by a standard add-on module that resides along with the operating system in RAM- or ROM-based libraries. This provides high levels of interactivity, but with dependents on the architecture and available resources of a single computer.

key-in   A command keyed in, rather than selected from a menu.

keyboard interface   As an input device, the keyboard is more efficient for sequential tasks, such as text entry.

key point   Point on an element, including vertices, to which you can snap.

kinematic analysis   The study of motion of a system, independent of forces that produce motion. All degrees of freedom must be specified as a function of time.

knot   Parameter value that indicates where on a curve or surface a pole's influence terminates.

knot line   Knot strong enough to form an intersecting line or create an angular vertex in B-spline geometry.

Knowledge-Based Engineering (KBE)   An engineering method in which engineering knowledge about the product (e.g., the techniques used to design, analyze, and manufacture a product) is stored in a product model which represents the engineering intent of the design.

lagrangian methods   Methods which use the kinetic and potential energy to form the equations of motion.

Laminated Object Manufacturing (LOM)   A patented process by Helisys, Inc. (Torrance, Calif.) of producing a physical prototype directly from a 3D surface or solid model.

LAN   Local Area Network. One of several systems used to link computers together in order to share data, programs, or peripherals.

large-amplitude motion   A mechanical system can experience large displacements. When a mechanical system goes through large-amplitude motion, the equations of motion cannot be represented as linear relationships. Same as *geometric nonlinearity*.

latent surfaces   Surfaces that are no longer visible after a boolean or intersection operation because they lie inside or outside the solid.

layer   A logical separation of data to be viewed individually or in combination. Similar in concept to transparent acetate overlays.

leaf   A part in a product structure tree that has no children.

legacy systems   Previously installed applications or systems software.

lift   To move the face of a solid so that the adjacent surfaces are extended or stretched.

light   A simple, ambient illumination source that can be moved and colored.

line   A 2D geometric entity represented by a directional vector. A line will occupy a finite section of the vector defined by two endpoints.

line segment   Part of a line having two endpoints.

line string   Series of line segments joined as a single element.

line style   See **style**.

line terminator   Symbol placed at the endpoint of a linear element; an arrowhead, for example.

line weight   See **weight**.

Linear   Having a single dimension; a line.

linear algebraic equations   A set of relationships between variables that are related linearly (i.e., no transcendental functions or powers used).

linear blend   A type of blend created by two profiles and a linear trajectory. An example would be a section of HVAC duct that transitions directly from a square to a round.

linear equation   In SM, a polynomial with no exponent greater than 1 (e.g., $ax + b = c$).

linear interpolation   A process used to create motion for an object. Linear interpolation moves an object in a straight line between user-specified locations, sometimes called *key frames*. Frame increments are usually equally spaced.

linetype   Sometimes called line font. It represents the appearance of a line. For example, a continuous line has a different linetype than a dashed line.

liveware   As opposed to hardware or software, liveware refers to people: designers, engineers, and managers of SM software.

local coordinate system   The coordinate system in which the geometry of the components of an assembly in the product structure tree is represented. By defining the components of an assembly in the assembly's local coordinate system, the assembly can be positioned and oriented as a whole with respect to the overall product in the global coordinate system.

local coordinates   The location of a point within a local coordinate system defined relative to the global coordinate system, to points on an entity, or to another local coordinate system.

local modifications   Changing geometrical and topological information by producing, deleting, and moving local elements of a solid, such as faces, edges, and vertices.

lofting   The process of fitting a surface between two or more differing control profiles.

Macintosh® OS   Operating System of the Apple Macintosh computer, first introduced in 1984 as the first mass-marketed computer to feature a high-resolution, bit-mapped graphic display and a direct manipulation interaction style.

macro   Generally, ASCII text files containing commands specific to an SM program. Once executed, macros are read by the SM program, and the commands are interpreted and executed one at a time.

manifold object   A solid in which every surface point has an infinitesimally small neighborhood which could be deformed into a flat surface (a "2-manifold" in algebraic topology). Informally, an object without topological difficulties such as self-intersecting surfaces. A nonmanifold object is one with self-conflicting topology and the opposite of a manifold object.

manufacturability   Related to the ease of the ability to manufacture a product. Implies the availability of information on the manufacturing process and the data to drive those processes.

mass   A measure of the basic property of matter—inertia, which is the tendency of an object to remain at rest or in motion in the absence of external forces. Also, a value calculated by the mass-properties analysis of a solid model.

material In viewing and display applications, a material is a predefined "color" applied to the surface of an object. It controls how an object appears when it is rendered. In addition to color, each material definition can include reflective properties such as surface shininess, dissolve (transparency), texture attributes, and reflection maps.

material density The quantity or mass of material per unit volume, unit area, or unit length.

material properties Properties which measure material stiffness, strain ratios, thermal characteristics, hardness, etc.

mathematical approximations The changes made to the mathematical definition of CAD/CAM entities during the conversion to other entity types, as during the IGES exchange process. Translators and flavoring utilities may be required to perform mathematical approximations in order to convert an unsupported entity into a supported entity. For example, a translator may perform mathematical approximations to convert NURBS curves to parametric spline curves.

mathematical rectification The process in which a piece of geometry is modified to meet a specified metric, such as length of a line, start radius or end angle of a circular arc, length of major half axis of an ellipse, etc.

matte Refers to information in a rendered image that defines the transparency of each pixel. A pixel can be opaque, partly transparent, or completely transparent. The unused pixels of an image (black space) have a completely transparent matte. Other types of images, such as scanned, painted, and frame-grabbed images, can contain matte information as well.

maximum element edge length In FEA, the maximum length of any finite element edge in a particular mesh.

maximum face-aspect ratio In FEA, the maximum ratio of any two edges of a finite element face. Edges that are approximately normal to each other are generally the two intended edges to use.

maximum subtended angle In FEA, the angle that the face or edge of a finite element subtends on a curved surface of the solid model.

MCA Micro Channel Architecture, developed by IBM Corporation.

MCAE Mechanical Computer-Aided Engineering.

mechanical loads Loads that cause stress, strain, and deformation of a structure. Thermal loads cause temperature distributions which may be a mechanical load.

mechanism modeling The use of assembly models to simulate a mechanism's behavior. If a product's function is kinematic or dynamic in nature, assembly modeling can simulate the relative interaction between components.

memory One of the essential components of a computer: where programs and data are stored. Memory includes both ROM (read-only memory) and RAM (random-access memory).

menus A means of command retrieval that enables an operator to see and point instead of remembering and typing. Menu systems greatly reduce problems caused by the limitations of human memory, but do so at the expense of motor performance.

merge To combine or unite graphic elements.

mesh A computational grid associated with one or more topologies.

mesh algorithm The rules and process used to create a finite element mesh.

mesh density The fineness/coarseness of a finite element mesh.

mesh elements Simplified states of stress and displacement characterizing the behavior in each finite element.

message boxes In GUI design, message boxes provide critical information which is not requested and typically appears only when the system has entered, or is about to enter, an unrecoverable and potentially dangerous state.

microcomputer A computer principally designed for use by a single person.

microprocessor An integrated circuit "chip" (or set of chips) which acts as a CPU of a computer. Examples of microprocessors are the Motorola 68020 and the Intel 80486.

Microsoft Windows® A Graphical User Interface (GUI) created in 1985 by Microsoft Corporation as a multitasking, graphics-oriented alternative to the character-based environment provided by MS-DOS on PC-compatible systems. The bit-mapped displays and mouse-driven menus provided by Windows first opened the door to graphics-oriented software on the PC.

midpoint Middle key point of an element.

MIL-STD-1840 Military Standard 1840 (A and B). The Automated Interchange of Technical Information; describes the proper method for reading and writing magnetic tapes to allow CALS documents to be transferred among different systems and installations.

minimum element edge length In FEA, the minimum length of any finite element edge in a particular mesh.

minimum element face corner angle In FEA, the minimum angle of the three or more corner angles of a finite element face.

minimum face-edge ratio In FEA, the minimum ratio of any two edges of a finite element face.

minicomputer A computer that is generally configured for use by a small number of people. It generally has more powerful resources and peripherals than a microcomputer.

mirror To create the reverse image of a display set through a plane or around a defined axis.

modal dialogues In GUI design, modal dialogue boxes require a response before any other action can be taken. Application modal dialogues prevent the operator from invoking any application functions until the dialogue has been satisfied.

mode A software setting or operational state.

model Graphic representation or schema.

model space An electronic space defined in terms of three-dimensional coordinates where 3D modeling takes place.

model-drawing associativity The associative relationship between a 2D drawing and a 3D model. The associativity is typically one-way where the model updates the drawing or two-way where both the drawing and the model can update each other.

modeless dialogues In GUI design, modeless dialogue boxes are limited in scope and do not restrict subsequent actions. Operators can continue to work without responding, if necessary, and may be allowed to keep the modeless dialogue on display even after a response has been made.

modeling precision The method of operational accuracy employed by the SM operator, such as making sure that arcs (fillets and rounds) are actually tangent to adjacent straight edges and that they actually connect. Higher modeling precision means that more SM data can be utilized by downstream processes.

modem Stands for modulator/demodulator. It is the device that allows a computer to send and receive data over telephone lines.

modularization Breaking up an application into discrete components such that developing each separately and then integrating them is significantly easier than developing the application all at once.

moments Forces that cause bending of a structure.

moments of inertia The measure of tendency to produce uniform motion of an object about a point or axis. A value calculated by the mass-properties analysis of a solid model.

motion The process of creating a sequence of frames in order to animate visualized data.

mouse An input device which is well suited to certain types of interaction tasks. The mouse provides an efficient means of accomplishing tasks that require spatial manipulation, such as menu navigation and window sizing and positioning.

mouse sensitivity control A preference variable that controls how sensitive the viewport response is to the mouse movement.

MRI Magnetic Resonance Imaging.

MRP Material Resource Planning.

multilinear Refers to a series of multiple line segments connected at their endpoints. Polylines are connected, multilinear line segments. A multilinear element can occupy 2D or 3D space.

multiuser The ability for a computer operating system to allow multiple users on different terminals to share resources such as the CPU, storage, and memory.

multitasking The ability for a computer operating system to manage concurrent tasks.

named element An element that is named and that can be placed or manipulated by specifying that name.

named view A defined view that is named and that can be recalled by specifying that name.

NC Numerical Control.

NC verification Method of simulation material removal. The actual numerical control code is used to drive the graphic display of material being machined from a part.

NCGA National Computer Graphics Association, administrator for the IGES/PDES Organization (IPO) and U.S. Product Data Association.

needs analysis A preacquisition evaluation of a company's computer needs. Management will normally use the results of such an analysis as a basis for the decision-making process which includes hardware and software purchase and implementation.

network Interconnection of host computers and workstations that enables them to share data and control. The term *network* can mean the devices that connect the system, or it can mean the connected system. Also referred to as the *process of discussion* between people.

NextStep® GUI A windowing system and graphical desktop environment originally intended for the NeXT Computer, which began shipping in 1988, but which ceased production in 1993. Nevertheless, the NextStep GUI has survived and is being made available on several types of workstations.

NFS Network File System (Sun Microsystems).

NIST National Institute of Standards and Technology. An organization within the U.S. Department of Commerce charged with administering standards and technology transfer.

NIUG National IGES User Group. An organization that promotes the sharing and exchange of information on the use of CAD/CAM data exchange.

node The basic graph element used to represent distinct items (vertices, faces, etc.). A single coordinate in a grid.

node displacement The imposed displacement of a node in a specified coordinate direction.

nonmanifold object See **manifold object**.

nonlinear algebraic equations A set of relationships between variables that may be related by nonlinear functions.

nonperiodic B-spline Another term for open B-spline.

nonrational B-spline B-spline curve or surface whose poles have no weighting factor.

nonuniform B-spline B-spline curve or surface where knots occur at varying U or V increments.

normal In SM, planar profiles have a front and a back side. For example, in an extrusion operation, "normal to the profile" means that the front of the profile is facing the direction of extrusion. Normals are displayed to indicate the orientation of faces (polygons or surfaces). A normal is displayed as an arrow originating at the center of and at right angles to each face. Normals point toward the viewer for faces drawn in counterclockwise order. Since faces are visible only when they are facing toward the viewer, it is sometimes necessary to reverse a normal to correct a face's orientation. For a solid, all surface normals should point outward. See also **surface model**.

NTSC An acronym for National Television Standards Committee. It describes the color television broadcast system used in North America and in many other parts of the world. Images are usually rendered at an NTSC aspect ratio so that they can be broadcast on television without distortion.

numerical instability In SM, the inability of a repetitive numerical procedure to converge on a solution.

NURBS Nonuniform Rational B-Spline. A spline and surface representation based on B-splines. Nonuniform refers to the fact that the control points of each curve segment do not have to be evenly spaced.

object-oriented   A way to develop computer systems such that the basic form of the program is an "object" that includes both data and instructions for manipulating data.

octree   An SM database method in which a solid is represented by a hierarchical tree generated by a recursive subdivision of a finite universe. Also called *O-Rep*.

off-the-shelf code   Programs or libraries that are already written and can be used as is or can be integrated into other programs.

omnidirectional light   Light that is emitted in all directions at equal intensities. The sun is an example of an omnidirectional light. Other types of lights are directional spotlights and directional infinite lights.

OODB   Object-Oriented Database.

open B-spline curve   B-spline curve that has start and end edges in either or both the *U* and *V* directions.

open B-spline surface   B-spline surface that has start and end edges in either or both the *U* and *V* directions.

Open Look® GUI   A Graphical User Interface (GUI) developed jointly by Sun Microsystems and AT&T as the standard operating environment for UNIX System V.4. Open Look exists as a layer on top of a base windowing system that provides an imaging model (management of how graphical parts are displayed) and network communication services.

operating system   Software that manages computer resources and allows user access and control.

operator-defined primitive   Refers to any valid solid that is a result of one or more solid geometric operations. This is opposed to system-defined primitives that are operations built into the SM software. See also **primitive**.

order of continuity   Number of poles that have an effect on a curve or surface at any given location on that curve or surface.

origin   The intersection point of the axes in a coordinate system. For example, the origin of a cartesian coordinate system is where the *x, y,* and *z* axes meet, at (0,0,0). Also, the center of the boundary that encloses a data volume or geometry.

origin, B-spline   Start of a B-spline curve where *U* = 0, or the corner of a B-spline surface where *U* = 0 and *V* = 0.

orthogonal   Characteristic of an element consisting completely of elements positioned at 90° angles. A square is an orthogonal element.

orthographic view   A view that shows an object in two dimensions without perspective foreshortening.

OS2 Presentation Manager®   A Graphic User Interface (GUI) developed jointly by Microsoft and IBM in 1987 and favored by IBM and some compatible microcomputer manufacturers.

OSF/Motif® GUI   A window manager and Graphic User Interface (GUI) tool kit developed by Digital Equipment Corporation and the Hewlett-Packard Company for the Open Software Foundation (OSF).

overlapping windows   In a GUI design, where the windows overlap and have associated depth values that represent their distances from the viewer.

paging   A software operation that swaps blocks of data and/or software between memory and disk storage during program operation. It is used when the amount of data and/or the size of a program exceeds the available memory in a computer.

parallelepiped   A solid with six faces that are parallelograms (polygons with four sides where opposite sides are parallel). Cubes and bricks are special cases of parallelepipeds.

parameter   Any piece of mathematical information used in the creation of, or extracted from, a geometric entity. *Example:* $y = mx + b$ represents a line with slope of *m* and *y*-axis intercept of *b*. Both *m* and *b* are parameters of the line. Its coordinates are *not* parameters. The parameters of a circular arc are start angle, end angle, and radius. If the arc had been defined as having passed through three points, the three points would be geometric constraints, not parameters. Also, the property that associates a variable name with a value.

parametric CAD system   A type of modern CAD system that lets you relate the geometry of different elements of a product. When you change one element, the geometry of the rest of the product changes as well.

parametric curves and surfaces   Mathematically described free-form curves and surfaces.

parametric element   Graphic element whose position is determined by a relationship with another element. Parametric elements are also called *associative elements*.

parametric equation   Equation expressing the coordinates of either a curve as a function of one parameter or a surface as a function of two parameters.

parenting   A technique used to link objects together with movable joints. An example of parenting would be rotating wheels parented to a car. When a parent is moved, all of its children (and grandchildren, and so on) move with it. A term also used in database tree structures where higher-level nodes are parents to lower-level nodes.

part   A construction that cannot be further reduced. SM parts consist of axial sweeps, rotational sweeps, and solid primitives, and can contain any number of features.

part classification   Mechanism to classify parts and other elements of a product by their function or by the processes used to manufacture them.

path   Sequence of directories leading to a file or a sequence of menus leading to a command.

pattern   To fill a defined area with repetitions of a predefined geometric shape.

PC   Personal Computer.

PDES   Product Data Exchange using STEP (see **STEP**).

PDM   Product Data Management. A technology for managing all engineering and manufacturing data for a product to control the product development cycle.

periodic B-spline   Another term for closed B-spline.

peripheral   An accessory device to a computer, such a plotter, printer, or a tape drive.

perpendicular bisector   Line at the exact midpoint of an element and exactly 90° to the element.

perspective projection   Graphics displays simulating depth and distance by representing parallel lines merging at a vanishing point or a specified center of projection.

PET   Positron-Emission Tomography.

PHIGS   Programmer's Hierarchical Interface Graphics Standard.

Phong shading   A display process that computes lighting and color for each pixel of a displayed object. Phong shading also blends the boundaries between adjacent polygons to make faceted surfaces appear smooth and continuous.

photorealistic rendering   Refers to the ability to display an object on screen with photorealistic qualities. Rendering techniques used can range from transparency, texture mapping, specular reflection, radiosity, bump mapping, shadowing, and multiple light sources.

picking   An interactive technique used to select and organize objects, elements, and points. Picking is performed using a mouse to select a single element or to stretch a "pick box" around the elements displayed on the screen.

pixel   The fundamental element of a computerized image (short for "picture element").

place   To create and position an element.

plane   Spatial element in 3D geometry that may or may not have a boundary, but is level (having no elevations or depressions) and is 3D.

plane strain model   A model of mechanical structural behavior in which all strain and displacement occur in a single plane. Stresses normal to the plane are not zero. The maximum length of any finite element edge in a particular mesh.

plane stress model   A model of mechanical structural behavior in which all stress, strain, and displacement occur in a single plane. Stresses normal to the plane are zero.

plotter   A computer-controlled device that produces text and images on paper or acetate by electrostatic, thermal, or mechanical means.

pocket menu   An icon menu generally accessed by tapping a mouse button; it contains input generation and other commonly used commands.

point   Graphic element representing a position in space.

point classification   An internal SM operation that determines if a given point is inside, outside (including interior voids), or on the surface of a solid model.

point forces   Forces applied at a point. Actual forces always distribute over a finite area of contact.

pointing device   A hand-held device (typically a mouse or puck and tablet) used to control the movement of the cursor on the display screen.

pole   Vertex of a polygon. Also called a *control point*.

pole, B-spline   Point of influence that controls the shape of a curve or surface. A curve or surface bends toward its poles.

polygon   Multisided shape. Also see **Face**.

polygonal geometry   Geometry that uses points, lines, and flat faces to define objects.

polygonal representation   A form of boundary representation (B-Rep) in which all enclosing surfaces are planar.

polyhedron   Refers to a multisided, closed volume. All valid solids are polyhedrons.

polyline   A geometric entity composed of one or more connected segments which are treated as single entity.

polynomials   Equations that consist of sums of terms with coefficients that are constants and where all exponents are positive whole numbers (e.g., $ax^2 + bxy + c = 0$).

postprocessing   Interactive query and display of finite element results.

postprocessor   Software that converts CAD/CAM data from the IGES format into the proprietary format for a particular CAD/CAM system. May be referred to as an *IGES translator*.

preprocessing   Creation of a finite element mesh, loads, restraints, etc.

preprocessor   Software that converts CAD/CAM data from its native proprietary format into IGES format. May be referred to as an *IGES translator*.

primary model   In SM, the solid model from which other representations are derived.

primitive   Simple or elemental. The lowest state of a solid model. A solid or surface that is not derived from other elements. A solid volume defined by simple standard geometrical shapes, such as a box, cone, and cylinder. Primitives are used by the CSG modeling method.

principal axes   The coordinate system of an object, oriented such that the products of inertia with respect to it are zero, and moments of inertia are at maximums or minimums. The axes of that coordinate system are the principal axes of the object. A determination calculated by the mass-properties analysis of a solid model.

principal moments   The moments of inertia of an object calculated with respect to the principal axes of the object. A determination calculated by the mass-properties analysis of a solid model.

prism   A solid primitive similar to a right-rectangular box, except it has more faces. Prisms are defined by the number of equilateral edges or facets on its base, the radius of the vertices of the base, and the height of the prism which is normal to the base.

procedural texture   A 1D, 2D, or 3D texture that is calculated from a mathematical formula. If you cut open an object that has a 3D procedural texture applied to it, you will see a texture on the inside.

process plan   A plan which defines the order of manufacturing operations needed to obtain a final part.

product life cycle   Refers to the cycle of a product from concept to design, manufacture, use, disposal, or recycle. Can also refer to the life span of a particular product model or version.

productivity analysis   A postacquisition evaluation of a company's computer implementation and future needs. The results of this analysis are used to evaluate productivity improvement opportunities.

productivity indicators   A group of indicators used as a standard or benchmark to quickly determine where you are on the road toward full productivity with SM.

products of inertia   The inertia of an element with respect to two axes. See also **moments of inertia**. A value calculated by the mass-properties analysis of a solid model.

proficiency tests   A method of determining knowledge and level of proficiency in the use of SM technology. Such tests are usually customized for relevance to a typical work environment.

profiles   A set of curves on a plane connected end to end and forming a cross section of a blend, sweep, extrude, revolve, etc.

project   To move an element or point along a straight line or vector (usually the view z axis) until meeting another element. Often a data point is moved down the z axis of the view until an element is found within a specified tolerance of the axis. The point is then calculated as the point on the element closest to the z axis.

project file   A file that provides environment-variable settings, history information, and descriptions of user-defined selections for a project.

prompt   A message from the computer software requesting a response from the user.

property thresholding   The use of one or more property values in a data set to determine visibility and visual characteristics (e.g., color or contrast) when displaying the data set.

PROSTEP   The center for STEP in Germany.

prototype   The act of creating test beds for ideas and concepts for the purpose of validation.

pull-down list   An interface object used to select from a large set of options. A pull-down list is typically characterized by an arrow button. Clicking on the arrow, which normally displays the current selection, posts a list of available options.

quadratic equation   In SM, a second-degree polynomial; that is, a polynomial where the largest exponent is 2 (e.g., $ax^2 + bx + c + 0$). With multiple variables, terms can contain no more than two variables, and variables in two-variable terms cannot be squared (e.g., $ax^2 + bxy + cxz = 0$).

quadric surface   Surfaces generated by quadratic equations (spheres, cylinders, cones, ellipsoids, paraboloids, and hyperboloids).

quadtree   The 2D equivalent of an octree.

query boxes   In Graphic User Interface (GUI), design query boxes appear in response to operator actions, but are not requested explicitly. Query boxes prompt for a single piece of information, such as a yes-or-no answer to a single question, and provide a context in which the necessary information can be provided.

R&D   Research and Development.

radiation   A process that transmits heat away from molecules undergoing internal chemical change.

radio button   An interface method for setting options where you must select one of the options, but only one.

radiographic viewing   The use of computed images where items in the data set are translucent rather than opaque (similar to x-ray images).

radiosity   A process where certain aspects of an object's reflective characteristics can be computed; then, when the point of view is moved, these do not need to be recomputed.

radius   Distance from the center or origin point to the edge on any curved element.

radius of gyration   The radius of gyration of a solid object is calculated with respect to a particular axis of rotation. It is the distance from the center of mass, or centroid of the solid, to the projection of the centroid on the axis of rotation. The distance is measured along a perpendicular from the centroid to the axis of rotation. A value calculated by the mass-properties analysis of a solid model.

RAM   Random-Access Memory. See also **memory**.

Rapid Prototyping (RP)   The process of producing a physical prototype directly from CAD 3D surface or solid modeling data by a number of patented processes such as SLA, LOM, FDM, SGC, or SLS.

raster   A regular array. A computerized image is composed of a raster array of pixels.

rational B-spline   Curve or surface that has weighted poles.

ray-tracing   A technique used to create realistic reflections and refractions on reflective surfaces. Ray-tracing is a high-quality alternative to reflection mapping.

real time   The execution of time during an actual solid modeling session as opposed to simply viewing the results of an execution previously performed. Similar to a live versus a recorded event on video.

record length   The length of one record in a neutral format file. Each line in an IGES file contains 80 characters, so the record length is 80 characters.

rectification   The process whereby a piece of geometry is modified to meet constraints which have been placed on it. The constraints can be mathematical or topological.

recursive subdivision   The process of subdividing a shape (e.g., square or cube) into successively smaller parts, usually of the same shape.

redraw   Redisplaying the display contents without recalculating the database. Also referred to as *refresh*.

reference plane   Any two of the three axes in a cartesian coordinate system form a reference plane. There are three reference planes of any given cartesian coordinate system, the X-Y plane, the Y-Z plane, and the X-Z plane. Sketch pads for variational profiles. They provide a frame of reference for spatial location of elements.

reflection map   A movable image to cast background reflections onto reflective surfaces. Reflection mapping is a faster alternative to ray-tracing, but it can only approximate simple reflections (like a windshield reflecting clouds) or enhance the reflectivity of metallic surfaces.

refraction   The bending of light as it travels through a dense material such as glass or water. Refraction is simulated by ray-tracing and is typically defined as an attribute of a material.

regular array   A rectangular array of spatial locations, usually in 2D or 3D, that have a constant spacing between adjacent locations.

regular grid   The definition of a grid and topology of a data volume. A regular grid always has regular spacing and a regular topology whose individual elements are simple hexahedrons.

regular topology   An implicit hexahedral data structure whose every node need not be specified. A regular topology can be used for a regular or irregular grid.

relational rectification   The process whereby both mathematical and topological justification are applied to a piece of geometry, constraining it in both size and spatial positioning.

relative coordinates   Coordinates specified by differences in distances and/or angles measured from a previous set of coordinates rather than from the origin point.

relative mesh density   The ratio of density of the finest and coarsest regions of a finite element mesh as measured by element edge lengths or sometimes face areas.

REMOVE   See **boolean SUBTRACT**.

render   Computing all information in a scene about objects, surfaces, lights, and cameras to create a photorealistic image.

report attributes   Attributes that let you generate output from a design instance.

reports   Textual output from a design instance. Typical reports include bills of material, routing sheets, etc.

revolve   A process used to convert a 2D profile or silhouette into a 3D object. The 3D object is created by revolving the 2D profile around a central axis to sweep out a surface. Examples of objects created using revolve are wine glasses, lamp shades, and vases. This is also referred to as a *surface of revolution*.

RGB   A color space used to specify a color using values for Red, Green, and Blue. Values are usually specified between 0 and 1 for each color to obtain a color mix for a material definition. For example, the values 0.4, 0.4, and 0 yield a dark yellow color. RGB color space is also used to specify the colors of individual pixels in a rendered image.

rho   Greek character representing an angle in the precision key-in for spherical and cylindrical auxiliary coordinates. In a rho conic, rho is the ratio between the height of a conic section and the height of a cone.

right-hand rule   Using the fingers of the right hand to remember the relative directions of the positive x, y, and z axes of a cartesian coordinate system, as well as the direction of a positive rotation.

rigid bodies   A body on which any two points remain the same distance apart during motion. The shape of the body does not change.

RISC   Reduced Instruction-Set Computing.

robotics   The study and use of robots.

ROM   Read-Only Memory. See also **memory**.

root   The design instance that is the top of the product structure tree. Also, element(s) upon which an associative element or macro depends.

rotate   A positioning mode for geometry. When selected, the current geometry swings around a specified line or vector.

RP   Rapid Prototyping.

rubber-banding   Attaching the cursor to a fixed display point with a line that appears to stretch and contract like a rubber band as the cursor is moved.

rule-based system   Another name used to describe a knowledge-based engineering system.

ruled surface   A surface generated by linear interpolation between two lines or curves, or a point and a line or curve.

SAE   Society of Automotive Engineers.

SC4/TC184   Subcommittee 4/Technical Committee 184. The ISO body responsible for STEP.

scalar texture   A texture that modifies the shininess, dissolve, or decal of a material.

scale   To enlarge or reduce the size of a defined element, modifying only the dimensions, not the ratio among the pieces.

scan line   A row of pixels in a rendered image. Stated another way, a rendered image is comprised of scan lines, which are in turn comprised of pixels.

scene   An arrangement of tools, geometries, labels, and annotations in 3D space that can be rendered or animated.

screen image   The current state of the CRT screen. Specially developed images of solid models can be displayed, saved for use in animations and simulations, converted to graphic files or 35mm slides, overheads, etc.

script   A set of command instructions. An operator may use a script when flavoring CAD data before transfers or when creating consistent test case files for data exchange testing. See also **macro**.

scroll bar   A bar on the side of a list that lets you scroll through the list by clicking on a direction arrow.

sculptured solid   A solid which contains sculptured surfaces.

sculptured surface   A free-form surface that is curved in more than one direction, typically defined by NURBS, Bezier, or other mathematical definitions.

secondary model   In SM, an object representation, not necessarily solid, generated from the primary model of a solid.

select   The term used to identify the procedure whereby an operator uses a mouse, direction arrows, tablet, light pen, or other mechanism to identify a specific entity being displayed as part of a design.

Selective Laser Sintering (SLS)   A patented process by DTM Corporation (Austin, Tex.) for producing a physical prototype directly from a 3D surface or solid model.

semiregular array   A spatial array in which the spacing of elements is the same in a principal direction but varies by direction.

server   A computer-running software that provides a particular capability to an entire network of interconnected computers.

session   The process of saving, recalling, or starting a new model.

SET   Standard d'Echange et de Transfert.

setup   In numerical control (NC), refers to the process of preparing a machine tool to produce a part. Material stock, clamps, and related items are positioned during setup.

sewing   The process of attaching surfaces at their mating edges to form a closed volume. Sewing can join two surfaces or allow the database to refer to them as a surface set as long as they share edges within a specified system tolerance.

shadow object   In viewing and display applications, objects created do not cast shadows unless they have been paired with a shadow object. A shadow object is invisible, except that it casts a shadow of itself. Shadows are visible only in a rendered image; they cannot be seen in flat shading or smooth shading.

shape 2D or 3D element.

shell A solid model defined by a surface, thickness, and surface normals, such as formed sheet metal.

silhouette lines The exterior edges of an object as perceived from a particular viewpoint. Some SM systems generate silhouette lines automatically to display the perceived edge of a surface with curvature.

simulation In SM, the act of displaying a predetermined sequence of events. Simulations can be interactive or self-running. An interactive simulation prompts for input to determine a course. A self-running simulation displays images or executes commands based on a predetermined plan. See also **animation**.

single curvature A surface entity that curves on only one direction, such as an extruded arc or spline.

single precision Numbers stored in a computer using a single computer word. See also **double precision**.

slide show The process of recalling saved images to animate, simulate, or present ideas.

smoothing A technique in which element normals are to be interpolated to give those elements a smooth, nonfaceted appearance. See also **Phong** and **Gouraud shading**.

snap To place the cursor using an Input Generation command, with the cursor appearing to jump or snap to the point.

software Computer code that operates and controls computer-related hardware. Software can be used for design, analysis, or manufacturing, and includes SM, FEA, and NC.

software array limit An array stores an ordered set of data. The maximum length of the array may be fixed, such as 500 array entries, or allowed a variable array length.

solid Geometric element, such as a cube or sphere, having three dimensions.

Solid Ground Curing (SGC) A patented process by Cubital, Incorporated (Troy, Mich.) for producing a physical prototype directly from a 3D surface or solid model.

solid model Mathematical model composed of primitives or enclosed by surfaces. Valid solid models have surface normals that point toward the exterior of the solid.

Solid Modeling (SM) A geometric technique used to build and manipulate solid objects and combine them into assemblies. Complex solid objects are built from primitive shapes using boolean operations. Primitive shapes usually include analytic solids such as a block, cylinder, cone, sphere, and torus, linear and rotational sweeps, and parametric free-form surfaces. Solid Modeling can determine and store physical properties of objects such as weight, volume, surface area, etc.

solid modeling engine A tool kit or package of core SM functions that can be used as a basis for the development of an SM program. The provided functionality of a solid modeling engine can range from purely math-related functions to a full-featured modeling, database, and display package.

solid of revolution Solid composed of one surface that is swept about an axis and closes on itself; sometimes called a *sweep*.

solids-based NC machining A process where both the design model and the NC source code are geometrically represented as part of the solid model.

source code The instructions that make up a program in ASCII or readable text format.

span Polynomial section.

specular reflection A mirrorlike reflection characteristic of metallic or glossy surfaces.

sphere A solid primitive defined as the volume generated by a semicircle revolved about an axis passing through the endpoints of the semicircle.

spline A mathematically defined curve through an ordered set of points.

split To divide a component into two parts that can be manipulated separately.

start point First point in a series that defines an element.

start-up file A macro or program that is executed automatically when an SM program is loaded into memory. Start-up files provide initial customization of the SM environment.

state tree Hierarchical diagram showing the global and local modifications of a solid model.

static analysis A special case of dynamic analysis that is the determination of an equilibrium position of the system under the action of forces that are independent of time.

static detection The act of analyzing a stationary assembly of solid models to determine if any intersect each other or in fact share the same volume.

status display Display of active default values.

STEP Standard for the Exchange of Product Model Data, a familiar name for the emerging international standard ISO 10303. The goal is a complete, unambiguous, computer-readable definition of the physical and functional characteristics of a product throughout its life cycle.

StereoLithography (SL) A patented process by 3D Systems, Incorporated (Valencia, Calif.) for producing a physical prototype directly from a 3D surface or solid model.

stress coefficient A factor that indicates the ability of a material to deform under pressure.

style Symbology of an element such as continuous dashes, dash dot, solid, and so forth.

stylus An input device used like a digitizer puck, but looks like a pen.

subdivision The process of dividing a solid model into smaller constructions to be operated on separately. The subdivision of a solid models saves CPU time.

subassembly A gathering together of piece-parts into a logical unit that will eventually be added to an assembly. An example of a subassembly would be the ring and rod in our test case.

subtree A subset of a tree that consists of a node and its descendants.

surface A boundary defining an exterior face of a solid model. The surface is typically defined beyond the limits of the face. Enlarging the extent of the face still yields a valid face on the solid.

surface area The amount of space occupied by the exterior surfaces of a solid object as measured in squared units. A value calculated by the mass-properties analysis of a solid model.

surface model   See **normal**.

surface of revolution   See **revolve**.

surface pressure   A pressure that is distributed uniformly or nonuniformly over a face.

surface region   A portion of a surface fully bounded by curves on the surface.

surface rendering   A rendering method for creating high-quality images with antialiasing, reflections, and transparency.

surface tangent   A directional vector which lies on a plane that is perpendicular to a surface normal at a specified point on the surface.

sweep   A solid geometric operation defined by sweeping a planar cross-section profile along an arbitrary curve.

symbology   Display style of an element, including color, style, and weight.

symmetrical   2D geometry that is typically mirrored or equal about a common axis line; 3D geometry that is typically mirrored or equal about a common plane.

symmetry surface restraint   The restraint of a surface normal to the surface. This implies that the structure and loads are symmetrical about this plane.

system crash   An internal conflict or error in hardware or software that causes the SM system to halt operations. A system crash can cause software to lock out any input or the hardware to shut itself down. SM data is usually lost unless automated recovery procedures were in place.

tabulated surface   A special case of the ruled surface generated by a straight line as it moves parallel to itself along a curve.

tangent   Point on an arc where a line or surface touches that one point.

tap   To quickly press and immediately release a button.

tessellating   Subdividing a patch element into face elements and a curve element into a line element (applied in polygonal modeling). Tessellation lines are lines which connect tessallated elements.

tetrahedron elements   Finite elements that enclose solid regions of a structure with four (tetra) triangular faces.

text   An annotation tool that allows the labeling of data, tools, and data sessions. You can use different fonts or enhancements such as italics, bold, super- or subscripting, light text, and color text.

texture   A preprocessed image that modifies surface detail. A texture is part of a material definition and can impart color, bump, and transparency effects to the surface of an object. Texture is mapped to the surface of an object to give it more detail.

thermal boundary conditions   Conditions that constrain thermal loading to known zero or nonzero values at specified surfaces.

thermal coefficient   A factor that indicates the ability of a material to transmit heat.

thermal loads   Loads that impart temperature distributions on a structure.

thresholding   Specifying a specific range of measurements you want to exhibit.

TIFF   Tagged Image File Format.

tiled windows   In a Graphic User Interface (GUI), design where the windows are arranged automatically by the windowing system to completely fill the available display space (which may be either the entire display screen or an entire content area of a window).

time history   A time grid over which a simulation is performed. A grid is often divided into intervals. At these intervals the solution of the equations of motion is reported.

time series data   A set of geometric or volumetric data representing changes over time.

toggle   State gadget that can be placed with text or symbols.

tolerance analysis   Refers to the ability to predict the statistical variation of tolerances with an assembly as they would naturally occur in the manufacturing process. See also **tolerance stack-up**.

tolerance balancing   The process of balancing a dimensional tolerance where both the (+) and the (−) tolerance values are equal about the nominal dimensional value.

tolerance stack-up   The accumulative tolerance of mating parts. For example, if three plates were stacked atop each other and each had a manufactured width of 1 ± 0.01 inches, the overall height of the stack would be 3 ± 0.03 inches.

tolerances   Refers to the limits of accuracy of an SM system. Similar to manufactured objects, computer-generated geometry can be constructed to varying tolerance levels.

tool kit   A set of prewritten functions and utilities that simplify or enhance the creation of programs.

toolpath   In numerical control (NC), the path of a cutting tool as it passes over stock material to produce a desired shape.

top-down design   An approach to assembly modeling where the organization or individual responsible for the overall assembly establishes the logical hierarchy of subassemblies and parts and assigns the creation of actual geometry to others.

topological data   Data which includes the connectivity relationships among geometric components.

topological rectification   The process whereby a piece of geometry is forced into a particular spatial relationship with another piece of geometry. *Examples:* a line which is parallel or perpendicular to another line, circles which are concentric, curves which are tangent to or normal to each other, etc.

topology   The properties of objects that remain unchanged under distortion (as long as no surfaces are penetrated or torn). In SM, refers to the connections of individual elements (vertices, edges, and faces) of a solid model.

torus   A solid primitive defined by the revolution of a circle about an axis in the plane of the circle. The axis must not pass through the center of the circle, and must lie outside the circle in most SM systems.

trace depth   A value used during ray-tracing to specify the complexity of reflections. For example, a trace-depth value of 1 may generate single reflections (a mirror reflecting a wall). A trace-depth value of 2 may allow reflections of reflections (a mirror reflecting another mirror, which is reflecting a wall).

trajectory Refers to the path used in solid geometric operations such as extrusions and sweeps. Trajectories can be linear, multilinear, or curvilinear.

transcendental functions Any function which is not an algebraic function. The most common transcendental functions are those which contain terms involving trigonometric, logarithmic, or exponential functions. *Examples:* $y = \sin(x)$, $y = e(x)$, and $y = \log(x)$ are all transcendental functions.

transformation matrix A mathematical matrix containing the coefficients needed to perform a transformation on geometric elements represented in a matrix form.

transformation node A tree node that performs a geometric or other transformation on the object represented by its descendants.

transformations Operations applied to a geometric database to perform translation, scaling, rotation, and perspective.

transition See **blend**.

transparency See **dissolve**.

tree A graph in which there is a path between each pair of nodes, no loops, and a single node identified as the root.

triad Display aid for determining the position of a coordinate system.

trial attributes Attributes whose values are computed by trying out new values until a successful value is found.

triangulated surface geometry A method to describe the surface of an object made up of entirely flat triangular faces.

trim surface A surface that has been reduced to a smaller region by curves on the surface.

tube A solid primitive defined by two concentric diameters and a linear or curvilinear path. Tubes can also be of nondiametric shape.

turnkey A computer system sold complete and ready to use for a specific application. You just "turn the key."

tweeking The process of modifying a solid locally without modifying its topology, such as moving an edge, deforming a surface, or moving and feature.

twin edges In a valid solid (polyhedron), exactly two faces meet along each edge of the solid. These two edges of adjacent faces are known as *twin edges* because they are coincident and identical.

U direction Path followed on a B-spline curve or surface for which U values increase.

U parameter Arbitrary parameter used in parametric equations that define a B-spline curve or surface. The value of U varies from 0 to 1.

unbound values An indication that the value of a particular attribute has not yet been computed.

unevaluated representation A solid model in which at least some face, edge, and vertex information is represented only implicitly.

uniform B-spline B-spline curve or surface where knots occur at equal U or V increments.

UNION See **boolean UNION**.

unit A user-defined distance. It may be inches, millimeters, meters, etc.

UNIX Engineering-oriented, multitasking operating system developed by AT&T.

unstructured mesh A mesh where the node coordinates, element type, and connectivity are explicitly defined by the user.

user coordinate system A movable, user-defined coordinate system used for convenient placement of geometry.

V direction Path followed on a B-spline surface for which V values increase and U values are constant.

V parameter One of two parameters used in the parametric equations that define a B-spline surface. The value of V varies from 0 to 1.

VAR Value-Added Reseller.

variable cross sections In a solid blend operation, varying closed cross-section profiles are blended. A cross section obtained at any given point along the blend would vary in size and orientation.

variational engine That part of a parametric/relational solid modeling system which is responsible for maintaining the variational aspects of geometry. See also **variational geometry**.

variational geometry A method of representing a solid model as a set of interrelated equations defining its shape and dimensions. Variational geometry is solved simultaneously, as opposed to parametric geometry which is solved sequentially.

VDA-FS Verband der Deutschen Automobilindustrie—Flaechenschnittstelle (Association of German Automotive Industry—Surface Interface).

VDA-IS IGES Subset of VDA-FS.

vector A mathematical entity with a precise direction and length (but no specific location).

vector field Data that has both magnitude and direction, such as velocity or flux.

vertex An x-y-z location (a point in space) used to define an element. All types of elements consist of one or more vertices. Faces, lines, and point elements use vertices to represent points along their perimeters. Patch and curve elements (Bezier and B-spline) use vertices to represent control points.

vertex normal Used to aid the smooth-shading of curved surfaces. A vertex normal is used to calculate the curvature of a surface at a particular vertex. Vertex normals are typically created automatically when autosmoothing and surface normals are applied.

vertical Located at a right angle to the plane of a supporting surface.

VGA Video Graphics Array.

view Defined area of vision on a screen. A view lets you see a prescribed volume of the design cube. Views are created with their own x, y, and z axes. The x-y plane of the view is parallel to the screen, while the z axis can be thought of as coming straight out of the view toward you. The view axes maintain this relationship regardless of the rotation with respect to the design cube.

viewpoint   A location in 3D model space from which a model is viewed.

viewport   The rectangular area on your screen that displays your data. Also referred to as the *display*.

virus   Software code designed to infiltrate and infect a computer system. Viruses can take many forms and cause far-reaching effects. Damage can range from video disarray to a complete loss of all data. Virus-detection software is available and recommended.

void   Typically referred to as a hollow pocket modeled within a solid. A solid with a void would contain at least two (interior and exterior) unconnected enclosed volumes. Voids can be modeled but cannot be physically produced.

volume   The amount of space occupied by a three-dimensional object as measured in cubic units. A value calculated by the mass-properties analysis of a solid model.

volume element   The smallest element of a data volume; synonymous to voxel.

volume rendering   The process of producing an image from a 3D volume of scalar data by casting rays through a transparent volume.

volumetric solid modeling   The use of solid models that are defined by spatial samples (such as CT scan data) rather than geometric shapes defined mathematically.

voxel   A 3D rectangular region of space that may contain one or more properties (e.g., an average density for the region). 3D arrays of voxels are often used to represent digitized solid objects. A voxel is the 3D equivalent of a 2D pixel and is short for "volume element."

WAN   Wide-Area Network.

wavefront   The difference in element numbers or degrees of freedom for a stiffness matrix stored by numerical ascending order of the elements.

weight   Thickness of a displayed element; usually represented as the number of strokes it would be plotted, plus the original stroke. For example, wt=5 means that the weight or thickness of the element is 6 strokes.

weighted pole   Pole whose tendency to bend the curve or surface toward or away from itself has been altered to achieve a particular shape such as a conic.

welding   Any operation used to close small holes in an object's surface or to eliminate seams or cracks between faces. Welding merges vertices that lie within close proximity of one another. This distance is the *weld resolution*.

window   Independent rectangular display area that can be moved, resized, reshaped, collapsed, or uncollapsed.

wireframe   A technique used to display an object as a framework of lines (as opposed to shaded surfaces). On most computers, objects displayed in wireframe can be rotated interactively. Wireframe is typically the default display style.

workstation   Terminal that contains an internal CPU and can operate in a stand-alone mode or as part of a network.

world coordinate system   Default rectangular coordinate system. Points are defined in terms of the ordered triple (x, y, z), where the range for x, y, and z is approximately 2 billion. Often, applications require alternate coordinate systems (often called *auxiliary coordinate systems*), usually having a different origin and orientation for the x, y, and z axes. Points in a auxiliary coordinate system (ACS) are transformed to world coordinate system coordinates before they are used by the software.

world coordinates   The location of a point within the permanent coordinate system of 3D model space. Also known as *global coordinates*.

x axis   The horizontal axis in a cartesian coordinate system.

X Window System   A base-level set of windowing functions developed by a consortium of computer companies and MIT.

y axis   The vertical axis in a cartesian coordinate system.

z axis   The depth axis in a cartesian coordinate system.

z-buffer   An array of depth values used when generating an image. It is used to determine what parts of a data set are closest to the viewer and should be displayed.

zoom   The process of reducing or increasing the magnification of graphics on the display screen.

Index

Editor's Note: Also refer to The Solid Modeling Adviser Master Table at the front of this handbook for a complete listing of each SMA entry, by section, topic, group, icon, number, name, originator, and page number.

Index to Advertisers

Company	Phone	Product/Service	Reader Service No.	Page No.
Knowledge-Based Engineering				
Concentra Corporation (ICAD, Inc.)	(617) 868-2800	ICAD	207	9.1
Rapid Prototyping				
3D Systems, Inc.	(805) 295-5600	Stereolithography Systems	210	19.1
3D Systems, Inc.	(805) 295-5600	RP Service Bureau	211	19.4
Solid Modeling				
American Small Business Computers	(918) 825-7555	DesignCAD 3D	212	1.3
Autodesk, Inc.	(800) 964-6432	AutoCAD Designer		10.1
EDS Unigraphics	(314) 344-2687	Unigraphics	205	6.1
Hewlett-Packard Company	(800) 756-9597	PE/Solid Designer	201	vii
IBM Corporation	(800) 395-3339	CATIA	206/209	8.1/18.3
Intergraph Corporation	(800) 345-4856	EMS	208/215	15.1/30.1
The MacNeal-Schwendler Corporation	(800) 642-7437	MSC/ARIES	203	2.1
Manufacturing and Consulting Services, Inc.	(800) 932-9329	ANVIL-5000	202	xix
SDRC	(800) 848-7372	I-DEAS Master Series	214	25.1
Varimetrix Corporation	(407) 676-3222	Varimetrix VX	213	25.1
Sketchers				
IBM Corporation	(800) 395-3339	Professional CADAM Sketchit	204	3.3